Life-Histories of the Frogs of Okefinokee Swamp, Georgia

Life-Histories of the Frogs of Okefinokee Swamp, Georgia

NORTH AMERICAN SALIENTIA
(ANURA) NO. 2

By

Albert Hazen Wright

New York
The Macmillan Company
1931

PRINTED BY
THE CAYUGA PRESS
ITHACA, N. Y.

TO DR. LEONHARD STEJNEGER
NESTOR OF AMERICAN HERPETOLOGY
AND KINDLY COUNCILLOR OF
YOUNGER BIOLOGISTS

Field Work Under Heckscher Grants Nos. 14 and 31

FOREWORD

In 1914 we wrote as an introduction to a similar work for Ithaca, N. Y., the following paragraphs:

"Notwithstanding the extensive use of our American Anura for anatomical and embryological purposes, comparatively little attention has been given to the collection of definite data bearing upon the breeding habits and larvae of this group. In this connection, Boulenger (1897), in the preface to his work upon 'The Tailless Batrachians of Europe', observes:

'I would also express a hope that a little book of this kind . . . may have the effect of stimulating interest in a subject that has been too much neglected, and in the cultivation of which new workers will find much to repay their efforts, especially if applied in other regions of the globe, which, though richer in Batrachians, have as yet yielded little or nothing to our knowledge of the life-histories.'

"Dr. Gill (1898), in his review of the work just mentioned, remarks that he hopes this monograph* 'may serve as a model for other lands, and not least for the United States. . . . Every sojourner in the country must have noticed the masses of transparent jelly-like spheres in the water, but none in the United States could refer such masses with certainty to the parent species.' To a local study of these very phases of Anuran life, my investigations for the past seven or eight years have been directed."

Since 1914 we have continued these studies from Ithaca to California. With these studies of the southeast, Storer's excellent accounts of the Pacific coast forms and Strecker's long continued notes on Texas species, the life histories of most of the Salientia of North America are now outlined. Some remain untouched and many details need to be filled in the outlines at hand.

*The material upon which this report is based is from two sources: the personal material collected in Okefinokee Swamp from 1909-1922; and the United States National Museum collection of the Okefinokee species herein considered. Before the completion of this manuscript Mrs. Wright and I examined also all of the U. S. National Museum frogs of North America north of the Mexican line. This material furnished comparative notes on the following topics: the range; structural differences between sexes; least and greatest breeding sizes; transformation data and sizes; measurements of frogs from transformation to largest adults for rate of growth; first appearance and autumnal disappearance dates; and other incidental data. Additional information came from the U. S. National Museum's unidentified and uncatalogued tadpoles and transformation stages which the present author is examining from time to time. To Dr. Leonhard Stejneger, Dr. Remington Kellogg, and Miss Doris Cochran we owe countless kindnesses.

To Doubleday, Doran & Co. we are indebted for permission to use excerpts from Miss M. C. Dickerson's useful work, The Frog Book.

The investigation upon which this work is based was supported in 1921 and 1922 by a grant from the Heckscher Foundation for the Advancement of Research, established at Cornell University by August Heckscher.

CONTENTS

LIST OF ILLUSTRATIONS

(Plates mounted by A. A. Wright)

1921 photographs by F. Harper and the author.
1922 photographs by F. Harper and A. A. Wright.
1923-29 photographs by A. A. and A. H. Wright.

(Photographs developed and printed by Troy Studio
Engravings by The Hurst Engraving Co.)

xi

TEXT FIGURES

INTRODUCTION

In 1915 we wrote: "The object of all the Cornell (1909-1914) expeditions was to study and put on record something of the biological conditions in this extensive fresh-water swamp, which still presents in a large measure primitive and interesting conditions of environment, before they should become forever changed by the now rapidly penetrating lumbermen."

From these private trips we published A Biological Reconnaissance of the Okefinokee Swamp in Georgia. (The Birds by A. H. Wright and Francis Harper, 1913; The Turtles, Lizards and Alligators by A. H. Wright and W. D. Funkhouser, 1915; The Snakes by A. H. Wright and S. C. Bishop 1915; The Fishes, by E. L. Palmer and A. H. Wright, 1922). Besides these, three more reports were prepared but not published, namely, The History of the Swamp by A. H. Wright, The Amphibia by A. H. Wright and Julia Moesel, and The Reptiles (2nd Report) by S. C. Bishop and A. H. Wright.

In 1921 the author was given a grant from the Heckscher Foundation for the Advancement of Research established at Cornell University and this was continued for the season of 1922 (see topic Subsequent Explorations, 1914 to 1922). This paper therefore includes notes and material from 1909-1922,— the period to 1914 or later in the center of the swamp before lumbering; the period 1921 with lumbering (Billy's Island the base); and the period 1922 on Chesser Island to have conditions more like those of 1914 and to study the surrounding biota of the swamp.

ACKNOWLEDGMENTS TO RESIDENTS

In 1915 we held that most valuable services were rendered to this party by the Lee family, (Mrs. Lee, the mother of the first generation, Jackson, David, Bryant, Farley, Harrison, Joseph of the second generation, and Marion and Ely of the third generation), living on Billy's Island, the only human inhabitants of the interior of the swamp, and practically out of touch with the outside world. Their primitive mode of living had adapted them to a marvelous degree to the appreciation of the wild life about them, and their observations and knowledge of natural phenomena proved to be surprisingly accurate. The older men and boys were indispensable as guides while the party was in the swamp, and on the exit of the party a container was left with them to be filled with specimens which might come to their hands later in the year. This container, full of material chosen with evident care and good judgment, was received November 15, 1912, and the specimens thus secured proved a valuable addition to those previously collected. In December, 1913, data were obtained on the winter condition of some of the forms here noted.

In 1921 Jackson, Harrison and David Lee were in the swamp and rendered invaluable assistance. From the next generation we also received continued service. These were Henry Harrison and Marion Lee and their brothers and cousins.

In 1921 we entered the swamp with letters of introduction from the Hebards of the Hebard Cypress Company. No one received finer courtesies or consideration than we all the while we were in their midst. We camped in the lumber settlement of 300 or 400 or more. The superintendents (John M. Hopkins, A. J. Armstrong), gave instructions and courtesies which lightened in many ways our search. To the superintendents on the island (H. S. Quarterman and V. Alex. Quarterman), to the boarding house (Mr. Wm. J. Wilson and his sympathetic women helpers), to the timber cutters, skidder force, pile driver force, girdling crew, commissary or store unit, the shop employees, we extended our thanks for countless favors. To eat and associate with this roster of real workers who were truly tolerant of frogcatchers, snake "doctors" and other such queer researchers as we is an opportunity and experience we will never have again. As irregular as we might be in our eating hours, Mrs. Wilson and her force were patient. To one group we owe much help. They are the train force. These twelve or fifteen men (engineers, firemen, flagmen) would stop a train in impossible places to pick us up weary and often laden, or with engines in rare cases come for us at distant points. For no one on Billy's Island's roster did the author feel more indebted than to Sam Edwards, the time keeper and in many ways chief *factotum.* He was a well read man who could well understand the import of our mission. All in interest, fine spirit, assistance and information contributed to the attainment of our material.

This official roster deserves considerable thanks but rest assured that we were wise enough to enlist as well the interest of the Quarterman, Edwards, Strickland, Woodward, Jordan, Craven, Carter, Cox, Bennett and other Juniors who were volunteer assistants.

Continually we interviewed the older inhabitants whose intimate experiences with the life of the region proved invaluable. Each of the Lee brothers and the next generation as well we thus quizzed from the mammals to the fishes. In the same way R. A. Chesser and his brother Sam with their sons Ben, Harry, Ridley and Tom have unsparingly helped and willingly recounted their knowledge and experiences.

Messrs. James Henderson, Walter Davis, J. D. Hendrix, Julius Godwin, Norman Godwin, each contributed notes as we went down the catalogue of forms from fish to mammals and many a long session ensued.

Two members of the Hebard Company who particularly had rich knowledge of the swamp, its out of way parts and its rare inhabitants were particularly Sam Mizzell and his brother Hamp Mizzell.

In 1922 we were the guests of the Chessers on Chesser Island and to them we can never fully express the joyous and profitable summer they gave us. In 1922 we returned to Billy's Island for a week or more and received countless favors from our old friends of 1921 or of 1912-1921. All in all the animal experiences related to us by the inhabitants and members of the lumber colony as well were very valuable, particularly so for the birds and mammals. For the cold blooded animals they had less observations. Nevertheless they knew where most of them occurred and helped in securing them.

To several people of Folkston and Waycross we owe kindnesses, particularly to Mrs. J. L. Walker and her daughter of Waycross, Georgia.

ACKNOWLEDGMENTS TO SPECIALISTS

To the constant interest and assistance of Mrs. Anna Allen Wright, my wife, attaches much of whatever merit this paper possesses. She was on the trip in 1922. In 1912 she helped to carry part of my teaching in my absence, and in 1921 purposed to be my associate. She has made the drawings, mounted the plates and helped Dr. Francis Harper in the photography in 1922.

Both in 1921 and in 1922 Dr. Francis Harper was on the trip. He gave intelligent interest in collecting material and notes and was my chief reliance in the photography of the frogs in 1921. In 1922 Dr. Miles D. Pirnie assisted me in general, Mrs. Wright in plant collecting and identifications, and Dr. Harper in the preparation of skins.

At the American Museum of Natural History the particular species sought on two different occasions were kindly placed at our disposal by Dr. G. Kingsley Noble, Messrs. C. D. Pope and Wm. Hassler. At the Museum of Comparative Zoology, Dr. T. Barbour and Mr. A. Loveridge made my search very expeditious and profitable. In the same way, several days spent on material at the University of Michigan proved pleasant and of interest, thanks to Dr. A. G. Ruthven, and Dr. F. M. Gaige, but particularly to Mrs. Helen Thompson Gaige. To M. Graham Netting of Carnegie Museum, Pittsburg, Pa. also goes our indebtedness for favors deeply appreciated.

PREVIOUS PERTINENT AMPHIBIAN EXPLORATIONS TO 1914

In 1913 we wrote the following general introduction to a contemplated paper on "The Biological Reconnaissance of the Okefinokee Swamp in Georgia. The Amphibians. By A. H. Wright and Julia Moesel." It never was published but excerpts from it appear throughout this work. In it the following introduction appeared.

For several decades the state of Georgia has received very little herpetological attention yet the history of North American batrachology proves it to be one of the most important in the Union. The most recent pertinent list comes from the immediate southeast in Florida. In 1911-1912, Mr. Richard F. Deckert collected the following Salientia near Jacksonville.

They are[1]

*Ranapipiens	*Hyla pickeringii
Rana sphenocephala	*Hyla squirella
*Rana aesopus	Hyla femoralis
Rana clamitans	Hyla cinerea
Rana catesbiana	Hyla gratiosa
Rana grylio	*Chorophilus nigritus
Engystoma carolinense	*Chorophilus occidentalis
Bufo lentiginosus	Chorophilus ocularis
Bufo quercicus	Acris gryllus

[1] Deckert, R. F. Copeia No. 3, Feb. 19, 1914; No. 5, April 15, 1914; No. 9, Aug. 29, 1914.

At an earlier date and slightly farther south from Green Cove Springs and Hastings, Fla., C. S. Brimley lists[2]

Plethodon glutinosus
*Desmognathus fusca auriculata
Diemyctylus viridescens
Amphiuma means
Siren lacertina
Bufo quercicus
Acris gryllus

*Chorophilus ornatus
Hyla cinerea
*Hyla squirella
Hyla gratiosa
Hyla femoralis
*Rana aesopus
*Rana catesbiana

At Nashville and Allapaha, Ga. to the northwest of the Okefinokee Swamp, Mr. W. J. Taylor secured the following forms:[3]

Bufo lentiginosus lentiginosus
Acris gryllus gryllus
Chorophilus occidentalis
Hyla squirella
Hyla femoralis
Hyla carolinensis

Rana virescens sphenocephela
*Rana virescens virescens
*Rana areolata areolata
Rana clamata
*Desmognathus fusca
*Amphiuma means

Thus, from these three lists we could compile a hypothetical (*) list of forms to be sought in Okefinokee Swamp or its environs in the year 1913. The following 11 forms might be thought the nucleus of it. They are

Rana pipiens
Rana areolata areolata
Rana aesopus
Rana catesbeiana
Hyla squirella
Hyla pickeringii

Chorophilus nigritus
Chorophilus occidentalis
Chorophilus ornatus
Desmognathus fusca
Desmognathus fusca auriculata

In the early part of the last century no state of the United States furnished more amphibian material than Georgia and its earlier herpetological writers and collecters included such worthies as Major J. LeConte, Dr. J. L. LeConte, Dr. Holbrook and his east Georgian correspondents and collectors like Dr. Couper of St. Simon's Island and Dr. Harden of Riceboro, Ga. This latter place, the type locality of five or six mammals is equally interesting in batrachology. Here the LeConte plantation is situated and no doubt it is the type locality for some of the Georgian species Maj. J. LeConte described.

In 1825 (May 16) he distinctly records three forms from Georgia[4]:

Hyla lateralis   Hyla femoralis
                    Hyla delitescens

---

[2] Brimley, C. S. Records of Some Reptiles and Batrachians from the Southeastern United States. Proc. Biol. Soc. Wash. Vol. XXIII, pp. 9-18, March 23, 1910.
[3] Cope, E. D. The Batrachia of N.A. Bull. U. S. N. M. No. 34, 1889.
[4] LeConte, J. Remarks on the American species of the Genera Hyla and Rana. Annals Lyceum Natural History New York, Vol. I, Part III, New York, 1825, pp. 278-282.

Thirty years later (1855) he gives 12 forms each of which "inhabits Georgia" or the southern states. The five species which are not yet recorded in the Okefinokee proper are[5]

Rana capito

Chorophilus nigrita

Hyla versicolor

Hyla delitescens

Scaphiopus solitarius

In 1832 to 1842 the ten volumes of Dr. Holbrook's epochal "North American Herpetology" appeared in two editions. Many of his Georgian specimens or records came from Dr. Harden of Riceboro, Ga., or from J. Hamilton Couper, of St. Simon's Island. The latter gentleman also knew the country south of the Altamaha quite well. Dr. Holbrook gives 25 forms from Georgia or from what might be termed more strictly eastern Georgia. The missing species from the Okefinokee Swamp in 1913 are[6]

Rana pipiens Latreille

Cystignathus nigritus LeConte

Scaphiopus solitarius Holbrook

Hyla squirella Bosc

Hyla delitescens LeConte

Bufo americanus LeConte

Salamandra auriculata Holbrook

Salamandra quadrimaculata Holbrook

Salamandra quadridigitata Holbrook

Salamandra fasciata Green

Triton niger Green

Menopoma fusca Holbrook

Siren intermedia LeConte

Siren striata LeConte

Seven years later, 1849, the same author compiled a catalogue of the Batrachia of Georgia and in addition to the forms given above he enumerates ten more. They are[7]

Cystignathus ornatus Holbrook

Bufo erythronotus Holb.

Salamandra guttolineata Holb.

Salamandra salmonea Storer

Salamandra erythronota Green

Salamandra bilineata Green

Salamandra melanosticta L Gibbes

Salamandra venenosa Bart.

Salamandra talpoidea Holb.

Bufo americanus LeConte

Most of the material which Cope had to examine from Georgia came from the southeastern or southwestern districts of the state. In the southeast at Riceboro or in Liberty Co., he had specimens collected by Major J. LeConte, two forms by Dr. J. L. LeConte, three secured by Prof. S. F. Baird, several by Dr. W. L. Jones and some not accredited to collectors. In the first group (of Maj. J. LeConte) occur,[8]

---

[5] LeConte, J. Proc. Acad. Nat. Sci., Phila. Vol. VII, 1854, 1855, pp. 423-431. Phila. 1856. Read Dec. 25, 1855.

[6] Holbrook, J. E. N. A. Herpetology. Vols. 4, 5. 1842.

[7] White, Geo. Statistics of the State of Georgia: etc. Savannah. 1849. Appendix p. 15.

[8] Cope, E. D. The Batrachia of North America. Bull. U. S. N. M. No. 34. Wash. 1889, pp. 1-515.

Chorophilus occidentalis   Rana catesbiana
Hyla squirella   Rana areolata capito
Hyla versicolor   Amblystoma conspersum
Scaphiopus holbrooki   Amblystoma opacum

His son, Dr. J. L. LeConte took two forms one of which is absent from the swamp, to wit, Chorophilus nigritus.

Dr. W. L. Jones collected 14 species of salamanders and three anurans from the same locality. The following nine forms are of interest.

Plethodon cinereus cinereus   Amblystoma punctatum
Spelerpes guttolineatus   Amblystoma talpoideum
Spelerpes ruber stictoceps   Desmognathus fusca
Manculus quadridigitatus   Desmognathus nigra
Amblystoma opacum

Whether "Dr. J. Jones, Georgia" collected or resided at Riceboro we do not know. He took

Hemidactylium scutatum   Stereochilus marginatus

From Riceboro Prof. Baird had three forms, two of which were

Rana virescens virescens   Rana catesbiana

Also from Riceboro, Ga. with no collector mentioned Cope lists six forms, the four pertinent records being

Hemidactylium scutatum   Manculus quadridigitatus
Gyrinophilus porphyriticus   Spelerpes bilineatus

Thus we have recorded (until 1914) to the immediate northeast 21 salamanders and 21 frogs, toads and tree toads, while in the swamp we have recorded, (until 1914) 5 urodeles and 10 anurans. The forms of Riceboro missing from the Okefinokee (as recorded until 1914) are

Ambystoma talpoideum   Desmognathus nigra
Ambystoma opacum   Notophthalmus v. viridescens
Ambystoma punctatum   Pseudobranchus striatus
Ambystoma conspersum   Bufo l. americanus
Hemidactylium scutatum   Scaphiopus holbrooki
Plethodon cinereus cinereus   Chorophilus ornatus
Plethodon cinereus erythronotus   Chorophilus occidentalis
Stereochilus marginatus   Chorophilus nigritus
Gyrinophilus porphyriticus   Hyla squirella
Manculus quadridigitatus   Hyla versicolor
Spelerpes bislineatus   Hyla delitescens
Spelerpes guttolineatus   Rana pipiens
Spelerpes ruber stictoceps   Rana catesbeiana
Desmognathus fusca   Rana areolata capito
Desmognathus fusca auriculata

To these forms there should be added the three following species from localities southeast or northwest of the swamp, namely

Rana aesopus   Rana areolata areolata
                    Hyla pickeringii

This hypothetical list from three regions near the swamp probably is far in excess of what will ever be found in the swamp or its immediate environs. These 18 salamanders and 13 frogs and toads—31 in all—emphasized in 1914 the need of further collecting in this region. No doubt some of them like the species of *Pseudacris* (*Chorophilus*) may be reduced in number and specimens comparable to both *Rana pipiens* and *R. sphenocephala* may be found. We were on the lookout for members of the *Rana areolata* group but none of the three forms appeared. The natives maintain that the bullfrog of the outside is different from the one of the swamp and the former may represent *R. catesbeiana*. The two great surprises are the lack of salamanders and the absence of such forms as *Hyla squirella*. The author in 1914 had the conviction that exclusive or extensive collecting of amphibia in this region would yield several more forms.

In 1871 and 1876 Paul Fountain visited this region and his amphibian notes which follow may have enough pertinent historical interest to warrant their inclusion in this paper.[9]

"Probably the next living creature we notice will be the bull-frog, which attracts us on account of its, to our eyes, huge size. There are at least four species of frogs in these swamps, including the largest and smallest of American frogs. The bull-frog is not, however, very abundant, and I have noticed that this frog seems to prefer clear running streams to swamps. It grows to a very great size in the Okefinoke swamp, and sitting up on a snag or mass of moss, it looks like a large stone or boulder. As we approach, however, we notice the exceedingly brilliant eye fixed steadily upon us, and on attempting to touch it, it springs away with an alacrity for which we were quite unprepared, considering its heavy, unwieldy build. It has an enormous head, a thick-set body, and strongly formed limbs, much thicker in proportion than those of the common European frog. Its croak is spoken of as "Booming" and is very loud. It can sometimes be heard appearing to come from every part of an extensive district, and from a mile or more distant. *I am not sure that the Okefinoke frog is not a distinct variety of the common bull-frog.* It is larger than those which I have seen in streams running into the Mississippi and its tributaries, and in other places, and seems to differ in colour, though neither of these circumstances is of much importance. Size may depend on locality and abundance of food, and coloration certainly does. The following are the measurements of the largest specimen that I could find: Length of body from nose to base, 8 inches; breadth across, nearly 5 inches; girth, 14 inches; length of hind-limb, 12½ inches; weight, within a fraction of three pounds. The usual size is about seven inches in length, half as much more

---

[9] Fountain, Paul. The Great Deserts and Forests of North America. London, 1901, pp. 62-64, 67-68.

for length of hind-limb, and a weight of over two pounds. It is remarkable that so small a snake as the mocassin can swallow a bull-frog whole. Of course the snake is greatly distended by such a meal, and is helpless until it has digested it.

"The bull-frog is said to eat small fish. I cannot say this of my own knowledge. They feed on slugs, larvae, beetles, flies, spawn, water-insects, and other frogs, for I saw a bull-frog one day pounce upon a grasshopper-frog and swallow it in a twinkling, and one that I killed had a dead grasshopper-frog in its stomach. I have also found the comminuted elytra of water-beetles in their stomachs, but no scales or other signs of fish. The prey is swallowed with great rapidity—in a flash of time.

"The colour of the bull-frog is dusky grey, lighter on the sides and limbs, and lighter still on the under parts; but the same tinge throughout. There are some dark spots on the neck and back, and the hind-limbs have leopard-like markings.

"The grasshopper-frog, referred to above, is very abundant in the swamps. It is the smallest frog in the States, being only an inch and a half in length, and weighing less than an ounce. It is greyish-green in colour, with some brown patches and light stripes on the body, and the legs barred with brown. There are discs to the toes, like those of a tree-frog, but its habits do not seem to be arboreal. On the contrary, I have only found it in stagnant swamps and marshes where there was a thick matting of water-plants. They sit on the floating leaves in great numbers, and are very agile, and they make a piping noise, quite unlike the ordinary croaking of a frog. Thousands of them fall a prey to the storks and other aquatic birds, yet there are myriads of them in the Okefinoke Swamp.

"In certain parts of the swamp you may see the tadpoles through the water, swarming on the bottom as thickly as the mosquitoes in the air. I suppose these to be chiefly the tadpoles of the grasshopper-frogs; those of the bull-frogs I could never find.

"The other two frogs found in these swamps are of species which I could not identify. They are of medium size and dull colour, and there is nothing remarkable in their habits.

"There are also one or two species of water-lizards—newts apparently.

"Should we dig in the mud near the centre of the swamp, where there is a sluggish current in the water, it is not improbable that we shall turn up a hellbender, a species of salamander, which is held in utter abhorrence by our friends the shingle-cutters. I heard one of these gentlemen refer to me in the following eulogistic terms: 'Never tell me that that there monkey-crank ain't in league with the devil. Gawd-a-mighty! I seed him strake a hellbender, and never no hurt come to him.'

"The hellbender is as harmless as a frog or toad, or any other causelessly persecuted reptile. It is an absolutely water-hunting species, which I have never seen on dry land. It is more abundant in the Mississippi and the great rivers which run into it than elsewhere, and is scarce in swamps, to which it seems to resort to bury itself in the mud to hibernate, and perhaps to breed.

At all events, I have seen the young in the Okefinoke, and they seem to be hatched from the eggs fully developed, which is different from other salamanders, which undergo several transformations before attaining full development.

"The hellbender is from fifteen to eighteen inches long, and usually weighs about two pounds. It has a somewhat eel-like head, a bulky body, and a flattened tail, adapted to its aquatic life; but it is not a swift swimmer, and is easily captured with the aid of a hand-net. The few that I have handled seemed to be lethargic creatures, and made no resistance to capture, or attempts to bite in which they also differ from most other salamanders. The colour is grey, with spots and zigzag blotches of darker grey. It burrows in the mud in search of prey as well as to hibernate, and devours every kind of slug, worm, fresh-water shrimp, insect, tadpole, or small fish which it can capture. Its haunts make its habits difficult to study, but I believe I am correct in stating that it lies hid in the mud, with only its head uncovered, for the purpose of surprising the fish as they swim by. I have seen one so lying with a fish in its jaws. The people of the country have a strong prejudice against it and never lose an opportunity of destroying it."

The collection of the amphibian material was made at four different periods. The initial party consisting of zoologists from Cornell University stayed from May 28 to July 13, 1912. It consisted of Professor J. C. Bradley, the leader of the party, and Professor C. R. Crosby, both of the Department of Entomology; Dr. A. H. Wright of the Department of Zoology; Principal W. D. Funkhouser of the Cascadilla Preparatory School; Messrs. M. D. Leonard, S. C. Bishop, and A. R. Cahn, all of the class of 1913, and Paul Battle of Bainbridge, Ga., Mr. E. L. Worsham, State Entomologist of Georgia, and Mr. Chas. S. Spooner were with the party for a week. A smaller party from the University spent two weeks in the swamp from December 18, 1913, to January 1, 1914. This party consisted of Professors J. G. Needham and J. C. Bradley, Messrs. Paul Battle and John T. Needham. Another container was again intrusted to the Lees until August 1, 1914 when it was returned. In addition, the amphibians collected May 6-23, 1912 by Mr. Francis Harper were given to our museum and were available for this study.

SUBSEQUENT EXPLORATIONS (1914 TO 1922)

In 1921 we proposed to enter Okefinokee to make a thorough study of its vertebrate life, particularly the life histories of the Salientia. With the support of the Heckscher Foundation for the Advancement of Research, Mrs. Wright and I planned to leave in April and spend the spring and summer in the swamp. Circumstances necessitated her presence in Ithaca and Mr. Francis Harper was secured as my associate. Together from April 21 to August 1 we collected in the swamp with Billy's Island as our base. The Hebard Cypress Company were operating from this island and to them (The Hebards, John M. Hopkins, A. J. Armstrong, Sam Edwards, Sam Mizzell and Hamp Mizzell, The Quarterman brothers, and other officials) and its numerous employees we extend our heartfelt thanks for numerous kindnesses, courtesies, and assistance in our work.

In 1922 we motored to the swamp from Ithaca and arrived June 11. This year we chose Chesser Island on the eastern edge of the swamp to study the surrounding region and less disturbed parts of the swamp. On August 2 to 7 we visited Billy's Island. We sought also to get more illustrations of the breeding stages of life histories we worked out in 1921 and fill in the gaps in life histories of species not known.

The party of 1922 consisted of Mrs. Anna Allen Wright, Messrs. F. Harper and Miles D. Pirnie and myself. With a Ford we were able to operate from Waycross to Jacksonville or from the island to mainland.

In 1921 and 1922 we added to our amphibian species of previous years these species:

Siren lacertina	Pseudacris nigrita
Pseudobranchus striatus	Hyla squirella
Ambystoma angulatum	Rana aesopus
Triturus viridescens dorsalis	Rana heckscheri
Scaphiopus holbrookii	Rana virgatipes

The frogs in this list are forms solely outside the swamp or mainly so.

THE OKEFINOKEE REGION

The region of this study is roughly the Okefinokee swamp.

The Okefinokee region falls largely in the Sabalian and Lower Austral life zones of Rehn and Hebbard (1916), or physiographic areas called Lower Coastal and Upper Coastal by the same authors. It is in the Coastal plain of the southeastern United States and very decidedly of the pine barren region variously placed in Flat Pine Barrens, East Florida Flatwoods section (Florida portion of region). In some interpretations it might fall into the Gulf Strip of the Lower Austral or in some discussions be thought of as a part of the northern portion of the range of some "Floridan forms."

The swamp covers parts of Charlton, Ware, Clinch, Pierce, Camden, and Brantley counties and extends into Florida if Bay Swamp be conceived as a part of its area. We have done desultory collecting in Nassau and Baker counties in Florida. In a previous discussion we have given its area as 660 square miles, 26 miles in greatest width and 39 miles in greatest depth. Possibly these dimensions are somewhat larger than they are now known to be. The chief effluent of the swamp is the Suwannee river. The St. Mary's also drains some of the eastern part of the swamp. The tributaries or branches on the east side of the swamp are mainly short and most of the larger creeks are tributary to the St. Mary's river, while on the west side and north many creeks of considerable length flow into the swamp and through it eventually into the Suwannee. This swamp then makes of east Florida an island, if one wishes so to term it.

PLANT HABITATS

In 1926 we prepared a paper on The Plant Habitats of Okefinokee Swamp (MSS) and therein expanded the habitats of the swamp. We will content ourselves in this discussion with a short general discussion from that paper.

The swamp's geographic subdivisions as given by residents and by the maps fall into four major groups: cypress bays (such as Billy Island Bay, Floyd Island Bay, Double-O-Bay, Jackson Bay); prairies (such as Floyd's Island Prairie, Grand Prairie, Chase Prairie, Honey Island Prairie); islands ("piney islands" such as Billy, Honey, Floyd's and Chesser Islands and "hammocks" such as Craven, Mixon, Hickory, Cedar); and water-courses, (a) wooded (such as Minne Lake, Minne Lake Run, Billy Lake, River Narrows, Suwannee River), (b) artificial (such as Suwannee Canal), (c) open channels through the prairies connecting lakes or water courses. These are usually made by the residents and often follow the alligator trails. In March 1915 (Phila. Acad. Sci. 1915, pp. 144, 145), Messrs. Bishop and Wright used these four divisions in classifying the snakes according to habitat.

In 1921 we used thirteen or fourteen groups for characterizing distribution of the animal forms within the swamp, namely pine barrens, island edges, hammocks, grassy fields, cultivated fields, around and in buildings, sand scrub (Floyd's) cypress bays, cypress ponds, cypress heads, prairies, sphagnum bogs, and watercourses.

In 1922 being located in Chesser Island near the swamps edge and roaming on the mainland as we did the list reached 23 or 24 separate habitats or headings on our plant sheets. Categories such as these were used in gathering our notes together: St. Mary's river; sand bluff, St. Mary's river; sand scrub; sand ridges or hills; dry pine barrens; Camp Cornelia; cleared and cultivated fields; around buildings, roadsides and railroads; village streets; Spanish Creek moist woods; hammocks; moist pine barrens; edge of islands; cypress ponds; river swamps, branch swamps; bays; strands; edge of wooded lakes; borders of prairie lakes.

The major natural plant ecological communities or associations of the swamp proper might roughly be divided into six groups:

1. "Prairies" (including center of cypress pond, also open lakes).
2. "Bays" (including edge of cypress ponds, "heads in prairies," borders of wooded water courses such as Minne Lake).
3. Water courses (These merge with "prairies," open-centered cypress pond).
4. Hammocks (including cultivated fields, buildings, most "old fields").
5. Barrens (including pine barrens, moist and dry, sand scrub, sand hills or ridges, etc.)
6. "Strand" (including sphagnum bogs, fern bogs, fern prairie, sphagnum circle around "heads" and around cypress bases, etc.)

The "prairies" and cypress "bays" are peculiarly distinctive of the swamp. On the mainland, the open-centered cypress pond suggests these two elements. The water courses within the swamp can hardly be thought of as distinctive botanically as the "prairies," "bays," hammocks and barrens. The islands of the swamp are like a piece of the cut-off mainland with its hammocks and barrens. Witness the mainland extending into the swamp, as, The Pocket, followed closely by Jones Island, Gallberry Island, and Billy Island. The "strand" or sphagneous formation in different forms extends from the pine barrens to the "prairies."

If we proceed from the "prairies" on the eastern edge of the swamp over Chesser Island to St. Mary's river we have (without consulting notes) these impressions on breeding habitats based on our 1922 experiences.

Open prairies:

Acris gryllus	Hyla cinerea

Rana grylio

Outer edge of cypress "bay;" open cypress pond in "bay"; edge of lakes in "prairies":

Acris gryllus	Hyla cinerea

Rana grylio

"Strand" of "prairies":

Rana virgatipes

Cypress "bay" itself:

Hyla (in next category)
Three species of "prairies,"
Rana clamitans at island's edge.

Cypress pond on Chesser Island:

Acris gryllus	Bufo quercicus
Hyla cinerea	Bufo terrestris
Hyla femoralis	Rana aesopus
Hyla gratiosa	Rana clamitans
Pseudacris ocularis	Rana sphenocephala

Gastrophryne carolinensis

"Dreen" (Cypress "bay" between island and mainland)

Acris gryllus	Rana grylio
Hyla cinerea	Rana clamitans

Rana virgatipes

Permanent open ponds in pinelands on mainland. (Anna's Pond, Petty Pond, etc.)

Rana sphenocephala	Hyla squirella
Rana aesopus	Hyla gratiosa
Hyla femoralis	Bufo terrestris
Gastrophryne carolinensis	Bufo quercicus

Ponds (with shrubs or cypress)

Pseudacris ocularis	Hyla gratiosa
Gastrophryne carolinensis	Rana aesopus
Hyla femoralis	Rana sphenocephala

Roadside low flat temporary pools, no shade:

Bufo quercicus   Hyla gratiosa

Bufo terrestris   Hyla squirella

Gastrophryne carolinensis   Scaphiopus holbrookii

Camp Pinckney pools, high oak banks:

Bufo terrestris   Rana sphenocephala

Scaphiopus holbrookii   Hyla cinerea

Rana clamitans   Hyla versicolor

River swamp (St. Mary's River) pools:

Rana clamitans   Rana heckscheri

Et al.

A CATALOGUE OF THE SPECIES OF SALIENTIA OF THE OKEFINOKEE REGION (1922)

(Plates I, II, III)

The Salientia of this region include species, representing seven genera. These are *Scaphiopus, Bufo, Acris, Pseudacris, Hyla, Rana,* and *Gastrophryne.*

1. *Scaphiopus holbrookii* (Harlan). The spade-foot.
   This subterranean species was found only in the region east of the swamp. We recorded it from Braganza, Georgia to Hilliard, Florida. Usually our records are from tadpoles and not from the adults.

2. *Bufo quercicus* Holbrook. The oak toad.
   This is an abundant breeder in shallow pools during warmer rains. It may hide during the day or travel abroad in the heath or grassy cover of the pinelands.

3. *Bufo terrestris* Bonnaterre. The southern toad.
   This terrestrial species is abundant, being found in almost every land habitat where cover exists, particularly in pine barrens and hammocks. At breeding season it seeks shallow water for breeding.

4. *Acris gryllus* (LeConte). The cricket-frog.
   These little jumpers are in myriads on the prairies and in cypress ponds, and after rains may be common on the moist islands.

5. *Pseudacris nigrita* (LeConte). The black chorus frog.
   In early spring this species breeds in shallow water not within the swamp. After breeding it is found on pinelands or high sandy ridges (Trail Ridge, etc.).

6. *Pseudacris ocularis* (Holbrook). The little chorus frog.
   This midget of frogs of the U. S. A. breeds in the cypress ponds and thereafter is usually in the wet pine barrens of the islands' or swamp's edges, or around the edges of ponds.

7. *Hyla cinerea cinerea* (Schneider).   The green tree frog.
The "bellfrog" inhabits waterlily prairies, cypress ponds, swampy thickets, and proves one of the commonest anurans of such a habitat.

8. *Hyla femoralis* Latreille.   The pine woods tree frog.
This tree frog is a common inhabitant of the high long-leaved pines of pinelands and other trees of hammocks except at breeding times when it frequents cypress ponds and temporary depressions and ditches.

9. *Hyla gratiosa* LeConte.   The Florida tree frog.
This, the largest treefrog of the region, is scarce within the swamp but common enough in trees on the outside of the swamp.   It breeds in cypress ponds and other ponds.

10. *Hyla squirella* Latreille.   The Southern tree frog.
This species was not found within the swamp.   It normally lives about domiciles along water courses, and in other habitats in trees, but breeds in ponds, temporary pools, roadside ditches, etc.

11. *Hyla versicolor versicolor* (LeConte).   The tree toad.
We found this common species the rarest Hyla in this region.   We took it only along the St. Mary's River.   Here it bred in pools under oak trees.

12. *Rana aesopus* (Cope).   The gopher frog.
This inhabitant of gopher turtle holes along the Trail Ridge repairs to cypress and other ponds for breeding.

13. *Rana clamitans* Latreille.   The green frog.
This species is considerably smaller than in the north, less common than several Ranas, and frequents the edges of cypress ponds, cypress bays, border of streams, etc.

14. *Rana grylio* Stejneger.   The southern bullfrog.
This species is common on the prairies, along the edges of open water lakes, or in openings in the cypress bays.

15. *Rana heckscheri* Wright.   Heckscher's frog.
This species described from this region is an inhabitant of river swamps, swampy tangles outside Okefinokee swamp proper.   In these places it breeds.

16. *Rana sphenocephala* (Cope).   The southern meadow frog.
This is the common spotted frog of the region, breeding in cypress ponds, cypress bays, and ponds of other description as well as streams, runs, dreens, etc.   Later it travels more on the land in moist cover.

17. *Rana virgatipes* Cope.   The carpenter frog.
This species was not common in the center of the swamp.   In the cypress edge of Black Jack Island and in the cypress bay edges of the east edge of the swamp, and in the prairies in the nearby region we recorded it.   It breeds in the cypress bays.

Plate I

Lateral aspects. *Bufo, Gastrophryne, Pseudacris, Scaphiopus*

1. *Bufo americanus*, male, Ithaca, N. Y., May 4, 1929. From W. J. Koster.
2. *Bufo fowleri*, female, Mt. Vernon, Va., Mr. and Mrs. M. C. Brady and author June 3, 1928.
3. *Bufo terrestris*, male, Gainesville, Fla., May 4, 1929. From O. C. Van Hyning.
4. *Scaphiopus holbrookii*, male, Mobile, Ala., Apr. 18, 1929. From H. P. Löding.
5. *Bufo quercicus*, male, Gainesville, Fla., May 7, 1929. From O. C. Van Hyning.
6. *Gastrophryne carolinensis*, female, New Orleans, La., May 25, 1928. From Percy Viosca, Jr.
7. *Pseudacris ocularis*, Billy Id., May 20, 1921.
8. *Pseudacris ornata*, male, Helotes, Texas, Feb. 22, 1925.
9. *Pseudacris nigrita*, Chesser's Id., July 16, 1922.

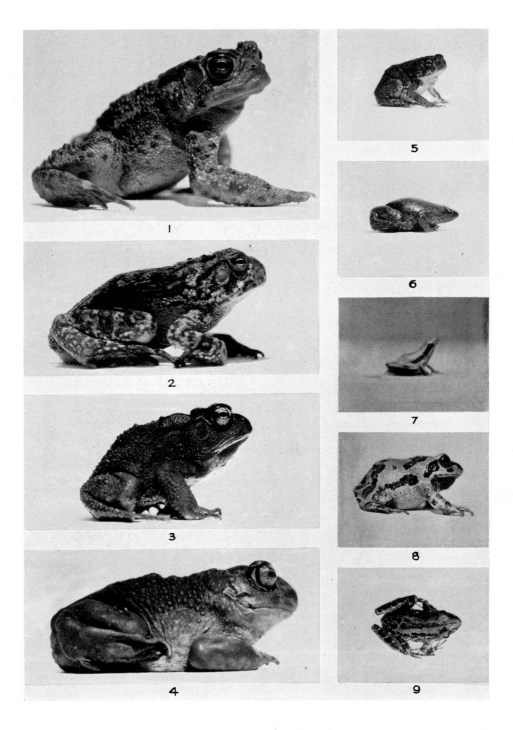

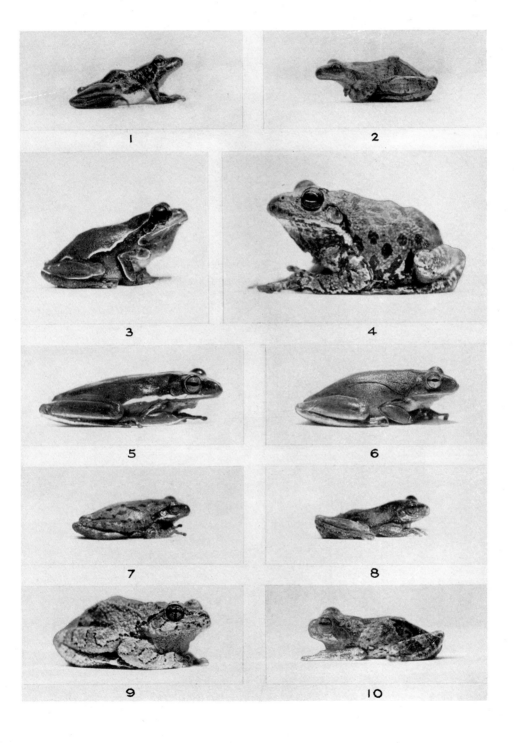

Plate III

Lateral aspects. *Rana* males

1. *Rana septentrionalis*, Onekio, N. Y.   July 14, 1923. × 1.0
2. *Rana clamitans*, Billy Id., Ga.   May 23, 1921. × 0.8.
3. *Rana virgatipes*, Chesser Id., Ga.   July 22, 1922. × 1.1.
4. *Rana heckscheri*, half-grown adult, Hilliard, Fla.   August 17, 1922. × 0.75.
5. *Rana aesopus*, Chesser Id., Ga.   1922. × 0.65.
6. *Rana pipiens*, Vermont.   Oct., 1928.
7. *Rana sphenocephala*, Billy Id., Ga.   May 18, 1921. × 0.5.
8. *Rana grylio*, Billy Id., Ga.   May 9, 1921. × 0.8.

18. *Gastrophryne carolinensis* (Holbrook). The narrow-mouthed toad. This subterranean species becomes abundantly evident when suitable rains occur. Then its sheep-like bleat is heard frequently in the pine barrens, edges of hammocks, etc.

HYPOTHETICAL SPECIES TO BE EXPECTED OR SOUGHT IN THE OKEFINOKEE REGION

In view of the foregoing discussions there is more or less (sometimes remote) likelihood of the following species being recorded near or in the Okefinokee swamp.

Bufo fowleri · Hyla andersonii

Pseudacris occidentalis · Hyla avivoca

Pseudacris ornata · Rana catesbeiana

Rana pipiens (see R. sphenocephala)

In this paper the life history of *Hyla andersonii* is considered and a few observations passed on *Pseudacris occidentalis* and *Pseudacris ornata*. The life histories of the common forms *Bufo fowleri*, *Rana catesbeiana* and *Rana pipiens* are omitted. For comparison with *Rana virgatipes*, the life history of the northern mink frog (*Rana septentrionalis*) is incorporated.

GENERAL DISCUSSION OF THE OKEFINOKEE SALIENTIA

RANGE

It would be natural not to expect truly tropical Floridan species such as *Scaphiopus holbrookii albus* or *Eleutherodactylus ricordii* (West Indies—Gainesville, Florida) in the Okefinokee swamp, yet on the Keys and in this southern tropical region such Sabalian forms as *Hyla squirella* and *Hyla cinerea* and *Bufo quercicus* occur.

The Sabalian frogs comprise the bulk of the swamp's amphibian inhabitants. About eleven species occur mainly in the Sabalian region. They are all, with two exceptions, in the Swamp (I.O.) or outside (O.O.) The two exceptions may later be found when better understood.

O.O.	*Hyla squirella*	Va. —Tex.
I.O.	*Hyla femoralis*	N.C.—Fla.—Tex.
I.O.	*Bufo quercicus*	N.C.—Fla.—Ala.
	Pseudacris occidentalis	S.C.—Tex.
	Pseudacris ornatus	S.C.—Tex.
O.O.	*Pseudacris nigrita*	S.C.—Fla.—Miss.
I.O.	*Hyla gratiosa*	S.C.—Fla.—La.
I.O.	*Pseudacris ocularis*	S.C.—Fla.
O.O.	*Rana aesopus*	S.C.—Fla.
O.O.	*Rana heckscheri*	S.C.—Fla.
I.O.	*Rana grylio*	Ga. —Fla.—La.

Four of these are solely outside and *Hyla gratiosa* mainly so.   *Rana aesopus* is absent within the swamp because of its subterranean habits.

There are about nine species of frogs which might be considered Austral. Three of them are absent such as *Bufo fowleri*, *Pseudacris feriarum* and *Hyla andersonii*. The latter ought to be present since its associated species *Rana virgatipes* occurs in the swamp.   The six Austral species are

	Bufo fowleri	N.E. —Ga.—Tex.
O.O.	*Scaphiopus h. holbrookii*	Mass. —Fla.
I.O.	*Acris gryllus*	N.Y. —Fla.—Tex.
I.O.	*Hyla cinerea*	N.J. —Fla.—Tex.
I.O.	*Rana virgatipes*	N.J. —Ga.
	Hyla andersonni	N.J. —S.C.
I.O.	*Gastrophryne carolinensis*	Va. —Fla.—La.
I.O.	*Bufo terrestris*	S.C. —Ga.—La.

The widespread *Hyla versicolor* was recorded on St. Mary's River at Folkston, Ga. and *Rana catesbeiana* has been at times reported to be near the swamp though we did not take it.

COLORATION OF SPIRIT SPECIMENS (1912)
AND MEASUREMENTS OF 1912 MATERIAL

These are parts of the 1913 manuscript. They were painstakingly made and are herein included as contributory to an understanding of the species. They can be interpreted in part as more pertinent to the 1912-1914 period in amphibia of the U. S. A. but in part they are apropos to the present discussion and paper, because partially they pertain to species little understood and partially because they were conceived from a different angle than the coloration from life or the scheme of measurements (relative) especially employed in this paper.

MEASUREMENTS

We have made relative measurements of the Okefinokee frogs to accord with a system we are employing for all the frogs of the United States. We choose from our and U. S. National Museum collections (supplemented from the collections of other institutions) representatives of each species and subspecies which measure in body length 20 mm., 28 mm., 36 mm., 44 mm., 56 mm., 66 mm., 68 mm., 82 mm., 95 mm., 108 mm., 125 mm., 136 mm., and 150 mm.   In this way if one of each of the Ranas of the swamp are measured at the same body length we have all our actual measurements in part also relative if they be put in a table.   For example at 56 mm., such a table as the following might be constructed. (Table 1)

TABLE I

NUMBER	1	2	3	4	5	6	7	8
Rana	*virg.*	*sept.*	*clam.*	*heck.*	*gryl.*	*spheno.*	*aeso.*	*cates.*
Sex	♂	♂	♂	im.	im.	♂	im.	im.
Length (sn.-vent)	56	56	56	56	56	56	M	56
Head (tympanum)	21	24	26	23	21.5	23.5	i	22
Head (angle mouth)	15	19	19.5	20	20	21	s	20
Width of head	18	23	24	24	21	21	s	23
Snout	8	9	10	10	10	10.5	i	9
Eye	6.5	7	8	7	6.5	7	n	7
Interorbital space	2	3	3.5	3	3.5	4.0	g	4
Upper eyelid width	4.5	6	5.5	6	5	6		4.5
Tympanum	7	10	9	5	5	6	i	5
Intertympanic width	12.5	11	12	15.5	12	14.5	n	15
Internasal space	4.5	4	6	5.5	3.5	5.5		6
Forelimb	23	30	31	29	27	30	t	31
1st finger	7	7	9	9	9	9.5	h	10
2nd finger	7	9	8	7.5	9	7	i	10
3rd finger	9	10.5	12	10	13	11	s	12
4th finger	6	9	7	7	10	7		10
Hind limb	75	88	86	84	71	104	s	82
Tibia	23	29	31	29		36	e	28
Foot	25	32	33	30	25	33	r	28
1st toe	7	7	8	8	9	6	i	9
2d toe	13	13	12	12	13	13	e	13
3d toe	18	20	18	17	18	18	s	18
4th toe	24	28	30	27	25	30	.	27
5th toe	16	19	20.5	18	23.5	20		20

In this paper we will not attempt to include all the measurements for the species of the Okefinokee region. These are reserved for a growth paper in process of organization and therein will be incorporated.

This chart means that if one finds a specimen 6-10 mm. in body length it might be a transforming or transformed frog of nine species; or at 11-20 mm. it might be one of 16 frogs (one of 15 transforming species or young of 14 species, or a male of 6 species or a female of 5 species); at 68 mm. there are ten species to consider, a male or a female of *Bufo terrestris, Scaphiopus holbrookii, Hyla gratiosa, Rana sphenocephala, Rana septentrionalis,* or *Rana clamitans,* a male of *Rana aesopus,* or immatures of *Rana heckscheri, R. grylio,* or *Rana catesbeiana*; at 95 mm. four species only are to be considered, a female *Rana aesopus* or either a male or a female of *R. heckscheri, R. grylio* and *Rana catesbeiana*; at 150 mm. only two species enter, a male or female each of *R. grylio* and *Rana catesbeiana.*

This chart might suggest the desirability of a key at each size for true comparisons. At 6-10 mm. it might thus prove a more desirable key because each of the nine species are at transformation and are comparable. In the same way at 95 mm. we have mature males and females of the green frog, gopher frog, Heckscher's frog, southern bullfrog, and bullfrog. Even here however we have the green frog and gopher frog nearing the extreme of their size and females of the other three just about beginning breeding. Possibly

TABLE 2

Identification Index
Legend—
t—transformation stages
i—immature or young
m—breeding male
f—breeding female

	Body Length in millimeters																
	6 to 10	11 to 20	28	36	44	56	66	68	82	95	108	113	125	136	150	180	200
Pseudacris ocularis	t	ti	mf														
Pseudacris nigritus	t	ti	mf														
(Pseudacris ornatus)	t?	i	im	mf													
Gastrophryne carolinensis	t	ti	m	mf	f												
Acris gryllus	t	ti	mf	mf													
(Eleutherodactylus ricordii)	t	ti	mf	mf													
Bufo quercicus	t	ti	i	i	mf	mf	mf	mf	f								
Bufo terrestris	t	ti	i	i	mf	mf	mf	mf	f								
Scaphiopus holbrookii	t	ti	i	mf	mf	mf	mf										
Hyla andersonii		ti	i	mf	mf												
Hyla squirella		ti	mf	mf	mf												
Hyla femoralis		ti	mf	mf													
Hyla cinerea		ti	im	mf	mf	mf											
Hyla versicolor		ti	mf	mf	mf												
Hyla gratiosa		i	mf	mf	mf	mf	mf	mf									
Rana sphenocephala			ti	i	mf	mf	mf	mf	f								
Rana virgatipes			t	i	mf	mf	mf	mf									
(Rana septentrionalis)			ti	i	mf					(north)							
Rana clamitans			t	i	i	i	mf	mf	mf	mf	mf						
Rana aesopus			t	ti	i	i	i		m	mf	mf	mf	f				
Rana heckscheri				ti	ti	i	i	i	m	i	f	f	mf	mf			
Rana grylio			ti	ti	i	i	i	i	i	mf	mf	mf	f	mf	mf	mf	mf
(Rana catesbeiana)			t	ti	i	i	ti	i	i	i	mf	mf	mf	mf	mf	mf	f

old age maximum frogs might not be comparable. In the same way if one glance at sizes from 11-20 mm. to 82 mm. one will find at any one size differences in maturity. Nevertheless keys at each size might prove useful and might in spite of their limitations prove suggestive of better characters than those we have chosen more at random in the past. In this connection, however, the keys of the past have not been so bad because they have generally chosen breeding adults. Possibly they will prove as good as some suggested by this identification index. (Table 2)

We have sought to measure the Salientia (frogs, toads, tree-frogs, etc.) of the United States and Canada at the 13 sizes given under the foregoing topic (see Measurements). Our intention was to present in this paper a series of keys at these various measurements. This will be delayed until the missing sizes can be found. Any student of the frogs of the Southeastern United States may find the following tables at 28 mm. (Tables 3, 4), 44 mm. (Table 6), 66 mm. (Table 7), 82 mm., 95 mm. (Table 8), 113 mm., 125 mm. (Table 5), and 150 mm. (Table 9) of use and they are included though our studies of these measurements and growth are not completed.

TABLE 3

Length 28 mm.	P. nigrita	P. nigrita	P. ornata	G. carolinensis	G. carolinensis	Acris gryllus	A. gryllus	E. ricordii	E. ricordii	B. terrestris	B. quercicus	B. quercicus	H. andersonii
Sex	♂	♀	♂	♂	♀	♂	♀	♂	♀	im	♂	♀	im?
H. tympanum							10		11	10	8.5	9.0	
H. ang. mouth				6	5.6		7.5		9	8.5	7	6	
Width head				8	8		10		9.5	12	10.5	9.5	
Snout				4	3.4		5		5	4.5	4	4	
Eye				2.2	3.2		28		4.5	4.0	3.5	3.0	
Interorb. sp.				2.2	3.2		1.6		3	3.5	3.5	3.0	
Upper eyelid				1.6	1.8		1.6		2.5	3.5	2.5	2.5	
Tympanum				—	—		2		3	3.5	2	2	
Int. tymp. sp.				—	—		8		8	9.5	8.5	8	
Int. nasal sp.				2.2	2.8		2.8		3	2.5	2.5	2.5	
Forelimb				12	11		15.8		16	15.5	14.5	14	
1st finger				2.0	2.2		4		3.5	3.5	3	3	
2nd finger				2.6	3.8		4			3.5	3	3.5	
3rd finger				5.0	5.6		7		5	6	5	5	
4th finger				4	3.8		4		4	3.5	3	4	
Hind limb				28	26.4		45		34	27	26	26	
Tibia				10.4	10.4		17.4		12	11	10	10.5	
Foot with tarsus				16	15.4		21.6		18	15	13	15	
Foot without tarsus				11	11		13.6		11	9.5	10	10	
1st toe				2.8	3		5		4	3	1.5	1.5	
2nd toe				4.6	5.0		7		6	5	3.5	3.5	
3rd toe				8	7.8		11		8	6	5	6	
4th toe				11	11		13.6		10	8	7.5	9	
5th toe				8	7		10.5		8	5.5	4.5	5	

TABLE 4

Length 28 mm.	H. squirella	H. squirella	H. femoralis	H. femoralis	H. cinerea	H. versicolor	H. gratiosa	R. sphenocephala	R. virgatipes	R. spetentrionalis	R. clamitans	R. aesopus
Sex	♂	♀	♂	♀	im.	im.	im.	ti	t	ti	t	t
H. tympanum	10.5	10	10	10	10	10	11	12.5	11.5	*	13	13
H. ang. mouth	9	8.5	8	9	8	9	10	10.5	10		10	11
Width head	10	10.5	10	10	10	12	11.5	10	10		11	12
Snout	5	5	4.5	5	5	5.5	5	6	5.25		5	6
Eye	4	3	3	3	3	4	4	4	4		4	5
Interorb. sp.	3	3	3	3.5	3.5	2.5	3	2.5	2		3	3.5
Upper eyelid	3	3	2	2.5	3	2.5	3	3	2		2.5	3
Tympanum	2	2	2	2.5	2.5	3	2	3.5	2.5		2.5	3
Int. tymp. sp.	8.5	8	9	8.5	8.5	9	9.5	8	8		8.5	10
Int. nasal. sp.	2	3	2	2.5	2	3	2.5	3.5	3		3	4.5
Forelimb	13	13.5	13	15	15.5	20	16	15	16		15	15
1st finger	4	3.5	4	4	3.5	3.5	4	4	4.5		4.5	5.5
2nd finger	4	4	4.5	5	4.5	5.0	4.5	3.5	4		4.5	5.5
3rd finger	5.5	6.5	6.5	6	5.5	8	6.5	5.5	6		6.5	7
4th finger	5	4.5	5	5.5	5.0	6	5.0	4	5		4.5	5
Hind limb	39	38	42	41	47	44	44	41	44		44	41
Tibia	15.5	—	14.5	15.5	17	16	17	15	13.5		15	—
Foot with tarsus		18					20	20			18	20
Foot without tarsus	11	11.5	11.5	10	11.5	14	12.5	—	13		13	14
1st toe	2	4	3	3.5	3.5	3	3	2.5	4		4	3.5
2nd toe	3.5	5	5	4	6	4.5	6	5.5	6.5		8	6
3rd toe	7	7.5	8	6	8.5	8	9	7.5	9		9	7.5
4th toe	9	9.5	10	10	10	11	11	11	12		13	14
5th toe	7	7	8	6	8	8	10	7	8		8.5	9

*U. S. N. M. & C. U. collections have 29, 30 mm. specimens not at .28 mm.

TABLE 5

	R. heckscheri	R. heckscheri	R. grylio	R. grylio	R. catesbeiana	R. catesbeiana	R. heckscheri	R. grylio	R. grylio	R. catesbeiana	R. catesbeiana
Sex	♂	♀	♂	♀	♂	♀	♀	♂	♀	♂	♀
Length	113	113	113	113	113	113	125	125	125	125	125
H. tympanum	44		44	39	40.5		43	46.5	42	45.5	43
H. angle mouth	40		39	38	36.5		41	40	39.5	41.5	41
Width head	48		43.5	38.5	41		47.5	46	42	49	45
Snout	17		16	15	17		19	16	17	18.5	17.5
Eye	12.5		10.5	12	11		13.5	13	13	12	12.5
Interorb, sp.	7		6	4.5	7		8	5	4	8	6
Upper eyelid	9.5		8	7.5	7		9.5	9	8.5	8.5	8
Tympanum	17		19	12.5	12		11.5	20	12	15	11.5
Inter-tymp. sp.	9		17.5	20	23.5		26	20	25	24	27
Inter-nasal sp.	9.5		7.5	7	9.5		9.5	6	8.5	8.5	9
Forelimb	45		52	57	61		56	57	62	45	67
1st finger	17		21	18	21.5		19	20	23.5	21	23.5
2nd finger	16		24	22.5	23		18	23	24.5	21	23.5
3rd finger	21		28	28.5	27		24	28	30	29	31
4th finger	17		23	23	24.5		20	23	24.5	22	25.5
Hind limb	160		153	145	169		160	168	173	168	180
Tibia	56		54.5	52	56		58	58	55	61	63
Foot with tarsus	78		80	77	82		81	84	86	87.5	97
Foot without tarsus	52		58	52	58		55	60	60	59	63
1st toe	18		23.5	23	22		20	26	25	22	23
2nd toe	27		33	33	31		28	36	34	32.5	34
3rd toe	38		46	44	44		42	52	47	46.5	49
4th toe	52		58	52	58		54	61	60	59	63
5th toe	38		46	44	41.5		40	51	48.5	46.5	49

TABLE 6

Length 44 mm.

	B. terrestris	S. holbrookii	H. andersonii	H. andersonii	H. cinerea	H. cinerea	H. versicolor	H. versicolor	H. gratiosa	R. sphenocephala	R. virgatipes	R. virgatipes	R. septentrionalis	R. clamitans	R. aesopus	R. heckscheri	R. grylio	R. catesbeiana
Sex	im.	im.	♂	♀	♂	♀	♂	♀	im.	im.	♂	♀	im.	im.	im.	ti	tim.	t
H. tympanum	15	17		13	14	14	14	13.5	18	18	16		16	17		16	16.5	16
H. ang. mouth	14	15		12.5	11	12	13	11.5	14	15.5	18		14	15		12	15.5	14.5
Width head	19.5	19		15.5	13	14.5	15.5	16	19	15	17		15	16		15	17	17
Snout	7	8.5		6.5	6.5	7.5	7.5	7	9	9	8		7	7		7	6	6.5
Eye	6	6		5	5	4	4	5	6.5	5.5	6.5		5.5	6.5		6.5	5.5	6
Interorb. sp.	4.5	6.5		4.5	4	4.5	4.5	5	4	3.5	3		3.5	3		4.5	2.5	3
Upper eyelid	4.5	5		4.5	3	3.5	4	4	4	4	3		3	4		4.5	3.5	3.5
Tympanum	3	4		2.5	2.5	2.5	3.5	2.5	4	5.5	4.5		4.5	4.5		3.5	4	3.5
Int. tymp. sp.	14	16		13	11	12	13	12.5	15	11	12		11	11.5		13.5	10	11.5
Int. nasal sp.	3.5	4		4	4	3.5	4.5	4.5	5	4.5	4.5		4	4.5		5	3.5	4.5
Forelimb	21	22		22.5	23	24	27	22.5	24	22	23		23.5	24.5		22	22	21.5
1st finger	5.5	5		6	6	6.5	8	7	7.5	8	6.5		8	7		7	6.5	7
2nd finger	5	5		8	7	7.5	10	10	9	5.5	7		8	7		7	7	7
3rd finger	7.5	8.5		10	9	9	13	13	12.5	7.5	9.5		11.5	11		10	10	10
4th finger	5.5	4.5		8	8	8	12	11	11.5	4.5	7.5		8	7		7	7	7.5
Hind limb	45	45		62	63	63	63	64.5	64	74	59		64.5	66		64	55	62
Tibia	16	15.5		—	23	25	21	19	23	26	—		22	22		23	21	21.5
Foot with tarsus	22	24		29	18	18	30	28.5	32	—	34		32	32		32	26.5	30.5
Foot without tarsus	14.5	16.5		17	15	18	19	18	20	23	22		25	21		23	21	20
1st toe	3	3		5	5	5	6	6.5	6.5	5	7.5		9	7		9.5	7.5	7.5
2nd toe	5	2.5		8.5	7.5	8	10	9.5	10.5	9.5	12		14	11		13	13	13
3rd toe	9	5		13	12	12.5	15	14	15	14	17		17	15		17.5	16	15.5
4th toe	14.5	9		17.5	16	16	19	18	19	21.5	22		25	21		21	21	20
5th toe	8.5	12.5		13.5	11	11	15	15	14	18.5	15		18	15		16	16	15

TABLE 7

	R. catesbeiana	R. grylio	R. heckscheri	R. aesopus	R. clamitans	R. clamitans	R. septentrionalis	R. septentrionalis	R. virgatipes	R. sphenocephala	R. sphenocephala	H. gratiosa	H. gratiosa	S. holbrookii	S. holbrookii	B. terrestris	B. terrestris
Length 66 mm.																	
Sex	im	im	im	im	♀	♂	♀	♂	♀	♀	♂	♀	♂	♀	♂	♀	♂
H. tympanum		25		26		27	23	24			27		22	22	24	22	22
H. angle mouth		22		26		22.5	19	20			23		21	18.5	20.5	20	19.5
Width head		24		28.5		25.5	21.5	25			25		24	24	25.5	27	26
Snout		9.5		13		10	9.5	9.5			12.5		12	10	10	9	10
Eye		8.5		8		9	6.5	8			8		7	8	7.5	9	8.5
Inter. orb. sp.		3		5		4	3	3			4.5		8	8	8.5	7	6
Upper eyelid		5		5		5.5	3	5.5			6.5		5.5	6	5.5	6.5	6
Tympanum		7		5.5		10	6	8.5			7.5		6	5	5.5	5	6
Int. tymp. sp.		13		20		13.5	14	12			17		19	21	23	21	20.5
Int. nasal sp.		6		7		6	5	6			6.5		6	5	6	5	4.5
Forelimb		32		29		29	28	30			35.5		35	31	30	37	34
1st finger		12		10.5		12	11	10.5			12.5		11.5	6	7.5	10	7
2nd finger		12.5		10.5		11.5	14.5	11			8		12	7	7	9	7
3rd finger		16.5		14.5		15.5	11	17.5			11		15	11	11.5	13	12
4th finger		12.5		11.5		11.5	11	13.5			7		11.5	6	6.5	9	7.5
Hind limb		87		82		95	91	96			118		92	62	64.5	66	69
Tibia		—		—		35	30	30			44		33	20	21	24	26.5
Foot with tarsus		43		43		48.5	41.5	47.5			38		33	33	33	37	39
Foot without tarsus		30		28.5		33	31	31			29		29	22	24	25	25
1st toe		12		10		11.5	10	11			8		8.5	4.5	4	6	5
2nd toe		18.5		15		17	14.5	18			13.5		12	8	8.5	9	8
3rd toe		24		21.5		24	23	22.5			20.5		19	12	13.5	15	14
4th toe		30		28.5		33	31	31			37		23	17	19.5	23	24
5th toe		24		19		23	21.5	25.5			22		17.5	11.5	11.5	12.5	14

TABLE 8

	B. terrestris	R. sphenocephala	R. clamitans	R. clamitans	R. aesopus	R. aesopus	R. heckscheri	R. grylio	R. catesbeiana	R. clamitans	R. clamitans	R. heckscheri	R. heckscheri	R. grylio	R. grylio	R. catesbeiana	R. catesbeiana	R. aesopus	R. aesopus
Sex	♀	♀	♀	♂	♀	♂	♂	♂	i	♂	♀	♂	♀	♂	♀	♂	♀	♂	♀
Length	82	82	82	82	82	82	82	82	82	95	95	95	95	95	95	95	95	95	95
H. tympanum	28	29	28	31	32.5	35	34	35	29	37.5	33	38		40	34	37	33	37	36
H. angle mouth	26	23	24	25	30	32	29	29	27	31.5	29	35		35	32.5	34	31	31	31
Width head	38	25	28	30	36	42	38	33	31	38	32	41		38	33	41	33.5	49	42.5
Snout	12	13	11.5	12	15	17	14	13	12	15	14.5	16		16	13	15	14	17	17
Eye	11	13	8	8	8.5	9	9	9	9	11	11	10		10	9	10	11	11	11.5
Interorb. sp.	9	5	3.5	5	5.0	7	7	5	6	5	6	9		7	5	6	5.5	5.5	6.5
Upper eyelid	6.5	7	7	7	6.0	7	8	6	5	8	7	7.5		6	7	7	7	7.5	6.5
Tympanum	8	8.5	8	13	8	7.5	12	13	7	14	11	13		16	9	11	10	9	8
Int. tymp. sp.	27	18	18	17	23	25	18	15.5	19	17.5	19	18		15	19	21	21	26	27
Int. nasal sp.	6	6.5	7	7	7.5	7	7	15.5	7	7	9	7		15	7	7	8.5	8	8
Forelimb	46	39	44	41	37	40	35	50	38	54	41.5	47		51	54	50	48	46	45
1st finger	11.5	11	14	12	15	15	12	14	13	15	17	13		15	18	17	19	15	17.5
2nd finger	11	9.5	13	11	13.5	10	11	16	13	14	16	12		16	19	16	19	10	12.5
3rd finger	16	12	18	16	19.5	16	13	18	18	19	21.5	16		20	22	20	24	17	16.5
4th finger	12	8	14	11	15	11	10	12	12	15	16	11		16	19	15	20	13	10.5
Hind limb	85	130	125	111	109	113	119	128	107	146	137	133		144	127	130	130	130	134
Tibia	32	45	41	41	—	43	41	42	37	50	47	45		46	—	45	44	48	50
Foot with tarsus	46.5	41	58		58	—					68				67		68		
Foot without tarsus	32.5	40	40	37	37	41	43	48	40	48	45	48		49	44	50	48	44	45
1st toe	6	8.5	14	10	12	9	11	15	12	11	16	13		17	20	15	17	10	11.5
2nd toe	11.5	15	21	18	18.5	17	18	24	18	19	24.5	21		25	28	23	25.5	18	19
3rd toe	20	21	30	22	27	23	23	29	26	27	32.5	25		34	37.5	31	36	23.5	29
4th toe	30	33.5	40	35	37	39	38	44	36	43	45	42		45	44	46	48	40	40
5th toe	18	21	30	27	26	22	28	35	30	29	31	30		37	37	35	35	24	25

TABLE 9

	R. grylio ♂	R. grylio ♀	R. catesbeiana ♂	R. catesbeiana ♀	R. grylio ♂	R. grylio ♀	R. catesbeiana ♂	R. catesbeiana ♀	R. catesbeiana ♂	R. catesbeiana ♀	R. catesbeiana ♀
Sex	♂	♀	♂	♀	♂	♀	♂	♀	♂	♀	♀
Length	136	136	136	136	150	150	150	150	180	180	184
H. tympanum	50		51	53		44.5	57	48	61		63
H. angle mouth	41		49	51		43.5	53	47.5	57		63
Width head	48		56	47.5		46	56	52	70		73
Snout	18		21	18		18	20.5	21	25		31
Eye	13.5		13	13.5		12	14	14	15		18
Interorb. sp.	5.5		6	6		6	10	6.5	10		9.5
Upper eyelid	9		11	9		9	10.5	10.5	12.5		12
Tympanum	22		18	13		13	22	13	22.5		19
Inter-tymp. sp.	20		28	26.5		25.5	29	29	32		40
Inter-nasal sp.	7		10	9		7	10.5	9.5	12.5		12
Forelimb	52		66	71		76	70	74	90		80
1st finger	22.5		20	22		22	28	26	35.5		32
2nd finger	24.5		19	22		26	27	26	38		32
3rd finger	32		26	32		31	34.5	31.5	48		40
4th finger	23.5		20	23		26.5	30.5	27	42		32.5
Hind limb	187		190	165		175	218	173	260		220
Tibia	63		66	57.5		61.5	73	61	92		82
Foot with tarsus	93		96	89		98	108	98.5	127		120
Foot without tarsus	65		—	60.5		66	73	66.5	94		75
1st toe	25		15	22		26	27	27	37		29
2nd toe	39		28	33		40	41.5	38	52		44
3rd toe	50		41	45		53	52	52	72		64
4th toe	65		60	60.5		66	73	66.5	94		75
5th toe	50		42	42.5		53	52	51	70		60

FIRST APPEARANCE AND AUTUMNAL DISAPPEARANCE

These two topics we can discuss in no way clearly or specifically because we were not in the swamp the last of September, October, November and December before the Christmas season, nor in the swamp from January to April 22. It is therefore apparent why we have no reason for a general discussion of these topics or hibernation. The U. S. National Museum collections have contributed some records for the above four months.

BREEDING SIZES

On the basis of least breeding sizes we have six groups in the 21 species considered. First come two forms, *Pseudacris ocularis* and *Acris gryllus*, which mature at 11.5-15 mm. for males and 12-16 mm. for females. The next group of five, namely *Bufo quercicus*, *Gastrophryne carolinensis*, *Pseudacris nigrita*, *Hyla squirella* and *Hyla femoralis*, matures for males at 19-

24 mm., and for females at 20.5-23 mm. The third group of four—*Hyla andersonii, Hyla versicolor, Hyla cinerea, Rana virgatipes,* matures for males at 30-41 mm., for females at 38-41 mm. The fourth group of six species, viz: *Rana septentrionalis, Hyla gratiosa, Rana sphenocephala, Bufo terrestris, Rana clamitans* and *Scaphiopus holbrookii* matures for males at 48-54 mm. and for females at 48-56 mm. The fifth group has one form, *Rana aesopus,* with first males at 68 mm. and first females at 77 mm. The final and sixth group comprise *Rana heckscheri, Rana grylio* and *Rana catesbeiana* with males maturing at 82-85 mm. and females, at 85-102 mm. The above data and more are summarized in the following table: (Table 10)

TABLE 10

	MALES	FEMALES
Pseudacris ocularis	11.5– 15.5mm.	12 – 17.5 mm.
Acris gryllus	15 – 29	16 – 33
Bufo quercicus	19 – 30	20.5– 32
Gastrophryne carolinensis	20 – 30	22 – 36
Pseudacris nigrita	21 – 28	22 – 30
Hyla squirella	23 – 36	23 – 37
Hyla femoralis	24 – 37	23 – 40
Hyla andersonii	30 – 41	38 – 47
Hyla versicolor	32 – 51	33 – 60
Hyla cinerea	37 – 59	41 – 63
Rana virgatipes	41 – 63	41 – 66
Rana septentrionalis	48 – 71	48 – 76
Hyla gratiosa	49 – 68	50 – 68
Rana sphenocephala	49 – 78	53 – 82
Bufo terrestris	51 – 74.5	56 – 82
Rana clamitans	52 – 72	58 – 75
Scaphiopus holbrookii	54 – 72	50 – 71
Rana aesopus	68 –101	77 –108
Rana heckscheri	82 –113	102 –125
Rana grylio	82 –152	85 –161
Rana catesbeiana	85 –180	89 –200

The relationship of egg diameter to smallest breeding size in each species is given in the following table (Table 11). With the smallest and largest egg vitelline diameters we divided the least breeding size of each species to see how many times bigger the body length was than the real egg diameter of each species. For example the smallest breeding oak toad in body length is only 13.6 times longer than the egg diameter of that species, wherein the smallest breeding bullfrog would be 50 times longer in body length than its own egg.

The five smallest species have relatively the largest egg vitelli, 13.6-15 times in body length. The bulk of the species (15 in number) have vitelli in body length from 17.5-30 times. *Rana grylio* has it 41 times and *Rana catesbeiana* has it 50 times.

TABLE II

Bufo quercicus	13.6–15.8
Pseudacris ocularis	14.4–19.0
Acris gryllus	15 –16
Pseudacris nigrita	17.5–28.2
Gastrophryne carolinensis	18.3–20
Hyla femoralis	19.1–28.7
Hyla andersonii	21.4–25
Rana virgatipes	22.7–27.3
Hyla squirella	23. –28.7
Hyla cinerea	23.1–46.2
Rana sphenocephala	24.5–37.7
Scaphiopus holbrookii	25 –36
Hyla versicolor	26.6–29
Hyla gratiosa	27.2–49
Rana aesopus	28.3–37.7
Rana clamitans	29 –37.1
Rana septentrionalis	30 –36.9
Bufo terrestris	30 –42
Rana grylio	41 –58.5
Rana catesbeiana	50 –70.8

VOICE

The species of *Bufo, Hyla, Acris, Pseudacris, Scaphiopus* have single vocal vesicles beneath the chin. The frogs go from single mental vocal inflation of *Rana clamitans, R. heckscheri, R. catesbeiana, R. grylio, R. septentrionalis* (slightly lateral as well), to round paired sacs of *Rana virgatipes,* elongate lateral sacs of *Rana sphenocephala,* to the side of body inflated as in *Rana aesopus.*

We will not attempt a general discussion of voice. It is a hard topic to characterize and the process of voice production in detail is a subject we plan to pursue at greater length in subsequent investigations.

MATING

Every species (*R. heckscheri* and *P. nigrita* not studied) in Okefinokee swamp doubtless mates or breeds more at night than by day, but inasmuch as heavy rains are most responsible for onset of breeding many of them may mate vigorously by day. Those we have thus found are: *Scaphiopus holbrookii, Bufo quercicus, Bufo terrestris, Acris gryllus, Hyla femoralis, Hyla gratiosa, Rana aesopus, Rana clamitans, Rana sphenocephala.*

The mating eagerness, or ardor has been much discussed as to the mutilation which males will endure when the clasping impulse is paramount. This we will not discuss in this paper. It is hard to measure which are the more tenacious—toads, frogs, treefrogs or narrow-mouthed frogs. All are examples of intense amplexation.

At this point I wish to observe that contrary to some statements that the extrusion of eggs usually occurs only after the male has clasped the female for several days, in the species of the United States this seldom obtains. We have seen mated pairs of at least 32-35 species and of some species many pairs. In general in nature the eggs are laid soon after amplexation. The females do not approach breeding grounds or males until ready or nearly ready. Occasionally or rarely a pair may be mated in toads while en route to pond, but normally they meet at the breeding grounds. Many times with laboratory mating or sometimes with pairs brought into capitvity several days elapse before ovulation and then often the eggs do not develop.

We have also seen little indications of unmated males fertilizing the eggs or egg masses already laid as has been recorded for European forms. One wonders how many of those observations were made in the field. Furthermore the unmated males will hang about the egg masses laid because usually this is where the non-ovulated females will lay. They often hide under the masses, about them, etc. In such areas we hunt for the frogs, males, females and mated frogs.

If the supernumerary males have accidentally or designedly fertilized egg masses it has not been observed by us. Query also has been asked what stimulus prompts the male to discharge his sperm thus without the female. If they do it maybe the same that has caused individual females of many species to ovulate without a male or ovulate if the male is removed. Possibly with some males as with these females the process has gone so far and the frenzy or intensity of mating so vigorous no stay is possible.

Fall or late summer copulation has engaged some workers' attention. In the northern states where the ovulation periods of species are short or in European species some assert that a male will copulate a second time. Whether it be a second time or a male which ripened late is not always ascertained. If one glance at the breeding seasons of these Okefinokee frogs as with desert species, he will discover some breeding from February or March to October 1, November 1, or December. This probably means that there are ripening individuals ready for each suitable rainy period, not necessarily one short crestal period as occurs in some northern species and that a male or female breeds only once that season.

Many of us in the north have been accustomed to thinking when we heard a common meadow frog croak in August or September or a peeper in September or October, that this is an exuberant salutation before it goes into hibernation. Possibly in some cases it means nothing. In other cases it may mean males which have ripened. For example, in September 1929 our automobile went bad at night before a farm in lower Wabash valley. The instant we got out we heard an immense chorus of southern meadow frogs, *Rana sphenocephala*. We asked ourselves if it were a play chorus. The next day on our way to Olney, Ill. in some ponds we found several fresh masses of eggs. The fall croaking then in some instances in the north may mean breeding or incipient urges to breeding.

COLORATION FROM LIFE

In this discussion we have attempted to give a Ridgway description of live Okefinokee representatives of males and females. Normally descriptions have been from spirit specimens. Furthermore the date of the description is given. A July description might be quite different from a March or an April one in color tones. True, we could not attempt to catalogue all the variations in color and these descriptions are only as representative as the season and circumstances would permit. In almost every species there were pronounced differences between the males and females of a species.

STRUCTURAL DIFFERENCES

In all the frogs (*Rana*) the enlarged thumb is the best criterion of maleness. None of these *Ranas* of Okefinokee have two excrescences on the male's thumb as in some of the Pacific coast species of *Rana*, and none seem to have the webs of the hind feet as in some northwestern and northern species. In the southern meadow frog and gopher frog we have not the distinctive differences, of tympana found in the green frog, carpenter frog, mink frog, Heckscher's frog, southern bullfrog or common bullfrog. There may be more yellowish tints in the throats of those five in the males than in the females.

In the *Hylidae* of the Okefinokee region the series may be separated by the different color on chin and throat except possibly at times in the pigmy *Pseudacris ocularis*. In the same way it is not always easy to separate a male narrow-mouthed frog from a female of the same species. In the solitary spade-foots the throats, excrescences on fingers and coloration of the back generally assist. In the toads the customary differences more or less obtain.

THE CUSTOMARY AMPLEXATION
(Pl. IV, Figs. 1-4; Pl. V)

In the two toads (*Bufonidae*) oak toad and southern toad the embrace is axillary or at times supra-axillary with the first two fingers folded back. In the nine species of tree frogs (*Hylidae*) herein considered, namely, the little chorus frog, black swamp cricket frog, cricket-frog, southern tree frog, pine woods tree frog, Anderson tree frog, green tree frog, common tree toad, and Florida tree frog, the embrace is axillary or supra-axillary. In the narrow-mouthed toad (*Brevicipitidae*) it is axillary. In the spade-foot (*Scaphiopodidae*) it is inguinal. In the eight species of frog (*Ranidae*) considered, it is pectoral. These eight are, southern meadow frog, gopher frog, carpenter frog, green frog, mink frog, Heckscher's frog, southern bullfrog, and bullfrog.

CROSS EMBRACES
(Pl. IV, Fig. 7)

In our study of the Salientia of Ithaca we were in the process several years and had ample material. But in a trip to other parts one's material is carefully isolated to insure normal life history notes in the short period at hand. In these trips little attempt or opportunity was given individuals for cross embraces in the camp laboratory. Some of the records given were field observations and casual notes.

Scaphiopus holbrookii ♂   X Hyla gratiosa ♀

Bufo terrestris ♂   X Rana sphenocephala ♂

Bufo terrestris ♂   X Rana sphenocephala ♀

Bufo terrestris ♂   X Hyla gratiosa ♂

(Rana septentrionalis ♂   X Rana clamitans ♀)

When ovulating is taking place in the same place for several species, embraces might occur. For example, a *Bufo terrestris* male might leap at *Hyla femoralis, Hyla cinerea, Hyla gratiosa, Scaphiopus holbrookii* or any other if it approaches its size.

Some workers on the basis of few observations may think the males can distinguish sexes but countless cases of males mating have been observed. We did not record all we saw, but have in our notes the following species where males amplexated:

Bufo quericicus	Hyla squirella
Bufo terrestris	Hyla versicolor
Acris gryllus	Pseudacris ocularis
Hyla femoralis	Rana sphenocephala

Or to make the case more pronounced males sometimes mate in a tier of three: one female below with a male atop the male mating with her. We recall such a case in *Pseudacris ocularis, Bufo quercicus* and *Scaphiopus holbrookii*.

Abnormal embraces with forms other than frogs were not sought or observed.

DEPARTURES FROM CUSTOMARY AMPLEXATION AND THEIR SIGNIFICANCE
(Pl. IV, Figs. 5, 6, 8)

In 1914 we remarked the emphasis laid by European workers on form of embrace or amplexation in differentiating or diagnosing certain families or genera. In Dr. Gill's comments on Boulenger's Tailless Batrachia he notes that differences may in part be due to differences in size between males and females and must vary.

Since the Ithaca paper we have seen the amplexation of almost every species of the southeastern United States. In general with eastern Salientia we can say that every species of *Rana* embraces pectoral-like; that every Hylid (*Acris, Pseudacris, Hyla*), each *Bufo* (*B. americanus, B. fowleri, B. terrestris, B. quercicus*), and the narrow-mouthed toad (*Gastrophryne carolinensis*) are axillary or supra-axillary in fashion while the spade-foot is inguinal. But every one of these may at times be varied from the normal.

Relative size, beginning, crest or waning of impulse or exhaustion of male or presence of other males may dictate the form of amplexation.

In most of the species of Okefinokee when enough pairs were at hand variations occurred.

Sometimes a male will seize a female in pre-axillary form (*Gastrophryne*). Or a small male may apparently have to be supra-axillary or pre-axillary in front of forearms over the tympanum (*Bufo terrestris*). Or a male if it has amplexated axillary for several times over several days may be pre-axillary with fore hands on lower throat or pectoral region (*Acris*), or on one side have arm to middle of female's throat and other arm axillary (*Hyla cinerea* or *Bufo terrestris*).

Axillary fashion in pectoral or inguinal species occurs. A *Scaphiopus* male once held a female with one arm above and behind a foreleg and the other just in front of a hind leg. Or a southern meadow frog, male, may seize a female *Rana clamitans* axillary-like, not have arms long enough to reach breast. Or an unusual pair of *R. grylio* might seem axillary like.

Pectoral amplexation might come in axillary forms when a male proves bigger than the female (*Hyla femoralis, Bufo terrestris, R. clamitans*). Sometimes both arms go on to the breast or only one. The other arm might be axillary like in embrace.

In toads and spade-foots ardor is very great. One toad we saw embracing a floating rootstock. Any frog its size it will seize. In the same way the spadefoot will seize southern meadow frogs, Florida tree frogs, southern toads or similar-sized anurans.

In spite of the variations given in the three preceding paragraphs we have never seen ovulation in any species where abnormal amplexation obtained and in general most of the preceding records must be preceding ovulation or where captives have long remained in embrace. Normally at ovulation in the field and usually in laboratory amplexation is normal.

OVULATION

In our study of ovulation we sought to capture mated pairs afield. These usually laid the night of their capture. There were a few exceptions to the rule as we found for the forms of northeastern United States, but in general all species follow it. It means that when the female appears at the breeding place she is usually ready to ovulate. If mating males be not present or if a female of a pair be separated from a mating male or if a female be caught in a congress just before mating, she may lay in captivity without the attendant male. We did not seek to see if such were possible for each species, but it is without doubt the case. At random with no attempt to secure such results we noted ovulation without attendant males in *Acris gryllus, Hyla versicolor, Hyla cinerea, Bufo terrestris, Rana clamitans, Rana sphenocephala* and *Rana virgatipes*.

In very early spring at least six forms begin to breed. Possibly *Pseudacris nigrita* may lead or come after the others. Its eggs we have not found. They are doubtless a loose small mass like those of *P. triseriata* or *P. feriarum* farther north. The southern meadow frog *Rana sphenocephala* begins laying its plinths from February to December; crest March to May. About the same time, February 15 or 20 to August 17 (crest March to May) the gopher frog *Rana aesopus* lays a larger plinth similar to that of the southern meadow frog. March 1 to September 1 seems the period, (crest March to May) for the long egg files of the southern toad *Bufo terrestris*. From March 10 to

Plate IV
Amplexation

1

2

3

4

5

6

7

8

PLATE V

Normal embraces.

1. *Hyla cinerea*, Billy Id., Ga.   July 7, 1921. Axillary amplexation.
2. *Hyla femoralis*, Billy Id., Ga.   May 20, 1921. Axillary amplexation.
3. *Hyla gratiosa*, Coat-bet pond, Chesser Id., Ga.   July 17, 1921.   Axillary amplexation.
4. *Hyla squirella*, Anna's pond, Folkston, Ga.   July 3, 1922. Axillary amplexation.
5. *Acris gryllus*, Startling Branch, Folkston, Ga.   July 2, 1922. Axillary amplexation.
6. *Pseudacris ocularis*, Billy Id., Ga.   May 26, 1921. Axillary amplexation.
7. *Bufo quercicus*, Billy Id., Ga.   June 4, 1921. Axillary amplexation.
8. *Bufo terrestris*, Billy Id., Ga.   July 6, 1921. Axillary amplexation.
9. *Gastrophryne carolinensis*, Billy Id., Ga.   May 21, 1921.   Axillary amplexation.
10. *Bufo fowleri*, Dinwiddie, Va.   June 1, 1917. Axillary amplexation.
11. *Rana clamitans*, Billy Id., Ga.   July 4, 1921. Pectoral amplexation.
12. *Rana sphenocephala*, Billy Id., Ga.   May 22, 1921. Pectoral amplexation.

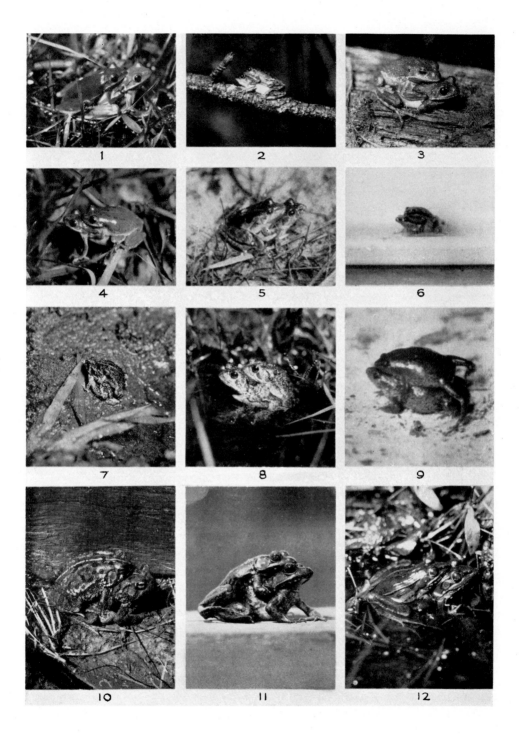

1

2

3

4

August 17 (crest April to June) the solitary spadefoot may begin its laying of bands (later cylinders). From March 18 to September 1, (crest April to June) the Florida tree frog (*Hyla gratiosa*) lays its single eggs. Thus we have in early spring six forms—a small loose egg mass, two plinths, egg strings, egg bands or cylinders, and single eggs. However different in form, they are all alike in being submerged.

Our evidence points to six forms as beginning ovulation in April. The southern tree frog, (*Hyla squirella*) lays single eggs in April to August (crest April to June). The cricket-frog (*Acris gryllus*) apparently comes next, April 15 to September 1 (crest May 10 to July 20) with its single eggs (rarely in masses). The cow bell frog (*Hyla cinerea*) lays its surface films or submerged masses from April 15 to August 15 (crest May 10 to July 15). Soon after, April 20 or 25 to September 1 (crest May 20 to July 15) the pine wood tree frog (*Hyla femoralis*) deposits its films on the surface. From April 24 to August 21 (crest May 20 to July 20) the little chorus frog (*Pseudacris ocularis*) emits single eggs on the bottom of ponds and on vegetation. From the last of April to August 11 the carpenter frog (*Rana virgatipes*) lays a plinth attached to sticks or stones like meadow frog masses, but the individual eggs have no inner envelopes. Three of the six lay single submerged eggs, one a plinth, one a surface film, and one sometimes a surface film, or sometimes a submerged mass. Possibly Heckscher's frog (*Rana heckscheri*) begins April 1 and stretches to August 1 (crest? May and June) but this period is uncertain as is the conjectural mass. Is it a film like *R. grylio*, *R. clamitans*, or if in April, a submerged mass like *R. virgatipes*, *R. sphenocephala*, or *R. aesopus?*

About May 1 four seem to start. From May 1 to August 11 (crest May 20–June 30) the common tree toad (*Hyla versicolor*) ought to deposit its surface films. From May 1 to August 31, (crest May 20 to July 23), the narrow-mouthed toad (*Gastrophryne carolinensis*) spawns clear marble-like eggs in films on the surface, these eggs truncated on the top. From May 1 to July 8 or later (crest May 20 to June 14) the Anderson tree toad might if in Okefinokee region lay its single submerged eggs. One more goes from May 1 onward to September 1 (crest May 23 to July 26) and it is the oak toad (*Bufo quercicus*) which deposits short bars of eggs on the bottom of ponds.

From the middle of May to September 1 (crest May 24 to July 28) the southern bullfrog (*Rana grylio*) has large films one by two and a half feet across, much as does *Rana catesbeiana*. If this latter form be near the Okefinokee it doubtless lays the last of May or from June to August 1 when the green frog (*Rana clamitans*) has been recorded laying its smaller surface films. From May 1 onward we thus have remarked seven forms of which five lay surface films and two submerged (one single eggs, one bars in different forms) eggs.

Some of the spawning dates, order of ovulation and humidity (Table 12) and temperature data (Table 13) appear in the following tables.

TABLE 12

SPECIES	SPAWNING PERIOD			CREST OF OVULATION		
Pseudacris nigrita						
Rana sphenocephala	Feb.	to	Dec.	Mar.	to	May
Rana aesopus	Feb. 15	Aug.	17	Mar.		May
Bufo terrestris	Mar. 1	Sept.	1	Mar.		May
Scaphiopus holbrookii	Mar. 10	Aug.	17	Apr.		June
Hyla gratiosa	Mar. 18	Sept.	1	Apr.		June
Hyla squirella	Apr.	August		Apr.		June
Acris gryllus	Apr. 15	Sept.		May	10	July 20
Hyla cinerea	Apr. 15	Aug.	15	May	10	July 15
Hyla femoralis	Apr. 20	Sept.	1	May	20	July 15
Pseudacris ocularis	Apr. 24	Aug.	21	May	20	July 20
Rana virgatipes	Apr.(last)	Aug.	21	May		July
Rana heckscheri	(Apr. 1?	Aug.	1?	May?		June?
Hyla versicolor	May 1	Aug.	11	May	20	June 20
Gastrophryne carolinensis	May 1	Aug.	31	May	20	July 23)
(Hyla andersonii	May 1	July	8	May	20	June 14)
Bufo quercicus	May 1	Sept.	1	May	23	July 26
Rana grylio	May 15	Sept.	1	May	24	July 28
(Rana catesbeiana	June	July		June	20	July 15)
Rana clamitans	June 2	Aug.	10	June	14	July 15
Rana septentrionalis	June 25					)

TABLE 13

	MINIMA		MAXIMA		
	RANGE	AVERAGE	RANGE	AVERAGE	HUMIDITY
Pseudacris nigrita					
Rana sphenocephala	50–74	65°	66–78		Rain
Rana aesopus	68–74	71	81–91	86	Inch or more of rain
Bufo terrestris	50–78	66	73–97		.90–2.60 inches
Scaphiopus holbrookii					Heavy rains
Hyla gratiosa	62–83	70	78–98	90	.91–2.40 inches
Hyla squirella	62–74	70	81–96	90	1.42–1.80 inches
Acris gryllus	58–73	69	73–97	89	Heavy rains
Hyla cinerea	60–74		75–91		.84–2.80 inches
Hyla femoralis	61–74		81–96		.48–3.47 inches
Pseudacris ocularis	70–79	74			Rains
Rana virgatipes	70–82				Rains
Hyla versicolor	68–74		83–96	91	1.48–4.06 inches
Gastrophryne carolinensis	66–77	72	78–97	89	T–5.00 inches
Bufo quercicus	64–74		79–96		T–5.31 inches
Rana grylio	68–78		85–96		Humid or rain
Rana clamitans	68–75		88–94	90	None-considerable
Rana heckscheri					

Quite obviously the evidence of minima, etc. for *Rana aesopus, Scaphiopus holbrookii, Pseudacris ocularis, Rana virgatipes* and *Rana heckscheri* is too scanty to be sure of their place in this table. In Okefinokee swamp humidity is the great factor in precipitating ovulation.

THE EGGS
(Pls. VI, VII, VII, IX; Text Fig. 1)

Incorporated with this consideration of our southeastern species is a previous key to the eggs of our northeastern forms. The combination may be termed "A key to the eggs of the Salientia east of the Mississippi River."

Workers will discover the following species missing from the key because the authors themselves have had no opportunity to secure both fresh and preserved materials of these species:

Hyla andersonii—Eggs first found by T. Barbour and later by G. K. and R. C. Noble.

Hyla c. evittata—Eggs found by M. K. Brady. Quite similar to *H. cinerea*.

Pseudacris ornata—Eggs not known. Described by J. K. Strecker.

Pseudacris nigrita—Eggs most certainly like *Pseudacris triseriata*, *P. feriarum*, and *P. septentrionalis*.

Rana areolata—Eggs described by H. P. Wright and G. S. Myers.

Rana cantabrigensis—Eggs very similar to *R. sylvatica*.

The season of breeding for species in the north is marked both at the beginning and at the end. Each species occupies four or five weeks except *Bufo americanus* and *Rana clamitans*. The exceptions may require two or three months for ovulation. In the southeastern states when once a species has begun, its season of breeding may extend throughout the summer or even into the early fall, dependent upon the high crests of precipitation. These species, although of a swampy region, wait for the rains and in this reliance on precipitation they suggest our desert species of Texas and Arizona. Those which do not begin until June have at least eight to ten weeks of ovulation. This minimum period for a species of the south is the maximum period for a northern form. Species such as *Rana sphenocephala*, *Bufo terrestris* and *Acris gryllus*, which begin early in the season, breed during 25–30 weeks of the year, if not longer or from February to September or October.

The number of eggs in a complement may vary from 100 in the smallest species, *Pseudacris ocularis*, to 20,000 in *Rana catesbeiana*, the largest form. The range in the tree frogs (*Hylidae*) is from 100 (*Pseudacris ocularis*) to 2,084 (*Hyla gratiosa*); in the toads (*Bufonidae*) from 610 (*Bufo quercicus*) to 8,000 (*Bufo americanus*); in the frogs (*Ranidae*) from 349 (*Rana virgatipes*) to 20,000 (*Rana catesbeiana*). The complements of the narrow-mouthed toad *Gastrophryne carolinensis*) and the spade-foot (*Scaphiopus holbrookii*) are, respectively, 869 and 2,332.

The eggs of seven species, *Hyla cinerea*, *H. femoralis*, *H. versicolor*, *Rana catesbeiana*, *R. clamitans*, *R. grylio* and *Gastrophryne carolinensis* float on the surface of the water; the eggs of the other 17 species are submerged. In northern or southeastern states no form with buoyant eggs lays before May 10. The 11 or 12 early breeders have submerged eggs. These are usually with firm jelly envelopes except for *Pseudacris triseriata* and *Scaphiopus holbrookii*, which have the consistency intermediate between the firm jellies of early breeders and the loose surface films of late breeders. One form, *Gas-*

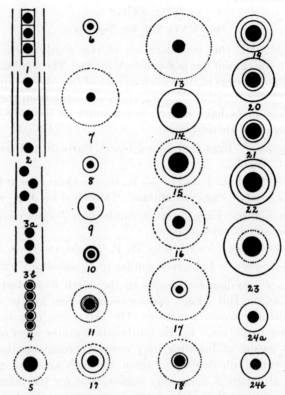

FIGURE I. INDIVIDUAL EGGS. × 2.3

1. Bufo americanus	8. Hyla crucifer	17. Hyla femoralis
2. Bufo terrestris	9. Acris gryllus	18. Hyla versicolor
3. Bufo fowleri	10. Hyla squirella	19. Rana palustris
4. Bufo quericus	11. Hyla gratiosa	20. Rana pipiens
5. Scaphiopus holbrookii	12. Hyla cinerea	21. Rana sphenocephala
6. Pseudacris ocularis	13. Rana catesbeiana	22. Rana aesopus
7. Pseudacris triseriata	14. Rana virgatipes	23. Rana sylvatica
(From Buffalo, N. Y.)	15. Rana grylio	24. Gastrophryne carolinensis
	16. Rana clamitans	

In No. 15 the vitellus was inadvertently drawn too large.

trophryne carolinensis, although it lays at the surface, has the most beautifully distinct, firm eggs of all the species considered.

The difference in jelly consistency in an early spring laid egg and late summer laid egg of the same species has not been studied for differences. Nor have we fully determined whether heavier rainfall is needed for the tardy breeders than for the early ones of a species. The eggs of *Rana heckscheri*, and *Pseudacris nigrita* of the Okefinokee forms remain yet to be described by someone.

The eggs were laid in camp and in the laboratory by mated pairs caught in the field. Later the eggs in the field were determined by these original checks. Occasionally the process of egg laying was observed in the field. Two species, one of the north and one of the south, were identified by the positive elimination of all the other resident forms.

The measurements and color descriptions are based on fresh eggs. Later, these were checked with preserved material. The eggs with loose outer envelope have the outer margin indicated by dots. In one species the vitelline membrane is far separated from the vitellus and the space is indicated by cross hatching. A summary of the egg characters of each species follows in the accompanying key:

A. Eggs deposited singly.
    a. Envelopes two
        Outer envelope diameter 1.4-2.0 mm.; inner envelope diameter 1.2 to 1.6 mm; vitellus diameter 0.8 to 1.0 mm; eggs brown above and cream below. Egg complement, 942. Season, June 10 to August 21 (Fig. 10)...... *Hyla squirella.*
    aa. Envelope single
        b. Envelope 2.3 mm. or more.
            c. Vitelline membrane far from vitellus, appearing as inner envelope 1.6 to 2.0 mm; outer envelope loose, glutinous, indefinite in outline 2.3 to 5 mm; vitellus 1.0 to 1.8 mm. Egg complement, 2084. Season, June 10 to August 21 (Fig. 11)............ *Hyla gratiosa.*
            cc. No inner envelope or appearance as such, envelope firm, definite in outline 2.4 to 3.6 mm; vitellus 0.9 to 1.0 mm. Egg complement, 241. Season April 15 or earlier to September 1 (Fig. 9) .. *Acris gryllus.*
        bb. Envelope 1.2 to 2.0 mm.
            c. Vitellus 0.6 to 0.8 mm. Egg complement, 100. Season, May 16 to August 21 (Fig. 6) ... *Pseudacris ocularis.*
            cc. Vitellus 0.9 to 1.1 mm. Egg complement, 800 to 1,000. Season, March 30 to May 15 (Fig. 8)................................*Hyla crucifer.*
AA. Eggs deposited in a mass.
    a. Egg mass, a surface film.
        b. Egg envelope outline always distinct, never lost in the mass; eggs firm and distinct like glass marbles, making a fine mosaic; envelope a truncated sphere, the flat surface above; envelope single 2.8 to 4.0 mm; vitellus 1.0 to 1.2 mm; color black above and white below. Egg complement, 869. Season, May 21 to August 17 (Fig. 24)........................*Gastrophryne carolinensis.*
        bb. Egg envelope outline indistinct, more or less merged in the jelly mass; jelly glutinous; egg brown above, cream or yellow below.
            c. Egg packets small, masses seldom if ever over 20 sq. in. (125 square centimeters), or 4 by 5 inches in diameter (10 by 12.5 cm.).
                d. Inner envelope large 2.2 to 3. mm; outer envelope 3.2 to 5.0 mm; vitellus 0.8 to 1.6 mm; Egg complement, 343 to 500. Season, May 19 to August 21 (Fig. 12)..........................*Hyla cinerea.*
                dd. Inner envelope small 1.4 to 2.0 mm; outer envelope 4 to 8 mm.
                    e. Packets small, seldom over 30 to 40 eggs; vitellus 1.1 to 1.2 mm. Egg complement, 1,802. Season, May 10 to August 13 (Fig. 18)....................................*Hyla versicolor.*
                    ee. Packets large, sometimes 100 to 125 eggs; vitellus 0.8 to 1.2 mm. av. 0.95 mm. Egg complement, 768. Season May 16 to August 21 (Fig. 17)................................*Hyla femoralis.*
            cc. Egg packets large, loose, glutinous films, 35 sq. in. to 675 sq. in. (218 to 3,721 sq. cm.).
                d. Inner envelope absent; vitellus 1.2 to 1.7 mm; egg mass 144 to 675 sq. in. (900 to 3,721 sq. cm.) in area, or 12 by 25 inches (30 by 61 cm.) in diameter; egg masses amongst brush around the edge of ponds or encircling *Pontederia*-like vegetation in midpond. Egg complement, 10,000 to 20,000. Season, June 1 to July 10, (Fig. 13)............
                        Rana catesbeiana.
                dd. Inner envelope present, 2.8 to 4.0 mm; vitellus 1.4 to 2.0 mm.
                    e. Egg mass seldom 1. sq. ft. (35 to 144 sq. in. or 218 to 900 cm) in area or 5 by 7 to 12 inches in diameter; usually around edge of ponds; inner envelope elliptic, pyriform or circular, av. 3.05 mm; vitellus 1.4 to 1.8 mm, mode 1.4 mm. av. 1.5 mm. Egg complement, 1,451 to 4,000. Season, May 23 to August 21 (Fig. 16)...
                        Rana clamitans.
                    ee. Egg mass over 1 sq. ft. in area (144 to 288 sq. in. or 900 to 1,800 sq. cm.) or 12 by 12 inches to 12 by 24 inches in diameter; usually in midpond; inner envelope av. 3.45 mm; vitellus 1.4 to 2.0 mm, mode 1.8 mm, av. 1.7 mm. Egg complement, 8,000 to 15,000. Season, May 24 to August 21 (Fig. 15)............*Rana grylio.*

aa. Egg mass submerged.
  b. Eggs in files or bands.
    c. Eggs laid in bands which soon become loose cylinders extending along plant stems or grass blades; vitellus 1.4 to 2.0 mm; envelope 3.8 to 5.6 mm. Egg complement, 2,332. Season, April 15 or earlier to August 17 (Fig. 5)..*Scaphiopus holbrookii.*
  cc. Eggs in files.
    d. Files short (4 to 10 mm in length); 4 to 8 eggs in short bead-like chain or bar or many such files radiating from one focus; vitellus 0.8 to 1.0 mm; tube diameter 1.2 to 1.4 mm. Egg complement, 610, 766. Season, June 4 to August 21 (Fig. 4)................*Bufo quercicus.*
    dd. Files long (several feet in length or often a meter or more long); vitellus 1.0 to 1.4 mm; tube diameter 2.6 to 4.6 mm.
      e. Inner tube absent; outer tube 2.8 to 3.4 mm; vitelli crowded in the files; at first in a double row, later more spread out but still crowded; 22 to 24 eggs in 30 mm (1 3/16 inches). Egg complement, 7,750. Season, April 15 or earlier to August 17 (Fig. 3)..*Bufo fowleri.*
      ee. Inner tube present.
        f. 18 to 20 eggs in 30 mm (1 3/16 inches); partition apparent between eggs; inner tube 1.6 to 2.2 mm; outer tube 3.4 to 4.0 mm. Egg complement, 4,000 to 8,000. Season, April 5 to July 25 (Fig. 1).......................*Bufo americanus.*
        ff. 7 to 8 eggs in 30 mm (1 3/16 inches); distinct space between eggs; no partition apparent; tube inclined to be slightly emarginate between the eggs; inner tube, 2.2 to 3.4 mm; outer tube, 2.6 to 4.6 mm. Egg complement, 2,888. Season, April 15 or earlier to August 13 (Fig. 2)...........*Bufo terrestris.*
  bb. Eggs in lumps.
    c. Egg mass a firm regular cluster.
      d. Egg mass a sphere 2½ to 4 in. (6.35 to 10 cm) in diameter, containing 2,000 to 3,000 eggs; outer envelope distinct.)
        e. Eggs black above and white below; inner envelope apparently absent, slightly evident under lens, 3.6 to 5.8 mm; outer envelope 5.2 to 9.4 mm; vitellus 1.8 to 2.4 mm. Egg complement, 2,000 to 3,000. Season, March 19 to May 1 (Fig. 23)....*Rana sylvatica.*
        ee. Eggs brown above and yellow below; inner envelope distinct 2.3 to 3.0 mm; outer envelope 3.6 to 5.0 mm; vitellus 1.6 to 1.9 mm. Egg complement, 2,000 to 3,000. Season, April 6 to May 18 (Fig. 19)................................*Rana palustris.*
    dd. Egg mass a plinth.
      e. Without inner envelope, complement small, 349 to 474; eggs black above and sulphur or primrose yellow below; eggs further apart than in *R. pipiens* or *R. sphenocephala;* outer envelope 4.9 to 6.9 mm; vitellus 1.5 to 1.8 mm. Egg complement, 349 to 474. Season, June 21 to August 11 (Fig. 14).........*Rana virgatipes.*
      ee. With inner envelope, complement large, 1,000 to 5,000 or more; eggs black above and white below.
        f. Vitellus average 2.0 mm (range 1.8 to 2.4 mm); inner envelope 3.1 to 4.4 mm; outer envelope 4.4 to 6.0 mm, mode 5.2 mm, av. 5.3 mm. Egg complement, 5,000 or more. Season, (?) to August 17 (Fig. 22).....................*Rana aesopus.*
        ff. Vitellus average 1.4-1.7 mm (range 1.3 to 2.0 mm); inner envelope 2.3 to 3.2 mm; outer envelope 3.4 to 6.6 mm. Egg complement, 1,000 to 5,000.
          (g. Average outer envelope 5.0 or larger.
            (h. Average outer envelope 5.1 mm. (range 4.2 to 6.0 mm, mode 5.0 mm.); vitellus 1.7 mm. average (1.4 mm-2.0 mm). Egg complement, 3,500 to 4,500. Season, March 30 to May 15 (Fig. 20) *Rana pipiens.*
            (hh. Average outer envelope 6.3 mm. (5.6-6.6 mm); vitellus 1.4 mm. average (range 1.3 to 1.6 mm); vitellus black or brown above, white or yellowish below. Season, June 25 to July 25. *Rana septentrionalis.*
         gg. Average outer envelope 3.8 mm (range 3.4 to 5.4 mm, mode 4.0 mm). Egg complement, 1,054. Season, April 15 or earlier to August 21 (Fig. 21)........*Rana sphenocephala.*

cc. Egg mass a loose irregular cluster.
    d. Egg mass small, less than 1 in. (2.5 cm) in diameter. 20 to 100 eggs in the mass; outer envelope merged; the one envelope 5.0 to 7.8 mm, rarely 3.0 mm; vitellus 0.9 to 1.2 mm. Egg complement, 500 to 800. Season, March 19 to May 1 (Fig. 7)..........*Pseudacris triseriata.*
   dd. Egg mass an irregular cylinder 1 to 6 in. (2.5 to 15 cm) in length, extending along plant stem or grass blade; envelope, single, 3.8 to 5.6 mm; vitellus 1.4 to 2.0 mm. Egg complement, 2,332. Season, April 15 or earlier to August 17 (Fig. 5).......*Scaphiopus holbrookii.* (See also (c) under (b) Eggs in files or bands.)

EGG-LAYING PROCESS

In most of these southeastern frogs the actual ovulation and fertilization process has not been observed. Generally we would return after midnight or later with a pair or more and had to sleep to conserve our energies for daytime observations where and when congresses occurred. The opportunity to observe this process was therefore often deliberately passed by. These are points the resident naturalists can do better in any event. At this juncture we will not enter into any discussion of the process, though we have opinions, but in some cases not all the facts we want.

HATCHING PERIOD

Scaphiopus holbrookii	1–2 to 6 days	Submerged masses
Gastrophryne carolinensis	1½–3 days	Surface films
Pseudacris ocularis	1½–1¾ days	Single submerged
Hyla squirella	1½–2 days	Single submerged
Hyla gratiosa	2 days	Single submerged
Hyla cinerea	2–3 days	Surface or submerged
Rana grylio	2–3½ days	Surface film
Bufo terrestris	2–4 days	Submerged files
Hyla femoralis	3 days	Surface film
Bufo quercicus	3–3⅓ days	Submerged bars
Acris gryllus	3–4 days	Single submerged
Hyla versicolor	3–5 days	Surface film
Rana sphenocephala	3–5 days	Submerged mass
Rana virgatipes	3–5 days	Submerged mass
Rana clamitans	3–6 days	Surface film
Rana aesopus	4–4½ days	Submerged mass
Rana catesbeiana	4–5 days	Surface film
Rana septentrionalis	5–13 days	Submerged mass.

From a glance it will be seen that the minimum period for each Okefinokee species is from 1 to 4 days for hatching, or the maximum period for each species from 1¾ to 6 days. This would imply temperatures of 60°–80° Fahrenheit or higher if our table of 1914 (p. 19) be correct. I still believe there is much to be said for that table. However, if one observe the table herewith given he will note that the shortest periods of hatching are not necessarily the surface films. Of the first five species with lowest hatching periods, four have submerged eggs. Strangely enough the single eggs in general have a tendency to hatch quicker than the masses. Probably in Okefinokee Swamp the egg complements of all species are under more uniform water conditions in temperature than we have in the north.

THE LARVAL PERIOD

According to the length of the larval period, the species of the Okefinokee region fall into two major groups: those which transform during the season in which the eggs are laid (14 or 15 species) and those which require one or more years for their development (5 or 6 species). The data are as follows: (Table 14)

TABLE 14

Larval periods	Egg season		Average transf. size	Vitelline diameter (mm.)	Larval period
Short larval period:					
Scaphiopus holbrookii	Mar. 10 to	Aug. 17	10 mm.	1.4 to 2.0	14 – 30 days
Gastrophryne carolinensis	May 1	Aug. 31	11	1.0 to 1.2	23 – 67
Bufo quercicus	May 1	Sept. 1	8	1.2 to 1.4	33 – 44
Bufo terrestris	Mar. 1	Sept. 1	8	1.0 to 1.4	35 – 55
Hyla femoralis	Apr. 20	Sept. 1	13	0.8 to 1.2	35 – 65
Pseudacris nigrita					40 – 60
Hyla squirella	Apr.	Aug.	12	0.8 to 1.0	40 – 60
Hyla gratiosa	Mar. 18	Sept. 1	20	1.0 to 1.8	41 – 65
Hyla versicolor	May 10	Aug. 13	16	1.1 to 1.2	45 – 60
Pseudacris ocularis	Apr. 24	Aug. 21	8	0.6 to 0.8	45 – 70
Hyla andersonii	May 1	July 8	12	1.2 to 1.4	49?– 74?
Acris gryllus	Apr. 15	Aug. 15	13	0.9 to 1.0	50 – 90
Hyla cinerea	Apr. 15	Aug. 15	15	0.8 to 1.6	55 – 63
Rana sphenocephala	Feb.	Dec.	23	1.3 to 2.0	67 – 86
Rana aesopus	Feb. 15	Aug. 17	27 to 35	1.8 to 2.4	85 –106
Long larval period:					
Rana virgatipes	Apr. (last)	Aug. 21	27	1.5 to 1.8	300 –365
Rana clamitans	June 2	Aug. 10	25	1.4 to 1.8	300 –400
Rana septentrionalis	June 25		34	1.3 to 1.6	365 –400
Rana heckscheri	Apr. 1 ?	Aug. 1 ?	35	( )	365?–730?
Rana grylio	May 15	Sept. 1	44	1.4 to 2.0	365 –730?
Rana catesbeiana	June	July	53	1.2 to 1.7	365?–730

The forms with long larval periods, namely carpenter frog, green frog, mink frog, Heckscher's frog, southern bullfrog and common bullfrog are generally mid-summer breeders, require 25–53 mm. for transformation size (usually 30–53 mm.) and have uniform-sized vitelli (1.3–2.0 mm.) relatively small for the transformation size required.

The forms in the short larval group fall into three groups: The first assemblage of four—solitary spade-foot, narrow-mouthed toad, oak toad, and southern toad—have small average transformation sizes 8–11 mm., relatively larger vitelli 1.0–2.0 mm., and may require a larval minima of 14 to 35 days. The second group comprehend nine forms, namely the tree frogs (*Hylidae*) of the swamp. They have larger average transformation sizes (12 to 20 mm) and actually smaller vitelli and larval minima of 35 to 55 days. The average of the minimum sizes of the vitelli of the nine species is between .8 and .9 mm. wherein in the first short larval group of four it is 1.15 mm.

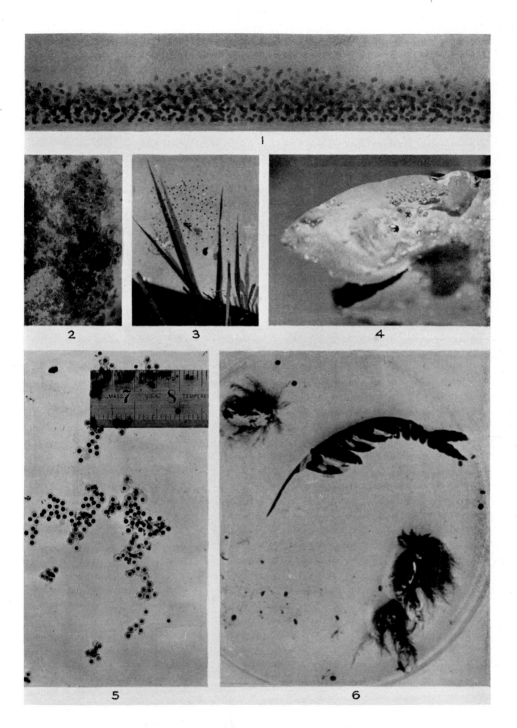

Plate VIII

Egg masses

1. *Rana clamitans* egg mass, partly hatched in white clayey pool at Thompson's Landing, St. Mary's River, Ga. July 9, 1922.
2. *Bufo quercicus*, single egg bar, on bottom of pond near Starling Branch, Folkston, Ga. July 27, 1922.
3. *Bufo quercicus*, clustered egg bars, laid in camp, Billy Id., Ga. June 5, 1921.
4. *Rana grylio* egg mass, Long Pond, Billy Id., Ga. May 24, 1921.
5. *Bufo terrestris* egg strings in field, Billy Id., Ga. June 6, 1921.
6. *Bufo terrestris* egg strings in camp, Billy Id., Ga. April 24, 1921.

Plate IX

Rana egg masses

1. *Rana septentrionalis*, Hellgate ponds, Onekio, N. Y. July 14, 1923. × 1.3.
2. *Rana virgatipes*, Chesser Id., Ga. July 22, 1922. × 1.0.
3. *Rana sphenocephala*, Billy Id., Ga. May 22, 1921. × 0.5.
4. *Rana aesopus*, Hilliard, Fla. August 17, 1922. × 0.45.

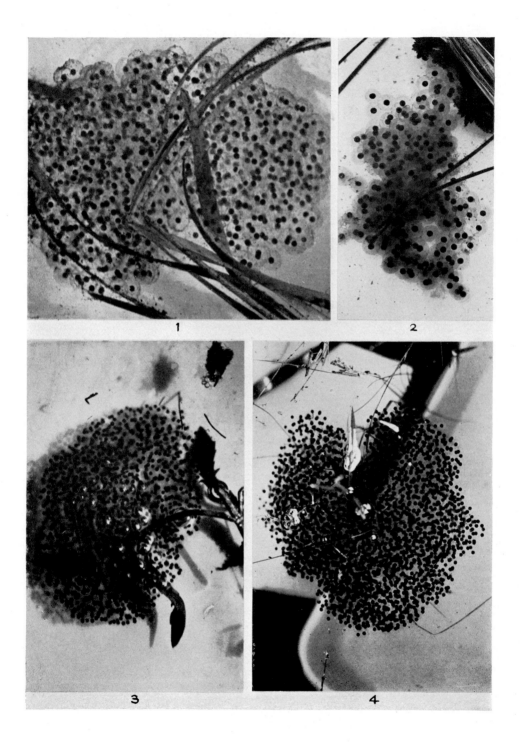

1   2

3   4

The last group in the short larval group comprise two species; the southern meadow frog and the gopher frog. These have transformation sizes from 18–35 (average 23–30 mm.) larger vitelli if anything than the winter (long larval) group and minimal larval periods of 67–85 days.

We wished to see if the larval period lengths in any way corresponded with the relation of the egg diameters (vitelli) to the transformation sizes. We divided the minimum transformation size by minimum vitellus size for column one. For column two we used the maximum transformation size and maximum vitellus. Column three is the mean of the two. The order of this table (Table 15) accords quite closely with the table of larval period lengths and there is surely a relationship. For example in the table a transformed solitary spade-foot is in body length only six times as long as the diameter of the egg vitellus from which it came. Or a transformed bullfrog is thirty-five times as long as the diameter of the egg vitellus from which it came.

TABLE 15

	1.	2.	3.
1. Scaphiopus holbrookii	6.07	6.00	6.03
2. Bufo quercicus	5.0	7.5	6.25
3. Bufo terrestris	6.5	7.5	7.00
4. Gastrophryne carolinensis	7.0	10.0	8.5
5. Hyla andersonii	11.0	10.7	10.85
6. Pseudacris nigrita	? 10.0	? 12.0	? 11.0
7. Hyla cinerea	14.3	10.6	12.45
8. Hyla femoralis	12.5	12.5	12.5
9. Acris gryllus	10.0	15.0	12.5
10. Hyla squirella	13.7	13.0	13.35
11. Hyla versicolor	11.8	16.6	14.4
12. Rana aesopus	15.0	14.6	14.8
13. Rana sphenocephala	13.8	16.5	15.15
14. Pseudacris ocularis	16.6	13.7	15.15
15. Hyla gratiosa	18.0	12.7	15.35
16. Rana virgatipes	15.3	17.2	16.25
17. Rana clamitans	14.6	18.6	16.6
18. Rana septentrionalis	22.3	25.0	23.65
19. Rana heckscheri			
20. Rana grylio	22.8	24.5	23.65
21. Rana catesbeiana	35.8	34.7	35.25

TADPOLES
(Pls. X, XI, XII, XIII, XIV)

The following table of tadpoles:—total length, greatest length of body, and tail, greatest depth of body and transformation size reveals a correlated ascending scale for all five characters. Usually the body length of a mature tadpole will be slightly greater than the average transformation size, but in several instances the same. Wherever it is smaller than the average transformation size we have added the range of transformation size. Usually in most of the tadpoles the body depth averages from 1.6–2.5 times in the size of transformation or body depth of tadpole in tail length from 2.5–4.5 times depending on the species. The order of size for the tadpoles usually accords with the order for size of adults with the exception of *Bufo terrestris, Scaphiopus holbrookii, Acris gryllus,* and corresponds very nicely with the order given in table (Table 16) on transformation size.

TABLE 16

	Greatest length	Greatest body length	Average transf. size	Greatest body depth	Greatest tail length
Pseudacris nigrita	? 23.0 mm.	? 8.8 mm.	(8–12 mm.)	? 5.0 mm.	? 14.2 mm.
Pseudacris ocularis	23.0	8.8	8	5.0	14.2
Bufo terrestris	24.0	9.8	8	5.0	14.2
Gastrophryne carolinensis	26.4	10.0	11 (7–12)	4.8	16.4
Scaphiopus holbrookii	28.0	12.0	10	5.0	16.0
Hyla squirella	32.0	12.0	12	6.5	20.0
Hyla femoralis	33.0	10.0	13 (10–15)	5.0	22.5
Hyla andersonii	35.0	12.0	12	5.5	23.0
Hyla cinerea	40.0	15.0	15	6.0	25.0
Acris gryllus	42.2	13.0	13	6.6	29.2
Hyla versicolor	46.6	15.8	16 (13–20)	10.0	30.8
Hyla gratiosa	50.0	19.0	20 (18–23)	12.0	31.0
Rana sphenocephala	62.5	25	23	15.0	37.5
Rana clamitans	84.8	27.8	25	17.2	57.0
Rana aesopus	81.0	29.0	(27–35)	14.0	53.0
Rana virgatipes	92.0	30.0	27	15.0	63.0
Rana septentrionalis	99.0	32.0	34 (29–40)	19.5	67.0
Rana heckscheri	95.0	41.5	35	17.0	53.5
Rana grylio	100.0	35.6	44 (32–49)	20.0	64.4
Rana catesbeiana	142.0	45.0	53 (42–59)	38.0	97.0

A synopsis of the tadpoles of the Okefinokee species with a few hypothetical and other species (put in parentheses) follows:

Some may attempt to use this synopsis as a key. It may work and at times it will not. To any worker who has had much field experience it is apparent that tadpoles of closely related species like other animate things are no respectors of man-made keys. Variations in individuals will occur. This is a synopsis of mature larvae. Half grown larvae or larvae close to transformation or almost transformed are often quite abnormal in the usual characters used in larval descriptions. For example we raised *Rana virgatipes* larvae from eggs but they did not attain a size large enough to get the labial teeth well developed. We had to secure another series of mature larvae before the description was completed.

Mouthparts. Boulenger (1898) labelled the labial teeth row from the upper edge of upper labium inward toward the horny mandibles and from the lower edge of the lower labium inward toward the mandible. The author (1914) labelled the labial teeth "from the outer edge of the lip to the inner row nearest the beak and the lower labial teeth from the row nearest the beak to the outer one next the papillose border." Possibly when our North American forms are described Boulenger's system may prove the better but we have kept to the first for consistency and other reasons. In the *Scaphiopodidae* sometimes the small upper row of teeth in labial border is lost yet the variations come most frequent in the small rows at either corner of the horny mandibles. In the *Ranidae* the greatest loss comes also in this same region near the ends of the horny beak. In the Hylidae, forms like *Hyla crucifer*, however, often lose the third outer lower row, the goatee.

a. Mouth disk absent; no labial teeth; no papillae; no horny beaks; spiracle median near anus; nostril within edge of mouth fold; eye on a canthus; tadpoles (23–26.4 mm) small; black or grayish olive tadpoles with a stripe on the middle of the tail musculature..........*Brevicipitidae.*

  b. Tail sometimes with black tip; eyes plainly visible from ventral aspect; inner face of upper labial edge with no black pointed escrescences; lower mandibular prolongation light; general coloration black with purplish gray or hair brown dots; venter with white or yellowish bands and large blotches; sides of body with same coloration; light band at base of tail musculature prominent (even in alcohol). Egg with truncate outer envelope, giving mass a mosaic appearance on water's surface. Virginia—Florida—Texas, and up Mississippi River to Indiana.....................*Gastrophryne carolinensis.*

aa. Mouth disk present; upper and lower labial teeth; labial papillae; horny beaks present; nostril free of mouth; eyes dorsal close together; tail tip rounded.

  b. Spiracle sinistral; upper labial teeth not with two close rows on each ridge; labial teeth 1/3, 2/2, 2/3, 2/4, 3/3, 3/4, 4/4 to 6/5; upper and lower horny beaks, papillae on lower edge of labium absent or one or two rows:

    c. Anus median; spiracle lateral below the lateral axis (of tail musculature projected forward) sometimes as much ventral as lateral; upper tail crest extends on to the body to a vertical nearer hind legs than the spiracle or only half way; viscera visible (in preserved specimens) through the skin of the belly.

      d. Labial teeth 3/4 to 6/6; papillae extending completely around the border of the labium except for a short toothed median interval above (sometimes absent in one species); papillary border not emarginate on each side; eyes nearer mid-dorsal line than lateral outline, on lateral axis; tadpoles 24.5–65 mm. in length; spiracle a slit, very low on side, about on the level of the mouth; in general very bronzy tadpoles; myotomes of tail musculature well indicated . . . . . .
           . . . . *Scaphiopodidae.*

      e. Teeth 6/6, 5/6, 6/5, 5/5; inner papillae present; spiracle equidistant between eye and base of hind legs or vent; eye 1.4–1.8 nearer tip of snout than to the spiracle,

average 1.52; internasal space in interorbital space 1.28
–1.83, average 1.56; depth of body 1.74–2.5 in body
length, average 2.04; muscular part of tail in depth of
tail 1.45–2.5, average 1.98; last lower row of teeth
longer than horny beak. Last lower row of teeth 1.5
times in next to lowest row of teeth. Egg mass an irregular cylinder, at first bandlike.

Massachusetts—Florida—Texas and Arkansas. . . . .
. . . . *Scaphiopus holbrookii.*

dd. Labial teeth 2/3; papillae confined to the sides of the labium
(on lower half only in *Bufo punctatus*) upper and lower edges
toothed; papillary border on each side emarginate; eyes
slightly nearer lateral outline than mid dorsal line, above
lateral axis; spiracle small, a porelike opening; tadpoles 24–
28 mm. in length . . . . *Bufonidae.*

e. Papillae on upper and lower halves of lateral labial
margin; some inner papillae.

f. Black or blackish tadpoles; in life intestine shows
through the skin of the belly; third lower row of
labial teeth long, 1.2–1.6 in first lower row; third
lower row 1.0–1.5 in horny beak; median space
between lateral parts of the 2nd row of upper labial
teeth small, contained 2.0–4.0 times in either lateral
half, not greater than lateral half.

g. Papillae plainly visible.

h. Tadpole to 24 mm; horny beak in upper
fringe 1.75, in first or second lower row
1.5; horny beak equal to or less than the
3rd lower row of teeth; median space between two parts of second upper row 1.4–
2.1 in either lateral part; third lower row
of teeth in first lower row 1.2–1.4; two or
more rows of strong papillae from end of
upper fringe to end of third lower row,
sometimes 3–5 rows at side of labium;
lower loop of papillae far below level of
third row and with at least two rows of
papillae; mouth in interorbital space 1.0–
1.5, average 1.17; mouth larger than internasal space 1.2–1.6, average 1.36; depth
of tail in tail length 2.4–4.5, average 3.27;
eye nearer snout than spiracle 1.0–1.56,
average 1.2; nostril nearer eye than snout
1.1–1.8, average 1.48. Egg mass long
file, inner tube no partitions. North
Carolina—Florida—Louisiana . . . .
. . . . *Bufo terrestris.*

hh. Tadpole to 27 mm; horny beak in upper fringe 1.2–1.5, in first or second lower row of teeth 1.1–1.2 or 1.2–1.3; horny beak greater than 3rd row of lower labial teeth; median space 1.15–2.0, 1–4, or 1.3–3.0 in either lateral part; third lower row of teeth 1.3–1.5 or 1.4–1.5 in first lower row; one row of weak papillae from upper fringe to end of third lower row of teeth with a few scattering papillae at the side of the labium; lower loop with only 2 or 3 scattering papillae beside the outer row of weak papillae:

i. Mouth in interorbital distance .77–1.0, average .92; horny beak in upper fringe 1.2–1.4; horny beak in first or second row 1.1–1.2 times; third row in first lower row 1.3–1.5; depth of tail in tail length 1.25–2.7, average 1.97; spiracle nearer eye than vent 1.04–1.54, average 1.28; eye nearer snout than spiracle 1.0–1.27, average 1.16; mouth larger than internasal space 1.4–2.2, average 1.76; papillae of lower labial loop do not extend under the end of the end of the third row of labial teeth; tail musculature in tail depth 1.26–2.66, average 2.04; internasal space 1.2–1.6 in interorbital distance, average 1.6; spiracle 1.05–1.55 nearer eye than vent, average 1.28. Egg mass long file, partitions, inner tube present. Eastern North America, from Hudson Bay southwest . . . . *Bufo americanus.*

ii. Mouth in interorbital distance 1.07––1.5; horny beak in upper fringe 1.4–1.5; horny beak in first or second row 1.2–1.3; third lower row 1.3–1.6 in first lower row; depth of tail in tail length 2.88–3.83, average 3.33; spiracle nearer eye than vent 1.25–1.7, average 1.45; eye nearer snout than spiracle 1.0–1.6, average 1.16; mouth larger than internasal space 1.1–1.83, average 1.47; papillae of lower labial loop slightly extend or do not at all

extend under the end of the third lower
row; tail musculature in tail depth
1.6–2.3, average 1.85; internasal space
1.5–2.16 in interorbital space, average
1.86; spiracle 1.25–1.7 nearer eye than
vent or base of hind legs, average 1.45.
Egg mass long file, no inner tube, sometimes two rows of eggs. Michigan—New
England—Florida—Texas *Bufo fowleri.*

cc. Anus dextral; spiracle distinctly lateral on or near body axis;

  d. Papillary border on side with an emargination; tadpoles 50–
149 mm. in length; papillary fringe on upper labium extends
not at all inward beyond the end of the upper fringe of teeth
or only 1/8 to 1/16 of the length of the fringe; length of
horny beak in upper fringe of teeth 1.0 to 1.5 times; labial
teeth 2/3 or 3/3 or 3/4 or more . . . . *Ranidae.*

    e. Labial teeth 2/3 occasionally 3/3 rarely 1/3; tadpoles
74–150 mm. in length; dorsal crest not extending to
vertical of the spiracle, but usually just ahead of the buds
of the hind legs; tail always elliptical not spathulate;
upper fringe of teeth equal to or slightly larger (never
1.5 times) the horny beak.

      f. Tadpoles 74–84 mm.; tadpoles usually transform the
same season they are born; transformation sizes 18
to 30 mm. average 24 mm. (except *R. aesopus*);
tadpoles (except in *R. aesopus*) not strongly pigmented on belly, viscera plainly showing through skin (in
spirit specimens.) Egg globular or plinthlike beneath surface of water.

        g. Body in tail 2.15–2.85, average 2.6; depth of
tail in length of tail 2.6–3.5, average 3.0;
nostril 1.0–1.5. nearer eye than snout, average
1.25; eye 1.0–1.3 nearer spiracle than snout,
average 1.12; median space between the second
upper labial row 1.0–2.0 times the length of
either lateral part of this row; third lower row
.33–.66 shorter than the first or second rows;
tail covered with large prominent dark spots;
belly strongly pigmented, in spirits it looks
white; viscera not visible. South Carolina—
Florida—Louisiana. (Viosca) . *Rana aesopus.*

      gg. Body in tail 1.3–2.2, averages (1.53, 1.6, 1.7);
depth of tail in length of tail 2.3–3.4, averages
2.7, 2.65, 3.0; belly not strongly pigmented, in
spirits dark, viscera show through the skin.

h. Median space in second labial row 2–4 times the length of either lateral part; third row of lower labial teeth .33–.66 shorter than the first or second rows, usually at least .50; eye nearer the snout than spiracle or equidistant; nostril nearer eye than tip of snout; depth of tail in length of tail 2.3–3.2, average 2.7; spiracle 1.5–1.8 nearer eye than snout, average 1.63. Hudson Bay to Louisiana and Eastern States .... *Rana palustris.*

hh. Median space .5–1.0 or 1.0–1.5 times either lateral part of the second upper row; third row of labial teeth .22 or .285–.33 shorter than the first lower row; depth of tail in length of tail 2.0–2.8 or 2.7–3.4.

i. Median space of second upper row .5–1.0 times either lateral part; third lower row of teeth .285–.33 shorter than the first lower row; nostril to snout equal to nostril to eye; eye 1.15–1.3 nearer tip of snout than spiracle, average 1.2; body length in tail length 1.35–1.66, average 1.5; mouth .9–1.6 larger than internasal space; depth of tail in length of tail 2.0–2.88, average 2.65; tail crest usually with quite prominent dark spots; greatest length of tadpole 74 mm; spiracle 1.1–1.86 nearer eye than snout, average 1.46. Southeastern States to Louisiana . .

.... *Rana sphenocephala.*

ii. Median space 1.0–1.5 times either lateral part; third lower row .22 shorter than the first lower row; nostril 1.1–1.5 nearer the eye than snout; eye nearer spiracle than snout 1.1–1.3; body length in tail length 1.3–2.0, average 1.7; mouth larger than internasal space; depth of tail in length of tail 2.7–3.4, average 3.0; tail crest usually translucent with fine spots or pencillings; greatest length of tadpole 84 mm; spiracle 1.4–1.86 nearer eye than snout, average 1.59. North

America east of Sierra Nevada southward into Mexico . . *Rana pipiens.*

ff. Tadpoles 84 to 142 mm; tadpoles usually winter
over at least one season; transformation sizes 28 to
59 mm. (except *R. virgatipes* 25 to 35 mm., possibly
R. onca); tadpoles usually with strongly pigmented
bellies, viscera not plainly showing through the skin
(in spirit specimens).

  g. Tadpole with prominent continuous black crest
  margins and a black musculature band; belly
  bluish; tadpoles to 95 mm.; young tadpoles
  black with transverse yellowish band on the
  body; spiracle .86–1.2 nearer vent or base of
  hind legs than snout, average 1.0; spiracle .85–
  1.2 nearer eye than base of hind legs or vent,
  i. e., usually equidistant; eye equidistant from
  spiracle and tip of snout; muciferous crypts very
  distinct; spiracle below lateral axis; tail tip
  acuminate; second upper labial row in upper
  fringe 1/3 to 1/4; upper fringe distinctly
  greater than horny beak; median space between
  two parts of second upper labial row 1–1 1/2
  of either lateral part; third labial row equal to
  horny beak; third lower labial row longer than
  single row of lower papillae; third lower labial
  row 1/4 to 1/5 shorter than 1st lower row. Eggs
  unknown. South Carolina—Mississippi . . .
  . . . . *Rana heckscheri*

 gg. Tadpole without black crest margins or lateral
  band; belly white, cartridge buff or yellow to
  maize yellow; no transverse yellow band in
  young tadpoles; spiracle nearer vent than snout
  1.1–1.8; spiracle to eye rarely less than 1.25
  greater than spiracle to vent; eye nearer tip of
  snout than spiracle 1.–1.4; second upper labial
  row in upper fringe 1/4 to 1/15; upper fringe
  equal to or slightly greater than horny beak;
  median space in either lateral part 1 1/2 to 11;
  third lower labial row much less (about 1 1/2)
  than horny beak; third lower row much shorter
  or equal to single row of lower labial papillae.

  h. Tadpoles to 140 mm; eye well above
  lateral axis; muciferous crypts indistinct;
  spiracle just below lateral axis; spiracle
  1.06–1.44 nearer base of hind legs or vent
  than tip of snout, average 1.25; depth of

Plate X

Mature tadpoles. × 1.0

1. *Hyla andersonii* (two tadpoles), Lakehurst, N. J. June 28, 1923.
2. *Hyla cinerea*, Chesser Id., Ga. August 12, 1922.
3. *Hyla crucifer*, Ithaca, N. Y.
4. *Hyla femoralis* (two tadpoles) Anna's pond, Folkston, Ga. June 27, 1922
5. *Hyla gratiosa*, Petty pond, Folkston, Ga. July 31, 1922.
6. *Hyla gratiosa*, young tadpoles, Trader's Hill, Ga. June 24, 1922.
7. *Hyla squirella* (two tadpoles) Anna's pond, Folkston, Ga. June 27, 1922.
8. *Pseudacris ocularis*, Saddlebag pond, Trail Ridge, Folkston, Ga. June 30, 1922.
9. *Hyla versicolor*, Camp Pinckney, Ga. June 22, 1922.
10. *Hyla versicolor*, Ithaca, N. Y.
11. *Acris gryllus*, Board Pile Pt.. Ga. July 14, 1922.
12. *Scaphiopus holbrookii*, Camp Pinckney, Ga. June 22, 1922.
13. *Bufo quercicus*. Chesser Id., Ga. August 10, 1922.
14. *Gastrophryne carolinensis*. Trader's Hill, Ga. June 24, 1922.

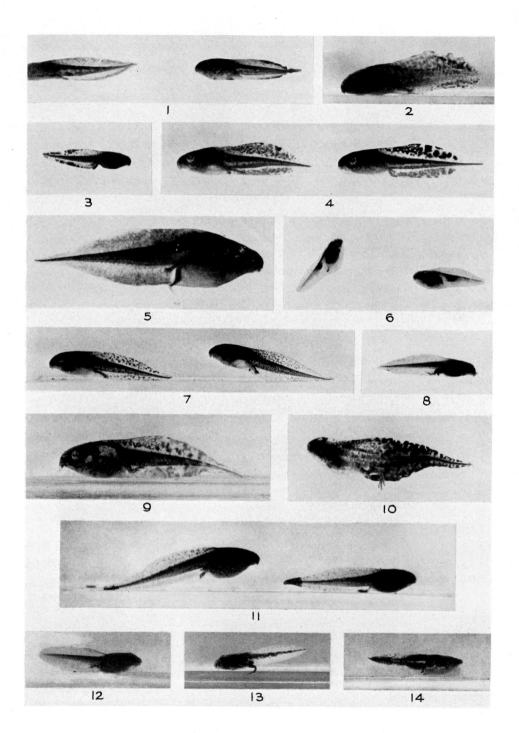

PLATE XI

Rana tadpoles. Mature. × 1.0

1. *Rana aesopus*, Chesser Id., Ga. August 10, 1922.
2. *Rana aesopus*, Petty pond, Folkston, Ga. July 29, 1922.
3. *Rana clamitans*, Near Spanish Creek, Folkston, Ga. July 17, 1922.
4. *Rana clamitans*, Ithaca, N. Y.
5. *Rana grylio*, Billy Id., Ga. May 11, 1921.
6. *Rana grylio*, Billy Id., Ga. August 4, 1922.
7. *Rana heckscheri*, Alligator Swamp, Callahan, Fla. July 20, 1922.
8. *Rana heckscheri*, Young tadpoles, Thompson's Landing, St. Mary's River, Fla. July 17, 1922.
9. *Rana sphenocephala*, Chesser Id., Ga. July 25, 1922.
10. *Rana sphenocephala*, Anna's pond, Folkston, Ga. July 10, 1922.
11. *Rana septentrionalis*, Onekio, N. Y. July 4, 1923.
12. *Rana pipiens*, Ithaca, N. Y.
13. *Rana virgatipes*, Lakehurst, N. Y. July 4, 1923.
14. *Rana palustris*, Ithaca, N. Y.

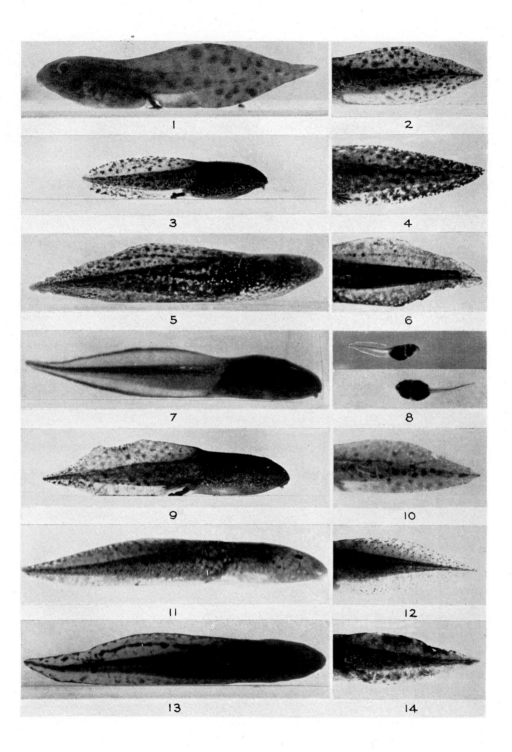

tail in tail length of tail 2.4–3.5, average
2.8; tail tip obtuse; second upper row in
upper fringe 1/4 to 2/7; median space in
second upper row 1 1/2 in either lateral
part; third lower row in first lower row
1/4–1/5 shorter; teeth 2/3 rarely 3/3.
Transformation size 43–59 mm. Egg
mass, a surface film. North America east of
Rockies . . . . *Rana catesbeiana.*

hh. Tadpoles to 84–100 mm.; eye on or just
above lateral axis; tail tip acute or acuminate (rounded in *R. onca*) teeth 2/3;
second upper row in upper fringe 1/6 to
1/15: median space in second upper row
2.5–11 in either lateral part; third lower
row in first lower row 1/2–1/3 shorter.

  i. Depth of tail in length of tail 1.45–1.8,
  average 1.7; tail tip acuminate; dorsal
  crest equal or less than tail musculature; muciferous crypts indistinct;
  spiracle 1.08–1.44 nearer vent than
  snout; mouth in interorbital distance
  1.5–2.37, average 1.94; internasal
  space in interorbital distance 1.8–2.6,
  average 2.16; 2nd upper row 1/6 to
  1/8 of the upper fringe; median space
  of 2nd upper row 2 1/2 to 4 1/2 times
  either lateral row; third lower row 1.5
  less than horny beak, much shorter
  than single row of lower labial papillae
  and 1/3 shorter than first lower row of
  teeth; 1st row of lower teeth equal to
  horny beak. Transformation size 32
  or 37–48 mm.; Egg mass, a surface
  film. Georgia—Florida—Louisiana . .
  . . . . *Rana grylio.*

  ii. Depth of tail in length of tail 2.5–4.7
  averages 3.1–3.87; tail tip acute;
  dorsal crest less than tail musculature;
  muciferous crypts distinct; spiracle
  1.07–1.08 nearer vent than snout;
  mouth in interorbital distance 1.3–1.8,
  average 1.5; internasal space in interorbital space 1.25–2.0, averages 1.6–
  1.75; second upper row of teeth equal
  to or greater than horny beak;

(j. Tadpoles to 99 mm.; transformation sizes at 29–38 mm; depth of tail in length of tail 3.2–4.7, averages 3.87; spiracle just touches lateral axis; eye just above lateral axis; spiracle 1.06–1.38 nearer eye than base of hind legs or vent, average 1.24; spiracle 1.25–1.6 nearer eye than vent, 1.45; mouth in interorbital distance 1.3–1.75, average 1.55; width of body in its own length 1.3–2.1, average 1.56; third lower labial row of teeth 1.25 less than horny beak, about equal to single row of lower labial papillae, 1/3 shorter than 1st lower row; sometimes a row of inner papillae below the 3rd lower row of teeth; median space in second upper labial row 3.5–4.5 times either lateral portion; second upper row 1/6 to 2/15 of the upper fringe; belly straw yellow, colonial buff or deep colonial buff; tail with round cartridge buff or pinkish cinnamon spots; no black line in dorsal crest as in *Rana grylio* or *R. virgatipes*. Eggs in a compact submerged mass. Hudson Bay — Minnestoa — New York—New England. . . . . *Rana septentrionalis.*

jj. Tadpoles to 92 mm.; transformation sizes at 25–38 mm. depth of tail in length of tail 2.5–3.7, spiracle just below lateral axis; eye on lateral axis; third lower labial row of teeth 1.5–1.25 less than horny beak, much shorter than single row of lower labial papillae, almost 1/2 shorter than 1st lower row; median space of second upper row 6–11 times the length of either lateral portion; second upper row 2/15 to 1/15 of the upper fringe.

k. Spiracle nearer vent than snout, 1.35–1.8; mouth 1.3–

1.8 times in interorbital distance, average 1.5; width of body in its own length 1.25–1.7, average 1.47 belly deep cream color; tail green mottled with brown and covered with fine yellow spots.

Egg mass, surface film.

Canada—Louisiana, Florida, New England *Rana clamitans*.

kk. Spiracle nearer vent than snout 1.07–1.45 averages 1.23–1.3; mouth 1.0–1.37 in interorbital distance, average 1.12.

l. Teeth 2/3 or 1/3; four to six rows of inner papillae from end of upper fringe to end of lower labial row; a row of heavy inner papillae below the third lower row of teeth; spiracle nearer eye than vent 1.42–1.82, average 1.62; nostril nearer eye than snout; 1.0–1.42, average 1.2; width of body in body length 1.45–1.86, average 1.6; tadpoles large (92 mm.); second upper row 2/15 or 1/15 of the upper fringe or second upper row absent; belly pale chalcedony yellow, sulphur yellow, vinaceous, pale grayish vinaceous or vinaceous buff; tail: *upper tail crest with a black line or row of large black spots, more prominent than in R. grylio; middle of musculature with another black line; tail dark with pale chalcedony yellow spots.* Transformation size 25–35 mm. Eggs, a submerged mass .

New Jersey to Georgia
. . . *Rana virgatipes.*

dd. Papillary border on side of labium without an emargination; tadpoles 23–50 mm. in length; labial teeth 2/3 or 2/2 . . . . *Hylidae.*

e. Labial teeth 2/2; eye dorsal just inside the lateral outline in dorsal aspect (more like Ranids) eye 1.0–1.66 (av. 1.22) nearer tip of snout than spiracle; depth of tail in length of tail 3.25–5.0, average 4.0; suborbital region oblique not vertical; spiracle to eye usually equal distance from spiracle to vent or base of hind legs; spiracle plainly showing from dorsum; *spiracular tube in life stands out at an angle from the body and opening is apart from the body proper*; tail tip conspicuously black (at times lost); papillary border does not extend above the end of the upper fringe (like *Rana*); length of horny beak in upper fringe of teeth 1.2–1.35 times; Eggs single, rarely a mass.
New York—Florida—Texas, up Mississippi Valley to Canadian Northwest . . . . *Acris.*

ee. Labial teeth usually 2/3 (rarely 2/2); eye lateral, visible from ventral as well as the dorsal aspect; eye 1.0–1.75 nearer the spiracle than tip of snout; depth of tail in length of tail 1.6–4.4, average 2.1–3.55; suborbital region vertical; spiracular tube in life parallel with body and opening at inner edge closely connected with or near to body proper . . . . . . *Hylidae exclusive of Acris.*

f. Labial teeth 2/2:

g. Teeth occasionally 2/2; tadpole to 33 mm. spiracle 2.0–2.6 nearer base of hind legs than tip of snout, average 2.16; nostril to eye 2.0 in nostril to snout; tail crests clear, heavily pigmented with purplish black blotches on the outer edge; no prominent dark lateral band with a clear light band below; upper fringe not perceptibly angulate in the middle; two rows of papillae on lower labial border below second lower row of teeth; median space between second upper rows of teeth 2–3 in either lateral row; ends of second lateral row extending beyond end of upper fringe for 1/4 to 1/6 of the length of either upper lateral row; horny-beak 1.75–2.25 in length from one end of lateral row to end of the other lateral row. Eggs, single, submerged. Manitoba—New Brunswick, South Carolina, Louisiana . . . . *Hyla crucifer.*

ff. Labial teeth 2/3:

  g Third row of labial teeth short, shorter than horny beak or .20– .40 of the first lower row in length; upper fringe slightly or not angulate at all; no flagellum ordinarily present; tadpoles 23–50 mm.; light papillary development, lower labial corner not with 3 or 4 strong rows of papillae; one or two rows of papillae below third lower row of teeth; the papillae extend above and beyond the end of the upper fringe for about .14–.285 of the length of the upper fringe.

    h. Tadpoles 23–33 mm.; eye equidistant between spiracle and tip of snout; spiracle 1.4–2.6 nearer vent or base of hind legs than tip of snout; spiracle 1.0–1.6 nearer eye than vent; papillae extend above the fringe for .16– .25 of the length of the fringe.

      i. *Musculature* with *no distinct brown lateral band with light area below*; crests usually heavily pigmented with purplish black blotches on outer rim; nostril to eye in nostril to snout 2.0; depth of tail in tail length 2.4–3.15, average 2.7; spiracle 2.0–2.6 nearer vent than snout, average 2.16; *no papillae below third lower labial row of teeth, thus appearing as a goatee*; median space between second upper labial row 2–3 in either lateral portion; horny beak in upper fringe 1.75–2.25. Eggs single, submerged . . . . . . *Hyla crucifer*.

     ii. *Musculature with a distinct brown lateral band with light area below*; crests usually clear with fine scattered fleckings, sometimes with fleckings gathered nearer outer rim; one or two rows of papillae below the third lower labial row of teeth; nostril to eye in nostril to snout 1.25–2.0; depth of tail in tail length 2.9–4.4, average 3.4, 3.55; spiracle 1.15–2.1 nearer vent than snout, average 1.5–1.875; median space between second upper labial row 2 1/2 or 3–7 in either lateral portion; horny beak in upper fringe 1.5–2.0.

j. Dorsal crest to vertical of spiracle; spiracle 1.0–1.66 (average 1.33) nearer eye than vent; spiracle 1.15 –1.95 (average 1.5) nearer vent than snout; mouth 1.0–1.25 larger than internasal space; two rows of papillae below third lower row of teeth; third labial lower row .25– .33 of the first lower row; first and second lower labial rows 1.25–1.6 greater than the horny beak; horny beak in upper fringe 1.5–1.75; median space between second row of upper lower row 2 1/2 or 3–7 in either lateral portion . . . . . .
. . . . . *Pseudacris (Raleigh.)*

jj. Dorsal crest to vertical midway between spiracle and eye; spiracle equidistant between eye and vent; spiracle 1.7–2.1 (average 1.875) nearer vent than snout; mouth and internasal space equal; one row of papillae below the third lower row of teeth; third lower labial row of teeth .33 of the first lower row; *dorsum of body in life with definite scattered black spots*; musculature with three bands, apricot buff (light) chestnut brown(dark) martius yellow (light); first and second lower labial rows 2.0 greater than the horny beak; horny beak in upper fringe 2.0; median space between second row of upper labial teeth 3–4 in either lateral portion. Eggs single.
South Carolina—Florida—Louisiana, (Viosca) *Pseudacris ocularis.*

hh. Tadpoles 35–50 mm.; eye 1.0–1.75 nearer spiracle than snout; spiracle 1.0–1.6 nearer vent than the tip of the snout; spiracle 1.25–2.5 nearer eye than vent or base of hind legs; papillae extend above the upper fringe for .14–.285 of the length of the fringe.

i. Tadpoles 50 mm. in length; body in tail 2.3–3.25, average 2.5; depth of body in width of body .83–1.0, average .9; depth of tail 10–14 mm.; beautiful green tadpoles; young tadpoles with a black saddle spot on the back of the musculature near its base and with a light line from eye to tail; one row of papillae below lower third labial row; papillae extending above upper fringe for .25–.285 of the fringe's length; dorsal crest extending to a vertical halfway between eye and spiracle. Eggs single, submerged. South Carolina—Florida—Louisiana. (Viosca) . . . . *Hyla gratiosa.*

ii. Tadpoles 35–45 mm.; body in tail 1.1––2.0, average 1.6; depth of body in width of body 1.0–1.8; depth of tail 5–9 mm.; no black saddle spot in young tadpoles.

(j. Tadpole small (35 mm.); dorsal crest extending to vertical halfway between spiracle and the base of the hind legs; depth of tail in tail length 2.5–3.5; average 3.0; nostril to eye 1.2–2.1 in nostril to snout; mouth in interorbital space 1.33–2.6; internasal space in interorbital distance 1.33–2.2; eye just touches lateral axis or is below it; horny beak in upper fringe, 1.5–1.7; papillae extending beyond the end of the upper fringe .25–.285 of the length of the upper fringe; two rows of papillae below third lower third lower labial row; median space between second upper labial row 1.25–2.0 in either lateral portion; third lower labial row .20–.22 of the first lower row; first row of lower labial teeth 1.0–1.5 times the horny beak. Eggs strewn in water amongst sphagnum (Noble & Noble.) New Jersey—South Carolina .
. . . . *Hyla andersonii.*

jj. Tadpole medium (40 and 45 mm.) Dorsal crest extends ahead of spiracle or to eye; depth of tail in tail length 1.5–3.2, average 2.75; nostril to eye 1.0–1.7 in nostril to snout; mouth in interorbital space 1.4–2.0; internasal in interorbital space 1.25–2.0; eye on lateral axis; papillae extending beyond end of upper fringe 1.4–2.5 of the length of the upper fringe; median space in second upper labial row 3–5 in either lateral portion; third labial row .25–.40 of the first labial lower row; first row of lower labial teeth 1.0–1.3 greater than horny beak.

     k. Dorsal crest to the vertical halfway between spiracle and the eye; depth of body in body length 1.7–2.5; musculature of tail in depth of tail 1.75–2.4 average 1.9; spiracle 1.4–2.3 nearer eye than vent; mouth 1.0–1.4 larger than internasal space, average 1.25; two rows of papillae below the third lower row of labial teeth; papillae extend beyond the end of the upper fringe .22–.25 of the length of the fringe; horny beak in upper fringe 2.0–2.3; third labial lower row .25–.40 the length of the first lower row.

     Eggs surface or submerged irregular mass.

     Virginia—Florida—Texas to Illinois . . . . . . *Hyla cinerea*.

gg. Third row of labial teeth long, longer than horny beak, or .75–1.00 of the first lower row in length; upper fringe very angulate in middle; flagellum on tail; tadpoles 32–50 mm.; heavy papillary development, lower labial corner with 3 or 4 rows of papillae; two more or less complete rows of papillae below third row of teeth (except in *Hyla arenicolor*); papillae extend

PLATE XII

Tadpole mouthparts (*Hyla, Acris, Pseudacris, Bufo*)

1. *Hyla crucifer.*
2. *Hyla gratiosa.*
3. *Hyla andersonii*
4. *Hyla cinerea.*
5. *Pseudacris feriarum.*
6. *Acris gryllus.*
7. *Bufo fowleri.*
8. *Pseudacris ocularis*
9. *Hyla squirella.*
10. *Bufo americanus.*
11. *Bufo terrestris.*
12. *Hyla versicolor*
13. *Hyla femoralis.*

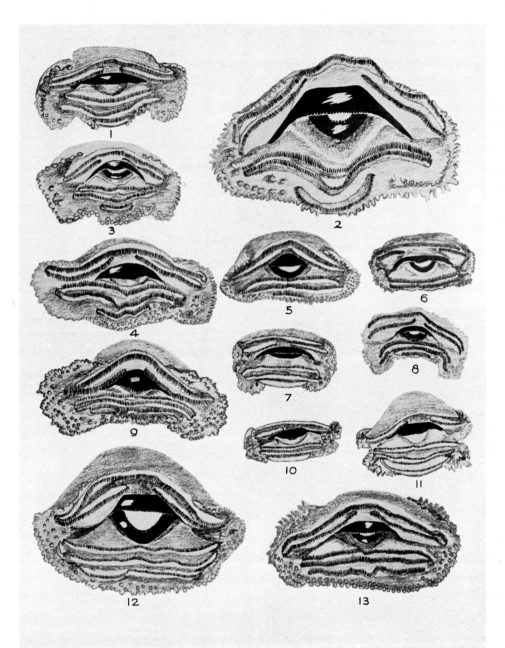

PLATE XIII

Tadpole mouthparts (*Rana*)

1. *Rana catesbeiana.*
2. *Rana sphenocephala.*
3. *Rana palustris*
4. *Rana aesopus.*
5. *Rana pipiens.*

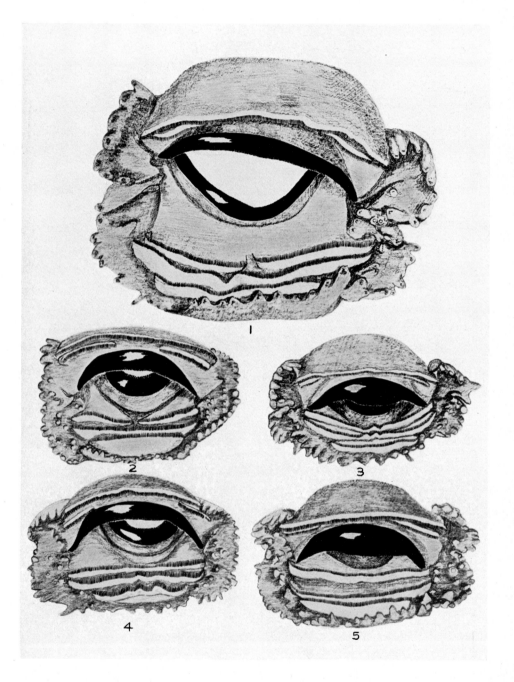

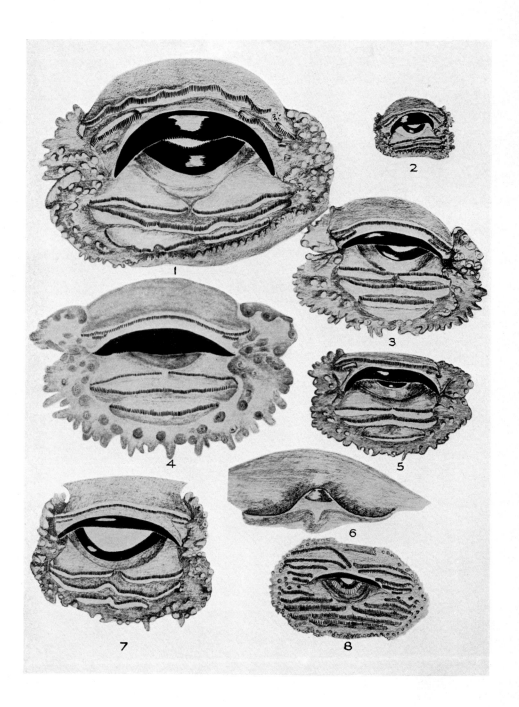

above and beyond the end of the upper fringe for about .30–.40 the length of the upper fringe.

h. Third lower labial row .80–1.00 of the length of the first lower row; dorsal crest extends to the vertical halfway from hind legs to spiracle, to spiracle or halfway from spiracle to eye; dorsal crest equal to, greater or less than depth of tail musculature; tadpoles 36–50 mm.; red may be present in the tail; tail crest distinctly or more or less clear of spots next the musculature; tail heavily blotched with dark blotches or spots.

  i. Medium space between lateral upper rows 5.0–10.0 times in either lateral row; spiracle 1.44–2.5 nearer eye than vent; width of body in its own length 1.6–2.1; eye 1.0–1.7 nearer spiracle than tip of snout; tail sometimes suffused with coral red, coral pink, or "reddish" or "orange."

    j. Medium space between lateral upper rows of teeth contained 6.0–10.0 in either lateral row; 1st and 2nd lower rows of teeth 1.4–1.6 greater than horny beak; mouth equal to internasal space; depth of tail in length of tail 1.6–2.75, average 2.25; muscular part of tail in depth of tail 1.8–2.3, average 2.1; depth of body 1.33–2.2 in body length, average 1.68; dorsal crest usually equal to or greater than musculature depth; center of belly solid sulphur yellow; *tail 3–5 banded*; light lateral band bounded below and above by a brown band; flagellum clear of pigment; body olivaceous black.

    Eggs a surface film.

    North Carolina—Florida—Texas
    . . . . *Hyla femoralis.*

  ii. Medium space between lateral upper rows contained 3.25–5.0 times in either lateral row; spiracle 1.12–1.5 nearer eye than vent; eye about equidistant between spiracle and tip of snout; internasal space in mouth .7–1.0; dorsal crest extends to vertical of spiracle or halfway between eye and spiracle; dorsal crest equal to or greater than musculature depth; muscular part of tail in depth of tail 1.72–1.9, average 1.8; depth of tail in length of tail 3.1–4.0; width of body in its own length 1.3–1.7; *no lateral bands in tail; tail more or less scarlet or orange vermillion with black blotches more prominent near the margins of the crests.* Body olive green; belly conspicuously white or very light cream. Eggs a surface film.

Minnesota — Texas — Maine — Florida . . . . *Hyla versicolor.*

hh. Third labial lower row .75 of the length of the first row; dorsal crest extends to the vertical of the posterior edge of the eye; dorsal crest usually less than depth of the musculature; tadpoles to 32 mm.; width of body in its own length 1.7–2.2, average 1.875; depth of tail in length of tail 2.2–3.3, average 2.8; third lower row of teeth not equal to first lower row; median space between lateral upper rows contained 3.25 –5.0 times in length of either lateral row; papillae extend above and beyond the ends of the upper fringe for .3–.33 of the upper fringe; horny beak in upper fringe 1.8–2.0; no bands nor red in tail; tail crest clear, *uniformly sprinkled with distinct black dots:* body greenish (like *H. cinerea* or *Hyla gratiosa*); belly testaceous, or chalcedony yellow. Eggs single, submerged.

Texas—Indiana; Florida to Virginia.
. . . . *Hyla squirella.*

TRANSFORMATION PERIOD
(Pls. XV, XVI)

Transformation for some species in Okefinokee may begin by April 1 or earlier, but it occurs principally from May to August, especially from June 10–July 27. Thereafter to October 1 or 15 or November 1, stragglers may transform. The approximate order of transformation is given in the following condensed table. (Table 17)

TABLE 17

	Spawing order	Larval period	Transformation dates	
			Average	Range
Rana clamitans	20	Over	April or May	Apr. 1 to Sept.
Rana grylio	18	1	June 1	Apr. 24 to July 19
Rana heckscheri	13	winter	June 10	May to July 15
Rana virgatipes	12		June 14	May 15 to Aug. 15
(Rana catesbeiana	19		June	May to Oct. 1)
(Rana septentrionalis	21		June	June or earlier to September)
Pseudacris nigrita	1	Short	(Early)	to July 1.
Rana sphenocephala	2	larval	June 21	–Apr. 1 to Oct. 1
Rana aesopus	3	period	— — —	May 1(?) to Nov. 1
Bufo terrestris	4	in the	June 15	Apr. 27 to Oct. 1
Scaphiopus holbrookii	5	year eggs are laid.	— — —	Apr. 15 to Oct. 1
Acris gryllus	8	,, ,,	July 14	May 29 to Oct. 1
Gastrophryne carolinensis	15	,, ,,	July 13	June 12 to Oct. 15
Hyla femoralis	10	,, ,,	July 17	June 16 to Oct. 1
Hyla squirella	7	,, ,,	July 3	June 26 to Oct. 1
Hyla versicolor	14	,, ,,	— — —	June 27 to Aug. 1
Hyla andersonii	16	,, ,,	July 19	June 29 to Sept.
Pseudacris ocularis	11	,, ,,	July 15	June 30 to ————
Hyla gratiosa	6	,, ,,	July 27	–July 1 to Oct. 1
Hyla cinerea	9	,, ,,	— — —	July 2 to Oct. 1
Bufo quercicus	17	,, ,,	July 21	July 7 to Aug. 16

There are many discrepancies in this table. Of the first four species which winter over we collected few transformed individuals. The earliest we reached the swamp was April 24. All may begin to transform earlier than the table shows. Doubtless the bulk of their transformation comes before the bulk of transformation for the first five breeders of the spring, i. e. the February to March 10 beginners. From *Acris gryllus* onward to the end of the table the spawning order seems to have little relation to transformation dates. This is more from insufficient data than anything else. In the table the least significant item is the average date. In some cases it means little. From *Acris gryllus* onward our transformation data come all from June 1 onward with one exception and all average dates are in July whereas the first early breeders have transformation from April 1 onward and averages in June or earlier.

If a composite curve were made of the 21 curves of transformation–sizes, we would have a continuous record of sizes from 6 to 59 mm. The transformation sizes fall into four groups of sizes. (Table 18) The first group of 6–12 mm. in size, (average 8–11, mode 7 to 11 mm.) comprises 6 species of four families: The toads (*Bufonidae*), namely oak toad and southern toad; two swamp cricket frogs or chorus frogs (*Pseudacris* of *Hylidae*), little chorus frog, black cricket frog; the narrow mouthed toad (*Brevicipitidae*), and the solitary spade-foot (*Scaphiopodidae*). The second group of seven species are from 9–23 mm. in range, 12–20 mm. in average size, and 12 to 20 mm. in modal size. They are all the remaining tree frogs (*Hylidae*). The third group of four species com-

TRANSFORMATION SIZE

TABLE 18

	Transformation size (mm.)				Adult size, (mm.)	
	Range		Average	Mode	Largest adult	Smallest breeding adult
Bufo quercicus	6 –	10.5	8	7	32	19
Bufo terrestris	6.5	10.5	8	8	88	42
Pseudacris ocularis	7	11	8	9	17.5	11.5
Pseudacris nigrita	(8?	12?)			30	21
Gastrophryne carolinensis	7	12	11	11	36	20
Scaphiopus holbrookii	8.5	12	10	10	72	50
Hyla squirella	11	13	12	12	37	23
Hyla andersonii	11	15	12	12	47	30
Acris gryllus	9	15	13	13	33	15
Hyla femoralis	10	15	13	13	40	23
Hyla cinerea	11.5	17	15	16	63	37
Hyla versicolor	13	20	16	16	60	32
Hyla gratiosa	18	23	20	20	68	49
Rana sphenocephala	18	33	23	25	82	49
Rana clamitans	20.5	33.5	25	24	75	52
Rana virgatipes	23	32	27	—	66	41
Rana aesopus	27	35			108	68
Rana septentrionalis	29	40	34	36	72	48
Rana heckscheri	31	49	35	33	125	82
Rana grylio	32	49	44	43	161	82
Rana catesbeiana	43	59	53	54	200	85

prise the southern meadow frog, green frog, carpenter frog and gopher frog. They range from 18 to 35 mm., average 23 to 27 mm., mode 24 to 25 mm. Two of these are transformers which winter over as tadpoles. The last group of four frogs (*Ranidae*) comprise the winter tadpole group, 29 to 59 mm. in range at transformation, average 34 to 53 mm., mode 33 to 54 mm.

The first 14 species are of species which normally transform the summer the eggs are laid. Of the last 7 species (larger transformation sizes) six are of the group which winters over as a tadpole.

Viewed from the point of transformation size and smallest breeding adult in each species the interval order between ranges of transformation size and smallest breeding size is as follows: (Table 19)

TABLE 19

	Interval (mm.)		Interval (mm.)
Acris gryllus	0 – 6	Rana sphenocephala	16 –31
Pseudacris ocularis	.5– 4.5	Rana clamitans	18.5–31.5
Bufo quercicus	8 –11	Hyla cinerea	20 –25.5
Gastrophryne carolinensis	8 –13	Hyla gratiosa	26 –31
Hyla femoralis	8 –13	Rana catesbeiana	26 –42
Pseudacris nigrita	9 –13	Rana terrestris	31.5–35.5
Rana septentrionalis	8 –19..	Rana aesopus	33 –41
Rana virgatipes	9 –18	Rana grylio	33 –50
Hyla squirella	10 –12	Rana heckscheri	33 –51
Hyla versicolor	12 –19	Scaphiopus holbrookii	38 –41.5
Hyla andersonii	15 –19		

Or if each species be considered from the point of view of least and greatest transformation sizes, least breeding size and greatest breeding size, how many times bigger will a little transformed anuran of each species have to grow to attain least breeding size and greatest breeding size: (Table 20)

TABLE 20

	To attain least breeding size		To attain greatest breeding size
Bufo terrestris	6.4 –4 times	Bufo terrestris	13.5–8.4 times
Scaphiopus holbrookii	6.0 –4.18 times	Scaphiopus holbrookii	8.5 –6.0
Hyla cinerea	3.2 –2.2	Hyla cinerea	5.5 –3.6
Bufo quercicus	3.16–1.8	Bufo quercicus	5.3 –3
Gastrophryne carolinensis	2.85–1.65	Gastrophryne carolinensis	5.14–3
Hyla gratiosa	2.7 –2.12	Rana grylio	5.0 –3.3
Hyla andersonii	2.7 –2.0	Rana catesbeiana	4.6 –3.3
Rana sphenocephala	2.7 –1.5	Rana sphenocephala	4.6 –2.5
Pseudacris nigrita	2.62–1.8	Hyla versicolor	4.5 –3.0
Rana heckscheri	2.6 –1.6	Hyla andersonii	4.3 –3.1
Rana clamitans	2.6 –1.5	Rana aesopus	4.0 –3.0
Rana grylio	2.55–1.6	Rana heckscheri	4.0 –2.6
Rana aesopus	2.5 –1.9	Hyla femoralis	4.0 –2.6
Hyla versicolor	2.5 –1.6	Hyla gratiosa	3.7 –3.0
Hyla femoralis	2.3 –1.53	Pseudacris nigrita	3.75–2.5
Hyla squirella	2.1 –1.77	Rana clamitans	3.65–2.2
Rana catesbeiana	2.0 –1.45	Acris gryllus	3.6 –2.2
Rana virgatipes	1.8 –1.3	Hyla squirella	3.3 –2.8
Rana septentrionalis	1.75–1.2	Rana virgatipes	2.9 –2.0
Pseudacris ocularis	1.64–1.04	Rana septentrionalis	2.5 –1.8
Acris gryllus	1.6 –1.0	Pseudacris ocularis	2.5 –1.6

RATE OF GROWTH
(Pl. XVII)

Knowing the transformation size and average, mode and maximum adult size we have certain starting points. But our conclusions on the number of years of growth are based on presumptive evidence, namely on the measurements of frogs taken at the same time or place, e.g. if at one time and place we take a 14 mm. transformed frog, a 22 mm. frog, a 31 mm. frog, and a 40 mm. individual of *Hyla femoralis*, we might infer we had four age groups: 14 at transformation, 22, one year old, 31, two year old, and 40, three year old. But what the resident naturalists can do is to mark frogs or keep them in some pond inclosure and get the real growth of an individual or individuals. My notes are to stimulate work along this line, little having been done in this country.

Of course great variations might happened with some northern species which might have extended periods of breeding, such as *Bufo americanus*, *Scaphiopus holbrookii* or *Rana clamitans*, but in the south or southwest it becomes more complicated with frogs which may breed from February or

TABLE 2I

		1st year	2nd year	3rd year	4th year	5t year	6th year	7th year
Pseudacris ocularis	7 –9	11.5–13.5	14 –17.5					
Bufo quercicus	7 – 8	10.5–18,20	19,21–28,30	28,30–32				
Bufo terrestris	6.5–11	13 –25	25 –35	34 –47	48 –59,60	59– 68	69– 79	
Gastrophryne carolinensis	8.5–12	15 –18,20	20 –27	25 –31				
Acris gryllus	9–12.5,15	15 –23	22,23–33					
Scaphiopus holbrookii	8.5–12	18 –24	26 –36	38 –50	51 –61	62– 72		
Hyla femoralis	10 –15	17 –26	26 –34	32,34–40				
Hyla squirella	11 –14	17.5–25.5	25 –36					
Hyla andersonii	11.5–15		(26? –34?)	(35? –44?)				
Hyla cinerea	11.5–17	20 –30	30 –42	41 –50	50 –60	63–		
Hyla versicolor	14 –20	20 –30	30 –42	42 –53	53 –59			
Hyla gratiosa	18 –23	28 –34	37 –45	47 –56	56 –68			
Rana clamitans	29 –33	33 –43	43 –52	52 –62	64 –77			
Rana virgatipes	23 –29,31	32 –39	40 –48	49 –56	60 –66			
Rana sphenocephala	20 –33	35 –50	52 –65	67 –78				
Rana septentrionalis	29 –40	40 –48,50	47 –58	59 –72				
Rana aesopus	28 –38	38 –52	52 –65	66 –77	78 –88	89–102	102–108	
Rana heckscheri	32 –49	(46 –63)	(63 –80)	(80 –96)	(97–113)	(114–125)		
Rana grylio	32 –49	56 –69	73 –86	91 –102	107–125	125–141	141–161	
Rana catesbeiana	43 –59	59 –73	73 –80	92 –100	108–130	130–148	150–166	170–180*

*Based on the Cornell and U. S. N. M. collections.

March to November 1 or later. Some have assumed that if at outcoming in the spring the collector find several separate size groups around certain means we might have year groups. If however a species breeds from February to December 1 he might have a variation from 4 months to 14 or 15 months. One needs to know transformation sizes (range, average, mode), transformation periods (average, mode, range), breeding periods and countless other factors to make a decent approach to a presumptive determination of year groups. The following table is therefore provisional, based on what evidence we have, and may be easily assailed or in part controverted but may lead to long continued careful studies by subsequent workers.

In view of the fact that each of these series of presumptive ages was determined from plotting the sizes of each species with no thought of previous plottings for kindred species there are quite close parallels in this table. Still one might ask how *Rana sphenocephala* might reach 78 mm. at the end of the third year when *R. clamitans* takes 4 years according to the table? The plotting for one or the other may be wrong or each individualistic. *Rana clamitans* in the south is small for its species. The south is the optimum for *Rana sphenocephala*.

In the same way Viosca has called my attention to the rapid growth of bullfrogs in the south as contrasted to the north. The growth given for *Rana catesbeiana* is for the north, may be very presumptive and far from the truth for Texan, Louisianan, Georgian and North Carolinian frogs. Bullfrogs I have found breeding in February at San Antonio, Texas, but in Ithaca, N. Y. never until June or July. The *Rana catesbeiana* figures in some ways do not strictly belong in this table. (Table 21)

In Table 21 we have underscored the year each is held to breed. From this we discover that *Pseudacris ocularis*, *Pseudacris nigrita* probably, and *Acris gryllus* breed at 1 year old. These are the small tree frogs. Then comes the oak toad (*Bufo quercicus*) and narrow-mouthed toads (*Gastrophryne carolinensis*) breeding at 2 years of age. In the tree frogs four species (*Hyla femoralis*, *Hyla squirella*, *Hyla andersonii*, *Hyla versicolor*) apparently fall in the two year old class, and three frogs (*Rana virgatipes*, *R. sphenocephala* and *Rana septentrionalis*) also breed two years after transformation. This gives representatives of four families, nine species in all, or about one-half of the table maturing in 2 years or thereabouts. Two tree frogs (*Hyla cinerea* and *Hyla gratiosa*) breed as 3 year olds, and five frogs (*Rana clamitans*, *Rana aesopus*, *Rana heckscheri*, *Rana grylio*, and *Rana catesbeiana*) fall in the same class. The last group is one of the most precocious groups of early transformation, namely the southern toad and solitary spade-foot. They transform quickly at small sizes, but have to grow apparently for 4 years before breeding.

In interpretation of age groups more chance for personal equation comes in the early sizes. For example from transformation onward some would make the frogs grow much faster the first year or so. Some no doubt would merge my first year and second year group into one (namely yearlings). Herein is one of the crucial periods needing more study.

FOOD

No phase might prove more profitable than the study of the food of these species. Former associates of the author such as Drs. P. A. Munz and S. W. Frost have pointed out how engaging this topic might be and how valuable anura are in collecting the lowly and rare insects the entomologist might miss. In this paper this topic is one of its weakest phases treated. Only three of the Okefinokee forms have been carefully studied with Okefinokee material. Dr. Vernon Haber published his interesting paper on "The Food of the Carolina Treefrog, *Hyla cinerea* Schneider" (Journ. Comp. Psych. Vol. VI, No. 2, Apr. 1926, pp. 189–220). Out of this study come G. Steiner's significant "Some Nemas from the Alimentary Tract of the Carolina Tree Frog (*Hyla carolinensis* Pennant) with Discussion of Some General Problems of Nematology." (Journ. Parasitology, Sept. 1924, Vol. XI, pp. 1–32).

One never knows whither these food studies of frogs as well as other groups will lead. In a somewhat similar fashion we have a by-product in the study of the food of the oak toad (*Bufo quercicus*). Dr. Remington Kellogg examined all our *Bufo quercicus* and *Bufo terrestris* from the Okefinokee swamp and these studies are incorporated in his two forth-coming papers. But some of the spiders of the *Bufo quercicus* food contents were submitted to Prof. C. R. Crosby. He picked up one vial of spiders collected by *Bufo quercicus* (Dr. T. Barbour collection) in Florida. He secured a new genus and new species. The next vial were spiders collected by *Bufo quercicus* (A. H. Wright collection) from Okefinokee swamp and the new genus from Florida appeared and another new species of it. Professor Crosby gives it the amusing title "A New Genus and Two Species of Spiders Collected by *Bufo quercicus* (Holbrook)," but the title nevertheless expresses the real situation. Other species ought to prove equally attractive forms for study.

ENEMIES

No article is more sought for or more relished as a food by a diversity of animals from fish to man than frogs. The latter's defense consists in concealment and in the possession of poison glands in the skin, neither of which means is aggressive in its nature. Insects and plants may prove a more constant fare, but to any fair-sized animal a frog diet is one of the preferred menus, if obtainable. Man is not content with cleaning up and draining the "frog holes" or swampy stretches, but he kills the frogs at all seasons. He takes the frogs when they congregate for breeding purposes and such a toll hardly accords with the ideas of conservation held at the present day for birds or mammals. The day may come when every farm will have its pond for cattle and hence frogs, but swine are amongst their worst enemies. (For longer discussion of this topic see the topic *enemies* under each species account.)

AFFINITIES

We are starting with the better known comparative characters of adults and are adding a supplement out of our actual experiences with these frogs

Plate XV

Transformation

Transformed frogs. Lateral aspect.

1. *Hyla andersonii*, Lakehurst, N. J. July 5, 1923. × 0.75.
2. *Hyla cinerea*, Billy Id., Ga. July 25, 1921. × 1.0.
3. *Hyla femoralis*, Chesser Id., Ga. July 2, 1922. × 1.0.
4. *Hyla gratiosa*, Chesser Id., Ga. July 27, 1922. × 1.0.
5. *Hyla squirella*, Folkston, Ga. June 27, 1922. × 1.0.
6. *Hyla versicolor*, Chesser Id., Ga. June 29, 1922. × 1.0.
7. *Acris gryllus*, Chesser Id., Ga. July 8, 1922. × 1.0.
8. *Pseudacris ocularis*, Saddlebag Pond, Trail Ridge, Folkston, Ga. June 30, 1922. × 1.0.
9. *Scaphiopus holbrookii*, two transforming frogs, Chesser Id., Ga. June 29, 1922 × 0.9.
10. *Gastrophryne carolinensis*, Chesser Id., Ga. June 25, 1922. × 1.0.
11. *Bufo terrestris*, Trader's Hill, Ga. June 24, 1922. × 1.0.
12. *Bufo quercicus*, Chesser Id., Ga. July 13, 1922. × 1.0.

Typical series, tadpole to transformed frog.

13-16. *Hyla gratiosa*, Chesser Id., Ga. July 25, 1922. Dorsal aspect. × 1.2.

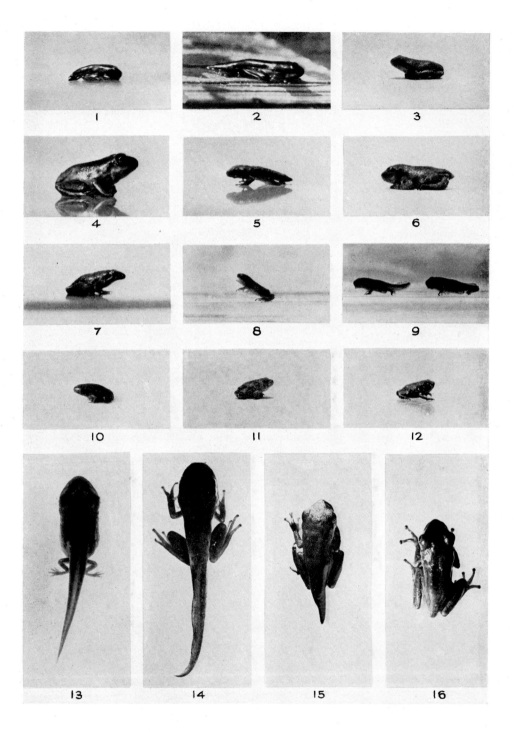

PLATE XVII

Chart of growth

Ranges of transformation sizes in comparison with the greatest mature sizes of males and females of twenty species.

(measurements in millimeters)

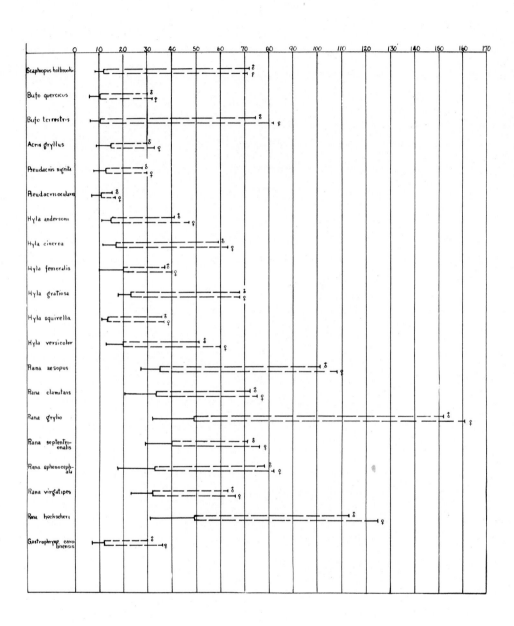

in camp, in the field and with them alive. One needs to gather much material alive in its own haunt and seek it oneself over a period of time, to appraise affinities and then he may be far amiss. Some of the evidences may be as follows:

1. *Adult characters.* Some may think or hold too little attention has been given comparative morphology and structural characters of the adults. Heretofore these have been largely used and are the common presumptive evidence already known and most easily sought with preserved material. Had Holbrook known that *Acris gryllus* and *Hyla crucifer* laid single eggs he would have been more confirmed in making them *Hylodes gryllus* and *Hylodes crucifer* which he did on adult characters. When one knows *Rana virgatipes* lays different egg masses from *Rana grylio* then do the adult resemblances become so overpowering in assignment of relationship? If we relied on egg mass, *R. virgatipes* might be put far removed from *R. grylio*, yet somewhere near *R. grylio* it doubtless belongs.

2. *Voice characters of males.* On the basis of sacs *Bufo quercicus* belongs in a different group from *Bufo terrestris*, *B. americanus*, or *Bufo fowleri*, and other characters bear out this judgment. Vocal sacs, however in the *Hylidae* of Okefinokee are not so useful in separation of racial groups. In the *Ranidae* the order of vocal sac development seems least in *R. clamitans*, *R. catesbeiana*, *R. heckscheri*, *R. grylio*, *R. septentrionalis*, and *R. palustris*. There is a group with prominent lateral sacs, to wit, *Rana sphenocephala*, *R. pipiens*, *R. virgatipes*, *R. areolata*, and *R. aesopus*. The first assemblage seems natural, but does *R. virgatipes* belong in the second group on other grounds? The second assemblage is as natural except for *R. virgatipes*. From another vocal point of view, *R. virgatipes* and *R. septentrionalis* must be close because each independently has been dubbed a Carpenter Frog.

3. *Breeding maturity.* On this basis we would put the small *Bufo quercicus* apart from *Bufo terrestris*. In the *Hylidae*, *Acris gryllus*, the species of *Pseudacris*, *Hyla squirella* and *Hyla femoralis* would form a small sized group; *Hyla andersonii*, *Hyla versicolor*, *Hyla cinerea*, and intermediate group; and *Hyla gratiosa*, a large sized group. Or *Rana virgatipes*, *R. septentrionalis*, *R. sphenocephala*, *Rana pipiens*, and *R. clamitans* might make one group and *Rana areolata*, *R. aesopus*, *R. heckscheri*, *R. catesbeiana*, and *R. grylio* another group. Are these groups good criteria of relationship in each case? I fear not.

4. *Breeding season.* In the Ranas it would seem as if *Rana sphenocephala* (also *R. pipiens*) and *Rana aesopus* (also *R. areolata*) fall in the very early group, and *Rana virgatipes*, *R. heckscheri*, *R. grylio*, *R. catesbeiana*, *R. clamitans* and *R. septentrionalis* form a later group. They seem natural groups, but does *R. palustris* fall intermediate?

In the *Hylidae*, *Pseudacris nigrita* comes very early. *Hyla gratiosa* and *Hyla squirella* and *Acris gryllus*, single egg layers, fall into early spring breeders. Are the two *Hylas* related? The next group seems *Hyla cinerea*, *Hyla femoralis*, *Pseudacris ocularis*, *Hyla versicolor*, *Hyla andersonii*, the first and last possibly related, the second and fourth, but the third apart.

5. Egg mass. In the frogs, *Rana catesbeiana, Rana grylio, (R. heckscheri), R. clamitans* lay films; *Rana palustris, Rana pipiens, Rana sphenocephala, Rana aesopus, Rana areolata, Rana virgatipes* and *Rana septentrionalis* lay plinths or masses beneath surface of water. In the *Hylidae, Hyla squirella, Hyla gratiosa, Pseudacris ocularis, Hyla crucifer, Acris gryllus* lay single eggs, *Hyla andersonii* and *Hyla cinerea* are in an intermediate group, and *Hyla versicolor* and *Hyla femoralis* lay surface films. Again we have recurring some of the groupings of the other headings. *Bufo quercicus* and *Bufo terrestris* are separate groups entirely on this basis.

6. Individual eggs. In the Hylidae possibly *Acris gryllus, Hyla crucifer* and *Pseudacris ocularis* should go together into one group of single eggs, *Hyla squirella* and *Hyla gratiosa* into another, and *Hyla cinerea* and *Hyla andersonii* into an intermediate group between single eggs and surface films. Of the latter type we have *Hyla femoralis* and *Hyla versicolor*. In the Bufos, *Bufo quercicus* belongs nearer *Bufo compactilis* or others of the southwest than with *B. terrestris* which in turn is as near *B. fowleri* as *B. americanus*. In the Ranas, *Rana pipiens, R. sphenocephala, Rana aesopus, R. areolata,* and *R. palustris* fall together on this character, while *Rana catesbeiana* and *Rana virgatipes* have no inner envelope and *R. grylio, R. septentrionalis* and *R. clamitans* have an inner envelope of jelly.

7. Larval period. The over-winter group of *R. virgatipes, R. clamitans, R. septentrionalis, R. heckscheri, R. grylio,* and *R. catesbeiana*, seems a natural group. They are later breeders than the short larval period group of *Rana pipiens, R. sphenocephala, R. aesopus, R. areolata,* and *R. palustris* which breed earlier except *R. palustris*. The Hylids, nine species, separate in no such clearly cut fashion.

8. Mature larvae. The tadpoles of *R. pipiens, R. sphenocephala, R. aesopus* and *R. areolata* fall more or less together as do those of the wintering tadpole group of six species (*R. clamitans, R. catesbeiana, R. grylio, R. heckscheri, R. virgatipes,* and *R. septentrionalis.*) In the Hylids, *Acris* appears as much a Ranid as a Hylid in character. *Hyla crucifer* and the species of *Pseudacris* apparently fall together into another group. *Hyla gratiosa, Hyla andersonii,* and *Hyla cinerea* seemingly are another group. And *Hyla femoralis, Hyla versicolor* and *Hyla squirella* form a fourth group.

9. Transformation period. The six Ranas (*R. clamitans, R. grylio, R. heckscheri, R. virgatipes, R. catesbeiana, R. septentrionalis*) begin to transform early the following season. Later come *Rana pipiens, R. sphenocephala* or *Rana aesopus* and *Rana areolata*. In the Hylids *Pseudacris nigrita* transforms early, the others much later and over a larger period. So in the Bufos, *Bufo terrestris* transforms early and *Bufo quercicus* much later.

10. Transformation size. Apparently this gives little clue to relationship. The group of *Rana sphenocephala, Rana pipiens, Rana aesopus, Rana areolata* may have smallest transformers (the first two) or larger transformers (the last two) or in the same way these groups may attain medium size or large size as adults. In the same way *Rana virgatipes* is small in transformation and adult size in its group (*R. grylio* group) which in the main is large in these particulars.

11. Transformation structures. Often at transformation it is extremely difficult to determine the Hylids or tree frogs. They are frequently each of them green at this stage. The taking on of their color pattern from transformation onward may often give a clue to relationship. For example, on this basis one might be tempted to place *Hyla cinerea, Hyla andersonii,* and *Hyla gratiosa* together.

HYPOTHESES

This topic is dangerous. It might give a fine chance for pleasurable writing. One might develop it with increasing confidence as one grew older. None of the following suggestions do we urge and their tentative characters merely show some habits of mind which have pervaded previous attempts at the relationships, distribution and origin of American biota. I hope no one will expend most of their energy on this part of our paper and tilt any hypothesis hard until he or she has labored industriously on the forms in question.

Some of these fancies are: 1. Is it worthy of consideration that those forms of Europe which Boulenger places below 4,200 feet elevation (namely, *Rana agilis, Rana esculenta, Bufo calamita, Hyla arborea, Pelobates fuscus,* and possibly others) might have counterparts in our Atlantic coast region in *Rana sylvatica, Rana virgatipes, Bufo fowleri, Hyla andersonii, Scaphiopus holbrookii,* etc.? Three of them are yet unrecorded from Okefinokee region and one not common and one on the outside of the swamp.

2. Is the Okefinokee region near the center of distribution of the forms of the United States of America with its eight Hylids (2 *Pseudacris,* 1 *Acris,* 5 *Hyla*), and three more possible Hylids, (2 *Pseudacris* and *Hyla andersonii*) or six Rana species or two diverse *Bufos* or 1 *Scaphiopus* and 1 *Gastrophryne*— 18 species with 4 or 5 more possible, or 22 or 23 in all? For example, would it be safe to say the region of the south eastern United States is the center of the single laying Hylids, namely *Hyla squirella, Hyla gratiosa, Acris gryllus, Pseudacris ocularis,* and that from one of these came the lone northern species, *Hyla crucifer*? Or from a *Rana grylio*-like form came the more widespread northern *R. catesbeiana, R. virgatipes,* and *Rana septentrionalis,* all very aquatic? Or from *Rana sphenocephala* came the widespread northern *Rana pipiens,* or from *Rana aesopus,* the more widespread northern *Rana areolata*?

3. Or are some of the Okefinokee species so limited in distribution (South Carolina to Louisiana, or less) to be merely Sabalian representatives of northern species? Shall we call the aberrant *Pseudacris ocularis* a Sabalian offshoot from the northern *Hyla crucifer, Rana grylio* a bigger *Rana virgatipes, Rana heckscheri* a bigger *Rana clamitans, Hyla gratiosa* a bigger *Hyla cinerea*?

4. Did most of our southeastern forms come from the southwestern or Mexican center, another favorite method of explanation? Did *Bufo quercicus* come from *Bufo compactilis, Bufo cognatus* or some southwestern form, or *Bufo terrestris* from *Bufo valliceps*? Is *Hyla squirella* of the *Hyla eximia, Hyla regilla* group? Or are *Hyla versicolor, Hyla avivoca, Hyla phaeocrypta, Hyla femoralis* from a *Hyla arenicolor* center? Is it reasonable to hold that

the center of *Scaphiopus* (*S. hammondi, S. hurteri, S. couchii*) is southwestern and that *S. holbrookii* came from *S. couchii*? Or are the two diverse *Pseudacris* lines: *P. nigrita* (clarkii) and *P. ornata* the center of all the others unless it be *P. ocularis*? Or is *Gastrophryne carolinensis* the one eastern fringe species from a Mexican center with several species?

5. Or must we think of some of the southwestern forms as outliers from an eastern center? *Hyla arenicolor* a sole representative of *Hyla femoralis* and *Hyla versicolor*? Or is *Hyla regilla* the one western approach to *Pseudacris* species?

6. Are *Hyla gratiosa, Pseudacris ocularis, Bufo quercicus, Rana heckscheri*, archaic or primitive relicts of an old faunal center in central Florida or elsewhere in the southeast comparable to the peninsular forms such as *Neoseps, Rhineura* and several snakes?

7. Or have some of these had ingress quite recently or accidentally, possibly like *E. ricordii*, geckos, etc.?

8. Are no certain Nearctic or Holarctic types like *Rana sylvatica*, or some Pacific *Ranas* or *Ascaphus truei* represented in the Okefinokee region? Just as in mammals, birds, etc. slight if any true upper Austral or Transition Zone forms appear.

9. Are the Atlantic coast forms like *Bufo fowleri, Hyla andersonii, Rana virgatipes* absent or scarce just as *Chrysemys picta, Clemmys muhlenbergii*, etc. are absent, *Clemmys guttata* very rare, etc., i.e. is the Atlantic coastal influence attenuated almost to nothing and Sabalian conditions predominant?

10. These queries might be expanded with no positive statements made but enough herein appear to show the bases for these imaginative indulgences or speculations.

SUMMARY OF AFFINITIES

In a sentence we might venture the following tentative assertions regarding each species of this study.

Scaphiopus holbrookii falls in relationship with *Scaphiopus couchii, S. hurteri* and less so with *S. hammondii*.

Bufo quercicus belongs near some western or southwestern forms such as *Bufo compactilis* and others.

Bufo terrestris may be of the *Bufo fowleri, B. americanus* group or related to *Bufo valliceps*.

Acris gryllus, the most aberrant Hylid, possibly more Ranid (see hind femur like *R. grylio* or *R. virgatipes* or tadpole) but possibly near *Hyla crucifer* or *Pseudacris ocularis*.

Pseudacris nigrita, much like *P. triseriata, P. feriarum*, etc., and possibly of a different line from *Pseudacris ornata*.

Pseudacris ocularis may be as related to *Hyla crucifer* or *Acris gryllus* as any of the *Pseudacris nigrita* assemblage.

Hyla andersonii probably falls close to *Hyla cinerea* group or possibly near *Hyla squirella*.

Hyla cinerea may be the same as *Hyla c. evittata* and close to *Hyla andersonii* or possibly to *Hyla gratiosa.*

Hyla femoralis is the *Hyla versicolor* representative of the piney woods.

Hyla gratiosa may be apart but possibly may fall with *Hyla cinerea* or *Hyla andersonii.*

Hyla squirella. Does it fall with *Hyla crucifer* and *Acris gryllus,* or *Hyla cinerea* (*cinerea, andersonii, gratiosa*) group, or *Hyla versicolor* (*H. arenicolor, femoralis*) group?

Hyla versicolor has as its nearest relative in Okefinokee, the piney woods treefrog *Hyla femoralis.*

Rana aesopus is close to *Rana areolata.* These in turn are close to *R. sphenocephala* and *R. pipiens.*

Rana catesbeiana doubtless has its nearest relative in *R. grylio* or *R. clamitans.*

Rana clamitans is probably nearer *Rana heckscheri* than *R. catesbeiana* or *Rana grylio.*

Rana grylio is a bullfrog, doubtless belonging in the *R. catesbeiana* group, yet it has affinities with *R. clamitans* or possibly *R. virgatipes.*

Rana heckscheri doubtless comes closest to *R. clamitans* though more must be known to place it carefully.

Rana septentrionalis is a puzzle. Is it close to *R. virgatipes* or near *R. clamitans,* or a holoarctic form from Eurasian stock like some northwestern species?

Rana sphenocephala is a southern *Rana pipiens.*

Rana virgatipes may be a relative of *R. grylio* or close to *R. septentrionalis.*

Gastrophryne carolinensis in tadpoles, eggs, etc. is different from *G. texensis.* Possibly this or a Mexican species may be its nearest form.

SUGGESTIONS FOR LOCAL OR RESIDENT NATURALISTS AND COLLECTORS IN THE SOUTHEASTERN UNITED STATES

GENERAL:

Topics in these life histories which in general are incomplete, fragmentary, or weak are:

1. First appearance.
2. Migrations to breeding places.
3. Range of cross-mating.
4. Egg-laying process.
5. Range in egg complements.
6. Hatching period in the field.
7. Variations in mouthparts of tadpoles
8. Larval periods made more exact.
9. Growth studies on marked individuals, not presumptive.
10. Food.
11. Autumnal disappearance.
12. Hibernation.
13. Sexual discrimination in mating as revealed in cross, abnormal, unisexual embraces.

SPECIAL:

Scaphiopus holbrookii
1. Experimental zoologists should canvass why its tadpoles develop into frogs in 17–30 days.
2. Why are sizes from 12–51 mm. scarce in collections?
3. Even presumptive growth data is scanty.
4. Food might prove very suggestive. Entomologists collect more frequently early night flying insects.
5. Post breeding studies to hibernation are fragmentary. This is the age-old question about spadefoots.
6. Why do *S. holbrookii* and *S. couchii*, large adults have small tadpoles, and transform at small sizes, and *S. hammondii* a small adult, transform at a large size?

Bufo quercicus
1. More observations on egg-laying process are neded.
2. The mature tadpole needs to be better described.
3. Transformation data scanty.
4. *Bufo quercicus* as an insect collector of small forms (see Dr. Remington Kellogg's and Professor C. R. Crosby's studies of this form).

Bufo terrestris
1. Tadpoles of *Bufo terrestris* need to be carefully described.
2. Are its affinities with *B. fowleri* and *B. americanus* or with *B. valliceps*, etc.?
3. Discrimination or non-discrimination of males at the breeding season.

Acris gryllus
1. How distinct are *Acris crepitans* and *Acris gryllus*?
2. Do 15 mm. transformed frogs breed at once or are they from 9 mm. transformed sizes?
3. Why superlarvation in *Acris*? Does it imply diverse larval periods?
4. Does it regularly lay single eggs or masses?

Pseudacris nigrita
1. We missed its life history completely. Every topic in our outline for each species needs attention.
2. Is it really different from *P. triseriata*, *P. feriarum*, *P. septentrionalis* and (old) *P. clarkii*?

Pseudacris ocularis
1. Does it belong in *Pseudacris*?
2. More evidence on breeding season.
3. Egg laying in field.
4. Larval period problematic.
5. Probable differences between tadpoles of *P. ocularis*, *P. nigrita*, and *P. ornata* not known. Lends an uncertain element in identification of *Pseudacris* larvae of southeastern U. S.
6. This mite of a frog ought in its food to collect unusual forms for entomologists and parasitologists.

Pseudacris occidentalis
Pseudacris ornata.
  1. One species or two?
  2. In either case complete life histories needed.
  3. Will the toadlike *P. ornata* be as diverse as *P. ocularis* or *P. triseriata*?
Hyla andersonii
  1. A better color description from life of the female is desirable.
  2. The breeding sizes (30 mm.–41 mm. males and 38–48 mm. females) are apparently lacking in breeding females below 38 mm. and breeding males below 30 mm.
  3. Is *Hyla andersonii* in other parts of its range always a sphagnaceous breeding frog? (See *R. virgatipes*)
  4. What is the hatching period in life?
  5. Larval period needs more evidence.
  6. Transformation period and size needs more observation.
  7. Even presumptive growth impossible because there are so few specimens in collections between 15 mm. and 35 mm.
Hyla cinerea
  1. Is it primarily a surface-film or submerged-strewn egg breeder?
  2. After the discovery (1922) of *R. heckscheri* young tadpoles, greater refinement of *H. cinerea* description is needed. Few *H. cinerea* tadpoles found in 1922.
  3. More transformations are needed.
  4. Rate of growth problematic in intermediate sizes until more material appears.
  5. Study transformed green tree frogs of *H. andersonii*, *H. cinerea*, *H. c. evittata*, *H. squirella*, and *H. gratiosa* for clues to relationships when they begin to assume their adult patterns.
Hyla femoralis
  1. This common Sabalian form could be used for cross breeding experiments and possibly hybridization with other Hylas.
  2. The larval period needs to be better determined.
  3. This denizen of the high long leaved pines would be a good subject for food studies. It would yield interesting material of the upper levels of the pine barrens.
  4. Abnormal variations in its tadpoles might be interesting to follow.
Hyla gratiosa
  1. What is the post and pre-breeding habits of this species?
  2. Why two dissimilar calls in this species?
  3. Egg-laying process in laboratory and in field needs to be watched.
  4. Intermediate sizes from 25–50 mm. are badly needed in collections for growth studies.
Hyla squirella
  1. Why is this Hyla more of a house treefrog or found more about human quarters, habitations, barns, cultivated yards, etc.?

2. Why do so many breeders choose such temporary pools?
3. Variations in the coloration are worthy of detailed study.
4. Does this species occasionally lay a surface film different from its normal singly laid eggs?
5. Larval period needs more attention.

Hyla versicolor

1. Why is this species not within the swamp?
2. Are these more marked in color than the northern forms?
3. Are the breeding periods of the north and south synchronous?
4. Why did the species average smaller in adults, tadpoles and transformation in southeastern United States?

Rana aesopus

1. Are *R. capito* and *R. aesopus* one?
2. Mating of the species unobserved.
3. Transformation notes in general are much to be desired.
4. Intermediate sizes from 35-48 mm. are very scarce.
5. What do the younger frogs do?

Rana clamitans

1. Not studied in as great detail because of northern notes on the species.
2. Why are breeding frogs much smaller than in the north and transformation at a smaller size?
3. Hatching period in field much desired.
4. Data on larval period needed.

Rana grylio

1. The egg laying has not been observed.
2. No field mated pairs have been taken.
3. Hatching records are not numerous.
4. The larval period is barely outlined.
5. What are its relationships in range to that of *R. catesbeiana*?

Rana heckscheri

1. Why has it been overlooked so long?
2. Intermediate sizes from transformation (31–49 mm.) to 82 mm. are needed.
3. Mating amplexation and habits not observed.
4. Method of ovulation and eggs not described.
5. Is its larval period one or two years?
6. Are albino tadpoles not infrequent in this form?

Rana septentrionalis

1. The breeding period needs to be outlined in better fashion.
2. Actual mating and amplexation we have not observed.
3. What is the normal hatching period?
4. More details of the variations in tadpoles are needed.
5. More positive evidence on larval period should be secured.
6. How long after transformation does or might a frog keep its tail?

Rana sphenocephala

1. What are the positive distinctions between *R. sphenocephala* and *R. pipiens*?
2. In the southeast does *R. sphenocephala* breed almost every month of the year?
3. Differences in young stages in tadpoles of *Rana aesopus* and *Rana sphenocephala*.
4. Are albino eggs often laid in coffee colored water?
5. Hatching period and larval period may be different with eggs laid almost every month of the year.

Rana virgatipes

1. Mating amplexation never observed.
2. Eggs needed to be identified other than by elimination. Check need from a mated pair.
3. Why have *R. virgatipes* and *R. septentrionalis* submerged egg masses?
4. The tadpole description needs supplementation and the tadpole period data is meager.
5. Transformation data is also fragmentary.

Gastrophryne carolinensis.

1. The vocal powers of the male and the process might be an interesting study.
2. The egg laying process has not been observed.
3. The food of the queer tadpole ought to be interesting.
4. Value of smooth or rough skin in taxonomic analyses of narrow-mouthed toads.
5. The spiracle, tadpole shape, intestine, absence of normal mouthparts, etc. of tadpole might be made a special study.

Bufo fowleri, Hyla avivoca, Rana catesbeiana

1. *Hyla avivoca* will doubtless be found eastward to Georgia and farther. Its life history is unknown.
2. The southeastern distribution of *Bufo fowleri* in distinction from *Bufo americanus* and *Bufo terrestris* and of *Rana catesbeiana* in distinction from *Rana grylio* and *Rana heckscheri* is needed.

GENERAL ACCOUNTS OF SPECIES

Scaphiopus holbrookii (Harlan)

(Pl. I, Fig. 4; IV, Fig. 2; VI, Fig. 2; X, Fig. 12; XIV, Fig. 8; XV, Fig. 9;
XVII; XVIII; XIX; Text Fig. 1, 5)

COMMON NAMES

Spade-foot. Hermit Spade-foot. Hermit Spade-foot Toad. Spade-foot Toad. Hermit Toad. Solitary Spade-foot. Solitary Toad. Holbrook's Spade-foot. "Storm Toads." "Storm Frogs."

RANGE

Check list. "Type Locality South Carolina. Range: Eastern States, Massachusetts to Florida, west to Louisiana, Texas to Arkansas." Stejneger and Barbour's Check List 1923, p. 23.

Supplementary records. Dr. Holbrook (1842, Vol. IV, p. 111) writes "Its range is more extended than I first apprehended. It is found in Carolina and Georgia. Dr. Troost sent me a specimen from Tennessee, and Dr. DeKay has observed it in the State of New York." In 1849 (Appendix, p. 15) Holbrook gives *Scaphiopus holbrookii* as a frog of Georgia. Dumeril and Bibron (1841, p. 474) expect it to be discovered "sur d'autres points des Etat-Unis."

In 1842 DeKay (p. 66) writes "We have now the pleasure to include it in the Fauna of New York. Specimens of this animal were found by Mr. Hill, in a garden near Clarkstown, Rockland County. . . . Dr. Pickering, I learn, has recently seen it in the neighborhood of Salem, where they appear in great numbers, at distant periods, after rains of long continuance."

The same year, 1842, DeKay was publishing, Andrew Nichols (1852, pp. 113–117) of Massachusetts was making the first extended descriptions of their habits. "Holbrook, in his N. A. Herpetology, Vol. I, pp. 85-87, says that he found these reptiles in three states only, viz: Georgia, South Carolina, and Tennessee—that they go in the water only in the breeding season, that which he observes in the spring; and that they live in holes in the ground of about six inches in depth, excavated by themselves—never coming out of these, except during the night and after heavy rains. This explains the mystery of their sudden appearance and disappearance, as above mentioned. It would also seem that they are Southern reptiles;—chilled by our northern climate, they want a more genial climate to celebrate their nuptials; and thus without a suitable pool to receive their spawn, year after year in this instance transpired, until a summer freshet filled their native habitat sufficiently."

"I have some reasons to conjecture that other colonies of these frogs exist in New England. An intelligent farmer of Topsfield (Mass.), to whom I showed my specimens, and related the foregoing story, told me he had several

73

times heard a similar croaking in a temporary pond of water near his dwelling, but he never went to see from whence the noise proceeded. Something of the same kind has been noticed in Framingham, in this State, by a student of medicine, who relates that he and a friend of his were kept awake on the identical night, June 16th, 1842, by the noise of frogs or something of the kind in a ditch of water near his lodging; that they went out to discover what they were, but on drawing near the place, the noise or cry, which resembled that of young crows, suddenly ceased, and nothing was to be seen."

In 1868 C. C. Abbott in New Jersey found that "This little frog is not abundant, and is generally met with when found, in the Southern counties of the State."

In 1909 Julius Hurter and John K. Strecker, Jr., record it in Greenway, Arkansas.

These previous records are not exactly supplemental but intended to show that quite early the extremes of its range were fairly well known.

In May, 1922, in Florida, "Richard Deckert (1922, p. 88) ran over one at Homestead, in the evening on the return trip." In 1923 A. H. Wright and A. A. Wright report this species from the Okefinokee region, Georgia and Florida. The same year Director T. VanHyning (1923, p. 68) of the Florida State Museum reports two found at night, March 18, at Gainesville, Florida.

In the summer of 1926 A. I. Ortenburger (1927, p. 46) in Western Oklahoma reports "*Scaphiopus holbrookii holbrookii* (Harlan) (in) Cimarron County 5 miles north of Kenton." In 1926 Wright (p. 83) gives this species as a Lower Austral species and gives its range as Massachusetts to Florida. The reason for the present author limiting it to Florida and not extending it to Arkansas and parts west of Florida is not now apparent.

Local Okefinokee records. In 1921 we were in the center of the swamp and did not record this species. Mr. Matt Hickox told us of a frog different from any we had on Billy's Island. His description of a special frog or toad which came at heavy rainy periods we suspected to be *Scaphiopus holbrookii.* He said it occurred in the vicinity of Braganza on the northeast border of the swamp.

In 1921 Mr. Harper heard from Mr. Dave Mizzell (on Folkston-Moniac road) who told him of a frog "called 'storm frog' because he appears when there are storms or floods. It hollers *wank!* It folds up so that you can't find its legs. It is larger than the 'hop toad'. One was dug up in a potato field."

In 1922 immediately after our arrival on Chesser Island on June 14, Mr. Ridley Chesser told us of frogs he heard near their barn that were neither carpenter nor gopher frogs. We suspected it of being spade-foots and on Chesser Island. A week later, June 22, in one of the deep pits at Camp Pinckney, Folkston, Ga., we found little else than spade-foot tadpoles. The pit was heavily shaded by oaks. The following day, June 23, we recorded tadpoles in a pond the Trader's Hill side of Brook's R. R. one mile from Trader's Hill. On June 27 we make the following note that "because of the discovery of these tadpoles in two different places this species seems a commonly distributed form in these parts." We found several people who knew about "storm toads" or "storm frogs."

Then on Aug. 16-17, 1922, near Hilliard, Florida, we camped beside a spade-foot congress in open cut-over pine-barrens, flooded because of an immense rain just preceding.

GENERAL APPEARANCE

This phase has aroused as much interest as any topic treated by authors. Its discoverer, Dr. Holbrook, (1842, Vol. IV, pp. 109-111) records "This singular animal approaches nearly to the toad in form." "This is a strange animal—an odd mixture of toad and frog, having the teeth of one, and the rudimental post-tympanal glands of the other; it approaches, however, nearest the toad in its form and habits, ..." "The skin is very delicate, and though warty or granulated after exposure, when first taken from its hole the *Scaphiopus* presents the etiolated appearance of a real subterranean animal." "Characters. Back olive coloured and somewhat warty, with two lines of pale yellow extending from the orbits to the vent, beneath yellowish white."

Harlan (1835, pp. 105, 106) says "This new species, first figured and des-scribed by Dr. Holbrook, (vide his valuable work on North American Reptilia) possesses very peculiar characters, displaying, in its external configuration, a strange mixture of the toad and frog. It has the contracted form of the first, with small typmanum, and rudimentary super-tympanal warts, without visible pores, and small warts disseminated over the back of the head; possessing palatine teeth and serrated maxillae, like the frogs, and like the *Rana cultripes* of Cuv. is remarkable in possessing a rudiment of the sixth finger, covered by a sharp horny plate, ..."

DeKay (1842, p. 66) gives as its "Characteristics. Ash grey, with two yellow curved lines from the eyes, dilated and subsequently united at the vent. Length two inches."

C. S. Brimley (1907, p. 157) gives upper jaw with teeth. Paratoids present. Hind feet webbed. Heel with a flat sharp edged spur" as enough to distinguish the Solitary Spadefoot. He uses the same characters in his revised key (1926, p. 80).

MEASUREMENTS
(Recent Material)

Head to angle of mouth 1.33 (28 mm.)—1.36 (44 mm. ♀)—1.35 (56 mm. ♂)—1.27 (56 mm. ♀)—1.27 (68 mm. ♂)—1.33 (68 mm. ♀) in width of head; head to rear of tympanum 1.09—1.11—1.19—1.09—1.07—1.12 in width of head; head to angle of mouth 3.1—2.99—3.02—3.1—3.09—3.24 in length of body; head to rear of tympanum 2.54—2.6—2.66—2.66—2.66—2.61—2.72 in length of body; snout—.54—.58—.71—.60—.66—.70 in first finger; snout .54—.62—.57—.56—.58—.64 in fourth finger; snout .36—.29—.47—.40—.37—.34 in first toe; eye 1.1—1.41—1.5—1.33—1.5—1.43 in snout; eye .4—.66—.71—.73—.81—.75 in tympanum; eye .6—.825—1.06—.80—1.0—1.0 in first finger; tympanum 5.5—4.0—4.2—3.4—3.4—4.0 in intertympanic width; tympanum 2.75—2.25—2.1—1.8—1.84—1.75 in snout; internasal width 1.16—1.25—1.0—1.0—1.8

—1.0 in upper eyelid width; interorbital width .77—.77—.625—.75—.72—.68 in upper eyelid width; interorbital width .66—.61—.625—.75—.66—.68 in internasal width; interorbital width 2.44—2.44—2.6—2.37—2.5—3.0 in intertympanic width.

Forelimb: Forelimb 1.86—2.0—2.43—2.0—1.74—1.7 in length of body; forelimb 2.13—2.04—2.39—1.75—1.87—1.7 in hind limb; first finger 1.5— 1.7—1.33—1.5—1.31—1.75 in third finger; second finger 1.5—1.7—1.33—1.63 —1.4—1.75 in third finger; second finger 1.0—1.0—1.0—1.09—1.06—1.0 in first finger; third finger .88—.59—.75—.72—.95—.64 in second toe; fourth finger 1.5—1.88—1.66—1.63—1.5—2.0 in third finger; fourth finger .66—.55— .825—.72—.64—.57 in first toe; internasal width 1.0—1.25—1.5—1.0—1.33— 1.4 in first finger; internasal width 1.0—1.25—1.5—.91—1.25 —1.25 in second finger; internasal width 1.5—2.12—2.0—1.5—1.75—2.5 in third finger; internasal width 1.0—1.12—1.2—.93—1.16—1.27 in fourth finger.

Hindlimb: length 1.14—1.02—.99—.87—1.07—1.0 in hind limb; tiba— 2.54—2.83—2.8—3.2—2.83—2.95 in length; tibia 2.9—2.9—2.75—2.8—3.04 —2.95 in hind limb; tibia 1.36—1.42—1.15—1.6—1.62—1.74 in fore limb; tibia 1.09—1.06—1.1—1.08—1.16—1.13 in hind foot; first toe 2.0—2.0—1.5— 1.625—2.22—2.25 in second toe; first toe 3.0—3.6—2.4—2.75—3.33—3.25 in third toe; first toe 4.5—5.0—3.3—3.5—4.9—4.75 in fourth toe; first toe 2.5— 2.8—2.125—2.0—2.7—2.62 in fifth toe; second toe 1.5—1.8—1.6—1.7—1.5— 1.44 in third toe; second toe 2.25—2.5—2.2—2.15—2.2—2.1 in fourth toe; second toe 1.25—1.4—1.33—1.3—1.25—1.16 in fifth toe; third toe 1.5—1.4— 1.37—1.27—1.46—1.46 in fourth toe; third toe .825—.77—.83—.77—.8—.80 in fifth toe; fourth toe 1.33—1.32—1.25—1.35—1.27—1.36 in hind foot without tarsus; fourth toe 1.2—1.24—1.2—1.25—1.09—1.21 in tibia; fourth toe 1.66—1.76—1.4—2.0—1.68—2.1 in fore limb; fifth toe 1.8—1.8—1.65—1.64— 1.76—1.8 in fourth toe; internasal width—.66—.625—1.0—.66—.75—.74 in first toe; internasal width 1.33—1.25—1.08—1.5—1.66—1.4 in second toe; internasal width 2.0—2.25—2.4—1.83—2.5—2.2 in third toe; internasal width 3.0—3.15—3.3—2.33—3.66—3.4 in fourth toe; internasal width 1.66—1.75— 2.0—1.41—2.08—1.9 in fifth toe.

HABITAT

Colonel Nicholas Pike (1886, p. 213) holds "It must, of course, be hunted for on secluded places and woody hillsides, but I will venture to say even the most knowing, in nine cases out of ten, will only find a Spadefoot by accident."

FIRST APPEARANCE

Holbrook places this in early March. Many authors have them appearing from April onwards.

On December 2, 1868 Dr. J. A. Allen (1868, pp. 186 & 187) speaks of their appearance at both Springfield and Cambridge, Massachusetts. He says: "On hearing the very peculiar notes of this species six years since, at the well-known locality near the Botanic Garden in Cambridge, I recognized it at once as being something I had heard occasionally at Springfield. It was not, however, till May 27th, 1866, that I happened to be fortunate enough to obtain specimens: I found two in a path, after heavy rain, several hundred yards from any permanent pool; and, during the day, several pairs spawning in different small transient pools, though at this time they appeared sparingly. I also heard them in Chickopee the following day, five or six miles distant from the first locality.

"In 1863, after unusually heavy rains towards the close of June, they came out in immense numbers, the transient pools formed by the heavy fall of rain seeming to be full of them; but they were heard only from 1 P. M. till about 3 A. M., of the following night; and being confined to the house by illness I failed at this time to obtain specimens. Not having been in Springfield at the proper time since, these are the only instances of their occurrence known to me. Specimens collected here in 1866 were deposited by the writer in the Springfield Natural History Museum, and in the Museum of the Essex Institute.

"The character of the season seems greatly to determine the time of the appearance of these animals, for they rarely, if ever, appear except after long continued rains, during which the fall of water has been sufficient to saturate the ground thoroughly, and to form pools in situations ordinarily dry. If the spring opens with heavy rains, it is not uncommon for them to appear during the last of March, or early in April, often before the snow is gone; if dry they are not seen till later, and if no heavy rains occur during the spring or summer months, as sometimes happens, they are not seen at all that year. If sufficiently heavy rains occur in May, or even in June, or in July, and not previously, as happened one year at Springfield, they may be expected even then. The present year, remarkable for its wetness, seems fully to demonstrate this, no less than four sets of the Scaphiopus having been observed at Cambridge. The first, few in numbers, appeared during the few warm days that occurred about April 1st; the second, much more numerous, April 15th; the third May 14th, and the fourth May 22d; each during, or immediately following, a very heavy falls of rain. They were observed not only at the old locality near the Botanic Garden, but in several others, including the pond west of the Museum of Comparative Zoology, and another east of it, formed by the temporary inundation of the marsh in Mr. Norton's woods. It takes but a few weeks for the young tadpoles to mature, the eggs generally hatching in from five to seven days, and the young being ready to leave the water in about three weeks; yet the pools selected by the Spadefoot for the home of their off-spring often become dry before the tadpoles are fully grown, and they consequently perish,—so that ordinarily but a small part mature. The wetness of the present year was not only favorable for their spawning, but also for the development of the young, so that the increase of the Spadefoots must have been unusually large."

GENERAL HABITS

Holbrook (1842, p. 111) holds that "it never ventures in water except at the breeding season; it lives in small holes about six inches deep, excavated by itself in the earth, which for a long time I mistook for holes of insects; here it resides, like the ant-lion, seizing upon such unwary insects as may enter its dwelling. It never leaves its hole, except in the evening, or after long continued rains. It shows great dexterity in making its dwelling, sometimes using the nates, and fastening itself by the spade-like process; at others it uses the legs with these processes, like a shovel, and will in this way conceal itself with great rapidity. In progression its motions are not very lively, and its powers of leaping but feebly developed."

Harlan (1835, p. 106) thinks the spade "must materially aid the animal in climbing steep and slippery ascents. Habits are said to be peculiar; about the size of the Esculent frog. Inhabits South Carolina."

DeKay (1842, pp. 66, 67) holds "It lives in small holes, in damp earth, a few inches below the surface, which it excavates with great ease by means of its spadelike processes. In these holes it lies in wait for such insects as may approach, and I suspect can spring forth to seize whatever may be passing incautiously near its hiding place. I remarked, at least in those which I had alive, that it leaped with great apparent ease to a considerable distance. To judge from those in my possession, although completely identical with the *solitarius*, I should be disposed to believe that our northern variety is less brilliant in its markings, and its general color is of a more grave and sombre hue."

LeConte (1855, p. 430) holds that "Although very seldom seen except when accidentally turned up by the spade or the plough, yet the *Scaphiopus* is a very common animal in Georgia. Whenever the Southeast storms occur at the Autumnal Equinox, the surface of the earth is covered with them, and their dismal croaking adds to the horror of the howling winds and the deluges of water which pour down from the heavens. They have also been found in Connecticut and Massachusetts. When placed upon the ground they dig with remarkable celerity, and soon entirely bury themselves in the earth."

Smith (1879, pp. 651, 652) observes: "For more than two years I have been looking for the 'spade-foot' (*Scaphiopus holbrookii*) in and about New Haven, confident that it occurred here and that careful search would reveal it; but my efforts have been vain until very lately. Thursday, April 24th, I saw some children gathered around an object on the pavement of Prospect street, and I asked them what they had. They replied that they had dug up a toad in the next yard. You can imagine my surprise and delight to behold a real live 'spade-foot,' the first I had ever seen alive. They willingly gave it to me, and I carefully took it home with me and kept it alive in a large box with plenty of earth and a tub of water.

"Tuesday morning (the 29th) I was shooting small birds near Fair Haven, when I heard a most peculiar bellowing from a pond near by. I am more or less familiar with all the ordinary sounds that come from a pond, and I jumped at the conclusion that I heard the 'spade-foot.' On reaching the pond I saw a sight I shall never forget; the pond was rather small, and was swollen and overflowing on account of the heavy rains of the two preceding days, and swimming all over the surface, and at times uttering their peculiar bellow, were forty or fifty of my long-sought friends. They would float or swim awkwardly

Plate XVIII

Spade-foot (*Scaphiopus holbrookii*)

1. Male and female, Chesser Id., Ga. August 18, 1922. Dorsal aspect. × 0.66.
2. Male and female (larger). Chesser Id., Ga. August 18, 1922. Ventral aspect. × 0.66.
3. Adult, Chesser Id., Ga. August 18, 1922. Lateral aspect. × 0.8.
4. Male, Chesser Id., Ga. August 19, 1922. Lateral aspect. × 0.8.
5. Egg masses, Hilliard, Fla. August 17, 1922.
6. Eggs, stained, Chesser Id., Ga. August 18, 1922. × 1.45.

1

2

3

4

5

6

along until they wished to favor me with a song, and then the accommodating soloist would suddenly assume a perpendicular position as if a plummet had been attached to his tail, his head alone swimming above the water, his white throat dilated till it was three times the size of the head, his mouth closed tight, he would sing his brief song and reassume his horizontal position. The pond was quite deep in the middle, but I secured some specimens to prove my statements on my return home.

"When I passed the pond again in the afternoon the same programme was being carried out, but I could secure no more specimens. On my return home I put my toad with the one I found Thursday, and in a few moments the male (the last caught) had clasped the female very tightly and I was expecting to raise some tadpoles, but they buried themselves in the earth the next day without laying any eggs.

"In the afternoon of Tuesday a friend of mine, Mr. W. H. Fox, found the *Scaphiopus* in a pond out on Prospect street, and secured quite a number of specimens together with some spawn which he thinks belongs to this toad.

"The next day (Wednesday, April 30th) I visited my pond again with net and pails, but the birds had flown without leaving a sign. Not a toad was to be seen or heard, and no spawn but frog spawn could be found; but they may have dropped it in the deeper water in the middle of the pond, out of my reach and sight. Mr. Fox visited his pond also Wednesday, but could not find a toad except the common one (*Bufo americanus*).

"When I brought my first specimen home she buried herself in the earth, but when I returned from Fair Haven she was swimming around in her tub of water like the rest of them, and when I put the male in they stayed in the water together. Wednesday morning when the toads in the two ponds had disappeared, my pair had also buried themselves again in the earth in their box. So I think I can judge of the movements of the free toads by watching the movements of my captives."

Pike (1886, pp. 213-215) writes "Many years ago I had several in my garden which became quite tame, and would allow me to take them in my hands. They made circular holes in the ground about six inches deep, somewhat turnip shaped. A few minutes sufficed for them to burrow out of sight. The long feet, with the horny excrescence serving as an additional toe, and the strong curved fingers enable the Spadefoot to make the excavation rapidly. This is not by any means the completion of its home. The inside has to be worked smoothly, and the earth prevented from falling in.

"This is done by the animal working its body with a circular motion, and the operation would go on for an hour or more, and the liquid exuding from its pores worked into the earth made it smooth, and formed a curious little dwelling when completed. Round the top was a layer of viscious matter, and woe betide any unwary insect that alighted on it. Closely concealed lay Spadefoot, only the bright eyes visible, ever on the watch, and unerring in its aim when any luckless fly intruded on the threshold. They appeared to be greedy feeders, and I often amused myself by giving them insects, which they seized with avidity as long as I supplied them.

"This I find is the usual summer residence of the Spadefoot, and when once domiciled, it rarely leaves home in the day-time. No two ever inhabit the same hole, hence the name Hermit Spadefoot, or *solitarius*.

"When sharp summer rains fell they would quit their houses and seek shelter under plants, but would not return to the holes they had left. As soon as it was fine, about sunset or in the night, new houses were constructed with great rapidity. In the fall, very heavy rains set in and one by one my pets disappeared, generally in the night, and though I searched diligently for them I could not find their hibernaculum, and presume they burrowed away under the fence.

"Thirty-five years ago I exhibited one of these habitations, which was made in a box sunk in my garden, with the animal in it, and read notes on it which were published in the Proceedings of the Brooklyn Natural History Society.

"The *Scaphiopus* changes much in color at various seasons. I have taken this animal late in the fall when it might easily have passed by as only a dingy young toad, but for the curious eyes which will always identify the Spadefoot, no matter what its dress. The irides are mottled gold and brown, and are divided into four parts by a notch at each quarter, giving a lozenge shape to the large black pupil.

"Quite late in November, I dug one up from about a foot below the surface of the earth, which was covered with decayed leaves. The head was smooth dark brown, and the whole body a dingy dark olive, with faint lines running from the eyes along the back, converging to a point at the rump. Every part of the animal was tubercled, even to the eyelids, and the parotid glands were greatly swollen. When first taken there was an orange tint over the thighs and hands, but this soon faded in confinement.

"The little fellow took kindly to its imprisonment, grew very tame, and looked quite comfortable in its large glass jar half filled with damp moss. Sometimes when the moss seemed too wet I put in a lot quite dry. The cunning animal would look at it, toad-like, with its head on one side, and take in the situation at once. It set to work and in a few minutes made a pretty little arbor, quite thick behind but so thin in front that it could see through the moss. It never appeared quite torpid, but only sound asleep at times, and would wake up quickly if disturbed. A favorite position of my Spadefoot was to crouch down flat with the hands turned in under the chin, the feet turned úp, and the long toes resting on the elbows.

"In April I took it out and found it as fat as when its winter rest began, although it had not tasted any kind of food for over six months.* During this long quiescence its coat had changed. The centre of the back was a bright sandy color with a large dark irregular star edged with black. The whole back and legs were heavily tubercled with a vivid red, chin white, abdomen and inside of thighs a reddish purple."

* "In autumn the *Scaphiopus* feed voraciously and become very fat, and this seems to keep them in good condition till spring again brings forth their insect food."

Hargitt (1888, pp. 535-537) writes: "A summer on Martha's Vineyard, and the occasion of a sudden and tremendous rainfall, afforded the opportunity for certain very interesting observations.

"My observations, as will be seen, add but little that is *new*; yet a record of them may contribute somewhat to corroborate and extend that which does exist.

"One afternoon, about August 10, 1887, while at work in the laboratory of the Martha's Vineyard Summer Institute, in company with Dr. H. W. Conn, Professor L. W. Chaney, and others, a very sudden and torrential rainstorm occurred, lasting some two hours or more. During an interval of cessation our attention was diverted by weird, plaintive sort of cries, which none at first was able to explain. Darting out through the still-falling rain toward a low sort of hollow, from which the cries seemed to come, it was found to have been converted into quite a pond, though previously quite dry. In this, and swimming about in a state of the greatest activity and excitement, were what looked to be scores of toads. No difficulty was found in securing a few specimens, which were at once identified as 'spadefoots.' Procuring a scoop-net we took several dozens of them, leaving many more in the pond.

"This was about four o'clock in the afternoon, and they continued their orgies till late at night. But I made careful examination the following morning, without finding a single specimen—not even a sign of one. In the water I found plenty of the spawn attached to grass and floating in strings, loosely attached to weeds—a fact which clearly indicated the purpose of their presence and peculiar excitement.

"On account of the pressure of other studies, I was not able to watch the development of the eggs. Indeed, I doubt whether they ever hatched, as the pond was nearly dry before the close of the following day, and the soil, being the loose sandy drift peculiar to that locality, would not certainly retain water for sufficeint time for the growth of the tadpole—if, indeed, for the hatching of the eggs, though, as to this, last, I cannot say, as I left before it could have occurred.

"This characteristic of the spawning habit is certainly peculair, and seems somewhat difficult to explain. First, the lateness of the season is remarkable. It is said that a related Eurpoean species breeds twice a year. Can it be possible that such is the case with *Scaphiopus*? There are some facts which seem to indicate that it might be, though it is hardly probable. Second, the places of spawning is still more remarkable. From the observations of Dr. Abbott and Colonel Pike, as well as my own, the choice seems to be for some temporary sink-hole or surface-pond. If the conditions for development in these places from speedy drainage, etc., were not so utterly precarious, it might be thought a shrewd precaution for evading the natural enemies common in the more permanent ponds and bogs. Altogether, the case seems to be quite anomalous.

"But to refer again to the adults in the pond: There they were by scores. Whence had they come, and in such numbers? In all probabilities, from the ground of the bordering hillsides and environs. But not a single specimen was seen out of the water, and that, too, notwithstanding we were at the pond almost immediately following their first coming. If they had come from any tolerable distance, it would seem that some late-comers would have been detected. Again, their retreat must have been almost as sudden as their appearance. I passed the pond about ten o'clock at night, and the air was perfectly vocal with their never-to-be-forgotten notes. I went to the pond early the following morning, but all was silent and deserted. Had they returned to the ground? Such seems the most probable explanation. Yet so carefully had they covered the retreat that not the slightest trace could be found.

"Furthermore, their appearance itself seems to be capricious and phenomenal. I made inquiries of persons of observant habits as to any previous occurrence in the vicinity, but was not able to find any account of them.

"It has been suggested that they are, doubtless, nocturnal in habit, and that this explains, in a measure, their comparative rarity, even where known to exist. I have no hesitancy in assenting to the nocturnal habit. It is quite in keeping with the habit of many of the order; and the vertical pupil of the eye points likewise to the same face. This, however, in itself, must be a comparatively small factor in the case, and, alone, would hardly insure it against frequent detection any more than does a similar habit in many other nocturnal animals. I had gone by this hollow repeatedly, night after night, both before and after this appearance, and, though constantly on the alert to notice anything of the sort, had no hint of their presence.

"Doubtless, the solitary burrowing habit goes much further in explaining its seclusion. But even this would be inadequate, unless the animal persistently avoided all open and cultivated grounds. Such, only, would protect it against frequent exposure by the spade or plow.

"Altogether, they are certainly the most peculiar and erratic of any of the order; and, under the peculiar difficulties in the way of continuous study, it will be long ere its life-history can be said to be thoroughly known. However, the very difficulties add a charm to the investigation, which we may hope will lead to success. To me, the brief research herein outlined has been full of the liveliest interest, and, while but a mite toward the solution of the problem, I shall hope that it may not be without some value when a final summary is made."

Cope (1889, p. 301) maintains that, "This species, though so widely distributed is seldom seen. After rains in spring and summer its cries may be heard at night, proceeding always, so far as my experience goes, from temporary pools. I have observed it twice in Pennsylvania, twice in New Jersey, once in Massachusetts, on the main land opposite Martha's Vineyard. Specimens from the latter locality which I kept in a vivarium buried themselves in the earth by day, but issued at night-fall, and industriously explored their surroundings. Their burrows were concealed by the loose earth which fell into and filled them, but below this the bony top of the head could be always found. Frequently one eye projected from the debris, presenting with its brassy-colored iris a most singular appearance. On being irritated with a hard object they utter a clattering note entirely unlike that of the breeding season."

In 1896 C. S. Brimley asserts, "I have occasionally dug them out of the ground."

In 1899 G. A. Boulenger (pp. 790-793) in his paper describes the external characters, measurements and skeleton in detail and remarks of its habits thus: "The habits, so far as I have been able to observe them, are very similar to those of *Pelobates*. They burrow in the soil in exactly the same manner and come out only at night to feed. All my efforts to induce them to produce, when irritated, the loud cries so striking in *Pelobates* have failed. On the contrary, when teased, they assume a very humble appearance, bending down the head at an angle to the vertebral column and shutting the eyes in a manner which is well represented on the accompanying plate."

In 1904 C. C. Abbott (pp. 163, 164) holds the Spade-foots may be one explanation of the reported showers of toads. He writes: "The frequent references in newspapers to occurrences of 'showers of toads' have suggested to the author that a condition in the life-history of the spade-foot toad, a little-known and strictly nocturnal species, living in the ground, might explain them more rationally than that the little batrachians are picked up by the wind in one place and dropped in another, perhaps miles away, or that other still more strange view quite common among the ignorant that toad-spawn is sucked up by the sun and hatched in clouds, where the tadpoles remain until they have advanced to the dignity of hoppers, when they fall to the earth. Unlike the common toad and the frogs, the spade-foot toad (Scaphiopus solitarius) does not have a regular season for deposition of ova, but the eggs may be laid at any time from April 1 to August 31. Furthermore, this batrachian does not resort to permanent water-courses or ponds on such errand, but takes advantage of temporary pools formed by showers of longer duration than is usual. It is remarkable how admirably this strange irregularity of an important event should be adapted to transitory conditions. Pools of rainwater seldom remain long on the ground's surface. Soakage and evaporation soon obliterate them; but that this may not prove a fatal objection, the eggs of the spade-foot toad hatch in about ninety-six hours, and in less than two weeks, or fourteen days at most, the tadpole has become a terrestrial animal or a 'hopper' and leaves its nursery. The development is even more rapid occasionally, I am led to believe, being accelerated by excessive warmth or retarded if the days are cool and cloudy.

"It will be readily seen that young spade-foot toads, congregated in or immediately about a temporary pool, will not wander far from it when their subterranean life begins, but will bury themselves in the comparatively moist ground where they happen to be. Should, at this time of their limited wandering, there occur one or more violent showers, the ground being wetted and little pools formed, the young spade-foot toads would necessarily, we might say, wander over a much wider extent of territory, and, escaping notice when confined to one fast disappearing pool, would be observed when dotting the ground over an extent perhaps of an acre or more. Seen thus, immediately after rain, and not previously noticed, the inference is not so strange that they came to the earth with the rain, or that there had been a shower of toads as well as of water."

In 1905 Fowler (1906, pp. 92, 93) writing of New Jersey forms gives, "the following notes are on an example which I received from Mr. James A. G. Rehn, during August of 1905. As it was brought alive from Palatka, Florida, by Mr. Rehn I give it place only as a foot note. —This toad has a very peculair habit of attempting to dig backwards by means of the black-edged spur on the hind foot, which it will rub rather fast and with good force against the palm if held in the hand. By a similar process it sinks into the ground or among grass. The eyes can be depressed considerably and give the head quite a different appearance if the animal is annoyed. It progressed usually by short hops or leaps, though sometimes crawled or walked slowly a few steps. In repose the usual position is to squat flat, and if then disturbed to inflate the flanks greatly. When held in hand it uttered a note similar to the call of *Rana clamata*, which may be said to resemble somewhat a smothered rattle or trill of rather harsh and low tone. The throat is inflated, though not very abnormally. This note seems to be due rather to discomfort than anything else. In captivity I could not induce the specimen to eat."

W. T. Davis (1908, pp. 48, 49) gives the following observations on spade-foots at Lakehurst, N. J., in 1906 and 1907. "During the heavy storms of August 1 and 2, 1906, Mr. Louis H. Joutel observed many of these toads at Lakehurst, N. J., in a depression temporarily filled with water. Their discordant notes could be heard a long distance. On July 20, 1907, I found at Lakehurst two partly grown individuals that had fallen into a cemented drain, up the steep sides of which they could not climb. On August 17 another was found in the same drain, and still another at the bottom of a shallow well that had become nearly dry. On October 12, 1907, with Professor Wm. M. Wheeler and Mr. G. P. Engelhardt, we found a somewhat larger individual in the same cement-lined drain. One of these toads was kept alive some time and fed on flies, but died after being fed on green flies. Mr. Engelhardt also had a frog die suddenly after it had devoured meat flies. The spade-foot toad has also been found on Staten Island."

Dr. Frank Overton (1914, pp. 29, 30) who unselfishly introduced the frogs and toads of Long Island to the naturalists of Greater New York, just as earlier W. T. Davis did the same for some of the rarer species of New Jersey, has in recent years given more attention to spadefoots than any naturalist in the North. From him we cull excerpts under several topics. He writes thus: "Spadefoot toads are considered to be rare, and few detailed observations of them have been made. Dozens of them suddenly appeared in a temporary pool near the Bay Avenue school building in Patchogue during the first week of April, 1912, after a series of hard rains. April seventh was warm and pleasant, and the toads were noisy all day. The temperature fell below freezing in the evening, and all the toads disappeared until the sixteenth, when the air again became warm, and a number reappeared from that day only. The temperature again fell in the evening, and no more spadefoots were heard until the twenty-seventh, when a few were heard after a hard rain. None were heard or seen after that date. A great number of eggs were laid, but no tadpoles survived the frosts.

"The spadefoot toads suddenly reappeared on the evening of April 12, 1913, in several pools near Bay Avenue after a warm, hard rain. They were noisy on the thirteenth, but after that date the weather was cold and only a few were seen until the twenty-third. Then about fifty appeared in the pool which had just refilled on the site of the pool in which they were seen in 1912. After two or three days all the toads had disappeared. Hosts of tadpoles were hatched but most of them were destroyed on account of their pools being filled in with soil. Those that survived completed their transformation into fully formed toads by the middle of June.

"A few spadefoot toads appeared in a small permanent pool near the Bay Avenue school on April 27 and 28, 1914, and laid considerable amount of spawn. There was a prolonged rain on May fourth and fifth and on the evening of the fifth great numbers of the toads appeared in the pool. About one hundred pairs were mated in the pool all through the following day, and their method of laying eggs was readily observed. The chorus of unmated males was loud on the evening of the sixth, but not one of the toads could be found on the seventh, although the temperature continued warm. On July 7, 1914, numbers of spadefoot toads appeared on the salt marshes adjoining the shore at Bay avenue, Patchogue, after a week of rainy days. They sang in a loud chorus and many were mated. None could be found on the next day." "The tadpoles of spadefoot toads have been found in Oakdale and Speonk. The toads are widely distributed, and their times of appearance are as regular as those of other toads. They escape observation on account of their burrowing habits, and their short stay in the breeding pools. I made sure of finding them by hiring a small boy to visit the locality every evening." In many respects the author agrees with the last paragraph from observations made on *Scaphiopus couchi* and *Scaphiopus hammondii*. It is an interesting fact that Prof. R. J. Gilmore of Colorado College, Colorado Springs, Colo., regularly and yearly uses *Scaphiopus* for his class use in biological courses instead of *Bufo* or *Rana* species.

After the publication of his Long Island Frogs and Toads, Overton, 1915, pp. 17, 52, 53, followed the yearly appearance of spade-foots with two notes in Copeia. They are: "Spadefoot toads (*Scaphiopus holbrookii*) appeared in Patchogue on the evening of May 22, 1915, for at least the fourth successive year. The first hard rain of spring occurred on the night of May 21, and on the evening of May 22, great numbers of toads were present in the same pool in which they had been seen in previous years. On the morning of the 23rd nearly every blade of grass in the pool was covered with their eggs, and by night not a toad remained in sight. The sudden emergence of the toads from their underground retreats and their extremely short stay in breeding pools, probably accounts for the former belief that years usually elapse between their appearances."

Later that year he gave another note (1915, pp. 52, 53): "On the evening of Aug. 4, 1915, enormous numbers of Spadefoot Toads (*Scaphiopus holbrookii*) appeared in Patchogue, Yaphank, Middle Island and Coram. I made a twenty-five mile circuit through the villages named, and found the toads in practically every pool. There had been an extremely hard rain during the two previous days."

The next year on Long Island J. T. Nichols (1916, pp. 59, 60) makes the following observations: "The morning of June 17, 1916, after heavy warm rain the preceding night there were singing Spadefoot Toads in a woodland pool beside a road. At mid-day one was seen to cross the road and hop away from the pool into the woods. Its color matched the leaf-carpet wonderfully. Others remained all day.

"One was captured in the pool and liberated the following day. It is remarkable how completely it was able to hide in a closely cut green lawn in bright sunlight by crouching at the bases of the grass. When liberated in the woods it disappeared backwards under the leaves, and remained with just the nose showing at the bottom of its entrance. On June 25, it was found again in this same spot under the fallen leaves in a shallow burrow in the ground, its nose showing. When disturbed it turned sideways, thus withdrawing completely and filling the mouth of the depression with sandy soil. July 3, on scraping away the dead leaves, there was no sign of the toad, but a spot of loose soil detected was investigated disclosing it at a depth of about 1 1/2 inches. This was the last seen of that particular individual, as on July 9, there remained only a neat steeply-slanting burrow, about 3 inches deep, empty.

"A steady rain commencing the night before, continued through July 23, on which afternoon Spadefoot Toads were singing in a pool in pasture land near stands of trees. During a temporary silence cattle came close to the pool, only to gallop away in alarm when the noise recommenced. Investigation disclosed singing Spadefoots also in the woodland pool occupied several weeks earlier, and a greater number in woods now flooded just across the road.

"Points of interest in these data are coloration in the woods, skill at hiding, recurrence in the same pool with favorable conditions after 36 days (See Overton, Copeia, Nos. 20 and 24), and an individual's remaining 15 days in one spot just under the fallen woodland leaves."

VOICE

Andrew Nichols (1852, pp. 113-115) gives considerable on the voice and habits of this species.

"In a shallow basin surrounded by ledges of green stone rock, which retains water during the winter and spring, and is occasionally filled in summer by great rains to the depth of one to four feet, on the brow of a hill in Danvers, over which the old Essex Turnpike crosses, and near the intersection of this road by the Newburyport Turnpike, an interesting colony of this rare reptile, hitherto unobserved north of South Carolina, has been lately discovered. Somewhere about the years 1810, 1811 or 1812, subsequent to a great rain in summer several frogs of this curious species were noticed by John Swinnerton Esq., now deceased, who resided very near this spot for sixty successive years, and had ample opportunity to observe them. Their numbers in this, their first appearance, were as great as any time since, determined by the testimony of several witnesses. At this time, during one or two days and nights, they were very noisy and actively engaged in fulfilling the great fiat of creation; and soon afterward they disappeared. Nothing more was seen of them for several years. Their voices or note so nearly resembled that of young crows that it attracted the attention of Mr. Elijah Pope, a farmer, who lived half a mile distant; and, accompanied by his son, sallied forth, gun in hand, to kill what he so naturally imagined was mischievous birds in his corn-field. From this little anecdote I am enabled to determine their first observed appearance with some degree of certainty; thus defining the time as about the first of September, when corn is in a state to be fed upon by a crow: while, again, the year mentioned above, agree with a statement of the son, Mr. N. Pope, who from his own present age, concludes that 1812 or a year or two earlier, was the time of their first visit.

"So far as recollection serves, nothing more was seen of them until July 1825, on a day memorable for the passage of La Fayette over the Newbury-port Turnpike close by, on his return to Boston from his eastern tour; at which time their voices added to the welcome greetings of a nation's guest! Since this last date, thus rendered conspicuous as well as certain, whenever the basin has been filled in warm weather, these reptiles invariably make their appearance. This has occurred, however, only three times, viz., August 12th, 1834; again in the summer of a year whose date is forgotten; and on June 16th, 1842. The forenoon of this day, last mentioned, was dark and rainy, as the day and night previous had been. Their croaking attracted the attention of an acquaintance of mine, and information of their appearance, with a pair of the frogs, was forwarded to me by Mr. Amos Swinnerton."

In 1884 both Dr. Charles C. Abbott in New Jersey and Col. Nicholas Pike observed this species in congress. The former reports on voice as follows:

"In a sink-hole in a dry upland field near Trenton, New Jersey, on April 10, 1884, there suddenly appeared a large colony of hermit spade-foot toads (*Scaphiopus holbrookii*), which, by their remarkable cries, attracted the attention of every one passing by. So unlike the cries of any other of our batrachians were their utterances, that all who heard them were attracted to the spot, and wondered, when they saw the animals, that so great a volume of sound could issue from so small an animal. One need not wonder, however, on this point if he will but examine the development of the animal's vocal cords.The machinery for producing sounds equal to an ordinary steam whistle are apparently contained in the throat of this rare and curious batrachian. Holbrook, in his diagnosis of the genus *Scaphiopus*, refers to the 'sub-gular vocal sac' of the males; but it must be inferred that the famales are voiceless. That they are not so noisy is probable, but occasion requiring, they can readily make themselves heard.

"It was not long, however, before the spade-foots again became the prominent figure of the fauna of the neighborhood. During the night of June 25-26, a violent north-east storm arose, and rain fell in torrents. The sink-hole, which for weeks had been nearly dry, was again flooded, and on the afternoon of the 26th was literally alive with these rare toads. Sitting upon every projecting stick or tuft of grass, or swimming with their heads above the surface of the water, were spade-foots by the hundred, and every one apparently uttering those shrill, ear-piercing groans that only these batrachians can utter. Not only during the day but all night their cries were kept up. The following day there was no abatement, but during the night the sound decreased. On the morning of the 28th not an individual was to be seen or heard.

"I have already referred to the wonderful noises made by these animals when they congregate in pools for the purpose of spawning. At no other time do they appear to be vocal, and the question naturally arises, why, when the animal leads a life that requires no such power except for two or three days in a year, should its utterances be far louder than any or all the frogs and toads of the same locality combined? Although the animal is strictly crepuscular and not diurnal, it could readily find a mate guided by sight, and the purpose of the deafening epithalamium is somewhat hard to determine. If it could be shown that they call to each other from far distant points, the difficulty would disappear, but this they are not known to do. Apparently it is not until they are congregated in some available pool that they sing, if singing it can be called. No words yet in use in our language can fairly describe their utterances, which, it may be presumed, are expressions of delight at meeting."

To Brimley (1896, p. 501) "The cry was not much louder than that of the common toad." To Ditmars (1905, p. 191) "the voice of the male resembles the tremulous call of the common toad, but is slightly louder."

Fowler (1907, pp. 96, 97) writes: "They are noted for their irregular and erratic appearance during warm weather, their burrowing in the ground tending to their escaping observation. About Trenton, according to Dr. Abbott, it may appear at any time between May and September, and erratically in abundance. They make a great noise, and as the egg-laying varies in time, their notes may also be expected to be heard at different times. During copulation, both animals roar so that they may be heard at the distance of half a mile. Their roar is not like that of the common toad, *Bufo*, and their vocal apparatus is not especially different during the operation. They will also roar at other times, as when disturbed or during heavy rains. Mr. C. C. Abbott informs me that he heard a few during the spring of 1904 and 1906. Dr. Dahlgren tells me that he secured examples near Trenton from the same locality where Dr. Abbott made his observations."

Dr. Overton (1914, pp. 28, 29) writes of its voice thus: "A mud puddle, or a temporary pool formed by a prolonged rain in early April sometimes swarms with toads that groan and squawk in a most unpleasant manner. Each squawk is like the groan made by a deep-voiced man having a tooth pulled. It may also be compared to the squawk made by a big rooster caught in the night.

Such a sound coming from a temporary pool in April is almost surely the voice of a spadefoot toad.

"A spadefoot toad makes its noise while it lies sprawled on the surface of the water. When it begins to sing, it suddenly distends its throat into a white pouch that is about double the diameter of its head. The result is that the pouch, floating on the water, lifts the toad's head up suddenly while the hinder parts of the body sink beneath the surface. At the expiration of the sound, the toad bobs back to its sprawling position. Each vocal effort lasts about a second. An active toad will repeat the sound about every ten seconds. A spadefoot singing in a pool on a dark night may be recognized by its vocal sac which appears like a big white bubble in the light of the lantern."

Shortly after Dr. Dunn's list of Reptiles and Amphibia of Virginia appeared H. W. Fowler adds *Scaphiopus holbrookii* to the list with these notes: "On July 15, 1906, Dr. Henry Fox obtained a fine example of *Scaphiopus holbrookii* which he forwarded soon after. He wrote: "The specimen as well as several other examples were exposed in plowing a stubble-field and attracted attention by the extraordinary loud and shrill cry they made when crushed by the plow. Mr. E. R. Dunn informs me this amphibian has not been definitely recorded from Virginia and the above examples all observed at Tappahannuk, are, therefore, of interest. In this connection I may also mention that under date of June 7, 1916, Mr. H. Walker Hand writes from Cape May, N. J. 'On May 28, Dr. J. S. Eldridge and myself were walking along a wood-road and heard a peculiar cry coming from the ground. I had heard the same before, but could not find the source. This time I dug down and the sound continued even as I was digging. At a depth of about three inches a spadefoot was found snugly fixed. He never stopped calling until I lifted him out.' "

In 1920 from Dade County, Florida, Deckert reports that "During a prolonged thunder-storm many of the Spadefoot Toads were encountered by the writer in the streets south of the Miami River on the afternoon of May 16, and during the night were found breeding at 19th Street and Avenue H., also at 22nd Street and Miami Avenue, and great numbers were reported from the low grounds near the 'Alligator farm,' Miami. Their cries sound like 'Ow, Ow,' and 'Miow,' but the latter much deeper in tone than the well-known cat cry. The noise made by a dozen males is deafening when one is near, though the call lacks carrying power."

On August 16, 1928, about one mile southeast of Hilliard, Florida, we were slowly travelling along the Dixie Highway detour. We were helping tourists over an overflowed area when Mr. Francis Harper espied a curious hawk and started after it. The search led him across the Dixie Highway and he heard what he at first mistook for young crows. (In this connection it is interesting to recall Mr. Andrew Nichols' account wherein spade-foot calls were likened to the call of young crows) they proved to be spade-foots. We, therefore, left the detour and went through the woods to camp beside the five or six ponds where the congress was. We could hear them for about a half mile's distance. Nearby it sounds somewhat like *where where, where, where* and so on. Once one of our party said it sounded at a distance like the calling or snarling of a cross baby. To the writer at first they sounded like some *Rana* in distress, much as they call when a snake or turtle have them. At a distance at other times they sounded like young herons in a heronry. They may make as much noise as a steam calliope but it hardly sounds like it. Mr. F. Harper characterizes the call as *"naarh, naarh*—complaining, nasal, not shrill or high pitched."

When we first approached the males called on all sides in full daylight, almost at our very feet. The throat by day is a beautiful glistening white when the male is croaking. The throat when inflated may be a ball from 1-1 1/2 inches in diameter. The male before he croaks lays on the water's surface with hind legs partially submerged. When he croaks he tips the hind end of the body and hind legs beneath the water and the head is reared to a 45°–75° angle with the water's surface. When at the height of the performance or slightly before he closes his eyes. Then the throat deflates and body inflates. It croaks about once in every two seconds.

Some occasionally question whether female frogs croak or assert they do not. Often a female when picked up will give a croak or squawk not like the breeding call of the male. Sometimes when two or more males are struggling for a female she will squawk, possibly because it may be almost too much for her to bear. Normally the male and female of a mated pair seldom croak. It is usually the males which are searching a mate or annoying the already mated pairs.

MATING

Male (From life, Aug. 18, 1922). Stripe from eye back to vent lemon yellow or greenish yellow. Snout mummy brown or prout's brown. Other light colors of the back are same as stripe from eye to vent, i. e., lemon yellow or greenish yellow, so also on the sides. Snout sometimes blackish brown (1) or bone brown. This is also the remaining color of the back. Sometimes the back color is virtually black. Limbs on dorsum much the same color or slightly washed out more greenish yellow than back light colors. Under parts of hind limbs, lower belly light grayish vinaceous. Rest of under parts white especially the white glistening throat when croaking is done. First three fingers with black excrescences. Space of hind foot dark-edged and tip of 1st toe. Web much darker than grayish vinaceous web of female. Male have wider and larger hind feet. Iris light greenish yellow with black on outer rim. Pupil vertical.

Female (From life, Aug. 18, 1922). Sometimes uniform warm sepia or bone brown above. Throat and breast white. Underside of forelimbs and hind limbs and lower belly light grayish vinaceous. Sometimes the stripe on females may be sulphur yellow instead of the intense greenish yellow of male.

Structural differences. The first character recorded is "Males with a subgular vocal sac (Holbrook 1842, p. 109). Dumeril and Bibron (1841, Vol. VIII, p. 472) write that "The males under the throat have an internal vocal vesicle which communicates with the mouth by two large longitudinal slits, placed one to the right and one to the left of the tongue." Or "Un sac vocal sous-gulaire, chesles males." (Same p. 471).

In the field we made the following notes:

(a) Strangely enough the croaking males were not so hard to approach in the daytime as at night when we tried to photograph them. At night we found them more wild and shy, restless. They proved harder to see and hold by flashlight than many species of toads or frogs. Often when croaking they were just out of the range of the flashlight.

(b) Almost always each male of a pair had a predominance of yellowish hues and the female inclines to the brownish hues.

(c) The throat when inflated glistened by day or under the flashlight in the night.

(d) Apparently the females seem to have hind feet very perceptibly smaller and lighter than in the male.

(e) "The male seemed to have the rear end of the body more of an extended ridge than in axillary, pectoral embracing forms."

(f) Often a male if placed on his back would draw up his hind legs and fore legs and rest on his back as a gopher frog will on his haunches if leaned up against some object.

(g) Males have the inner edges of first two fingers and sometimes the third finger with excrescences; and the first two fingers and the fingers in general are broader, less slender than in the females.

(h) The males and females are not so dissimilar in size as in some species. The males externally are visible as such at about 53 or 54 mm., the females at 50 or 51 mm. Presumably, according to our presumptive evidence of growth, these are 4-year-olds.

Duration, day or night. Pike (1886, p. 218) says "the Spadefoot has a great dislike to water, and when forced to it for breeding purposes does not remain in it long, from three to five days at most. The embrace often takes place on land, as it does occasionally in toads, so that they only enter the water for the purpose of spawning. Their wonderful screaming chorus is kept up the whole time the animals are *in coitu,* and is the love song of the males, the females having only a low guttural grunt. As soon as possible the sexes separate and seek their summer homes, where they lead solitary lives till they have to seek their winter's retreat." In 1920 we wrote that "The hermit spadefoot toad appears suddenly after prolonged rains in April and May or sometimes June or July. At the breeding season it is fond of sprawling out on the surface of the water as a wood frog does, and it is from this position that it croaks. This species gathers in large breeding assemblies like toads, and the matings are as spirited."

On August 16, 1928, beyond noon we found these spade-foots in congress. They continued all that afternoon and through the night, but early the next morning, August 17, not a one was to be found in pond nor nearby. All had left the pond or were in hiding in the pond or most presumably had burrowed in the nearby soil. If heavy rainy weather is on they like other species of spadefoots will breed by day, even start first in the daytime but darkness is the preferred period for spade-foots in general (*S. holbrookii, S. couchi* and *S. hammondii*).

The males in ardor are the equal of any toad. The tumbles and turmoils are just as numerous as in a toad congress.

Amplexation (Normal, abnormal, cross). Brimley (1896, p. 501) in observing fifty breeding frogs writes that "In every case the grasp of the male was inguinal." Richard Deckert's Fig. 1 in Overton's Long Island Frogs and Toads portrays an inguinal embrace, in all three pairs pictured. In 1920 (p. 22) we say that "The male seizes the female just ahead of the hind legs (inguinal fashion), a form of embrace not known in any other American form except in the narrow-mouthed toads . . . ." How the last slip on narrow-mouthed toads happened is beyond us now. *Gastrophryne texense* and *Gastrophryne carolinensis* embrace axillary fashion.

Normally a male embraces in inguinal fashion. In the five or six ponds we saw no other fashion for ovulating pairs. Even when fertilizing the eggs the male keeps the inguinal fashion but he draws up his vent near that of the female. A male of a mated pair can be taken away and another substituted. Almost invariably the second instantly remains on the female. Often one will see a male rush for another male or for a mated pair. Occasionally one sees a female with a mated male and another male atop the mating one. When spade-foots are actually ovulating the male usually closes his eyes.

Several abnormal embraces were observed. These are usually preliminary and not of ovulation period. One female was held by a male which had its left arm above and behind the foreleg of the female and male's right arm was just ahead of the right hind leg. Another male held her from below, his left arm behind her right arm and his right arm around her left side of waist. At times both of his arms were just in front of the hind legs.

In the ponds were narrow-mouthed toads (*Gastrophryne*) pine woods tree frogs (*Hyla femoralis*) cricket-frogs (*Acris gryllus*) and Florida tree frogs (*Hyla gratiosa*) breeding in great profusion. None were large enough for cross embraces except with the last. In one pond we found a male spadefoot 62 mm. long embracing a ripe female *Hyla gratiosa* 58 mm. long. In the ponds were several normal *Hyla gratiosa* pairs.

OVULATION

Habitat. The congress of ovulation we found Aug. 16 and 17, 1928 in cut over pine barrens in shallow depressions the water in one pond being 1–1 1/2 inches deep, in several 4–6 inches, in another 6–8 inches, and in a last pond 12–18 inches deep. The pools were in what might be called moist pine barrens or it might be an old field, a cypress pond not being far away. One pond was a depression in a wood road. Considerable of *Rhexia*, *Hypericum*, sedges and grasses were in the five or six ponds. In the ponds were numerous *Acris gryllus*, *Gastrophryne carolinensis*, *Hyla femoralis* and *Hyla gratiosa* breeding. All in all the pools were indeed very temporary.

Period. In South Carolina Holbrook (1842, p. 111) found that "It appears early in March, after the first heavy rains of spring, and at once seeks its mate."

Pike (1886, p. 220) writes: "In the pond where I found them in 1884 there was abundant water in 1885, fed by springs, and to my eye the same conditions obtained this year. It is evident Spadefoot thought differently, and resorted to a pool a quarter of a mile away, for some reasons unknown to me. I believe they breed every year, but change their locality, as the winters, though often severe on Long Island, certainly do not diminish the numbers of the *Scaphiopus*."

In Raleigh, North Carolina, Brimley (1896, p. 59) recorded "Last May I collected fifty breeding in a pool only a few yards from my house." In Florida, T. VanHyning (1923, p. 68) writes: "On the night of March 18, while some of the boys of the biological class of the University of Florida, Gainesville, Florida, were collecting frogs, among other species taken were thirty specimens of the Florida Tree Frog, *Hyla gratiosa* LeConte; eight specimens of the Gopher-Frog, *Rana aesopus* (Cope), and two of the Spadefoot Toad *Scaphiopus holbrookii* (Harlan).

"These and other species were all in a pond breeding near the University. One of the party collected eggs, and brought living specimens which have spawned since . . . ."

The summation of 23 congresses from 1910 to 1922 give two for March, four for April, five for May, three for June, three for July, three for August and two for September, or eleven for the spring months, nine for the summer months, and three for September, the modal month being May. The two March records are: the first for South Carolina and Georgia; and the second for Florida.

Our only record of ovulation observed is for August 16, 17, 1928.

Temperature and humidity. On August 16 and 17, 1928, when we found the spadefoot congress we had no thermometers with us. We record that the water must have been 75° to 80° when the rain was on and much higher when the sun came out. The rain was so heavy that many cars were stuck on the detour ahead of us and streams were flowing over the wooded bridges.

For five stations around the swamp for the two days, August 16 and 17, the air minima ranged from 69°–74°, with an average of 71° and the maxima ranged from 82°–91°, with average of 87°. These stations average .70 inches of rain, e. g., Glen St. Mary, Florida, had 1.80 inches August 16 and a trace the next day; Waycross had .69 inches August 16 and .55 inches August 17. But Hilliard where we were had .56 inches August 16 and 3.47 inches August 17 or 4.03 inches when the congress was in progress.

Egg-laying process. Overton (1914, p. 29) describes it thus: "The only time when spadefoot toads are not shy is while they are actually laying thier eggs. A pair of toads about to deposit a mass of eggs will cling to a stiff spear of grass about a foot beneath the surface of the water and will slowly crawl up the stem, depositing a string of about two hundred eggs enclosed in a gelatinous envelope about as large around as the toad's leg. Each batch will be laid within five minutes, and during that time the pair may be approached readily. A toad will lay its eggs at intervals within a very few hours, and will then disappear from the pool." Deckert's drawing (Fig. 1, p. 39), May 12, 1914, in this work is a very good portrayal of the process and in accord with our experiences in northern Florida.

One of our short field notes is as follows: "Spade-foots lay eggs on twigs (upright). Water 6 inches or more deep in first pond. Pair lays a band on a twig in about a minute or less. Female seizes the twig with forelegs and climbs branches with forelegs and hindlegs. Male embraces inguinal fashion.

"Must be 50 pairs or more in one pond which is 4 or 5 inches deep. The pair leave the surface and start for the bottom and the female moves up the stem toward the surface to the end of the twig. Sometimes horizontal position in laying, usually vertical. Intervals of laying. One pair has 15 seconds laying. Rested one minute. Laid. Rested 3 minutes. Ten seconds for laying. ...

Often a female will hold her head downward at first. From time to time the female will cross fore feet and hind feet as she climbs a stem."

To make sure our lone opportunity for observation on the breeding of the Spade-foots in 1921 and 1922 was used to its utmost we asked Mrs. Wright to record independently her own findings. Under egg laying we presented her notes: "We started from Callahan in a hard rain, a little before noon. On a detour two miles south of Hilliard, we stopped for cars going across a swollen creek. Francis went to look for birds and heard Spade-foots calling. We drove through the woods and back on the Dixie Highway and pitched camp, one mile south of Hilliard on an oak ridge. An old road filled with water made a shallow pond, and here we saw the males croaking, their white throats looking like shiny white golf balls. Just beyond was a shallow surface pool, caused by the heavy rain. The ground was covered with herbs; a little *Xyris*, a few sedges, *Rhexias*, small umbelliferous plant with violet shaped leaf, wire grass and a few *Hypericums*. The Spade-foots were calling here, and in another similar pool and in a third deeper pool as well. At a distance the chorus sounded like young crows trying to call. The pond was filled with mated pairs.

"A few eggs had been laid. The eggs were laid in more or less irregular band form along the grass blades or plant stems. In the third pond where the water was deep, the bands were long. The pair might be floating on the surface. When ready to lay, they went to the bottom of the pond, often the male with his eyes closed, and the female with her's partly closed. They moved around slowly on the bottom, or rested a minute. When she found a stem to suit her, she seized it with her front feet and pushed with her hind feet. The male clung close to her back, his chin tight against her back. (One we photographed had an abrazed chin as if from pressure). He held his knees against her knees, or sometimes his feet which are conspicuously broad, were pressed against her feet. She walked or climbed up the grass blade or along it, if it fell to horizontal position, pressed vent against the blade as she laid the eggs. He humped his back to press his vent close to her's while she was laying. As they reached the top of the blade, they sometimes moved immediately to a nearby one, or rested a short period. When first laid the eggs had a irregular band appearance as they were strung along the blade, sometimes

Plate XIX

Spade-foot (*Scaphiopus holbrookii*)

1. Rain filled depression in the pine barrens, Hilliard, Fla. August 17, 1922.
2. 3. 4. Males croaking, Hilliard, Fla. August 16, 1922. Flashlights.
5. Eggs, Hilliard, Fla. August 16, 1922.
6. 7. Tadpoles, Camp Pinckney, Ga. June 22, 1922.
8. 9. 10. 11. Tadpole and transforming frogs, Chesser Id., Ga. June, 28 1922.
   × 1.0.

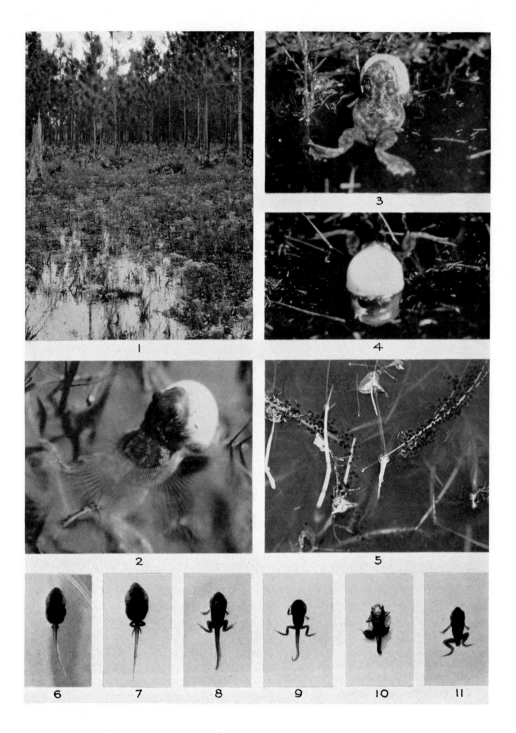

being much thicker as if more eggs had been emitted at such periods. When first laid, they had a brownish appearance with conspicuous creamy-white vegetative pole. As the jelly swelled and the eggs all turned right side up, they looked very black.

"By the next morning, some eggs were almost ready to hatch (these must have been the ones we found when we first found the pond). The other clusters were swollen into loose, irregular, elongate bunches attached to the stems which were tipped so that many times the bunches lay lengthwise on the water. There seemed to be a tendency for the bunches of eggs to be more or less clustered in areas. We noticed many pairs close together that first afternoon, and unattached males trying to get at a female making tangled masses of toads. There was a strong chorus that night and by the next morning the pond was all churned up and muddy. Many, many eggs were there, but no toads. The story was told for the season."

EGGS

Attachment, egg mass, egg description. On May 4, 1863 Mr. F. W. Putnam (1863, p. 229) made some statements concerning the frogs and toads found about Cambridge, Mass.

"The *Scaphiopus solitarius* Holbrook appeared in their old place, near the Botanical Gardens, in large numbers on the 19th of April, and commenced the same day to lay their eggs in bunches of about one, two and three inches in diameter; these bunches were floating on the water and were not attached to the grass, as was the case when seen in the previous years. On the 29th of April, another set of *Scaphiopus* visited the place, and laid eggs, which were attached to the grass as formerly. The tadpoles of this species are hatched in about six days."

Pike (1886, pp. 218, 219) compares these eggs and toads eggs. "On the ridge extending from East New York to Jamaica, one of the most elevated parts of Long Island, there are ten or twelve ponds, some fed by springs and constant, others often filled by winter's snows and rains. This spring I worked them all over with my net, and though I heard no screeching, yet as the *Scaphiopus* is far from rare on the hills near by, I felt sure they must breed in some of these ponds. Toads, I know, also swarm in the vicinity, and on the 17th of July I fished up what I took to be toad spawn, although not in chaplets, and only slightly attached to some weeds floating about in the water. The eggs were evidently laid only a few days before."

In 1897 Wm. L. Sherwood (1898, p. 18) holds that "The eggs are laid any time from April to June in bunches from one to three inches in diameter, and are placed around a spike of grass."

In 1899 G. A. Boulenger speaks of their eggs and breeding thus: "I had applied last summer to Messrs. Brimley, in North Carolina, where the Spade-foot is abundant, who kindly informed me that the eggs are laid early in spring, in strings resembling those of toads, but thicker and with the vitelline spheres more irregularly disposed—in fact, as I infer, not unlike those of *Pelobates*. They added that the season was then too far advanced for tadpoles to be procured, as their development is comparatively rapid, and the pools in which they are reared dry up by the end of spring. I have therefore to postpone a description of the tadpole, which I hope, however, to supply ere long."

Ditmars (1905, p. 191) holds "The eggs are similar to those of the toad, and are laid in strings." By no stretch of description could one hold them the same as those of the common toad.

(See Overton's notes under egg laying process and Deckert's Fig. 1 for the appearance of eggs at or immediately after ovulation).

In 1920 (p. 27) before our own first-hand experience with spade-foot eggs we repeated that "the hermit spadefoot lays eggs in bands like the European forms of this family, ..." But it should be said that soon these bands appear as cylinders. In 1923 (a p. 406) we speak of the "eggs in bands, later cylinders." Or 1923 (b p. 34) we hold that "from April 15th or earlier to Sept. 1st., six forms breed. . . . . *Scaphiopus holbrookii* lays bands of eggs which soon become cylinders." In 1924 (pp. 377, 379) we record the "egg mass (as) submerged. Eggs laid in bands which soon become loose cylinders extending along plant stems or grass blades; vitellus 1.4 to 2.0 mm.; envelope 3.8–5.6 mm. Egg complement 2,332. Season Apr. 15 or earlier to August 17." "These (early species) are usually with firm jelly envelopes except for *Pseudacris triseriata* and *Scaphiopus holbrookii*, which have the consistency intermediate between the firm jellies of early breeders and the loose surface films of later breeders."

In one pond in an area 4 feet square were 12 pairs. Before a congress is over the stems and vegetation at times gets tied up in a tangle with the interlocking and heavy egg masses. Some stems are with egg masses bent over and such horizontal stems are often connected to a vertical one by other jelly masses. A few fresh laid bands were as follows: 1 inch long, 2 inches, 4 inches. When the bands expand the band may be 1 1/3–1 3/4 inches in diameter. Usually the bands were about as long as the pond was deep. Most were, therefore, 1–6 inches long. But in the one deep pond were bands very much longer, 8–12 inches. In other words the female goes to the bottom of pond and crawls up to or almost to the surface before she ceases ovulation.

The next morning at 10:00–10:30 A.M. the spade-foots having left before daybreak, in an area 6–8 feet in diameter every grass blade was covered and bent over from the weight of one or more masses. The masses were swollen (not now band-like) and some almost hatched. Masses around the stems were 1 inch wide or sometimes 1 1/2–2 inches in width. If the original band be short, the final swollen mass may at times look squarish at the surface or be cuboid in reality. Most of the masses looked like cylinders of jelly or round masses. The pond was just packed with these masses and the water had a milky appearance.

We made several field observations and measurements on the individual eggs. Mrs. Wright made these three determinations: In one lot, the vitelli were 1.6 mm., 1.6, 1.8 mm., and envelopes 4.8 mm., 4.8 mm., 5.2–5.0 mm., and in mass the jelly more or less merged. Another set had measurements: 1.4

mm., 1.6, 1.6, 1.6, 1.8 mm. for vitelli and 3.8, 4.0, 4.0, 4.0, 4.5 for envelopes. A third group had 1.4, 1.6, 1.6 mm. for vitelli and 4.0, 4.0, 4.2 mm. for envelopes.

On three other lots the writer secured the following: One set give 1.4, 1.6, 1.6, 1.7, 1.8 mm. for vitelli and 4.2, 4.6, 5.4, 5.5, 5.6 mm. for envelopes. Another group where egg envelope a day old or not fresh, tended to be elliptical, we had vitelli 1.5, 1.7, 1.7, 1.7, 1.7, 2.0 mm. and envelopes 4.0, 4.1, 4.4, 4.5, 4.5 mm. The third group were one day or a little less old when preserved and jelly was more or less merged or there was no regularity of envelope outline at all. At times an egg would hang at the end of a jelly cylinder as if stalked with an egg in the end like a stalked egg—somewhat as occurs in egg masses of *Scaphiopus hammondii*.

At this writing (Dec., 1928) the fresh eggs of Aug. 16, 1922, now preserved in formalin surely look to be cream colored below and brown above. Another accession of some fresh laid eggs in deeper water have the eggs appearing blackish. Furthermore, these eggs were preserved when mass was still in the band form, the jelly unexpanded. Each band is from 4–6 eggs wide. The width of some of these bands ranges from 5-8 mm. in breadth.

Dangers. Dr. Abbott emphasizes this point. "During this brief interval these animals spawned, the eggs being attached to blades of grass and slender twigs. These eggs hatched on the 2nd of July and a larger series were gathered a week later.

"To return to the eggs. During the time that intervened from the laying of the eggs until I gathered specimens of the tadpoles, there occurred four moderately heavy showers, so that the water in the sink-hole at no time disappeared, but was much below the level that it reached during the protracted rainfall of June 26. Very much, therefore, of the spawn that was laid was high and dry for from two to four days before hatching, and I suppose was destroyed.

"On the evening of July 9 I found the water in the sink-hole confined to a very few shallow pools of limited area, and in these pools were a few hundreds of *Scaphiopus* tadpoles. In comparison with the abundance of eggs seen June 26, and of young seen a week later, it is evident that a large portion of the eggs were destroyed and a vast number of very young tadpoles were killed by the soaking away of the water.

"I have never known any like disparity between the ages of frogs or common toads and the young in the tadpole state; and it is at once very evident that if the spade-foot habitually or usually deposit their eggs in temporary pools, then we have an obvious reason for the positive rarity of the animal, as apparently it is the rule, rather than the exception, for the egg to be destroyed or the young perish."

The eggs usually hatch before the water evaporates enough to do damage except to the bunches which are near the shifting borders of these transient pools. Few are infertile. A few masses so appeared and one mass we tried to hatch so proved.

HATCHING PERIOD

Andrew Nichols (1852, p. 115) writes: "In five days after I found the spawn had become tadpoles, . . ." C. C. Abbott (1884, p. 1076) says: "During this interval (June 26–28) these animals spawned, the eggs being attached to blades of grass and slender twigs. The eggs hatched on the 2nd of July. . . ." This makes 4 to 6 days for hatching. Sherwood (1896, p. 18) gives the hatching period as "about a week."

On Aug. 4 and 5, 1915 Dr. Overton (1915, p. 53) records "a great congress—enormous numbers of eggs of the spadefoot and Fowler's toads were readily identified in the pools. On the 7th, the eggs were hatched" or 2 or 3 days after eggs were laid.

In this southern clime development is apparently even more rapid than in the north. On Aug. 18, 1928, we have the field note that two lots "are hatched early morning of August 18. In fact, some in pond were almost hatched August 17 at noon or 1–1/4 days after laying. Certainly 1 1/2–2 days after egg deposition these have hatched. Water must have been 75° or 80° when rain came and more when the sun came out. This hatched tadpole is from dorsum very broad in head, has large gills, has body very narrow as compared to head. The tail is dorso-ventrally very broad. The creature is mainly head and tail and odd in appearance.

MATURE TADPOLE

Color description from life. (*June 23, 27, 1922*). General color bronzy. Upper parts brownish drab, benzo brown, vinaceous drab. Upper parts with many close set spots of apricot orange or vinaceous tawny which on the top of upper tail crest become merged into a conspicuous bittersweet orange ridge of color. Throat and gill region with little of the orange vinaceous spots of upper parts. Gills can be seen through the skin. Spots on belly clear yellow green in places.

Tail. Muscular part brownish drab, benzo brown, vinaceous drab. Crests translucent. Upper crest with thin edge of dots and interlacing lines. This arrangement goes around the tip. Rest of under crest translucent—no edging. On the caudal half of lower edge of the muscular part the muscle segments are more or less outlined by the light color making emarginations between the black dots. The same arrangement for the dorsal third of the muscular part of the tail.

Iris and eye black, small; eye close together.

General appearance. Tadpole small (28.0 mm.) broad and large bodied but not deep. Body has from dorsal aspect a *Limulus*-like appearance. Tail short, tip blunt, rounded. Body unlike *Bufo*, broader nearer eye than vent. Dorsal crest extends on to the body to a vertical just ahead of the developing hind legs, is perceptibly nearer hind legs than spiracle. Spiracle sinistral, far below lateral axis, as much or more ventral than lateral, opening more rectangular or slitlike than in our tadpoles in general. Spiracle about on the level of the mouth. Eye on the lateral axis, very dorsal in position. The eyes close together, nearer the mid-dorsal axis than the lateral outline, in fact nearer together than in *Bufo*. Anus median at the end of the edge of the ventral crest. Muciferous crypts in preserved specimens at least indistinct.

Mouth parts: Teeth 6/6, 6/5, 5/6, 5/5. Whole labium (upper and lower) with continuous row of papillae except on the upper labium where a pronounced median interval is toothed. This median row is about equal to the first lower labial row of either side. From upper labial interval of teeth downward either side and across the lower labial border there is at least one row of inner papillae. Opposite the ends of the horny beaks are several rows of them filling in the space between upper and lower labia. The next series of teeth (the second) below the upper toothed interval is usually not continuous, rarely continuous. Usually one median end slightly overlaps the end of its counter part of the other side. The third series has a short medium interval one half the distance of the upper toothed interval or first series or slightly more than a similar interval in the third lower labial series. Either half of the upper third series is slightly less in depth than the horny beak and about equal to either half of the lower third series.

Measurements. Length of body (10–12.2 mm.) in tail (12.8–17.6 mm.) 1.1–1.7, average 1.34. Width (6.0–7.4 mm.) of body in its own length 1.4–1.8, average 1.64. Depth (4.8–6.8 mm.) of body 1.03–1.50 in body width, average 1.23. Depth of body 1.73–2.5 in body length, average 2.04. Depth (3.4–5.4 mm.) of tail in length of tail 2.5–4.0, average 3.14. Muscular part (2.8–3.0 mm.) 1.45–2.4 in depth of tail, average 1.98. Spiracle 1.24–1.66 nearer base of hind legs or vent region (4.4–6.0 mm.) than the tip of the snout (7.0–8.0 mm.), average 1.41. Spiracle equidistant between eye 1.44–5.8 mm. and base of hind legs or vent, 1.44–6.0 mm., average 1.0. Eye 1.4–1.8 nearer to tip of snout (3.0–3.6 mm.) than to spiracle (4.4–5.8 mm.), average 1.52. Nostril 1.5–2.26 nearer eye (1.0–1.8 mm.) than snout (2.0–3.0 mm.), average 1.9. Mouth (3.0–4.0 mm.) usually 1.56–2.5 larger than internasal space (1.2–2.0 mm.), average 2.08. Mouth usually contained 1.0–1.66 larger (average 1.3) than in interobital distance (2.0–3.2 mm.). Internasal space contained in interorbital space 1.28–1.83, average 1.56.

The dimensions of the largest tadpole are:

	mm.		mm.
Total length	28.0	Spiracle to vent	6.0
Body length	12.0	Spiracle to eye	5.2
Body depth	5.0	Eye to snout	3.6
Body width	6.4	Eye to nostril	1.8
Tail length	16.0	Nostril to snout	2.4
Tail depth	4.4	Mouth	3.0
Tail, musculature of	3.0	Interorbital distance	3.0
Spiracle to snout	7.6	Internasal distance	2.0

General remarks. After Nichols, Abbott is next to remark about the tadpoles. He notes that "The tadpoles gathered July 9th, which were then seven days old, were curious creatures. At this time the hind legs were well developed, although small, and did not interfere with the animal's natatorial locomotion. The bodies of these young Scaphiopi were short, stout and oval, and, when viewed in the water, deep velvety black; but when closely examined it was found that the two irregularly parallel yellow dorsal stripes, that are so prominent a feature in the coloration of the adult male, were plainly discernible.

"The movements of these tadpoles were not different from that of the young frogs and toads in this stage of their existence. Those that I had in an aquarium moved in companies as though following a leader, and occasionally one would drop out of the ranks, come quickly to the surface, eject a bubble of air, and dive again quickly to the bottom of the tank. Like all tadpoles they had enormous appetites, and when fed with bits of raw meat quickly attached their sucking mouths to the food offered, and did not remove it, I think, while a particle of blood remained in the mass.

"A week later, July 16, the majority of these tadpoles had acquired their front legs, and the tail had perceptibly diminished in size, but still was used by them when moving through the water. At this time, however, the movements of the animal are far less active than before or soon after, and for a few days, if exposed to the attacks of any enemies, would suffer far more than at any other period of their lives.

"A very curious feature in the growth of these animals is now to be noticed. Of the specimens I had under examination, in an aquarium, about five percent did not progress beyond the condition in which all were in July 9. These 'retarded' tadpoles proved to be voracious cannibals. They seized their more matured companions by their tails and legs, swallowing the member and thus sustaining their own lives at the expense of their fellows. They generally killed their victim in the course of twenty-four hours, and often in less time, and then promptly seized another. So bloodthirsty were these few 'retarded' tadpoles that I was compelled to protect the lives of the little hoppers, their brethren, which now, in spite of stumps of tails, sat in frog-like fashion on their haunches, and were in all respects miniatures of the adult spadefoots that in April and June made night hideous with their unearthly cries."

Pike (1886, pp. 219, 220) compares Spadefoot tadpoles to toad tadpoles. His account pertinent to this topic is: "The first week I had them was warm and sunny, and in about seven days the first tadpoles appeared, but a gloomy cold spell following, the rest did not hatch out under twelve and even fifteen days. At this stage they look black in the water, but are really black. In about ten days the color broke out into blotches, with little white scattered dots. Certain signs at this time led me to suspect I had found a treasure, and the metamorphosis was watched with renewed interest. Having bred toads, and my cabinet containing a series of these tadpoles of different ages, I soon found a difference between them and my new acquisitions.

"The toad tadpoles are oval, of a dusky black, with a clear white fin on the tail. The Spadefoots are brown and chubby, the tail narrow and blotched all over. Then they swim differently; the latter with the body depressed, and they skim around the aquarium with the greatest rapidity. The tadpole is of good size before the hind legs develop, and the back and abdomen gleam with gold; the latter is dark gray, the former brown, with dark marks on it showing the outline of the star of the adult starting from a broad dark disk between the eyes.

"As soon as the hind legs are out, both body and tail diminish, and they are as ravenous as other tadpoles, devouring both meat and fish greedily. As soon as the thread-like front legs show, they must have cork or clips to sit on, as their perfection is close at hand. I neglected this at first, and some that were ready to leave the water August 18, actually atrophied till they were barely an inch long from snout to hind toe, the smallest live reptiles I ever saw, and died evidently from inability to remain in their watery home. It was only by giving them resting places, and a way out into a dry house, that I succeeded in bringing out strong young ones, and the first act of their terrestrial life seems to be to provide a home by burrowing.

"When the front legs are well out in the toad, the whole under part assumes a yellowish-white hue, the thighs are finely granulated, and on the insides of the hands and feet the joints are thick and white. From between the eyes and all over the back are the outlines of the future warts, increasing in size daily. When the Spadefoot is at the same stage of growth the whole underneath is dusky gray; feet and hands are slighter and smoother; the body more drawn in behind the arms, and the tail is narrower."

In 1923 (p. 406) we held "*Scaphiopus holbrookii* has bronzy tadpoles, translucent crests, rounded tail tip, oblique black bars on musculature; labial teeth 4/5."

LARVAL PERIOD

Nichols (1852, pp. 115, 116) gives the first account of this phase: "In examining the water, however, we found it filled with spawn—and two females were drawn from the bottom of the pool. . . . The old frogs were not seen again. In five days after, I found the spawn had become tadpoles, of which about a hundred I took home—kept them in glass globes,—fed them on fish and flesh—scarcely one died. They remained longer and grew larger in the tadpole state than did those left in their native pool, which later became perfect animals in less than four weeks. On the other hand, those kept in water, without any opportunity to crawl on land, or on any substitute for it, such as floating chip, or some foothold firmer than water, were slower in their development. It seems then, that the development and successive changes of the organs, confirm to circumstances. So long as water is wholly their residence, their caudal appendage is necessary and accordingly used, retaining its proportionate size and strength, and the growth of the legs is in the same proportion. If the water be gradually withdrawn, and mud, moist earth and then dry, gradually substituted, they will much sooner undergo the change from the embryonic to the infantile condition of existence. Thus, at the end of four weeks, all the water in which the spawn was deposited had evaporated; in some of the lowest spots of the basin a little mud of the consistency of clay-mortar alone remaining. Here the young frogs were merrily hopping about, enjoying life on dry land, while those in confinement in water, were still increasing in size, and yet in an embryo condition. This very short natural period of the tadpole state admirably fits them for such breeding places as the one in which the subjects of this paper were found; a locality where water can remain for a short time only, and this is the most wet seasons."

Sherwood (1898, p. 18) gives "the metamorphosis being complete in about two to three weeks" or with his week of hatching 3–4 weeks from egg laying. Ditmars (1905, p. 191) has it that "The metamorphosis is completed within a few weeks from the time of hatching."

Overton (1914, p. 30) records for one group (1913) that eggs laid Apr. 13 or 23 transformed the middle of June or two months later. In 1915 eggs which were laid Aug. 4 and 5, he found as transformed frogs at least by Sept. 4 or about 30 days from egg laying or 27 days of tadpole life.

Most of the records imply a very short larval period such as 30 days, 14–21 days, 21–28 days, 60 days, 30 days. Normally they need a month or less before transformation. The eggs laid Aug. 16 and 17 were hatched August 17 and 18. Five days from egg laying these tadpoles were 14 mm. long, of which the body was 7 mm. On August 26 we started northward in a Ford and carried these tadpoles on the running board of the car. They nevertheless transformed Sept 2, or 17 days from egg deposition or strictly 15 days of larval life.

TRANSFORMATION

Period. Nichols found them transforming in mid July. Apparently Abbott's tadpoles under observation transformed in about 21–23 days or July 23–25. Pike had them transformed in August. Overton records some in September. In 1920 (p. 36) we held they transformed from June to August.

In 1922 we found in one place June 22 tadpoles, most of which were mature, quite a few with two legs and one with four legs. On July 24, one month later, there were none left in this pond. Transformation came from June 22–July 24. Some eggs which were laid at Hilliard, Florida, August 16 and 17, 1922, transformed on the running board of the Ford Sept. 2. The earliest transformation material we possess are some which Dr. Frank Overton gave us in 1915 bearing the data Aug.-Sept. 22, 1915, from Patchogue, L. I. In view of the short larval period some trasnformations must begin as early as mid April and some appear as late as October.

Size. In 1920 (p. 36) we give the "ranges of size from 0.3 to 0.5 of an inch at the time of transformation (see Fig. 2 and Pl. XXII, Fig. 11)." In the figure 2 the transformation size is given as about 0.4 of an inch and the adult as 2.7 inches. In the plate it is apparent the transformation spade-foot and the common toad are the two smallest of the 16 species figured.

A series of 13 transformed spadefoots given to the writer by Dr. Frank Overton, Patchogue, Long Island, and collected Sept. 22, 1915, range from 8.5–11 mm., mode 10 mm., average 10 mm. A transformed individual taken June 22, 1922, at Camp Pinckney, Ga., measures 10 mm. A series of 17 taken at the same place June 27 give a range of 8.5–12 mm., an average of 10 mm., a mode of 11 mm.

GROWTH

Colonel Nicholas Pike (1886, p. 218) writes that "When they leave the water they are smaller than the common toad, but if the season is favorable they grow rapidly in width more than length. I have some two years old one-quarter of an inch in length, and nearly as wide as long."

We took in Okefinokee region transformation sizes from 8.5–12 mm. and 28 adults. The latter were all breeding males and females from 51–71 mm. In the U. S. National Museum and our collections also intermediate sizes between 51–12 mm. transformation size are scarce. We have a specimen 28 mm., one 44 mm., two 45 mm., and one 50 mm. Do the 28 mm. and 44 mm. represent modes or two different groups? If so, we have four groups at least: 8.5–12 mm. at transformation; 28 mm., 44–50 mm., 51–72 mm. Doubtless the last group needs to be divided into two groups. From comparison with meager *S. couchii* material where a 21 mm. specimen and 56 mm. were taken at same place; and specimens 26, 27, 31, 31, 31, 31.5, 32, 36, 53, 56, 58, 59.5, 59.5, 60, 67 mm. were taken at another locality at the same time and from deductions from 59 adults of *S. holbrookii* above 44 mm., the evidence provisionally might be interpreted as: 8.5–12 mm., at transformation; 18–24 mm. one year olds; 26–36 mm. two year olds; 38–50 mm. three year olds; 51–61 mm. four year olds; 62–72 five year olds. It could be interpreted as 8.5–12.0 mm. at transformation; 21–28 one year olds; 31–40 mm. two year olds; 42–52 mm. three year olds; 53–60 four year olds; 62-67 or 68 five year olds and 70–72 six year olds. At present we incline toward the former, knowing the material is scant for careful conclusions.

FOOD

Holbrook alludes to its catching insects at the entrance to its hole. Andrew Nichols (1852, p. 116) "also kept a few of the old frogs, three in number, two females and a male in a barrel, a third part filled with moist peat muck, containing some earthworms (*Lumbricus terrestris* L.) and other small creatures. Occasionally I threw in a few garden snails (*Limax agrestis* L.), small pieces of meat, fish or insects. Whether they ate of those provisions is uncertain. Occasionally I found one or two of them out of the muck, in which they usually buried themselves, reserving only a small breathing hole, opening above their heads. . . . I kept them until the last part of November, when carelessly permitting the earth to become frozen, they were killed."

Pike (1886, pp. 217, 218) on Aug. 8, 1884 captured several of these animals in their exodus from the water and makes some food notes on them. "We carried our little treasures home in bags filled with grass, and so tired were we after our hunt we left them imprisoned all night. Some of them objected to being bagged, and made a faint squeaking noise when handled.

"Next morning I placed them in a large glass jar with earth, and in less time than it takes to write the fact most were buried, all but their noses. I fed them on flies and insects, and once I put in half a nest of young spiders. As soon as their little bright eyes caught sight of the moving game, a most animated scene took place. Every one was out jumping and capering about till not a spider was left, when back they all hastened to hide till new victims were provided. I turned many into the garden in the hope that I might see some come out this spring. I was, however, disappointed, and it was not until August 24 that by accident I discovered any were alive. On the night of the 22nd, and all next day, heavy rain fell, which washed the poor little fellows out of their homes and revealed their presence to me.

"Two days after the exodus we visited the same hillside, but with the exception of two or three belated in the pond, not one was visible. We hunted diligently for them, dug in all sorts of places, turned over heaps of stones, but all in vain; yet I do not doubt there were hundreds buried all around us had we only known where. It is evident they go far from their watery home, for they were marching steadily on, the column spreading out about fifty feet wide with none beyond it. Nor do I think they feed during the exodus. I saw an immense number of very small crickets in amongst them, but though I looked carefully I could not see any of the little Spade-foots eating them."

Fisher (1920, p. 77) had a captive of which he wrote: "While in captivity it was fed mainly upon earthworms. It also ate a grasshopper and a cricket or two. It is remarkable how it would always close its eyes when swallowing, and this seemed to be an important and necessary part of the act. When open, the eyes bulge out prominently, but when closed they are drawn back until they do not bulge at all. When the eyes are thus retracted, the roof of the mouth is lowered and this doubtless helps to force food down the throat in swallowing."

AUTUMNAL DISAPPEARANCE

Holbrook (1842, p. 111) says "I have met them even in very cold weather, with snow on the ground." Col. Pike (1886, p. 215) writes of this species and cold weather as follows:

"When the cold nights of fall begin, the Spadefoot leaves its summer home and looks out for one more suitable for the winter season. It generally chooses the warm southerly side of a hill, and excavates deeply for its new quarters. It was only after many year's studying of this animal that I was able to verify this fact.

"About four years ago I found one by accident in winter, over three feet below the surface. On December 27, 1884, I was in Cypress Hills Cemetery when a laborer who was digging a grave called my attention to a toad snugly imbedded in the side of an opening he had just made. His spade had slightly grazed the body of the animal, which I saw at once was a Spadefoot. I asked him not to disturb it till I had made a careful examination of the burrow. The man had dug down nearly four feet, but the distance the creature had burrowed was by exact measurement three feet two inches.

"The most careful search round the hibernaculum failed to discover any outlet. It had left no trace of burrowing behind it, having evidently covered up all tracks to its lair. The soil was closely packed about it, and the round hole was perfectly smooth, just large enough to contain the body in the crouching posture I mention its assuming in confinement. I have since been told that the Spadefoot has been found at a depth of six feet, but this I cannot vouch for.

"When the weather is not too severe, even while the last snow is on the ground, the *Scaphiopus* often makes its appearance, but then it only roams aimlessly round, hiding under dead leaves and taking little food. The usual time of awakening to renewed spring-life is the end of April or beginning of May, and if the weather is unfavorable, not till June or even July."

Dr. G. Clyde Fisher (1920, pp. 76–78) says that "On August 14, 1918, I captured a Spadefoot . . . in the basement of my house in Douglaston, Long Island, which is inside Greater New York. It was taken in a small cavity in the damp earth, which it had probably made, in a break in the concrete on a level with the floor. It was in excellent condition, and apparently it was fully grown. We had seen it hopping about at night several days previous to this, but we do not know how long it had been in the cellar or how it got there.

"For several weeks we kept it in a large box of earth. At night it was generally out on top and active, but in the day time it was usually underneath the soil. It would always dig in backwards, making good use of the horny processes or spades on the hind feet. It was surprising how quickly it could burrow out of sight.

"On the night of October 12 it sang a few times without being disturbed. . . . It would usually sing or squawk when tickled on the throat or breast.

"This specimen dug in on October 13 and stayed in so far as we could tell, until dug out by us on October 21. It dug in on October 21, on which date it ate an earthworm. On October 27, in order to make an experiment upon its hibernation, it was placed out of doors, but unfortunately it escaped the first night and was not seen again."

AFFINITIES

Holbrook's "General Remarks" (1842, p. 111) are: "This animal is perhaps somewhat allied to the Ceratophris of South America, which has teeth, the posterior extremities short, and the hind feet furnished with a movable unarmed tubercle. The *Rana cultripes* of Cuvier (Regne Animale Tom. II, p. 105) would seem to be furnished with a process more nearly resembling that of our animal.

"The animals of the family Ranoidea delight in the sun, and may at all times be seen sitting half emersed in water, even when his days are the most intense. They are all diurnal, or seek their food in the day time, with one exception only, the *Scaphiopus solitarius*, which passes its days in holes prepared by itself, and feeds on such insects as may unwarily enter its dwelling." Harlan (1835, p. 106) notes its likeness to *Rana cultripes* Cuvier. Dumeril and Bibron, 1841, recognize its relation to *Pelobates cultripes* in their arrangement. DeKay (1842, p. 66) holds that "With the teeth of a frog and parotid glands of a toad, its natural place is between these two genera."

LeConte (1855, pp. 429, 430) writes "This curious animal so much resembling a frog in its maxillary and palatine teeth, and a toad in its parotids, the form of its body and its subterranean life, gives a fair example of some of our systematic arrangements. It has been placed by M. Dumeril among the frogs, of the genus *Bufo*. The flat spur, as it has been called, at the root of the first toe on the internal margin of metatarsus, is nothing more than a much developed form of a scale or a disk occupying the same situation in most animals of this family."

In 1855 Baird describes *Scaphiopus couchii* and in 1859 *Scaphiopus hammondii*. In 1882 Boulenger places *Scaphiopus holbrookii*, *Scaphiopus couchii* and *Scaphiopus rectifrens* in the same portion of the key under "Derm of head involved in cranial ossification" as opposed to "Derm of head free from dermal ossification" in which group he places *Scaphiopus hammondii*. The latter in 1866 Cope placed in *Spea* on the character Boulenger employs above. In 1889 Cope still retained *Spea* for *S. hammondii* and *S. multiplicata*.

BIBLIOGRAPHY

1868   Abbott, C. C. Catalogue of the Vertebrate Animals of New Jersey. Appendix E. in Geology of New Jersey by George H. Cook, p. 804.

1884   ———. Recent Studies of the Spade-foot Toad. The American Naturalist, Vol. XVIII, No. 11, Nov. 1884, pp. 1075-1080.

1904   Abbott, C. C. One Explanation of Reported Showers of Toads. Proc. Am. Phil. Soc. Jan.-Dec. 1904, April 8, 1904, Vol. 43, pp. 163-164.

1868   Allen, J. A. Catalogue of the Reptiles and Batrachians found in the Vicinity of Springfield, Mass., with notices of all the other species known to inhabit the State. Proc. Bost. Soc. Nat. Hist., Dec. 2, 1868, Vol. XII, pp. 171-204.

1882   Boulenger, G. A. Catalogue of the Batrachia *S. ecaudata*. British Museum 1882, pp. 433, 434.

1899   Boulenger, G. A. On the American Spade-foot (*Scaphiopus solitarius* Holbrook) Proc. Zool. Soc. London June 20, 1899, pp. 790-793.

1896   Brimley, C. S. Batrachia found at Raleigh, N. C. American Naturalist, Vol. 30, June, 1896, p. 501.

1907   ———. A Key to the Species of Frogs and Toads Liable to Occur in North Carolina. Journ. Elisha Mitchell Scientific Society, Vol. XXIII, Dec. 1907, p. 157.

1926   ———. Revised Key and List of the Amphibians and Reptiles of North Carolina. Journ. Elisha Mitchell Sci. Soc., Vol. 42, Nos. 1 & 2, Oct. 1926, p. 80.

1889   Cope, E. D. The Batrachia of North America. Bull. No. 34, U. S. Nat. Mus., pp. 298-301.

1908   Davis, W. T. Notes on New Jersey Amphibians and Reptiles. Proc. Staten Id. Assoc. Arts and Sciences, Feb.-May 1908, Vol. II, Part II, pp. 48, 49.

1920   Deckert, R. T. Amphibian Notes from Dade Co., Florida. Copeia, Mar. 15, 1921, No. 92, p. 22.

1922   ———. Notes on Dade County *Salientia*. Copeia, November 1922, No. 112, p. 88,

1905   Ditmars, R. L. The Batrachians of the Vicinity of New York City. The Amer. Mus. Journal, Vol. V, pp. 190-191. Photographs by Hubert Lang.

1841   Dumeril, A. M. C. and Bibron, G. Erpetologie Generale, Vol. VIII, p. 472.

1920   Fisher, G. Clyde. A Spadefoot in Summer. Copeia, Aug. 18, 1920, No. 85, pp. 76-78.

1907   Fowler, H. W. The Amphibians and Reptiles of New Jersey. Rept. N. J. State Museum, 1906, Trenton, pp. 92-97.

1918   ———. The Spade-foot Toad in Virginia. Copeia, March 19, 1918, No. 55, p. 44.

1858   Gunther, A. Catalogue of the Batrachia Salientia. London, 1858, p. 38.

1888   Hargitt, C. W. Recent Notes on Scaphiopus holbrookii. Amer. Naturalist, June 1888, No. 258, Vol. 22, pp. 535-537.

1835   Harlan, R. Medical and Physical Researches, Phila. 1835, pp. 105-106.

1902   Hay, W. P. A List of the Batrachians and Reptiles of the District of Columbia and Vicinity. Proc. Biol. Soc. Wash., June 20, 1902, Vol. XV, p. 128.

1842   Holbrook, J. E. North American Herpetology, 2nd edition, Vol. IV, 1842, pp. 109-111.

1849   ———, In George White's Statistics of the State of Georgia. Savannah, Appendix, p. 15.

1856   Le Conte, John. Descriptive Catalogue of the Ranina of the United States. Proc. Acad. Nat. Sci. Phila., Dec. 1855, Vol. VII, pp. 429, 430.

1852   Nichols, Andrew. Occurrence of *Scaphiopus solitarius*, in Essex County, with Some Notices of its History, Habits, etc. Read June 17, 1843, Journ. Essex County Nat. Hist. Soc., No. 3, 1852, pp. 113-117.

1917   Nichols, J. T. Spade-foot Toad at Mastic, Long Island. Copeia, June 24, 1917, No. 45, pp. 59, 60.

1927   Ortenburger, A. I. A List of the Reptiles and Amphibians from the Oklahoma Panhandle. Copeia, April-June, 1927, No. 163, p. 46.

1914   Overton, Frank. Long Island Fauna and Flora III. The Frogs and Toads. Mus. Brooklyn Inst. Arts and Sciences, Science Bulletin Vol. II, No. 3, Nov. 3, 1914, pp. 28-30.

1915   ———. Annual Occurrence of Spade-foot Toads. Copeia, July 27, 1915, No. 20, p. 17.

1915   ———. Late-Breeding Spade-foot Toads, etc. Copeia, November 18, 1915, No. 24, pp. 52, 53.

1886   Pike, Nicholas. Notes on the Hermit Spadefoot—. Bull. Am. Mus. Nat. Hist., Vol. 1, 1881-1886. Bull. No. 7, Art. XIV, July 1886, pp. 213-220.

1865   Putnam, F. W. Some Statements Concerning the Frogs and Toads found about Cambridge, Mass. Proc. Bost. Soc. Nat. Hist., Vol. 2, (1862, 1863) 1865, pp. 229-230.

1898   Sherwood, Wm. L. The Frogs and Toads Found in the Vicinity of New York City. Proc. Linn. Soc. of New York, 1897, 1898, No. 10. Read Apr. 13, 1897, pp. 17, 18.

1879   Smith, F. S. The Spade-foot Toad in New Haven, Conn. American Naturalist, Oct. 1879, Vol. XIII, No. 10, pp. 651, 652.

1923   Van Hyning, T. A Collecting Note on Florida Batrachians. Copeia, May 20, 1923, No. 118, p. 68.

1920   Wright, A. H. Frogs: Their Natural History and Utilization. U. S. Bur. Fisheries, Appendix VI, Doc. 888, 1920, p. 22, 27.

1923a   ———. The tadpoles of the frogs of Okefinokee Swamp, Georgia. The Anatomical Record, Jan. 20, 1923, Vol. 24, No. 6, p. 406.

1923b   ———. The Salientia of the Okefinokee Swamp. Copeia, Feb. 1, 1923, No. 115, p. 34.

1926   ———. The Vertebrate Life of Okefinokee Swamp in Relation to the Atlantic Coastal Plain. Ecology VII, No. 1, January 1926, p. 83.

1924   Wright, A. H. and A. A. Wright. A Key to the Eggs of the Salientia East of the Mississippi River. The American Naturalist, Vol. LVIII, July-August 1924, p. 379.

Bufo quercicus Holbrook

(Pl. I, Fig. 5; V, Fig. 7; VIII, Fig. 2; X, Fig. 13; XV, Fig. 12; XVII; XX; XXI; XXII, Fig. 7, Text Fig. I, 4)

COMMON NAMES

Oak Toad. Dwarf Toad. Oak Frog.

RANGE

Check list. Type locality: Charleston, South Carolina and Smithville, North Carolina (Löding says this is now Southport).

Range. North Carolina to Alabama and Florida—Stejneger and Barbour 1923, p. 26.

Supplementary records. Since 1923 it has been recorded in Mississippi and Louisiana. In 1922 H. P. Löding (p. 17) records these "Alabama records: Mobile and Baldwin Counties." In 1923 Viosca (p. 37) records it in Southeastern Louisiana. In 1924 (p. 59) G. S. Myers takes it in Wilmington, N. C. The same year Schmidt (1924, p. 68) has it from Mt. Pleasant, S. C. The same gentleman took it at Natural Well, Magnolia, N. C., on July 10, 1915. In 1926 (p. 80) C. S. Brimley gives it as an inhabitant of Craven, Carteret, Duplin, Edgecombe, Lenoir and New Hanover Counties, N. C.

In 1908 (p. 19) Brimley held "Dwarf Toad (*Bufo quercicus*) "to be in the Lower Austral Zone.   In 1926 (p. 82) Wright held "*Bufo quercicus* N. C.— Fla.—Ala." to be one of the eleven species of frogs of the Okefinokee region which might be held to be in the Sabalian Zone or region.   The same year 1926 Percy Viosca Jr., in species of "Group I, Species Common to the Atlantic and East Gulf Coastal Plains" writes "Excepting where governed by strictly local ecological conditions, we can consider it axiomatic that species found on the Atlantic Coastal Plain occur at least as far west as the Florida parishes of Louisiana, an area lying in the extreme Southeastern corner of the East Gulf Coastal Plain.   My own observations have already extended westward the known range of a number of species, the following of which can be included in Group I: *Bufo quercicus, Hyla gratiosa, Abastor erythrogrammus, Leimadophis flavilatus* and *Tantilla coronata*.   Those which have not previously been recorded as far west as Louisiana, I have taken in St. Tammany or Washington Parishes."

Local Okefinokee records.   In 1912 we wrote of it as follows: Twenty-four specimens were taken in 1912, sixteen May 28, 1912, on the trip into the swamp, three from May 3–June 2, two June 6, and three June 24.   They were secured on Billy's Island, Honey Island and at Mixon's Ferry.   Their occurrence in Okefinokee comes well within their range.   There is no definite place given for the Georgia records which LeConte (Cope '89, p. 292) made in 1855.   This species seems most common in Florida, where Brimley ('11, p. 11) added four stations to Cope's three records for the State and Miss Dickerson ('07, p. 105) has it from Ozona, Fla.   It reaches its northern limit in North Carolina.

In 1921 we took it on every island visited (Billy's, Floyd's, Honey, Black Jack, Jones, Middle, Chesser and others); in the country surrounding the swamp, such as The Pocket, from Hopkins to Waycross, from Folkston to Waycross, along the Suwanee River to Fargo and along the St. Mary's River from Moniac to Camp Pinckney (in 1922 from Camp Pinckney to St. Mary's at its mouth).   It is a very abundant and universally distributed species.

GENERAL APPEARANCE

Holbrook (1842, Vol. V, p. 13), its describer, gives its characters as follows: "Head short; snout pointed; superciliary arches slightly elevated; body short, very flat, rounded at the flanks, above dusky, with a yellowish vertebral line, on each side of which are black blotches; abdomen silvery-gray; throat dusky; groins tinged with yellow."   DeKay (1842, Vol. III, p. 68) speaks of this extra-limited species as "very small."   Cope (1889, p. 292) speaks of it as "the smallest known species of the genus Bufo."

C. S. Brimley (Dec. 1907, p. 157) has it as "Size small, length of head and body one inch.   Skin very rough.   Bony ridges turning inward almost at right angles just back of the eyes."   In 1926 (p. 80) he characterizes it as follows: "Size small, length of adult only 1 1/4 inches, a white line down middle of the back, skin very rough especially on legs."   Cope (1889, p. 261) thought "One smaller metatarsal tubercle; superciliary crests incurved posteriorly so as to be transverse; a supratympanic crest; parotoid gland descending on sides to inferior part of the tympanum,"—the diagnostic characters of *Bufo quercicus*. Miss Dickerson (1906, p. 45) emphasizes the "Cranial crests, inconspicuous; skin very tubercular, spinous on legs and arms; size small (1 1/4 inches)." Both LeConte and Loennberg and others have found that the superciliary crests can be straight at times.

The identifications of the oak toads in the past have emphasized their smallness, their scarcity in most collections, the paucity of good accounts of them, and other factors. For example, it is not surprising to find a young *Scaphiopus holbrookii* identified as *Bufo quercicus* or the young of other *Bufo* species thus termed. We have seen as many as ten different accessions in collections of earlier years dubbed "Juvenile," "Young," "Half-grown" when in almost every instance they were full grown males and females externally apparent as such. The collectors did not distinguish them as oak toads nor were they used to seeing the species.

COLORATION OF SPIRIT SPECIMENS (1912)

Coloration.—Upper parts greyish through light to dark brown or almost blackish. From the tip of the snout to the vent runs a sharply defined white or yellowish white line and even in the darkest-colored individuals. In the series of comparable small southern toads this vertebral color is absent or if present, is irregular and primarily along the middle third of the back. There are 5 or 6 pairs of black spots along this line. Usually from the nostrils of either side there extends backward a black or brownish bar which makes a right angle turn to the front of the eyelid; the second pair begins on the posterior part of the eyelid and extend rather obliquely to the vertebral line and along it inside of the supraorbital crest to its end. These two pairs of black or brown spots produce on the head a cross of intervening white color one bar being the median longitudical vertebral line and the other a transverse line from the middle of one eyelid to the other eyelid. Sometimes just inside the anterior end of the parotoid and somewhat away from the vertebral line is a pin point of a spot comparable to the same one in *B. terrestris* and *B. fowleri*. On a line with the posterior ends of the parotoid are two other large prominent spots which may be longitudinal or oblique in relation to the median line. Halfway between the posterior ends of the parotoids and the vent is another pair of spots and just ahead of the vent a sixth pair. This sixth pair may be absent at times as are the 3rd pair. In some of the lighter colored specimens from the posterior end of the parotoid there leads backward along either side a prominent black band bordered above by an almost equally wide white band. Also from the front part of the parotoid a dark bar leads downward to the arm insertion. All of these spots and the whole dorsal coloration pattern is very suggestive of the detailed color description of *Bufo fowleri* (Dickerson, '01, p. 94) and of some of our *B. terrestris* already described, but if these specimens be compared with *B. terrestris* representatives of the same size, the latter have the spots more irregular, usually more or less obscured by reddish brown tipped warts, smaller spots back of the posterior ends of the parotoids. The fourth pair of spots of *B. quercicus* have their counterparts in *B. terrestris* in two pairs of spots, the anterior pair pin-head spots which usually meet and fuse across the middle line.

The underparts are grey or greyish-white *spotted* or unspotted. Most of our specimens fall in the former group. Possibly Florida specimens (like our St. Petersburg material) may be unspotted but all of our specimens but two are more or less spotted and we have from Natural Wells, Magnolia, N. C., a specimen collected by Mr. Karl P. Schmidt, which is spotted and even darker beneath than our Okefinokee forms. In some the spotting is very faint on the breast and pectoral region. In others it occupies much of the upper belly and one has all the underparts dark except the very wrinkled oval patch on the buttocks which is pure white or yellowish-white. Usually when dark enters the ventral coloration the throat is darkest. Most of these specimens have the palm and sole dark but not all of them, and our young southern toads have these parts white in the main except in a few which are dark colored.

STRUCTURAL CHARACTERS (WRITTEN IN 1912)

Structural characters.—In the structural characters we have our best distinctions between the oak toads and immature southern toads. The throat pouch or vocal sac of the male is distinctive but sexual characters are tantalizing key distinctions unless given for both sexes. In the cranial crests these differ from *Bufo terrestris* at the same size. In *Bufo terrestris* there are no crests or the supraorbital crest is very faintly outlined. In *B. terrestris* these ridges decidedly bend inwards at the posterior ends and the interval between these two converging ends is contained 2.5–3.0 times in the length of the crest to the nostril while in *B. quercicus* the ends are divergent or very slightly convergent and the interval is contained in the crest to the nostril 1.5–2.0 times. Whenever the crests show in these 20–35 mm. southern toads the posterior end of the continuous supraorbital crest is invariably beyond the inner posterior-dorsal angle of the upper eyelid and opposite or behind the anterior end of the parotoid while in *B. quercicus* adults 20–30 mm. it ends ahead of the anterior end of the parotoid and frequently stops at the above mentioned angle. Behind this angle it frequently extends as a series of interrupted raised warts. In none of the southern toads are the posterior supraorbital crest ends connected across the middle line by a ridge, or series of warts, but is always open while in the oak toads there is always a transverse series of raised warts which give the cranial hollow a parapet behind as well as on either side. In very warty specimens the other crests loose the distinctiveness and only this parapet of three sides shows. In southern toads 20–35 mm. there are no postocular and supratympanic crests at all. In oak toads the postocular ridge is never continuous with the supraorbital crest and the gap is bridged by a series of warts. The supratympanic crest from the postocular to parotoid is very prominent and very broad in *B. quercicus* while in small *B. terrestris* (20–35 mm.) it is absent and in 50–70 mm. adults it is always a smooth edged horny ridge not with numerous warty tubercles on it.

PLATE XX

Oak toad (*Bufo quercicus*)

1. *Ilex myrtifolia—Bufo quercicus* pond, about four miles E. N. E. of Chesser Id., Ga. July 15, 1922.
2. Male croaking, Billy Id., Ga. July 3, 1921. Flashlight.
3. Male croaking, Billy Id. Ga. May 26, 1921. Flashlight.
4. 5. Male croaking, Billy Id., Ga. June 4, 1921. Flashlights.
6. *Bufo quercicus* on sand, Honey Id., Ga. July 3, 1921.
7. Egg string, attached to leaf blade, Coat-bet pond, Chesser Id., Ga. July 17, 1921.

1

2

3

4

5

6

7

The parotoids of the oak toad are finely spinose while those of a small southern toad are no more than tuberculate at the most; the parotoids of the former are relatively shorter their width 1.25–1.5, usually 1.5 times in the parotoid's length, while in the latter the parotoids are more elongate, 1.8–2.0, usually 2.0 in their length. The posterior ends of the parotoids of *B. quercicus* are far more divergent than those of *B. terrestris*, i.e., set more obliquely to the vertebral line. The parotoids of *B. quercicus* in many send a downward portion to the lower level of the tympanum while in these young *B. terrestris*, as in adults, the lower edge of the parotoid, is little if any below the upper border of the tympanum. The tympanum is in contrast with the postorbital ridge. Upper parts including upper eyelids rugose, on the fore-limbs and sometimes on the tarsus, spinose; symphyseal tubercle as in young southern toads; underparts granulate in young and females, rugose often in the larger males; first finger shorter than second and about equal to the 4th; outer metacarpal tubercle quite large, inner tubercle small; subarticular tubercles often in a double series, the tubercle at the base of each finger transverse or double in nature and as wide as finger tips; the other sole tubercles and subarticular ones are circular. Outer metatarsal tubercle small; inner tubercle large and brown-tipped; plantar tubercles relatively smaller than the palmar tubercles.

In all except six of the 24 specimens the tongue is small, narrow, elongate and elliptical with the posterior third or half free. In one it is as broad as long; in four quite broad and much shorter and in one specimen the front half is broad and the free half narrow.

MEASUREMENTS
(1912–1914)

The measurements of 8 adults are as follows: In length they are 21–30 mm., average 25.3 mm., the head including the tympanum is 7–9 mm., average 8 mm., *usually* 3 sometimes 3.5 times in the length of the body, or head measured to rictus oris is 4–4.6 in the length, or the head measured to posterior end of the supraorbital crest is 3.3–4.3 in the length; width of the head 7–10.5 mm., average 9 mm., usually 1.1 times greater than the length of the head, equal to the femur and tibia; snout 2.75–4 mm., average 3.3 mm., less than the eye which is 3.5–4 mm., average 3.5 mm. while in small *B. terrestris* of the same size usually the two are equal; tympanum indistinct, 1.25–2 mm., average 1.65 mm., much less than the interorbital distance or eyelid; interorbital distance 2.25–3.5 mm., average 3 mm., usually greater than the upper eyelid which is 2–3 mm., average 2.5 mm.; femur from 6.5–10.75 mm., average 9.35 mm., *slightly more than tibia* which is 7.5–10 mm., average 8.8 mm., femur slightly more than foot without tarsus; tarsus 4.5–6.75 mm., average 5.75 mm.; rest of foot 6–9.75 mm., average 8.3 mm., equal to or slightly less than the tibia; anterior limb from axilla 9–16 mm., average 12.2 mm.; posterior limb from groin 18–29 mm., average 22 mm. or forward on body to posterior part of the posterior part of the parotoid or to the arm insertion.

In all these measurements we compared these *B. quercicus* specimens with about 40 *B. terrestris* of the same size and season of capture, and must confess we could find no constant relative measurement of the above categories to set one apart from the other. It seems that usually the breadth of these oak toads in the length is 1.5–2.0 while with almost all of the small southern toads of the same size the ratio is 2.0 or more, but this is not always absolute.

(Recent Material)

Head to angle of mouth 1.6 (20 mm. ♂)—1.6 (28 mm. ♀)—1.5 (28 mm. ♂) in width of head; head to rear of tympanum 1.14—1.07—1.24 in width of head; head to angle of mouth 4.0—4.66—4.0 in length of body; head to rear of tympanum 2.85—3.1—3.3 in length of body; snout .71—.75—.75 in first finger; snout 1.0—1.0—.75 in fourth finger; snout .43—.37—.37 in first toe; eye 1.4—1.33—1.14 in snout; eye .4—.66—.57 in tympanum; eye 1.0—1.0— .87 in first finger; tympanum 7.5—4.0—4.25 in intertympanic width; tympanum 3.5—2.0—2.0 in snout; internasal width 1.33—1.0—10. in upper eyelid width; interorbital width 1.0—.83—.71 in upper eyelid width; interorbital width .75—.83—.71 in internasal width; interorbital width 3.75—2.66 —2.4 in intertympanic width;

Forelimb: Forelimb 2.0—2.0—1.93 in length of body; forelimb 1.9—1.85 —1.8 in hind limb; first finger 2.2—1.66—1.66 in third finger; second finger 1.83—1.4—1.66 in third finger; second finger .83—.86—1.0 in first finger; third finger .45—.70—.70 in second toe; fourth finger 1.6—1.25—1.66 in third finger; fourth finger .43—.375—.5 in first toe; internasal width 1.66 —1.2—1.2 in first finger; internasal width 2.0—1.4—1.2 in second finger; internasal width 3.66—2.0—2.0 in third finger; internasal width 2.33—1.6 —12. in fourth finger.

Hindlimb: length .95—.92—.92 in hind limb; tibia 2.87—2.66—2.8 in length; tibia 2.7—2.5—2.6 in hind limb; tibia 1.42—1.33—1.45 in forelimb; tibia .91—.95—1.0 in hind foot; first toe 1.66—2.33—2.33 in second toe; first toe 3.0—4.0—3.33 in third toe; first toe 4.0—6.0—6.0 in fourth toe; first toe 2.66—3.33—3.0 in fifth toe; second toe 1.8—1.7—1.43 in third toe; second toe 2.4—2.55—2.1 in fourth toe; second toe 1.6—1.4—1.3 in fifth toe; third toe 1.33—1.5—1.4 in fourth toe; third toe .9—.83—.9 in fifth toe; fourth toe 1.08—1.1—1.33 in hind foot; fourth toe 1.16—1.17—1.33 in tibia; fourth toe 1.66—1.56—1.9 in forelimb; fifth toe 1.5—1.8—1.7 in fourth toe; internasal width 1.0—.60—.60 in first toe; internasal width 1.66—1.4—1.4 in second toe; internasal width 3.0—2.4—2.0 in third toe; internasal width 4.0—3.6—3.0 in fourth toe; internasal width 2.66—2.0—1.8 in fifth toe.

HABITAT

Holbrook (1842, p. 14) found that "This beautiful little species of toad is mostly found about sandy places that are covered with a small species of oak which springs up so abundantly where pine forests have been destroyed; whence it is commonly enough called Oak Frog, which specific name I have preferred". At this time he limited it to South Carolina and North Carolina but in 1849 (Appendix, p. 15) he gives "*Bufo quercicus*—Oak Frog" as one of the Batrachia of Georgia.

LeConte (1855, p. 430) held it to be "Very common in Georgia in wet places, under logs and pieces of wood".

Loennberg (1895, p. 338) in 1892 and 1893 found it "very abundant on the dry sand hills about Oakland, Orange County, as well as in the 'flatwood' about Kissimee, Osceola County and in Hillsboro County".

Brimley (1909, p. 133) of Lake Ellis region had "About a half dozen taken in drier situations in May 1908 (also taken by Sherman on Shackleford's Banks, near Beaufort, N. C. in June 1901.)" The same author (1910, p. 11) "received (it) from Hastings, Orlando, Green Cove Springs and St. Petersburg, all in Florida. Evidently common at the first and last two places".

Ten miles south of Jacksonville, Florida, in 1911 and 1912 R. L. Deckert makes the observation that "*Bufo quercicus* Holbrook (is) common, in companies in temporary water, or scattered on cultivated ground".

In Alabama Löding (1922, p. 17) writes "In Mobile County this little toad is rather common in high sandy locations with Scrub Oak and Palmetto undergrowth".

In Louisiana in 1923 (p. 37) Viosca places this species in his "Division 4, Longleaf Pine Flats" of "The Uplands". This Division he characterizes as follows: "Abruptly bordering the pine hills on the south, lies this strip of flat lands characterized by a beautiful stand of longleaf pine interspersed with loblolly. The streams here, because of the lower elevation, are normally sluggish and often spread out over low areas forming swampy situations. These are characterized by swamp magnolia in the shallower areas and tupelo in the more permanent swamps.—Typically the country is north Floridian, rather than Louisianian, and several Southeastern species, not found elsewhere in our State, have congenial habitats here. *Bufo quercicus*, *Bufo terrestris* and *Hyla gratiosa* are significant examples".

In 1912 we wrote of their habitat somewhat as follows: "This little toad was found on the outskirts of the swamp in the cut-over lands where few pines remain and where the cover was solely low heaths. Here at noon when we arrived these creatures were hopping about little mindful of the sun. On Honey Island we took them on the sandy soil where the pines were abundant and on Billy's Island they occurred on the unshaded cleared cultivated fields of the Lee's. They seemed to have no particular preference for shade or exposure and apparently were quite generally distributed. The few specimens in our collection are not due to their scarcity so much as to our neglect. One might think them quite terrestrial from their spinose exterior but not only on the drier and higher outskirts did we find them but also on the islands and near their swampy edges. In fact, we even recorded some on the little islets of Honey Island Prairie."

After our 1921 and 1922 studies we think of this form as an essentially abundant pine barrens species though occurring in hammocks and elsewhere.

FIRST APPEARANCE

In 1912 we found them when we entered the swamp the last week in May. In 1921 we record them as early as April 25 when we entered the region and in 1922 we arrived June 13-14 when they were out in full force. Some of the U. S. National Museum material was taken in April, such as:

U.S.N.M., Nos. 29056-64, Apr. 3, 1901, adults, L. Kissimee, Fla., E. A. Mearns.

U.S.N.M., Nos. 49580-81, Apr. 16, 1912, Autaugaville, Ala.

U.S.N.M., No. 46147, Apr. 20, 1892, Mobile Bay, Ala., R. J. Thompson.

U.S.N.M., No. 46090, Apr. 23, 1892, Bay St. Louis, Miss., Mr. V. Bailey.

One record is for March, 1912, made by N. R. Wood at Auburndale, Fla., (U.S.N.M. Nos. 48771-76).

GENERAL HABITS

Variation in color. Holbrook (1842, pp. 13, 14) characterizes this species as follows:

"The head above is dusky, with a yellowish central longitudinal line; the superciliary ridges are grey, with a white mark in the centre; on each side of this longitudinal line is an oblong spot, extending from it to include most of the posterior part of the orbit of the eye; a small part only of the orbit in front of this is light coloured; the upper jaw is light brown.

"The back of the animal is dusky-brown, with a vertebral line of pale yellow, marked with a few scattered small warts of reddish-brown colour; on each side of this line are irregular black blotches, with here and there a slight tinge of reddish-brown; the back is covered with innumerable warts and granulations, of variable size and colour, generally black, but the smaller ones of dusky-red; on each flank, and extending from the axilla downwards towards the posterior extremity, is an oblong black blotch, bounded with white both above and below.

"The throat is dusky; the abdomen is silvery-grey, yellowish at the groins, and with a pale tinge of yellow around vent. The anterior extremities, as well as the posterior, are dusky-brown above, marked with black transverse bars or spots; their inferior surface is coloured like the abdomen, except the fingers and toes, which are reddish-brown".

For coloration of our 1912 material see topic Coloration in Spirits (1912), also the topic Mating—Colour—Male and Female. They may be any shade of grey, brown or reddish-brown or even be almost black. Loennberg noticed that some of his material from Hillsboro County were redder. Apparently his other material was grey or light brown. LeConte speaks of it as "dusky with a few irregular black spots, many of the warts, particularly those on the sides whitish or reddish; a very distinct line of one of these colours runs from the point of the nose along the vertebral column to the vent. Beneath the body is granulate, white, more or less varied, particularly on the fore part with black". Cope with his mistakes on this species we do not quote. Miss Dickerson (1906, p. 104) gives a good colour description and accompanying plate of the species. This species if it wishes can be as variable as *Bufo terrestris* or *Bufo americanus*.

General habits. Holbrook (1842, p. 14) held "it spends most of its time in concealment under fallen leaves, or partially buried in the sand, from which it is washed out by heavy rains".

Loennberg (1895, p. 338) says "This is a very active little animal considering the fact that it is a toad. It is seen in all kinds of places and at all times of the day, even in the brightest sunshine, but especially after rain".

VOICE

During the breeding season according to Holbrook (1842, Vol. V, p. 14) "the male (has) a slight chirp, not unlike some kinds of insects". To Deckert (1914b, p. 2) "its cry resembles that of a small chick, very loud and shrill, and may be heard at any time of day or night, sometimes from absolutely dry and dusky fields and roadsides, where these tiny toads hop about in the glaring sunshine, living on the smallest of insects. The full chorus, which is ear splitting, is, however, heard only at night, after heavy rains".

Miss Dickerson (1906, pp. 19, 21, 105, 106) speaks of *Bufo quercicus* thus: "Vocal bladders inflated from the middle of the throat are to be found in *Bufo cognatus*, *Bufo compactilis* and *Bufo quercicus*". "*Bufo quercicus* would seem to be expressing most active distress in its tones like those of a lost chicken". "They are difficult to see, but give notice of high-pitched sounds. The individual call is like that of a young chicken in distress, but considerably louder. The male alone gives the call, and while producing it seems to have in his mouth a transparent bladdder about the size of a man's thumb. The fact is that this toad has a large vocal bladder that can be extended from the mid-line to the lower throat region. This structure relates it to *Bufo compactilis* and *Bufo cognatus* of the Southwest. When taken in the hand, the Oak Toad gives a rather musical chirping sound, like that of a young bird".

The first day we recorded its calling in 1921 comes May 16. Then one of the lads brought in an oak toad he had taken on the edge of a cypress pond. A little later Mr. Harper "went off in the piney woods. He came back and reported one of the biggest queries he has yet encountered. He said he didn't know whether the caller was a bird, or beast, or whether it might be young bobwhites, queer, brownheaded nuthatches or some other bird? A rain came up and not until he was just ready to leave did he solve the note. It was that of *Bufo quercicus*. It seemed so unfroglike or untoadlike a call to him".

His journal note is as follows: "A baffling, peeping in several parts of the piney woods. Some strange *Hyla*, bobwhite or something althogether different? Nearly desperate over these peepings here and there in the piney woods, always stopping when I came close.—Scarcely know whether to look in trees or on the ground. Finally one peeped in a fairly open, burnt over space, and by hearing it from several directions at close range, I hit upon the spot pretty closely. Then getting on my knees I had scarcely gone a yard, when a little black toad, with a thin, golden-yellow stripe down its back, made a little movement among the grass and saw palmetto. *Bufo quercicus!* And meanwhile other peepings continue at intervals in the other parts of the piney woods; *pheep, pheep, pheep, pheep, pheep, pheep, pheep, pheep, pheep, pheep, pheep*,—a plaintive (rather shrill) high-pitched piping.

"When I 'froze' for several minutes, it quit 'freezing' on its part, and made a few leisurely forward movements, crawling with one leg at a time, lizard-like, with body off the ground. It made hops of a couple of inches or so only when I poked a straw at it. Meanwhile little loose fold of skin in the middle of its throat vibrates. Once in a while it seems to nab an insect.

"A cloudy, lowering, humid day, following a day and night of rain.—Finally it made off of its own volition,—hops of two inches or so, though it still mainly crawled. It was interested in ants running around near it, turning its body to watch them and finally thrusting out its tongue to lick one up—".

The afternoon of this day, according to my own journal, we "went out to Crosby Pond.—Where the road crossed a swale we heard a queer note and approached it from several angles. We found its author near the base of a stump in amongst saw palmetto, gallberry (*Ilex glabra*) and *Gaylussacia*. The oak toad male was calling before we approached. We got within ten feet. He piped only lowly. After we had worked him around for a photo for some time, he suddenly to our surprise backed into a hole at the base of a saw palmetto. The hole was 3/4 of an inch in diameter and not deep. Once when one of us made a pass at a fly the toad ducked farther into its hole. Its note is surely very birdlike. One will hear three or four calls like a piping chicken. Sometimes the notes are repeated three or four times. Then process repeated after a very short interval. There may be three or four groups of calling for one individual. There were several animals around. Once the note was likened to that of a swallowtailed kite. Truly the most unfroglike note I ever heard. It is very high pitched and some times sounds like some animal in distress. There are several calling in the piney woods. One calling from a tangle of chokeberries (*Aronia*), *Osmunda cinnamonea*, *Bamboo brier* (*Smilax*) and sweet bays. Couldn't find it. Are the toads moving pondward? Later in the evening we heard none". The next day the author visited this toad's burrow. When we ran a straw into it only a queer spider ran out. The toad had left.

In 1912 and in 1921 some of the residents both normally and almost invariably accurate assured me that the blacksnake had a whistle and that this note of the oak toad was the call in question. They readily acquiesced in our determination of it as that of *Bufo quercicus*.

On June 4, 1921, while the author was studying eggs Mr. Harper made the following field notes on peeping and intervals in *Bufo quercicus*. In the afternoon are the following: "Number of peeps during a calling period are about 25, 16, 13, 32, 37, 35, 32, 24 and 27 (for one observation). Only a few brief seconds between periods. One interval of 3 seconds; then records of about 35 peeps in 20 seconds, 16 calls in 8 seconds; 18 calls in 10 seconds; 30 calls in 15 seconds; 32 calls in 16 seconds; 29 calls in 14 seconds". "In the evening they were slower—perhaps exhausted with 4 to 5 hours of continual calling. 10 calls in 26 seconds; 22 in 16 seconds; 20 in 13 seconds; 22 in 17 seconds".

In inflation of the throat they are like *Bufo compactilis*, *Bufo cognatus*. The lower throat is the principal part involved in the process. The lower part of the throat is thrown out into an elliptical bag or sausagelike balloon. One can tell when a toad is going to thrill after a rest. The body will inflate to a large size and then the most ludricous sac projects out in the throat region. The tip of the sac when not really inflated comes close to the tip of the chin. Otherwise it appears as a little loose vibrating sac 1/2 inch out from the lower part of the throat. When deflated the body inflates. When body is compressed or deflated the sac inflates.

Its call may carry 1/8 of a mile or more. When this species is in chorus it is one of the most deafening ear deadeners I have encountered when in their midst. We often employed the method of varying the closure of our ears to pick out various notes and cut out other dominant notes. For example, Mr. Harper's note of a chorus 8:30—10:00 P. M., July 16 illustrates it *"Bufo quercicus*, abundant calling. All (*Hyla gratiosa, Chorophilus, Hyla femoralis, Bufo quercicus*) combined, enough to cave in our ear drums. By half closing ears we shut out the sound of *Hyla femoralis* almost entirely, and hear others, better than ever especially *Chorophilus, Bufo quercicus, Acris,* —".

The journal voice records for 1921 and 1922 are as follows:

1921

May 16. First heard to be recognized. Ventriloquial. Many heard.
May 17. Heard one or two more.
May 18. Heard sone *B. quercicus.*
May 21. After afternoon rain temperature 71° heard several oak toads.
May 22. Several heard noon-day sun. Only one heard near Oak Toad swale.
May 23. At 5:30 and 7:30 P.M. heard one near camp.
May 24. Hottest day yet, 94° at 3:00 P.M. Heard one, then later several.
May 26. Are *Bufo quercicus* bound for the ponds? Have taken and heard several. This afternoon when hottest an occasional *Bufo quercicus* spoke.
May 27. One calling 4:30 P.M.
May 28. One calling sundown.
June 1. Hear oak toads particularly near trestles. In cypress ponds hear occasional oak toads.
June 3. None calling this night.
June 4. Rained 2 inches or more. Here at congress. Heard plenty amongst saw palmetto. Lots croaking in the ponds.
June 5. Several calling during and after the shower. Few this evening.
June 6. No *B. quercicus* calling.
June 17. One heard.
June 20. One heard. From time to time we heard oak toads.
June 21. One heard.
June 22. Heard at 9:30 P.M. one oak toad.
June 23. In white quarters heard several croaking. Thunderstorm after evening began. *Bufo quercicus* calling.
June 25. Several heard 9:30 A.M. Hear none near camp.
June 26. One heard 6:30 P.M. Temperature 77°. Showery.
June 28. Rain in evening. Commonly calling.
June 29. Heard before and after thunderstorm.
June 30. Afternoon. Heard as I approached Billy's Island 6-6:30 oak toads in considerable numbers. Few calling near camp.
July 1. Few calling near camp.
July 3. Calling during and after rain. Numerous everywhere.
July 4. Evening at 9:00 P.M. 75° sultry. No *B. quercicus* calling.
July 5. One recorded in the evening and one in mid-afternoon.
July 6. One or two in afternoon after rain. Several calling in temporary pools.
July 15. One heard.
July 16. Abundantly calling at night.
July 19. 10:00 A.M., one heard.
July 23. Few *Bufo quercicus* calling.
July 24. One 12:30 P.M. (rain). Later calling commonly.
July 26. Quite a few calling at night.
July 29. Commonly heard in rain from Honey Island Prairie to The Pocket.
July 30. No end of oak toads calling. Rain in late afternoon.
July 31. Heard abundantly along the railroad in a good many places from Fargo to Moniac. Heard also practically every night along the St. Mary's—F. Harper.
Aug. 17. *Bufo quercicus* several heard at Camp Pinckney.

1922

June 13. Calling at 11:45 bright sun. Air about 94°.

June 15. Several calling on mainland.

June 19. Heard a few in woods after the rain of today.

June 21. One calling at 10:00 P.M.

June 22. Heard around camp a few calling.

June 23. Heard at R.R. ponds one mile south of Trader's Hill. Afternoon.

June 26. One calling. Cloudy weather. Cutover pine barrens. Several about Anna's Pond. Several on way to Folkston and back to camp.

June 27. One heard at 10:00 A.M. in cut pine barrens.

July 2. 8:30 P.M.—midnight. Heard a few. Some rain.

July 3. Last night to midnight or later in many places a deafening roar of *Bufo quercicus*. It began before dusk.

July 11. On the island heard oak toads everywhere at 5:00 P.M. after the rain. Temperature 70°.

July 12. Several calling this forenoon.

July 18. One or two heard at Murray Bay.

July 21. One or two heard in mid-forenoon. Showery.

July 25. Heard a few in mid-forenoon. Bright sun. Hear plenty calling west edge of woods at 9:00 in evening. Air 72°. Hard rain until 7:00 P.M.

July 26. Immense chorus on mainland and on Chesser Island. Tonight at midnight 75° big din.

Aug. 1. One calling mid-afternoon. Many heard at night.

Aug. 2. One or two heard at about 11:00 A.M.

Aug. 4. Several in pine barrens 8:00 P.M.

Aug. 5. Several heard tonight.

Aug. 8. No end of oak toads heard along old Okefinokee road 8:00-11:00 P.M. after rain. They are everywhere.

Aug. 9. Heard from 5:00 P.M. onwards at mainland and about camp. Common.

Aug. 10. Commonly heard near Petty Pond.

Aug. 11. Tonight 8:00-12:00 heard quite a few oak toads from Folkston to Chesser Island.

Aug. 13. St. Mary's Ga.,—Chesser Island. Strong Chorus 7:00-10:30 P.M.

Aug. 15. One or two late afternoon.

Aug. 16. Commonly calling in spade-foot ponds at night.

Aug. 17. On oak ridges near and around our camp never saw more oak toads. Some calling.

Aug. 20. One heard at daybreak. Temperature 72°.

In 1921 on the day of the record of calling the air minima of nearby stations (5 in all) were from 60°-70° in May, 61°-78° in June and 67°-73° in July or an average of 68°. Our camp records usually taken when we arose in the morning range from 64°-83° or average 73°.

In 1921 and 1922 when great congresses came, the following rain and temperature records for five nearby stations are as follows. The rain conditions at camp are in the last column.

1921

		Degrees	Degrees	
May 16	5.47 inches	81–83	66–67	Heavy rain
,, 21	3.13 ,,	79–80	66–67	Continual rain
June 3	4.04 inches	82–87	68–70	Sprinkles
,, 4	.70 ,,	83–88	64–71	Downpour
,, 5	.82 ,,	82–90	69–70	Shower
,, 30	3.37 ,,	81–89	66–67	Thunderstorm
July 3	4.25 ,,	86–91	70–72	Rain all P. M.
,, 16	1.16 ,,	85–87	70–72	Shower
,, 23	2.97 ,,			
,, 24	1.30 ,,	87–90	67–70	Rain
,, 29	4.66 ,,	73–84	70–72	Downpour
,, 30	1.74 ,,	85–95	71–72	

1922

July	2	5.31 inches	90–96	68–72	Heavy rain P.M.
”	11	1.16 ”	87–92	66–70	” ” ”
”	25	.73 ”	93–96	73–74	
”	26	T. ”	94	73–74	Rain P.M.
Aug.	8	3.64 ”	85–93	73–74	
”	9	.55 ”	81–93	71–73	Showers
”	10	1.24 ”	79–91	68–73	Sprinkles
”	11	.87 ”	85–91	65–69	
”	13	2.79 ”	87–91	68–73	Showers
”	16	2.05 ”	85–91	70–72	Rain most P.M.
”	17	4.53 ”	82–91	69–72	Cloudy

In 1921 in every instance rain came in nearby stations and at camp (one exception) when congresses came. The stations average .14–1.10 inches per station, the maxima range from 79°–95°, the minima 66°–72°. In 1922 rain came in every instance in nearby stations from 1 to 1.06 inches per station or always at camp (4 exceptions). The air maxima were 81°–96°, air minima 66°–74°.

With these subterranean animals, like the spade-foots, warm rains at least 0.5–1.0 inches or very humid conditions seem needful to start it calling vigorously. It may start at minima of 60°–67° but the minima of congresses are usually 66°–74°. Humidity is, however, the important factor.

MATING

Coloration (From life, June 8, 1921). Dorsal stripe white, pale orange yellow or maize yellow or sulphur yellow or cream buff. The dorsal spots are black. First pair between eyes usually not connected as in *Bufo terrestris*; spot in front of parotoid round one wart, not elliptic with two or more warts; spot between parotoids not connected, not a half moon made by connection; spots ahead of hump separate as in *B. terrestris*; spots ahead of vent prominent enough in oak toad but just two pin points. Upper parts with some gull gray or pearl gray or pale olive gray. Stripe from lower part of tympanum almost to groin in the above grays; also patch back of angle of mouth below tympanum also patch above arm insertion, in front of femur and back part of upper eyelid. All these lighter dorsal areas with burnt sienna colored tubercles which are especially prominent along either side of dorsal stripe from hump backward and on oblique lateral stripe, on posterior part of eyelid. The tubercles on black areas look black but many are really also burnt sienna. Parotoid with fine and thickly studded burnt sienna tubercles. Tubercles on palmar and solar surfaces, posterior surface of thighs (partially), groin (a little), pectoral region (a few tubercles) vinaceous rufous, Hay's russet or mars orange. Ventral parts smoke gray or grayish white or pale olive buff or even sometimes a cream color. Each tubercle stands out. On venter proper they are close together and black between, little apparent on the sides, tubercles wider apart and the intervening black more apparent. Same for underside of the limbs.

Iris cream color, rim around pupil and eye napthalene yellow; rest largely black with some cartridge buff or ivory yellow.

Male with lower throat between angles of mouth dark olive gray, more or less puffed out, pleated or wrinkled. All of throat darker than rest of ventral parts but lower half darker than mental part. Female with throat same as rest of venter. Slight dark spot in anterior posterior region.

Structural differences. Neither Holbrook nor LeConte indicated the sexual differences. Miss Dickerson was the first to indicate that the throat of the male is dusky. Deckert (1914b, No. 9, p. 2) says "The throat of the male is black, and when the pouch is distended, forms a small elongate bladder, slanting upward, and about 3/4 inch long and 1/4 inch in diameter".

In 1912 we made these notes on the males and females. "These four females are the lightest colored of the twenty-four, the upper parts being grayish-brown and the spots being most distinct. In one of the spent females the underparts are pure white and the other gravid female has only a few faint spots but the males are the darker specimens. In all of these a gular fold or flap extends acrosss the lower throat connecting the posterior ends of each ramus of the lower jaw. In the larger males when the vocal sac is not distended it lies behind this gular line, and looks like a triangular apron on the pectoral region the apex pointing backward and the base being on the gular line. On the females this gular barely shows. In the males we could discover no excrescences on the first two fingers. This breeding evidence is one of the strongest arguments to prove that this little animal is not a spinose young *B. terrestris* or *americanus* as Boulenger thought, and is corroborative of Holbrook's third reason for its establishment (Holbrook, 1842, V, p. 15)."

A study of our 1912, 1921 and 1922 specimens and such other *Bufo quercicus* material which has come under our observation resolve our data in the following categories:

1. The range of our males from Okefinokee is from 19–30 mm., of males from widespread parts of its range (U. S. N. material) 20–29 mm.

2. The range of our females from Okefinokee is from 20.5–32 mm.; of other females from U. S. Mus. collections (26 lots) elsewhere 22–28 mm.

3. The grand average of all females measured is 25 mm., mode, 26 mm. The 69 females measured were as follows: 1 at 20.5 mm.; 3 at 21 mm.; 7, 22 mm.; 9, 23 mm.; 4, 24 mm.; 12, 25 mm.; 13, 26 mm.; 8, 27 mm.; 6, 28 mm.; 2, 29 mm.; 2, 30 mm.; 1, 31 mm.; 1, 32 mm.

4. The grand average of all males measured is 23.6 mm., mode 25 mm. The 89 males measured were as follows: 5 at 19 mm.; 4, 20 mm.; 3, 21 mm.; 11, 22 mm.; 7, 23 mm.; 11, 24 mm.; 22, 25 mm.; 12, 26 mm.; 5, 27 mm.; 5, 28 mm.; 1, 29 mm.; and 1, 30 mm.

5. The measurements of 11 actual pairs are somewhat as follows:

    June 4, 1921   22♂ × 25♀ ; 26♂ × 30.5♀ ;
    July 3, 1921 25♂ × 26.5♀ ; 23♂ × 24.5♀ ; 24♂ × 26♀ : 25♂ × 26♀ .
    July 3, 1922 25.5♂ × 26♀ ; 26♂ × 28♀   24♂ × 31♀ .
    July 26, 1922 26.5♂ × 27♀ ;
    July 27, 1922 25.5♂ × 25.5♀ .

In no instance was female smaller; but the average is no more than 1 1/2 mm. greater in the females, the greatest range of difference 7 mm., the least 0 mm.

6. Several notes on males or possible males might be in place:
    (a) 15.5 mm. specimen has 1 transverse fold from mouth angle to other mouth angle. Is it to be a male? At this size these small oak toads are little beauties: stripe down back very prominent from mouth margin over snout to vent. Tubercles carmine tipped and at times making a margin along light vertebral line.
    (b) 16 mm. has 3 transverse edges across lower throat. Is it going to be a ♂? ♂ not functional at this size.
    (c) Of 4 specimens 14, 15, 16, 17 mm. we remark: two small ones darker in color and will probably develop into ♂'s. No signs now. The larger two are lighter, may develop into ♂'s.
    (d) One 18 mm. specimen black throat, two transverse folds, one of them connecting angles of mouth; probably going to be ♂.
    (e) One 19 mm. ♂, throat in general not black, the evertible sac not extening over pectoral region as lapette or apron. It is outlined in front by two transverse ridges and behind in pectoral region by two transverse ridges.
    (f) One 19 mm.♂, throat region with 5 or 6 transverse folds but no apron.
    (g) One 19 mm. ♂, lower throat with good apron on breast.
    (h) One 19.5 mm. ♂, dark throat and narrow dark triangle down middle of pectoral region.
    (i) One 20 mm. ♂, throat not very dark but has throat lapette.
    (j) One 20.5 mm. ♂, quite a throat apron. Do you suppose some queer oak toad noises are young males calling?
    (k) One 22 mm. Lapette extends forward beyond chin.
    (l) One 24 mm. Dark throat apron. No black excrescences revealed on thumb and second finger in alcoholics.
    (m) One 24.5 mm. Possibly first and second fingers in life may seem to be a little more horny but it is not very well revealed in preserved material.
    (n) One 26 mm. Apron on lower throat but throat light not dark while its mate, a female, has dark throat and heavily spotted breast.
    (o) One 28 mm. Dark throat. Lapette covering 3 or more folds underneath. One or two ridges on front of pectoral region hid by apron. No excrescences revealed. Forearm and possibly brachium in males thickened and relatively larger in this male. Probably a general rule.
    (p) One 30 mm. Beautiful. Long lapette with secondary one. Top of head reminds me in some ways of *Bufo hemiophrys*.

7. In a similar way a few notes on some females are:
    (a) 18 mm. specimen ♀ ? but not a male.
    (b) 18 mm. 2 transverse ridges on lower throat. Is it a ♀ ?
    (c) 21.5 mm. ripe, dark throat.
    (d) 22 mm. with dark triangle on pectoral region.
    (e) 25 mm. pectoral region with prominent black spots.
    (f) 25 mm. Very dark spotted throat and breast. (To distinguish from ♂ must look at throat vesicle. Other female throats like rest of under parts. Tympanum warty or may be free of warts. Sometimes tympanum in female so covered with warts tympanum is not revealed.) ♀ ripe. Surely a warty beast.
    (g) 25.5 mm. spent, 13 mm. wide.
    (h) 25.5 mm. ripe. Stripe more prominent in preserved ♀s, probably because they are lighter.
    (i) 26 mm. Dusky throat and breast.
    (j) 26.5 mm. Throat slightly spotted with darker.
    (k) 26.5 dark, ripe. Width 19 mm. Triangle on pectoral region.

(*l*) 26.5 mm. Ripe. Underparts generally light throat slightly darker. Width 15 mm.

(*m*) 27 mm. Throat dark extended on pectoral region and front belly as a triangle, the base of the triangle on the throat.

(*n*) 27.5 mm. Ripe. Stripe down back almost bluish-white in alcohol. Under parts unspotted.

(*o*) 28 mm. Solid black throat, heavily black spotted breast. Spent.

(*p*) 30 mm. Ripe. Width 18 mm. Underparts uniformly light.

(*q*) 30.5 mm. Dark throat and vestee. Spent. 14.5 mm. wide.

(*r*) 31 mm. Throat dusky. Middle of pectoral region with several big black spots. Width 20 mm.

8. In general it seems that males are revealed externally as such at 19 mm. or higher and females at 20.5 mm. or higher, that this is two years from transformation, i.e., the oak toad goes through two winters after transformation before breeding.

Duration, day or night. In 1921 almost the instant, April 25, we entered the swamp the boys brought us a ♂ oak toad. But it was not until May 16-21 we began to record the females. On the latter date we noted that "in the afternoon after the rain we started for turpentine still. Heard and saw *Bufo quercicus*. Picked up two, one a gravid female". Later "went to old and new hogshole. Heard a few males in the water. They all stopped except one which I could not find. On May 25 we took 2 males and 2 females."

On May 26 we made the following journal notes: "In pipewort, sedge and grass places at 10:00 a. m. found a female *Bufo quercicus*. Hear males in the woods. Is *B. quercicus* actually going to the ponds soon? *B. quercicus* calls are more lively and insistent. Have taken four or five this morning. Females are about more since last night's thunderstorm. Are females bound for any particular place on this piney island? They are moving somewhere. Does it mean the onset of breeding? In burnt-over area it seemed as if more were present. Possibly they are easier to find in this area. Found 3 ♂'s and 3 ♀ s. Males not in holes. Am getting so I can locate them easier. Returned to camp to find that the boys had taken 6 *Bufo quercicus* from the hammock west of camp. One male mated with another, made a terrarium for the oak toads. Now all 12 or 14 are out of sight in sand except two. They back into ground".

On June 1 we were still puzzling about them per the following: "An oak toad beside a log; very light in color; can squeeze into small space and freeze. It was near a ditch. Found two oak toads by a log near the trestle but still on dry ground. They are a pair but not mated. Will they go to water separately or mate on the way without rain or mate with first rain? Now have a plenty of them, 15 or 16".

Only three days later, June 4, many of our queries were answered. About two inches of rain dropped and the island seemed teeming with oak toads (see Ovulation for account). They bred almost everywhere. All about the cleared fields, in piney woods, in hammocks, and numerous other places we found oak toads that day. In one pond heard plenty of male oak toads amongst saw palmetto. We saw lots of *Bufo quercicus* croaking on floats, one on a pine cone in the water, others on logs, sticks, etc." "In one case a little ♂ oak toad faced a large southern toad (*Bufo terrestris*). Both were croaking and their inflated sacs would almost touch. A picture indeed. We found several pairs on the south side of this pond. They were in water 4-6 inches deep and easy of capture. They do not separate. Could have taken more in this little transient pond where there are no end of *B. quercicus*". On June 5 near our old camp of 1912 in a pond where vigorous matings were held on June 4 found a dead female, no doubt killed from rigors of mating or from exhaustion of ovulation or from both causes.

On June 28 at night we found *Bufo quercicus* calling vigorously. Francis Harper relates the following amusing incident: "A *Bufo quercicus*, on a floating chip, had to leave one foreleg suspended in air when 'hollering', the distention of body preventing the toad from reaching a foothold with it. Another seen on floating chips."

On July 3 "the species was abroad in great numbers. Every transient shallow pool filled by the rain had them calling. Took 3 or 4 pairs and 30 or 40 males in short order".

Amplexation (Normal, cross, abnormal). In all the amplexations of field mated pairs and also matings in captivity the typical axillary form obtained. Sometimes ovulation may come without attendant male. For example, "July 26, 1922, at midnight heard no end of *Bufo quercicus* in pond near Starling Branch crossing. Captured two pairs in an overflowed grassy area. One pair when we arrived at camp were broken. Put them together in fish can but they did not mate. Probably female laid her complement without mating. The other pair laid by morning of July 27".

In several instances we noted among our captives that a male might mate with another male. On July 5, 1921 "in my enclosure found three in tier arrangement with a female below, embraced by a male in axillary fashion and this male embraced by another male in typical axillary amplexation.

OVULATION

Habitat. "In the breeding season, they seek out stagnant pools, where they deposit their spawn, ... (Holbrook, 1842, Vol. V, p. 14). In 1920 (p. 30) we state that "the egg string is laid in warm, shallow ponds, ...". In 1921 we found them in any kind of impermanent pools after a heavy rain. They might be on the swampy edge of the island or in the highest normal dry parts of the island, might be in railroad ditches, excavations, shallow pools or ponds, cleared fields, corn patch puddles, depressions in roads, or any basin which will hold water for a time. At times, however, one is impressed with the observation that possibly they do discriminate permanent places. For example, on June 1, 1921, we observe: "Hear oak toads particularly near trestles. Do they know there is more permanent water in such places?" Many of them breed in shallow cypress ponds where development is assured.

One journal note (1922) will suffice to indicate their widespread distribution and choice of breeding. "July 3. Last night in *many places a deafening roar of Bufo quercicus*. Especially at a pond 1/2 mile west of Trader's Hill, Ga.,—a shallow grassy area. There were four Florida tree frogs (*Hyla gratiosa*) calling, some 10 southern tree frogs (*Hyla squirella*), some cricket-frogs (*Acris gryllus*) and no end of pine woods tree frogs (*Hyla femoralis*). Never heard such a din. Hard on the ear. Brought in 12–15 males of oak toads (*Bufo quercicus*). Also brought in three pairs of oak toads". The above species are frequent associates of the oak toad in breeding time and place.

Period. In 1912 we discussed the ovulation period from scanty evidence. It follows: Of all the 24 adults only four are females, three of which are spent and one of the four, the largest specimen (30 mm. long), has the ovaries full of eggs about to be laid. This specimen was taken June 1, just one day previous to the circumstantial record in the field and these four records give us little idea of the breeding range. Subsequent to June 2 we found no more of these small egg-strings nor ripe females and these facts force us to believe June 1 about the end of the egg-laying period. Five of the eight specimens were taken from June 1-7 and breeding impulses may explain their greater abundance during the first of June and not later.

In 1920 (p. 30) we held that "the oak toad breeds in May and June, most of the egg laying doubtless occurring before June 15". In 1923 (b, p. 34) we write from June 1st to 10th, three species begin (ovulation) *Bufo quercicus* ...". In 1924 (b, p. 379) we give as the "Season June 4 to August 21".

In 1921 on June 2 we noted that the "oak toads from Hopkins, Ga., have not laid as yet. The females have ripe eggs in them".

On June 4 we found our first eggs. It "rained" two inches or more. When we came out from dinner the island was afloat and everywhere oak toads were calling. Oak toads out where apparently no permanent ponds are but nevertheless in these ponds calling and mating. Found a pond where they were calling and laying".

The next congress came on July 3, 1921. Our terse note is "70° at 7:35 a.m. Trip by pond lever car to Honey Island, Honey Island Prairie and almost to Black Jack Island. On return to Honey Island began to pour, but a warm rain. Found oak toads in a shallow brushy basin. Immense choruses. Caught several. In fact, caught about 50. We took three pairs of oak toads. In an overflow area with *Woodwardia* (fern) the predominant plant, water 2-4 inches deep. This chorus at 3:30–4:00 p.m. Same condition all the way home".

In scanning our journals, work sheets and notes we find notations as to ovulation on the basis of different factors as follows: May and June, May 1–June 15, May 25–July 30, June 1–August 21, June 4 to August 21, June 4–August 27, June 4–August 17, May 25–   , June 4–August 8, June 4–July 17. These dates give the growth of our accumulating data but they also reveal that our knowlege of this abundant species is all to scanty. Doubtless if one were to choose the extremes above May 1–August 27 he could not be far astray, although the author would prefer May 15–August 15 or June 1–August 15 for the general period and bulk of ovulation.

If one occasionally finds mature tadpoles in mid June or unspent females (August 26, 1922) in late August then he realizes the possibility of May 1 or earlier as beginning of oviposition and September possibly as the end of straggling ovulation.

Since the above paragraphs were written we have examined very carefully our female series and the U. S. National Museum material with the following results: Spent May 23, May 25, June 1, June 4 (3 ♀), June 5, June 6, June 15, June 23, July 3, 4 ♀, July 4, 2 ♀, July 13–17, 2 ♀, July 15–   , July 27, 2 ♀ and August 8; unspent–May 29, June 1, June 2, June 15, June 16, 5 ♀, June 28, June 30, July 3, July 12, 2 ♀, July 15–   , July 17, July 26, 2 ♀. The range of ovulation on this basis might then be from May 23–July 26, a possibility, August 8. The May 23 date is from St. Petersburg, Fla., and one unspent record in peninsular Florida extends at least to July 17,—these stations south of the Okefinokee Swamp.

Temperature and humidity. In 1921 and 1922 when positive ovulation was known in seven instances, 3 in 1921 and 4 in 1922 our temperatures at camp range from 70°–82° and in every instance when rains from showers to drenches obtained. The minima of surrounding weather stations are from 64°–74°. In ovulation often the heavier part of the rain may have come the day before. The following night the immense chorus or congress may ensue. In June and July when a rain starts about noon and continues through the afternoon quite certainly that evening if minima be not below 60–64 the oak toads appear en masse. The minima of the 7 ovulation records 70°–82° in camp are somewhat higher than the minima recorded and derived for congresses, i.e., 64°–74° (see voice) but are exactly the same as temperatures above (64°–74°) derived from nearby weather stations for the seven dates.

Egg-laying process. Holbrook (1842, Vol. V, p. 15) writes "I have seen the male and female together, and have seen the female deposit her spawn, even when confined in a glass vessel". He does not, however, describe the process.

On June 4, 1921, the first congress we ever witnessed we did not see all the process. Some of the pairs laid eggs in a bunch reminding one of Chinese firecrackers (see egg description). "The oak toads began laying at 10:00 p.m. The female would emit some eggs. The male would draw up his legs as in *B. terrestris* and *B. americanus* and emit milt with two or three exertions. Then he would rest in drawn-up fashion for 1 or 2 minutes or sometimes less. Then eggs would drop down. At first one pair laid eggs only in bars of 2 or 3 or 4 or 5 or 6. Seemed so strange. Female then would lay 14–30 eggs at one time or 4–6 bars. Then once after egg-laying she dragged along and all the bars trailed behind showing they had a connection, a hyaline jelly connecting them. There is no outer envelope as in *B. americanus* and apparently eggs come out in bars of 4–6, then area between becomes stretched. At times several bars or free ends appear from the vent of the female and not just two ends, i.e., one from each oviduct".

For a month after first eggs in laboratory we did not see eggs in the field. We wondered if they were heavier than water, sunk to the bottom and were so small we could not find them on the bottom.

On July 3 and 17 we began to get our clues. On July 3 we found oak toads common in the furrows between rows of newly planted sweet potatoes. In the flooded furrows were no end of toads. Saw an oak toad pair swim to the bottom of a furrow in its deepest part and they deposited eggs.   They moved on.   They don't leave all eggs in one place.   Saw 7 or 8 oak toad pairs.   All amplexate axillary fashion".

EGGS

Attachment, egg mass. Holbrook, though he saw the female lay her spawn does not describe the eggs, their form and characters. In 1912 we made the following provisional identification:

On June 2, 1912, in a shallow pool in the hollow between two growing corn rows we found the small egg files of some kind of toad.   At the time we had no preservative or cans to take care of these and upon return the next day the pool had dried up.   Our one prominent impression was the smallness of the egg string.   The eggs were in one row like those of our northern *B. americanus* and rested on the muddy bottom of this shallow impermanent pool, but the egg-tube was much smaller in diameter and length. The egg string was not carefully examined at the time and we cannot compare it with the eggs of the common toads.   We are, however, firmly convinced that these files were those of the oak toad.   Deckert (1914b, No. 9, p. 2) speaks of "The spawn...laid in tiny strings,...".   In 1920 (p. 30) we speak of "The egg string or file is a small edition of the southern toad's egg string, the former being much smaller in diameter than the latter".   Deckert and we each should have used bars or short strings, for it better conveys the form of the egg mass.   In 1923 (p. 406) Wright and Wright speak of "Eggs in files. *Bufo quercicus*...".   In 1923 (b, p. 34) Wright holds "*Bufo quercicus* lays its short bars of eggs on the bottom of ponds".

In 1921 our first field notes on eggs came June 4.   They are: "Found a pond where male oak toads were calling. *Bufo quercicus* eggs.   Many parts of an egg complement will be two, three, four, five or six eggs in a string or bar independent of rest.   One pair, at first laid nothing else but these bars.   Often times 5 or 6 will radiate from one center.   These are all in same plane.   Sometimes from one center bars extend in all planes, e.g., one of 13 bars; another of 30 or 40 or 50 bars.   The jelly envelope closely fits the egg and the margin becomes slightly indented between each egg.   The eggs are black and white; last night by flashlight the eggs looked creamy but fear we were wrong on this observation.   Egg more brown or brownish-black on upper pole.   Apparently the bars of eggs is comparable to the inner tube of *B. americanus* eggs and the tube of jelly becomes pinched off or drawn out between each four or five eggs. Sometimes eggs separating to bars, sometimes not.   An egg bar will be from 2–3 mm. to 6 or 7 mm. in length.   Vitellus 1.0 mm.; 9.5 mm., 9.0 mm.; .8 mm.; 1.0 mm.   Whole bar 5.8 mm., leaves 1.15 mm. envelopes between on both ends or about 2 mm. between each egg.   A partition line between each egg".

On July 3 we did not get an entire clue to field deposition but on July 17 on Chesser Island "In water 3–6 inches deep with dip net discovered one or two strings of 4–6 eggs of *Bufo quercicus*.   Became accustomed to finding the 4–6 egg bars on the bottom without dip net.   The single bar or two of them seems a regular deposition form in the field".

Plate XXI

Oak toad (*Bufo quercicus*)

1. Habitat near Siren Run, Billy Id., Ga. May 27, 1921.
2. Toad looking out from entrance of hole in ground, Billy Id., Ga. May 16, 1921.
3. Toad in daytime retreat $1\frac{1}{4}$ inches deep and $\frac{5}{8}$ inch in diameter, beneath a slab of wood. Trail Ridge, Folkston, Ga. June 16, 1922.
4. Female and male, Chesser Id., Ga. July 4, 1922. Ventral aspect. × 1.0.
5. Cluster of egg bars laid in camp, Billy Id., Ga. July 4, 1921.
6. Egg bars, stained, Chesser Id., Ga. July 4, 1922. × 1.3.
7. 8. 9. Tadpoles, Chesser Id., Ga. August 10, 1922. × 1.0.
10. Transformed toad, Chesser Id., Ga. July 23, 1922. Dorsal aspect. × 1.0.

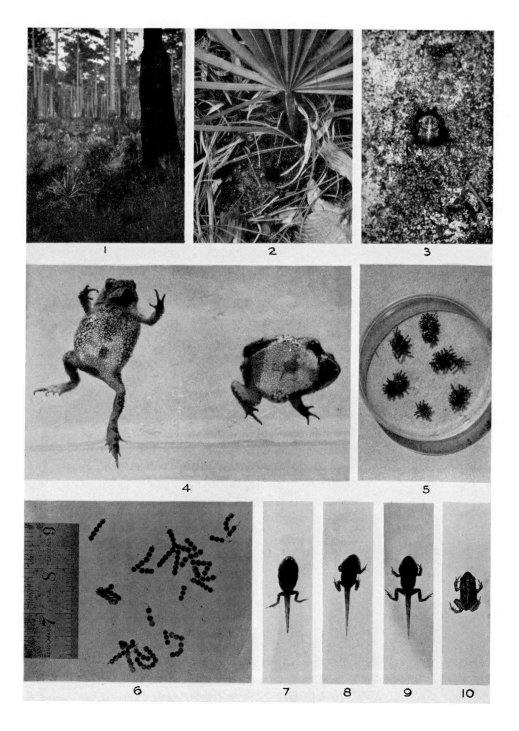

1　　　　2　　　　3

4　　　　5

6　　　7　　8　　9　　10

Egg description. In 1912 we made these observations on the species. A count of the eggs of the left ovary reveals 305 eggs and if there be the same in the right one the complement would be 610 eggs. Each of these ovarian eggs is .8–1.0 mm. in diameter, the average .9 mm. while in the common toad the egg is 1.0–1.4 mm., average 1.1 mm., mode 1.2 mm.

In 1920 (p. 30) we held that "The female oak toad may deposit 500 to 600 eggs, while a common toad produces 4,000 or more. The eggs of the oak toad are slightly smaller than those of the common toad". In 1924 (pp. 376, 377, 379) Wright and Wright give a diagram of a bar of 5 *Bufo quercicus* eggs quite unlike in egg string any *Bufo* east of the Mississippi. Of all *Bufo* eggs seen in the U. S. A. they remind us most of *Bufo compactilis* only its eggs are in long strings. Our characterization of 1924 (p. 379) is "Eggs submerged. Eggs in files. Files short (4 to 10 mm. in length); 4 to 8 eggs in short bead-like chain or bar or many such files radiating from one focus; vitellus 0.8–1.0 mm.; tube diameter 1.2–1.4 mm. Egg complement, 610, 766".

In 1921 we first positively identified this species (See egg mass, attachment, for 1921 notes). Two days after the July congress we observe that we made this note. "Noticed that the eggs of *Bufo quercicus* are decidedly brown and cream or yellowish".

In 1922 the following three notes might have pertinence: On "June 28 we found a female in a 'chufa' field at 9:00 p.m. Later made a count of the ripe eggs in her left ovary. There were 383 or if the same for the right, 766 for both ovaries, its entire complement". On "July 4 the pairs laid between 12 midnight and 7:00 a.m. The strings come out several eggs long but the jelly every 5 or 6 eggs seems to pull out. There is little jelly around eggs. There is little jelly apparent if stained with red ink or potassium permanganate (camp stains for writing and poison ivy respectively). "Finally on July 27 in a shallow *Quercus myrtifolia* pond we heard so many oak toads we looked for eggs. We find single bars of 2–6 or 8 eggs rarely attached to sticks at the surface, usually attached to grass blades .5 to 1 or 2 inches below the surface of the water. The water is 1–3 inches deep. Other bars are attached to pine needles. Most often grass is the point of attachment. Once in awhile two bars extend out from a common focus. Normally they are close together. Found a female dead. Did she die from ovulation or mating?"

Detailed measurements of preserved material by Mrs. Wright give the following results: 52 vitelli yielded 3 at .8 mm., 2 at .9 mm., and 47 at 1.0 mm., the average and the mode 1.0 mm.; 51 tubes of jelly gave 23 at 1.2 mm. in width, and 28 at 1.4 mm., the average 1.3 mm., the mode 1.4, but not one actually at 1.3 mm.; 4, 5 or 6 eggs within a tube, each egg in sphere, spheres stuck together, so partition between vitelli; of two 4-egg bars one is 4 mm. long, one 4.8 mm.; of two 5-egg bars each is 5 mm. long; of one 6-egg bar it is 6 mm. long. In two accessions of eggs she notes "Queer little yellow drops like drops of oil within egg tube and on outside". "Few drops like drops of oil".

Dangers. In 1920 (p. 30) we held that "Many of these eggs or the subsequent tadpoles are dried up by the rapid evaporation of the very transient breeding pools". No species suffers more badly than the oak toad from its choice of breeding places yet it is an abundant form. Two to six or eight inches are its usual depths for egg deposition. Often we made such remarks as these in regard to eggs "The loss must be frightful". "How does this species keep itself at abundance"? "The eggs in these furrows cannot escape drying". "The development must be rapid or the eggs or tadpoles will get caught".

HATCHING PERIOD

Our first record of ovulation in 1921 came June 4 at 10:00 p.m. Some of these in petri dishes hatched June 8 before 6:00 a.m. when we arose. This means from 72–80 hours from ovulation to hatching or 3–3 1/3 days.

MATURE TADPOLE

Color description from life (July 7, 1921). General coloration of the body is grayish olive, olive lake, grape green or ecru olive produced by close set dots of lighter color over a blackish background. Very few small black spots on the back. In one two legged specimen general color quaker drab or of the vinaceous group. There is a black spot over the nostril and one over each eye. The belly is pale purplish vinaceous; the throat and mentum with no bright color. Gill region with clusters of deep olive buff or the general colors above.

Tail. The upper crest much more heavily marked than in *Bufo terrestris.* Lower crest is also more or less marked with black. Along the dorsum of the muscular part of the tail are 6 or 7 black saddles. Along the ventral edge of muscular part are small black clusters but not so prominent as dorsal saddles. In a two-legged specimen alternation of dark and light on tail musculature for 8 or 9 spots. Along the back of body proper the characteristic paired spots (4 or 5 of them) appear.

Iris black and general colors above.

General remarks. In 1923 (a, p. 406) Wright and Wright has "*Bufo quercicus*—gray tadpoles, six or seven black saddles on musculature, heavily marked upper crest, venter one mass of color". There are plenty of oak toads in the Okefinokee region. We had difficulty getting mated pairs at first. Then when the developmental series of check pairs in the camp were fairly well advanced, a severe rain came, overflowed the pans and some *Bufo quercicus* tadpoles and *Bufo terrestris* tadpoles became mixed and our checks for *Bufo quercicus* were never brought to mature tadpoles in the camp thereafter. There is a possibility of uncertainty in some of our *Bufo quercicus* tadpoles, hence the unequal treatment given the tadpoles of this species.

LARVAL PERIOD

Deckert (1914 b, No. 9, p. 2) holds "the metamorphosis is very rapid". In 1921 we have the journal note July 7 that "*Bufo quercicus* eggs laid June 4 are approaching transformation. One with four legs today." This implies 33 days. In 1922 we took mature tadpoles on June 27 implying egg laying before our entrance to the swamp June 13-14.. In 1922 we recorded transformation

July 13 and 18. The earliest record of eggs we have in 1921 or 1922 is June 4. The intervals from June 4 to July 13 or 18 are 39 and 44 days. A period of 33–44 days does not seem unreasonable for such a summer breeder and shallow water inhabitant though our evidence is slender (see tadpoles General Remarks). Since the above was written we find that we captured a pair July 3. They laid July 4. The tadpoles were raised in camp and some went through to transformation by August 12 or 39 days after egg laying.

TRANSFORMATION

Period. In 1921 we recorded approaching transformation July 7. In 1922, on "July 12 found *Bufo quercicus* transformed in the edge of a pond in wet pine barrens." On "July 13 around Coat Bet (*Hyla gratiosa*) pond on its south side found plenty of young toads (*Bufo quercicus*) transformed. They were near the edge of the pond but in the moist pine barrens especially in clear areas". On July 18 (1922) found a few transformed around the shallow edges of Murray Bay (a sphagnum swamp overgrown with heaths and even trees). On August 16, 1922, near Callahan, Fla., we found them transformed. At Trader's Hill Pond (1/2 mile west) on July 3, 1922 we found them mated. Eggs from these were carried to camp. The transformed toads from this series transformed August 12.

In 1922 we then have transformation records from July 12–August 16.

Size. Deckert (1914 b, No. 9, pp. 2, 3) is the first to record anything on this phase. The metamorphosis he holds to be very rapid. Hence one would expect little pigmies of transformed frogs. "The young toads, when fully developed, are 1/4 inch or less in length. The adults measure: male, 1 inch; female, 1 1/8 or 1 1/4 inch".

On July 18, 1922 we secured five little toads at Murray Bay, Folkston, Ga., measuring 7, 7.5, 7.5, 8, 8 mm. respectively. They had "no stripes down back, were prickly all over". On August 16 near Callahan, Florida, we took one 8 mm. long. On July 30–31, 1922, we secured one on Chesser Island, 10.5 mm. long. It is just past transformation. The note on it reads: "Makes me think of *B. debilis* at this size". On August 12, 1922 we succeeded in transforming this species at 7 mm. in length. Our largest series came July 12, 1922. Some of them measured as follows: 6, 6, 5, 7 (median stripe), 7 ,7, 7, 7.5, 8, 8, 8, 8, 8, 8.5, 9, 9 (stripe down back), 9.5, 10 mm. respectively. Some of the larger were slightly past transformation. The very tuberculate under surface of forefoot suffices to distinguish it from *Bufo terrestris*.

GROWTH

This species transforms at 7–8 mm. On July 30, 1922, on Chesser Island, Ga., we secured one 10.5 mm. and the next day in the same place one 13.5 mm. In 1917 at LeRoy, Ala., we took 9 specimens 11, 12, 13, 14, 14.5, 15, 16, 16, 16 mm. respectively and one 21.5 mm., possibly two age groups.

In the swamp we have isolated records such as: July 9, 1922 one 16.5 mm.; May 6, 1921, one 15.5 mm.; August 13, 1922, 14, 15, 16, 17 mm. examples.

When we entered the swamp in 1912, May 28, we picked up at Mixon's Ferry, Suwannee River, the following: 1 at 15 mm.; 4 at 16 mm.; 1 at 16.5 mm.; 1 at 17 mm.; 3 at 17.5 mm.; 2 at 18 mm.; 2 at 18.5 mm.; 2 at 19.5 mm.; 1 at 20 mm., probably one age group. Shortly after we arrived in 1921 we secured May 1, 1921, two 16, 16.5 mm. and one 25.5 mm. ♀. Certainly two groups. It would seem as if these May and early June (to June 12 or 15) records from 11–20 mm. are toads which wintered over and are 1 year beyond transformation. At times it seems as if this group might be broken from the 2 year olds at 18 mm., but some of the 19–20 or 21 mm. are doubtful. Almost all our material is determinable as to sex from 19 mm. onward for males and from 20.5 or 21 or 22 mm. for females. Possibly the one year olds—if males to be are 11–18 mm., and if females to be 11–20 or 21 mm.

We have collections on which we take a 17 mm. unsexed specimen and four from 24–28 mm. sex determinable or a 18 mm. unsexed—apparently two clear cut groups. But on June 10, 1921, we took specimens, an 18 mm. unsexed and 19.5, 20 and 20.5 mm. males or June 1, 1921, two unsexed 16.5 and 18 mm. and three sexed individuals 19 mm. ♂, 21.5 mm. ♀ and 22 mm. ♀. Almost certainly as determined in previous paragraph the 16–18 mm. immature forms and mature group 19–22 mm. (sex revealed externally) are two groups.

Most of our big series are as follows:

June 16, 1922　9 from 20.5 mm. ♀–26.5 mm. ♀
14 from 24.5 mm. ♂–27.5 mm. ♂
July　3, 1921　7 from 23. mm. ♂–26.5 mm. ♀
1922　9 from 22. mm. ♂–26.5 mm. ♂

Because of records such as these one might think 28–32 mm. individuals 3 year olds but the evidence is slender. For example, on May 25, 1921, we take together a 19 mm. ♂ and two females 28 mm. and 29.5 mm. or June 4, 1921, a male 26 mm. and a female 30.5 mm., or July 12, 1922, two 26 mm. ♂s, 26.5 mm. ♀ and one 30 mm. ♀, or June 30, 1922, two 19 mm. ♂s, two 25 mm. ♀s and 26 mm. ♂ and one 28 mm. ♂, or July 1, 1922, a male 24 mm. and one male 29 mm.

In conclusion we hold transformation to come at 7–8 mm., a mean at 7.5 mm.; one year old stage 10.5 or 11 mm.–18 or 19 or 20 mm., or mean at 16.5 mm.; two year olds, 19 ♂ or 21 ♀–27.5 or 28 mm. (possibly to 30 or 32 mm.), mean at 25 mm. There may be a three year old class from 27.5 or 28 mm.–32 mm., with mean 29 mm., but this is not quite so certain.

FOOD

For this topic consult Dr. R. Kellogg's forthcoming economic studies of *Bufos*. He examined our series and found some very interesting things in its diet. Professors C. R. Crosby and S. C. Bishop in examining some of Dr. Kellogg's oak toad material thought so highly of the oak toad as an insect collector that they entitled one paper thus, "A New Genus and two new Species of Spiders Collected by *Bufo quercicus* (Holbrook)."

ENEMIES

In 1912 we wrote that the common garter snake ("highland moccasin") prefers toads, and the oak toad with the Southern toad receives more of its attention than any other prey.

In 1922 we felt that the spreading adder (*Heterodon*) is equally appreciative of oak toads as well as southern toads. The gopher frog has also been given as inordinately fond of oak toads.

AUTUMNAL DISAPPEARANCE

Our first record for the swamp is April 25 about the earliest we entered the swamp and our latest date August 26, 1922. After our 1912 trip we received specimens of this species collected from July 15 to November 1, but there is no certainty they were taken at the latter date though we suspect it near the period of the oak toad's retirement. We find in literature no record beyond our August 26 though it must stay out for two or three months beyond this date.

AFFINITIES

Holbrook who describes it spends most of this phase of his description to proving it is not the young of a large species. "That this little animal is not the young of any other species I am certain, for

"1. It cannot be the young of the *Bufo lentiginosus*, for the superciliary ridges are not elevated in proportion, the upper jaw is not emarginate, and with the young of that species I am well acquainted.

"2. It cannot be the young of the *Bufo americanus*, as that animal is not found near Charleston, and, besides, it wants the characteristic spade-like process to the foot.

"3. It cannot be the young of the *Bufo erithronotus*, for its whole form is different. It is not half the size, nor are its toes half as extensively webbed; it is, in fact, a distinct and adult animal, for I have seen the male and female together, and have seen the female deposit her spawn, even when confined in a glass vessel".

It is a natural tendency to wonder if it be not a young of some other *Bufo* when one first encounters it but it is very distinct as comparisons of an adult *B. quercicus* and a young of *Bufo lentiginosus* reveal in the plate given (Plate fig. 00).

LeConte did not make any mistake about it but Cope made it a new form, *Chilophryne dialopha*. Boulenger (1882, pp. 319, 309) retained Cope's *Bufo dialophus* of Sandwich Islands (p. 319) and places *Bufo quercicus* Holbrook in the synonymy of *Bufo lentiginosus americanus*. Cope led him astray and he, Cope, (1889, p. 292) alludes to it thus "The redescription of the species by myself was due to the omission of its characteristic peculiarities from extant writings. The erroneous locality (Sandwich Islands) is one of the several such errors, based on the incorrect labeling of the collections of J. H. Townsend, to which the specimen belonged."

In 1889 Cope (p. 292) writes of it as follows: "In some specimens the transverse posterior part of the fronto-parietal crest is broken up. It then resembles the young of the *Bufo lentiginosus*, with which it has been supposed to be identical by various authors. It, however, differs from this species in the differently shaped parotoid glands, the thickened posterior parts of the mandibles, and from all the subspecies, except the *B. l. woodhousei*, in the shorter head. There is no doubt but that Dr. Holbrook was correct in regarding this as a distinct species of very small size."

On the basis of vocal sac of male alone Miss Dickerson (1906, pp. 89–91) places *Bufo quercicus* with *Bufo compactilis* and *Bufo cognatus* in relationships. Other characters may bear her out in this determination.

In appearance one might place *Bufo quercicus* with *Bufo cognatus* and might call *B. quercicus* a small edition of it. Of course, there may be some relationship with *Bufo debilis* the other small toad of the U. S. A., but it is more remote from it than from *B. cognatus*. In the males the vocal vesicle is of the *Bufo cognatus* groups but so is also some others such as *Bufo compactilis*. Its note is quite different from the above species. We ourselves know first hand the eggs of *Bufo compactilis*, *B. punctatus* and *B. quercicus*. We have no positive eggs of *B. debilis* or *Bufo cognatus*. *Bufo punctatus* may lay single eggs black and white, or eggs in loose flat masses on bottom or quite a film on the bottom. *Bufo quercicus* lays brown and cream colored eggs, 4 to 6 or 8 in a bar with little or no jelly. *Bufo compactilis* lays brown and cream colored eggs in a file, one envelope wide and with little jelly. In known eggs of the United States *Bufos*, *Bufo quercicus* approaches closest to *Bufo compactilis*. Possibly when *B. cognatus* eggs are found they will appear to be related in appearance to *Bufo quercicus* and *Bufo compactilis*. This is, however, conjecture. The tadpoles of *Bufo quercicus* in coloration are lighter than many *Bufo* tadpoles and may approach the bicolored tadpoles of *Bufo compactilis* (as yet we do not positively know *Bufo debilis* and *Bufo cognatus* tadpoles).

Quite reasonably it seems to be in the *Bufo cognatus-compactilis-punctatus* (possibly *debilis*) assemblage.

BIBLIOGRAPHY

1907 Brimley, C. S. A Key to the Species of Frogs and Toads Liable to Occur in North Carolina. Journ. Elisha Mitchell Sci. Soc. Dec. 1, 1907, Vol. 23, pp. 157, 159.

1908 ———. Notes on Life Zones in North Carolina. Journ. Elisha Mitchell Sci. Soc., May, 1908, Vol. 24, pp. 17-19.

1909 ———. Some Notes on the Zoology of Lake Ellis, Craven County, North Carolina, with Special Reference to Herpetology. Proc. Biol. Soc. Wash., June 25, 1909, Vol. XXII, p. 133.

1910 ———. Records of Some Reptiles and Batrachians from the Southern United States. Proc. Biol. Soc. Wash. March 31, 1910, Vol. XXIII, p. 11.

1926 ———. Revised Key and List of the Amphibians and Reptiles of North Carolina. Journ. Elisha Mitchell Sci. Soc., Oct., 1926, Vol. 42, p. 80.

1862 Cope, E. D. Proceedings Acad. Sci. Phila., 1862, p. 341.

1886 ———. Proceedings Am. Phil. Soc., 1886, p. 516.

1889 ———. The Batrachia of North America. U. S. Nat. Mus. Bull. No. 34, pp. 291, 292.

1925 Crosby, C. R. and S. C. Bishop. A New Genus and Two New Species of Spiders Collected by *Bufo quercicus* (Holbrook) The Florida Entomologist. October 1925, Vol. IX, No. 3, pp. 33-36.

1914 Deckert, R. F. List of Salientia from near Jacksonville, Florida. Copeia Feb. 14, 1914, No. 3, p. 3.
1914 Deckert, R. F. Further Notes on the Salientia of Jacksonville, Florida. Copeia Aug. 29, 1914, No. 9, pp. 2, 3.
1842 DeKay, James E. Zoology of New York, or the New York Fauna.... Part III, p. 68.
1906 Dickerson, M. C. The Frog Book, pp 89-91.
1842 Holbrook, John E. North American Herpetology, 2nd Edition, Vol. V, pp. 13-15.
1849 Holbrook, John E. Batrachia of Georgia Appendix (p. 15) in George White's Statistics of the State of Georgia. Savannah 1849.
1855 LeConte, John. Descriptive Catalogue of the Ranina of the United States. Proc. Acad. Nat. Sci. Phila. Dec. 1855, Vol 7, p. 430.
1922 Löding, H. P. A Preliminary Catalogue of Alabama Amphibians and Reptiles. Geol. Survey of Ala. Museum Paper No. 5, Ala. Mus. Nat. Hist. Sept. 1922, pp. 16, 17.
1895 Loennberg, Einar. Notes on Reptiles and Batrachians Collected in Florida in 1892 and 1893. Proc. U. S. Nat. Mus. 1894, Vol. XVII, p. 338.
1924 Myers, George S. Amphibians and Reptiles from Wilmington, N. C. Copeia June 30, 1924, No. 131. p. 59.
1924 Schmidt, Karl P. A List of Amphibians and Reptiles Collected near Charleston, S. C. Copeia July 15, 1924, No. 132, p. 68.
1923 Stejneger, L. and T. Barbour. A Check List of North American Amphibians and Reptiles, 2nd Edition, p. 26.
1923 Viosca, Percy, Jr. An Ecological Study of the Cold Blooded Vertebrates of Southeastern Louisiana. Copeia Feb. 1, 1923, No. 115, p. 37.
1920 Wright, A. H. Frogs: Their Natural History and Utilization. Appendix VI. Rept. U. S. Commissioner of Fisheries 1919, Doc. 888, p. 30.
1923 ————. The Salientia of the Okefinokee Swamp, Georgia. Copeia Feb. 1, 1923, No. 115, p. 34.
1926 Wright, A. H. The Vertebrate Life of the Okefinokee Swamp in Relation to the Atlantic Coastal Plain. Ecology Jan. 1926, Vol. VII, p. 82.
1923 Wright, A. H., and A. A. Wright. The Tadpoles of the Frogs of Okefinokee Swamp, Georgia. The Anatomical Record, Jan. 20, 1923, Vol. 24, p. 406.
1924 Wright, A. H., and A. A. Wright. A Key to the Eggs of the Salientia East of the Mississippi River. American Naturalist, July-August 1924, Vol. LVIII, pp. 375-381.

Bufo terrestris Bonnaterre

(Pl. I, Fig. 3; V, Fig. 8; VIII, Figs. 5, 6; XII, Fig. 11; XV, Fig. 11; XVII, XXII, Text Fig. I, 2)

COMMON NAMES

Southern Toad. Carolina Toad. Grey Toad. Land-frog (Bartram). Land-toad (Catesby). Latreille's Toad. "Charming Toad." "Hop Toad."

RANGE

Check list. Type locality: "La Caroline."

Range. The Carolinas to Florida, west to the Mississippi.—Stejneger & Barbour Check List, 1923, p. 26.

Ranges along the seacoast from South Carolina to Florida, and following the Gulf through Alabama and Mississippi. Scattered individuals are met with across the mountains to South Carolina.—Girard 1854, p. 86.

Supplementary records. In 1922 Deckert (Copeia, Nov. 20, 1922, p. 88) found "*Bufo terrestris*" singing at Royal Palm Hammock, and in wet places northeast to Homestead." In June 1922 C. S. Brimley (1923, p. 4) in North Carolina "found (them) common at Laurel Hill, Scotland Co., June 1 and 2, 1922." Earlier he (1922, p. 48) records "Southern Toad (*Bufo terrestris*). One taken at Fayetteville, May 28, 1920, and two more on June 4 and 6, 1921. The common toad of this region (Raleigh), however, appears to be

Bufo fowleri." In 1922 in Duval Co., Fla., Thomas Hallinan at Fort George Island found several. Nieden (1923, p. 125) though he publishes in 1923 really comes about to the year 1914 in data so has little or no additional range evidence. He gives Southern United States, North America (east of Texas). K. P. Schmidt (1924, p. 68) records it at Mt. Pleasant, S. C., and *Bufo fowleri* at the same place. In South Carolina Pickens, 1927, has *B. americanus*, *B. fowleri* and *Bufo terrestris* in South Carolina. In 1923 Viosca (1923, p. 37) gives *Bufo terrestris* as one of the Southeastern part of Louisiana. At Wilmington, N. C., George S. Myers (1924, p. 59) took "*Bufo terrestris* Bonnaterre. Several.'' In North Carolina, C. S. Brimley (1925, p. 80) credits to to Jares, Onslow, New Hanover, Cumberland and Scotland Counties. In 1926 (pp. 82, 83) we considered it one of the "nine species of frogs which might be considered Lower Austral." "I.O. *Bufo terrestris* S. C.—Ga. La." Earlier in 1896 (p. 1011) Cope placed "*Bufo lentiginosus lentiginosus* Shaw" amongst the "Species which the Floridan subregion shares with the Austroriparian . . ." He also (p. 1007) gives it as a characteristic Austroriparian species. In 1889, Cope (p. 290) holds "The *B. l. lentiginosus* is confined to the Austroriparian region east of Texas, and all statements to the contrary are based on error. It does not ascend the Mississippi Valley, so far as is known." The next year 1890 H. Garman reports it from Southern Illinois and Kentucky. Did he have *B. fowleri* or is *B. terrestris* in Kentucky and Illinois? Miss Dickerson (1906, p. 39) also places it in the Austroriparian region. Brimley (1910, p. 11) has it from Bay St. Louis, Miss. to Bellair and Fort Meade, Fla., or Mimsville and Riceborough, Ga. Viosca (1926, p. 308) has it among "a few coastal plain species whose range from Virginia or North Carolina southward and westward to the Mississippi Valley seems fairly well established."

Shaw (1802, p. 173) credits it to the Carolinas and Virginia. Harlan (1825, p. 345 and 1835, p. 10a) does not consider *terrestris* alone when he has it inhabiting "the southern and middle states."

Local Okefinokee records. In 1912 fourteen adult or half-grown toads were secured and about 100 others in various stages of growth beyond transformation. Several adults taken from snake stomachs were used in this (1912) study besides a series of transformed individuals and numerous tadpoles.

This species we found generally on all the islands and all around the outskirts of the swamp. No enumeration of localities is necessary. It occurs throughout the pine barrens and hammocks in fact any land habitat. In breeding we find it in shallow water normally. One Okefinokee boy called them Charming Toad. "Charming toad because it charms you, turns your eyes right green."

GENERAL APPEARANCE

Shaw (1802, p. 173) held "This very much resembles the common toad (Europe) in its general appearance, but has a smaller head and sharper snout. . . . Its colour is a dusky brown, paler beneath or it is all over mottled with minute blackish or dark brown spots: the irides of the eyes are red."

In 1826 (pp. 344, 345) and in 1835 (p. 109) Harlan gives the following: "*Char.*—Above dark-brown, verrucose, with irregularly disposed fuscus, or blackish spots, edged with white: *beneath* dirty white, granulated: *sides* pale, spotted; *legs* barred, large oblong warts behind the eyes; a large blackish spot posterior to the tympanum; head above canaliculate; two tubercles on the heel of each foot; a longitudinal, vertebral, shallow, groove. Length of the body about 3 inches."

Holbrook (1842, Vol. V, p. 7) gives its characters as: "Head large; snout obtuse; superciliary ridges greatly elevated and terminating posteriorly in a knob; upper jaw emaginate, lower furnished with a hook in front; parotoid glands large, reniform, and reaching below the tympanum to near the shoulder; tympanum large; vocal vesicle internal; body above warty, dusky brown, with a tinge of yellow; beneath granulated, dirty yellowish-white. Length 3 inches." Cope 1889 (p. 278) holds its definition to be "Frontoparietal crests divergent, produced into a knob behind the short post-orbitals; super-tympanic well developed; head 3.5 to 4 times in length."

Miss Dickerson (1926, p. 43) chooses for distinction "head long (three and half times in total length); cranial crests greatly elevated and swollen behind; underparts unspotted." In 1907 Brimley (p. 157) chooses "bony ridges ending in a knob behind" for his key character. In 1926 he uses the same with the added note of "color usually dark and breast unspotted."

In 1914 Deckert (No. 9, p. 2) says "The toad itself, however, is differently (from *B. americanus*) built, the head being wider and higher, and the arms and legs shorter and more delicate. The eyes, also, are larger, and the enormous bony knobs on the large heads of some old females give them a sort of resemblance to species of the tropical cystignathoid toads *Ceratophrys*. Unlike the latter, our toads are gentle creatures, living their lives of usefulness in our farms and gardens."

Boulenger (1882, pp. 309, 310) gave his *Bufo lentiginosus musicus* these characters: "Supraorbital ridges swollen behind and produced beyond the angles of the postorbitals; subarticular tubercles generally simple, metatarsal tubercles moderate."

COLORATION OF SPIRIT SPECIMENS (1912)

General color from buckthorn brown to almost black. Bright colored forms have a prominent light vertebral band or line and a prominent oblique light band from form of parotoid to the groin. In darker specimens the lateral bands disappear before the vertebral line does. Many of the specimens have both absent. The under-parts of one half of the adult series have the breast and sides of the belly with fine spots like Holbrook's figure ('42, V, fig. 11) while the other half have unspotted venters.

STRUCTURAL CHARACTERS (WRITTEN IN 1912)

Cranial crest prominent; canthus rostalis low; preorbital ridge not extending below the level of the lower rim of the eye; supraorbital ridges divergent and ending in elevated inward curved knobs which are not united across the middle of the head by a flat bony rim except in one specimen. In this specimen (No. 6575) the supraorbital crests are lower, the furrow between them shallow and the two ends merge across the middle line and thus form an ovate bony-like plate between the eyes with the apex at the nostrils and the base on a line of the anterior ends of the parotoids. At right angles to the front of the supraorbital knob a ridge extends to a point just opposite the end of the eyelid; here the ridge sends a branch downward 1/3 of the way in front of the tympanum and sends another ridge backward over the tympanum to the parotoid; tympanic disk distinct, the cephalic border more sharply defined than the caudal edge. Parotoid in some narrow and elongate, in others shorter; in some reniform, in others oval; upper jaw slightly to decidedly emarginate; head smooth; upper eyelid with small warts; back and hind limbs with fine warts; a spinose group above the arm insertion; forearm with coarse granulations; under parts granulate; 3rd finger slightly longer than the first; 2nd finger longer than the 4th; tongue elliptical.

MEASUREMENTS
(1912—1914)

The measurements of 14 adults or half-grown toads are as follows: In length they are 40–67.75 mm., average 56.75 mm.; the head including the tympanum is 13.5–25 mm., average 18.8 mm., mode 20 mm., contained in length of body 2.9–3.4 times usually slightly over 3 times; or head to rear of cranial crest 3–3.8 in length of body; width of head 15.5–28 mm., average 23.7 mm., mode 23 mm., usually slightly greater than head length, femur or tibia; snout 5.75–8.75 mm., average 7 mm., mode 6 mm., equal to eye which is 5.5–8.25 mm., average 6.9, mode 6 mm.; tympanum 3.25–5.5 mm., average 4.3 mm., mode 4 mm., 1.2–2.0 in eye, usually at least 1.5 times; tympanum slightly less than eyelid which is 3.25–6.25 mm., average 5 mm., mode 4.5 mm.; equals the interorbital distance or occasionally is slightly less, the interorbital distance being 4.25–6.25 mm., average 5.1 mm., mode 5 mm.; femur 13.5–29.5 mm., average 21 mm., mode 22 mm., equal to or slightly less than rest of the foot, equal to or slightly more than the tibia which is 14–27 mm., average 20.5 mm.; rest of foot 15.5–29 mm., average 22 mm.; anterior limb from axilla 26.75–44.5 mm., average 32.2 mm.; posterior limb from groin 48.5–78.5 mm., average 62.5 mm., or 1.7–2.3, usually under 2.0 times length of anterior limb.

(Recent Material)

Head to angle of mouth 1.07 (20 mm.) 1.4 (44 mm.)–1.4 (56 mm.♂) –1.37 (56 mm.♀)–1.33 (66 mm.♂)–1.35 (66 mm.♀)–1.4 (82 mm.♀) in width of head; head to rear of tympanum (——)–1.3–1.16–1.26 —1.18–1.23–1.38 in width of head; head to angle of mouth 3.08–3.14 —3.75–3.2–3.4–3.3–3.14 in length of body; head to rear of tympanum (——)–2.93–3.1–2.9–3.0–3.0–2.9 in length of body; snout 1.0—.78 —.875—.875—.7—1.1—.96 in first finger; snout 1.0—.78—.875—.875—.75 —1.0—1.0 in fourth finger; snout .66—.50—.437—.437—.50—.66—.50 in first toe; eye 1.0—1.16—1.23—1.14—1.17—1.0—1.1 in snout; eye (——) —.5—.693—.71—.70—.55—.727 in tympanum; eye 1.0—.91—1.08—1.0 —.82—1.1—1.04 in first finger; tympanum (——)—4.6—3.75—3.6—3.41

—4.25—3.375 in intertympanic width; tympanum (——)—2.3—1.77—1.6
—1.66—1.8—1.5 in snout; internasal width 1.33—1.3—1.12—1.25—1.3
—1.3—1.08 in upper eyelid width; interorbital width 1.0—1.0—.9—.83—1.
—.92—.72 in upper eyelid width; interorbital width .75—.8—.8—.8—.75
—.71—.66 in internasal width; interorbital width (   )—3.0—3.4—3.0
—3.4—3.0—3.0 in intertympanic width.

Forelimb. Forelimb 2.0—2.1—2.0—1.75—1.9—1.8—1.8 in length of
body; forelimb 2.2—2.15—2.1—1.7—2.—1.8—1.85 in hindlimb; first finger
1.5—1.6—1.57—1.42—1.7—1.44—1.45 in third finger; second finger 1.5—
1.65—1.83—1.42—1.7—1.44—1.45 in third finger; second finger 1.0—1.2
—1.16—1.0—1.0—1.1—1.45 in first finger; third finger .88—.6—.63—.75
—.66—.72 in second toe; fourth finger 1.5—1.5—1.55—1.42—1.6—1.55—1.3
in third finger; fourth finger .66—.55—.5—.5—.66—.66—.50 in first toe;
internasal width 2.—1.6—1.75—1.75—1.5—2.0—1.9 in first finger; internasal width 2.—1.4—1.5—1.75—1.55—1.8—1.82 in second finger; internasal
width 3.—2.3—2.75—2.5—2.7—2.6 in third finger; internasal width 2.—1.6
—1.75—1.75—1.7—1.8—2.0 in fourth finger.

Hindlimb. Length 1.1—1.0—1.0—1.0—1.05—1.0—1.03 in hindlimb;
tibia 2.5—2.75—2.5—2.75—2.5—2.75—2.55 in length; tibia 2.75—2.8—
2.6—2.7—2.6—2.75—2.6 in hindlimb; tibia 1.25—1.3—1.36—1.6—1.3—
1.55—1.4 in forelimb; tibia .94—.9—.9—.9—.9—1.04—1.01 in hind foot
(without tarsus); first toe 2.—1.66—2.0—2.14—1.6—1.5—1.9—in second toe;
first toe 3—3—3.5—3.4—2.8—2.5—3.3 in third toe; first toe 3.75—4.6—5.4
—4.8—4.8—3.8—5.0 in fourth toe; first toe 2.5—2.8—3.1—2.9—2.8—2.8
—3.0 in fifth toe; second toe 1.5—1.8—1.8—1.6—1.75—1.66—1.75 in third
toe; second toe 1.87—2.9—2.7—2.26—3.0—2.5—2.6 in fourth toe; second toe
1.25—1.7—1.57—1.33—1.75—1.4—1.55 in fifth toe; third toe 1.25—1.6
1.5—1.41—1.7—1.53—1.5 in fourth toe; third toe .83—.94—.9—.83—1.0
—.83—.9—in fifth toe; fourth toe 1.3—1.5—1.6—1.7—1.55—1.6—1.55 in
fifth toe; fourth toe 1.6—1.1—1.15—1.1—1.1—1.05—1.06 in tibia; fourth
toe 1.33—1.45—1.5—1.9—1.4—1.6—1.53 in forelimb; fifth toe 1.5—1.7—1.7
—1.7—1.7—1.8—1.7 in fourth toe; internasl with 1.3—.9—.9—.9—1.1
—1.2—1.0 in first toe; internasal width 2.6—1.4—1.75—1.9—1.7—1.8—1.75
in second toe; internasal width 4.—2.6—3.1—3.—3.—4.6—3.3 in third toe;
internasal width 6.—4.1—4.75—4.25—5.3—4.6—5.0 in fourth toe; internasal
width 3.3—2.4—2.75—2.5—3.2—2.5—3.0 in fifth toe.

HABITAT

In 1892 and 1893 Einar Loennberg (1895, p. 338) finds "This is the most
common toad in south Florida. It is seen in great numbers about the houses
and other places in the evening. In the daytime, it hides under old logs,
boards, etc. at the shores of lakes and other moist places." Ten miles south of
Jacksonville, Florida, R. F. Deckert (Copeia, 1914, Feb. 14, No. 3, p. 3) records "*Bufo lentiginosus* Shaw common in companies in temporary water or
scattered on cultivated ground." Again the same author (1914, No. 9, p. 2)
writes "*Bufo lentiginosus* Shaw is the southern representative of our common

(northern) toad, and seems to prefer the neighborhood of human habitations for its abode. Near our house we found them under boards, logs, tubs, heaps of rubbish, etc." In 1921 he writes "It is found at any time of the year in gardens and cultivated grounds."

(For habitat notes see General Habits, Ovulation Habitat, and Local Okefinokee records).

FIRST APPEARANCE

Most of the records for the first half of the year come in April. In the U. S. National Museum collections we noted two collections in January, three in February, four in March, eight in April, four in May, two in June and eight in July.

In 1921 we entered about April 22 and secured specimens at once. Two days later they were breeding near our camp. This implies that they may have been out much earlier.

GENERAL HABITS

Variations in color. Shaw (1802, p. 173) notes "They vary somewhat in colour, being deeper or paler in different individuals."

Early naturalists in America began to find red toads and about them much difference of opinion obtained.

Bartram (1791, p. 279) writes "The highland frogs, commonly called toads, are of two species, the red and the black. The former, which is of a reddish-brown or brick colour, is the largest, and may weigh upwards of one pound when full grown; they have a disagreeable look, and when irritated, they swell and raise themselves up on their four legs and croak, but are no ways venomous or hurtful to man."

In 1827 J. L. Williams (A View of West Florida, 1827, p. 29) speaks of "The red and black toads are common and useful reptiles; in destroying insects they are extremely expert."

Harlan (1827, p. 345, 1835, p. 109) describes a "Var. A. The reddish-brown, or brick-coloured toad of Bartram; very large, weighing near one pound when full grown; legs and thighs marked with blotches and ringlets. Inhabits the Southern States. The Red toad of Pennsylvania is but little larger than the *B. musicus.*"

Holbrook (1842, Vol. V, pp. 11, 12) figures and describes *Bufo erythronotus* at considerable length. His last three topics might be repeated: "*Habits.* This animal is found in the deep forests of oak in the neighbourhood of Charleston, and is especially rare, as in nine years I have not seen more than a dozen specimens, consequently nothing can be said of its habits.

"*Geographical Distribution.* As yet this animal has only been observed in South Carolina.

"*General Remarks.* There is no doubt that this animal is an adult, though I was at first disposed to consider it the young of the large toad of similar colour mentioned by Bartram in his Travels in Florida, which as yet I have never seen. Subsequent observation has, however, convinced me to the contrary; for Bartram's animal weighed nearly a pound, while no specimen of the *Bufo erythronotus* exceeded twenty lines in length; nor can it be the young of *Bufo lentiginosus*, as the superciliary ridges are not elevated, and the slight elevation that does exist is between the nostrils and orbits; or the young of the *Bufo americanus*, which is sometimes red, for this latter animal does not inhabit the low country of South Carolina, nor has it the spade-like process at the foot, as in that animal; nor, in fact, is it the young of any animal, as might be inferred from its size, for I have seen the male and female together, and have seen their spawn."

In 1854 Charles Girard says little but it is direct. Under *Bufo lentiginosus* Holbrook he writes "*Bufo erythronotus* does not appear to us different from *B. lentiginosus*, since color alone cannot be taken as an exclusive guide amongst the bufonids."

In December, 1855, John LeConte (1856, p. 430) under *Bufo musicus* Daudin writes "This species like all its congeners varies very much in color and in the form and disposition of the spots. This variation depends entirely on the will of the animal. It is generally, however, of a very dark dusky, sometimes light grey and even reddish. I cannot conceive how it has ever received the name of *lentiginosus*, which as I have shown before under *Telmatobius* is as unlike this animal as any species can be. The *Rana lentiginosa* of Shaw, of which he gives in his general Zoology a tolerably good figure, although copied from Catesby, is perfectly smooth and more resembling a frog than a toad, and therefore well called by him the land frog; whereas the *B. musicus* is very rough and makes no approach to its form and habits. It walks rather than hops. Bartram's red toad of Florida was a mere variation of this species, the difference being nothing more than an accidental or voluntary change of color."

"*Bufo erythronotus* Holbrook, l.c.v. pl. 2. Not having been able for years to obtain a living specimen of this animal, I shall say nothing more of it than that it bears not the slightest resemblance to the *Bufo lentiginosus* (*B. musicus*) as stated by Mr. Girard in Proceed. A. N. S., Vol. p. 86."

General habits. In 1912 we write "This very abundant form is well known and no account of its general habits is needed. We found it on the outskirts of the swamp in the cut-over sections and it was common on the various islands of the swamp, especially in the Lee's cornfields."

Shaw (1802, p. 173) speaks of its locomotion thus "Its motion also is not that of crawling, but leaping." In general he says "These animals are said to be most common in wet weather, but are very frequent on the higher grounds, and appear in the hottest part of the day, as well as in the evening." This is a paraphrase of Catesby. Harlan (1825, p. 345) holds it "Mostly leaps, seldom crawls;" Holbrook (1842, Vol. V, p. 9) tells us "This animal is timid and remarkably gentle in its habits, remaining concealed during the day in some dark place, and only venturing out as the dusk of evening approaches." . . . "I have seen an individual kept for a long space of time, which became perfectly tame: during the summer months he would retire to a corner of the room, into a habitation he had prepared for himself, in a small quantity of earth, placed there for his convenience. Towards evening he would wander about the room in search of food, seizing greedily whatever insect came his way. Some water having been squeezed from a sponge upon his head one hot day in July, he returned the next day to the same spot, and seemed well pleased with the repetition; nor did he fail during the extreme heat of the summer to repair to it frequently, in search of his shower-bath." In 1914 Deckert (No. 9, p. 2) holds "Their habits are in every respect similar to those of *Bufo americanus . . .*"

VOICE

Holbrook (1842, Vol. V, p. 9) is the first who calls attention to its voice "The males at this season are extremely noisy, though at other times they are silent, or make only a slight chirp when taken. Like many of the Hyla tribe, they have a large sac under the throat, which is distended when the animal croaks."

In 1908 H. A. Allard in discussing *Bufo fowleri* in Northern Georgia (Gwinett & Jackson Counties) refers to the voice of *Bufo lentiginosus* thus: "In this region throughout March I heard the occasional prolonged trills of the so-considered common toad (*Bufo lentiginosus*). By the first of April these notes had become quite silenced, and the distinct chorus of congregations of Fowler's toads had begun. I first noticed these toads singing on the evening of March 26, although I think the first singers had appeared somewhat earlier. It was interesting to note that the voice of Fowler's toads were never heard with the appearance of cool, chilly nights, although the trilling of the common toad continued. Throughout the early spring, this contrast in the occurrence of the two notes, with respect to temperature changes was very marked." (Science, 1908, n. s. 28, p. 655).

H. Garman (1890, p. 189) says that "The note of this variety is a singular squawk which it is hardly possible to represent in words." Possibly the form he had might have been *B. fowleri*. Deckert (1914, No. 9, p. 2) writes "the call of the male cannot be distinguished from that of the Northern species." In 1921 he (Deckert) writes "this, the common Southern toad, was heard in May, June, July, August and September, its trilling call coming from rain-ditches in hammocks, pineland and from roadsides."

In 1921 we made these random notes on the first congress: April 24. The note sounds more like our droning *Bufo americanus*, not like the scream of *Bufo fowleri*. They are different . . . . Trill from 7 to 9 seconds in length, shorter than *Bufo americanus* possibly.

When we entered the swamp April 22 the toads were well advanced in their breeding period and less and less did they call in the day time unless a heavy rain or downpour came. Like the meadow frogs they called more and more in the evening and later and later in the evening as the season advanced.

The calling toads in cypress ponds and bays may be perched on a log, on a cypress knee or stub or stump at the base of a cypress tree or gum tree, on the moss, resting on aquatic plant stems, leaves, dead twigs usually in shallow water or on the edge of a pond. In overflow pools it may be anywhere in shallow places. Rarely, if ever, does it float when croaking. In flooded yam fields, cornfields, etc., it rests on the sides of the hills and may be a great nuisance to other frogs (Hylas especially). Along the railroad ditches and roadside pools it usually frequents the margins and edges when croaking. If the water be not deep it is not particular as to stance, but it is truly an alert, pert, "up on its toes" animal.

Some might think its note much like our Northern *Bufo*, some might call it a trill, a drone, a musical note in quality or a bass roar. Many of them nearby the observer are very deafening. Their choruses can be heard some distance away.

The note is of 7–9 seconds duration, with intervals from 4–60 seconds. Several counts Mr. Harper and I made were 14–23, 41–50, 4–11, 1 or 2 min., 18–27, 45–55, 8–15, 28–38, 55–3, 16–24, 41–55, 10–7, 31–38, 52–60, or an average of 31–55 seconds intervals. To Mr. Harper the "roar might be represented thus: "waghrrrrrr rrrrrr." Just like other species they may give weak notes; individuals may be freakish, hesitant, shrill or rarely open their mouth to scream or half inflate their throats to give puzzling notes. Usually when croaking the throat is distended to its full capacity with compressed body. The body is distended and the throat collapsed.

The voice record for 1921 is as follows:

1921

April 23.   Toads and southern meadow frogs began croaking in chorus in cypress ponds 1–4 mile southeast of camp. Air is 58°, water 60°. Began about 8:00 or 9:00 p. m.

April 14.   These began last night about 8:00. Air 66° at 9:15 a. m. Sun very bright Moonshine Pond. Plenty of toads calling later than 7:30 p. m.

"   25.   Bufo in chorus a. m.

"   30.   Tonight the air is cold. The thermometer at 7:00-8:00 p. m. is 58°. Over at Long Pond and elsewhere we hear no *Bufo terrestris*. Possibly because they are finished laying.

May 9.   A lone *Bufo terrestris* calling. Last night went out at 8:30 p. m. temperature 73°. Toads in bay at Billy's Lake were calling loudly. Could hear no toads in other ponds.

"   15.   *Bufo* calling at 9:00 p. m., temperature 65°. A cool wind and rain from the east.

May 16.   Many calling at night. Temperature 71°.

"   20.   Heard several.

"   30.   Heard a few *Bufo terrestris*. We need a rain.

June 4.   Downpour. In *Bufo* pond a few heard. In Crosby pond heard no end of them in deeper water. Temperature 70°. Hear plenty in negrao quarters. In *Bufo* pond more calling than when I went out tonight.

"   5.   Calling all about in rain puddles in cultivated fields at night.

"   17.   *Bufo terrestris* calling in evening.

"   21.   Late in night *Bufo terrestris* trilling.

"   22.   Calling at 2:00 a. m. Temperature 88°.

"   23.   Heard a few around Long Pond.

"   24.   Heard one calling at night.

"   29.   Commonly heard.

July 1.   Some toads going strongly.

"   3.   No end of *Bufo* calling after the downpour. Temperature 72°.

July   4.   Evening at 9:00 p. m.   75°, sultry. Toads are calling.
 ”   6.   Abundantly calling about 10:00 p. m.
 ”   23.   Last night I heard a few toads.
 ”   24.   About two or three calling near camp at night.
July 26.   Last night many toads calling.
 ”   28.   Several calling about camp.
 ”   29.   *Bufo terrestris* were commonly calling.
 ”   30.   Toads calling last night.
Aug. 10.   Several heard.
 ”   13.   One heard.
 ”   14.   Several heard.
 ”   16.   Several calling at Camp Pinckney.

1922

June 19.   Commonly calling at night in first dreen or slough.
July   2.   Assembly Starling Branch 8:30 p. m., many calling.
 ”   3.   Tonight from 8:00 p. m. to 1:00 a. m., July 4, heard toads. Some at
Trader's Hill Ponds. In many places they were heard.
 ”   11.   At second "dreen" several calling. A few heard at other places.
Temperature 70°.
 ”   25.   Hard rain. Plenty of toads to be heard in the woods to the west edge
of the island.
Aug.   1.   Several in gutters of Waycross. Weak voice not deafening chorus.
 ”   2.   One calling at night.
 ”   8.   A few lone voices 8:00–11:00 p. m., after a rain. Temperature 79°.
Aug. 11.   Heard some 8:30–10:00 p. m., but rather few. In overflowed area of
Spanish Creek only chorus.
 ”   13.   A few in road from St. Mary's to camp. In one or two instances a
fair chorus.
 ”   18.   Several calling in evening.
 ”   19.   One calling at night.   ..
 ”   26.   Several heard about dark.

Considering 12 choruses from April 23 to July 26, 1921, we have for nearby
Weather Bureau Stations maxima 72°–94°, usual range 81°–89°, average 84°,
mode 85°, for the day before; and minima from 50°–76° (one 45°), average
61°; for the day of the record, maxima from 80°–92°, average 86°, mode 86°;
minima of 50°–74°, average 66°. Heavy rains of .90–2.80 preceded most of
the choruses or at the time of the chorus. In the last of April maxima of
81°–89° and minima of 50°–62° obtained during croaking whether in chorus or
scattering calls. In the first half of May the maxima 72°–92°, minima 53°–67°
obtained. In the last of May maxima of 80°–97° and minima of 63°–72°
obtained. In the first half of June maxima were 83°–90°, minima 56°–71°.
In the last of June maxima were from 80°–98°, minima 67°–78°. In the first
of July maxima were 85°–92°, minima 67°–74°. In late July maxima were
85°–90°, minima 67°–72°. Thus we have minima of 50°–62°, 53°–67°, 63°–72°,
56°–71°, 67°–78°, 67°–74°, 67°–72°. The later the season of chorus quite
likely the greater the rain to start it.

The actual records of air temperatures taken by us in camp in 1921 when
we heard *Bufo terrestris* were 58°–88°. Most of the records range from
65°–75° and were preceded or accompanied by rain, or cloudy weather. When
we first entered the swamp on April 22 and 23 we had considerable rain.

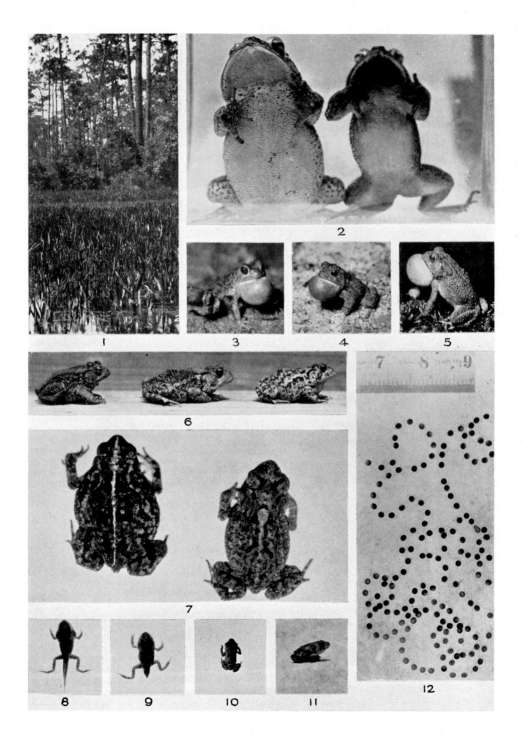

The species bred from April 23–25. We heard them at 60°–74°. On April 30 we had air 58° or less, in fact it went down to 50° or 51°. That night we heard no toads from 50°–58°.

In 1922 whenever we had a chorus or considerable calling from July 2 to August 18 downpours, rain or cloudy weather obtained. Our lowest temperatures during the day were from 70°–81°. The minima for nearby stations were from 62°–74°. The best choruses are at least 68°–74°. Rain is the important factor. Toads will call at 60° or lower but humidity dictates largely in the matter.

MATING

Male (From life, June 9, 1921). Line from front line of eyes almost to vent pale gull gray or mineral gray. Black spots along dorsum: one pair near cephalic edge of eye; one pair from upper eyelid connected across the meson; one in the mid dorsum between tympana; a pair either side of middle between the rear ends of tympana; a pair of small spots; a pair of large spots where hump comes; a pair of small spots; a pair just ahead of vent—all black spots of dorsum thinly encircled with chalcedony yellow. More or less broken pale gull gray or mineral gray line from tympanum to groin. Below this a prominent black area. Tubercles of back black or deep brown tipped. Lighter areas on rear of hind legs sulphur yellow. Either side of vent a few orange tubercles. Under parts pale smoke gray. Pectoral region, under parts of hind legs, and sides with black spots. Lower jaw rim like belly color. Throat deep mouse gray or dark mouse gray with widely spaced white dots. Gives throat discolored appearance. Light area of dorsum of hind foot same color as the rear of thighs. Very little rusty on front of thighs and groin. Top of first two fingers with excrescences and slight line of such on edge of third finger. Color of excrescences chocolate or better hay's maroon or maroon.

Female (From life, June 9, 1921). Lighter, larger. Practically no spots on pectoral region. None on throat. Throat same color as belly. Practically no rusty spots. Ground color of the dorsum more greenish olive. Sometimes at breeding season males and females may be alike in color, e.g., on April 24, 1921, several pairs were thus, several pairs reddish, one pair gray. Most of pairs, however, were diverse.

Structural differences. Some of the differences noted in the field are:

1. On April 24, 1921, we observed the following:
   a. One male of a pair was about 3/5 of the female in size.
   b. One pair, both male and female, were reddish. Two more pairs red. One pair grey.
   c. In some cases males and females alike in color but usually different.
   d. One pair with one hind leg of female freshly eaten off, possibly by a turtle.
   e. The backs of the thumb and second finger of the male have excrescences on the top and a slight excrescence on the inner edge of the third finger.

f.   The females usually have the head crests larger, thicker and more raised but this does not always obtain.

An examination of our and other collections reveal the following difference or notes:

a.   The range of 84 males is 42–68 mm., one 82 mm., average 55 mm., mean 55 mm.

b.   The range of 136 females is 44–88 mm., average 63 mm., mean 62 mm.

c.   Usually the females have throat like rest of underparts and the males have it discolored but some large females have throat clouded (e.g., a 64 mm. ♀) very clouded (e.g., a 76 mm. ♀) or a male may have throat quite light in color.

d.   We have given 42–50 mm. as within the range of adult males. As a matter of fact these have no excrescences on fingers or very slight ones, but most of these have fully or partially discolored throats. At about 54 mm. a male is sure to have excrescences and discolored throat.

e.   The heavy spotting in pectoral region may be in either sex or both. The one median pectoral spot (like that of *Bufo fowleri*) occasionally appears and may be in either sex.

f.   Sometimes in the external recognition of sexes in the debatable sizes of 42–49 mm. the higher or larger cranial crests in the females help in the determination.

Duration. Usually the amplexation may last only an hour or so; if the female be not ripe it may extend for days. Often the mated pairs in camp might not lay the first night of capture. For example, "on July 2, 1922, at Starling Branch Crossing 8:30 p. m. to midnight took one pair. Brought it to camp. It did not lay on the night on July 2–3 and yet another taken at same place July 3 from 8:00 p. m. to 1:00 a. m., July 4, laid between 1:00–7:00 a. m., July 4, or 0-7 hours later."

On April 24, 1921, two of the pairs were not broken by the next morning. On May 2, we have a note about these that "the two toad pairs collected April 23–24 are now broken," or 7 or 8 days later. On June 7 we have the note that a pair "Have remained in embrace June 7 from night of June 4. (Let them remain until June 9 when we forcibly broke them) "Or 5 days' duration. Or on July 11 "at the second dreen (Chesser Id.) we found a mated pair . . . Brought it into camp. . . . Temperature 70°. July 12. The pair has not yet laid. July 16. The pair of July 11 fixed July 14."

C. S. Brimley in his notes on North Carolina Herpetology (Copeia, 1923, p. 4) writes "Southern Toad (*Bufo terrestris*) found common at Laurel Hill, Scotland Co., June 1 and 2, 1922. On June 2 a number were found breeding on the edge of a roadside pool, and the following facts noted. The unmated male toads at nine in the morning were screaming loudly on the edge of the pool, but had not entered the water, while at noon they were in the water and mated, but almost silent."

Night or day.

April 23. Croaking in chorus in cypress ponds. Air 58°· water 60°. Began about 8:00 or 9:00 p. m. Went over at 10:00 p. m. Caught two mated pairs of *Bufo*. Took several males and one female. Brought these back. Mated two males with two females, expect four pairs tomorrow morning.

April 24. The male and female of a pair if not yet laying are when taken out of the water often given to urinating for protection. . . . Fifteen pairs in an area 6 feet square. Sun very bright.

May 15. Rather cool. Toads are travelling everywhere.

May 16. Crosby Pond at night. In the pond are no end of *Bufo terrestris*. Several mated pairs.

June 4. Everywhere in road home were toads. Hear plenty in lumber quarters. It was 70° last night when I returned. In *Bufo* pond were more *Bufo terrestris* than any night yet.

July 3. (In overflow area north of camp). Here in these temporary grassy pools were no end of *Bufo terrestris*, pairs and single toads.

Amplexation. Normally the amplexation is axillary. The last two fingers are not dug into the axil and often rest on the arm insertion of the female.

But, as with other toads, abnormal embraces are not unusual in this species. On April 24, 1921, we saw one lone male embracing the floating rootstock of *Pontederia*. This male on the *Pontederia* root could be pulled along or the root floated yet he would not let go.

Or, supra-axillary embraces may occur, e.g., June 7, 1921, "The male *Bufo* in camp of a mated pair is so small its embrace is supra-axillary. Had dug into sides of female at least 1/3 to 1/2 inch above arm insertion almost straight back from the tympanum and a little below middle of the parotoid."

Or subaxillary fashion may obtain. On July 3, 1921, we have the note. "In one mated pair of *Bufo* small male mating regular axillary fashion and slightly back of axilla of small female. A large male holding a small female behind fore limbs and its hands on the breast of the female and almost touching."

Occasionally a toad will attempt to embrace a meadow frog or leap at it. When toads are breeding where *Hyla gratiosa* are, the impetuous toad males will annoy the croaking *Hylas* considerably or any other *Hyla* or frog near its size.

OVULATION

Habitat. In 1921 we generally concluded that they preferred cypress ponds, but the following notes will give some idea of some other habitats found:

April 24. We captured some in recently dug post holes. After rain a night ago these toads began to assemble in the ponds.

April 24. Moonshine pond. At its north end shallow and amongst the gums plenty of toads calling.

May 9. Toads in cypress bay wooded swampy edge of island and also at Billy's Lake where railroad spur goes across it.

May 16. Crosby pond. No end of toads. Some would float on surface of pond. Many a toad would perch at base of a cypress tree or on a log or on a cypress stub 3–8 inches above the water. Several mated pairs in water 4 inches to 1 foot deep. Flashlighted only toads.

May 31. ˙No end of toads in temporary pools in negro quarters west.
June 4. Went to an open pond (no trees) south of our old camp. Here no end
of *Bufo terrestris* in deeper water.
June 6. Went to Oak Toad pond in cleared fields to photograph where oak toads
and Florida tree frogs were. Found plenty of *Bufo terrestris* eggs.
June 6. In temporary ponds in the street of the white quarters are toad's eggs.
July 3. In grassy overflow area toads common. Common in furrow pools of
newly planted sweet potato fields. In white quarters street pools no end of
Bufo terrestris.

Later we found them in roadside ditches, ditch pools beside the lumber
railroad, pools in tracks in wood roads, in dug pits, old field ponds, overflows
of branches, quiet waters of stream edges and countless other transient places.
On one occasion their eggs were so plentiful in impermanent pools that we
wrote June 4 "What a frightful waste of frog life in transient pools."

Period. Holbrook (1842, Vol. V, p. 9) speaks of "the male (seeking)
the female in the month of May, when hundreds of them many be seen together in some stagnant pool, on which they deposit their spawn, and then
return again to the land."

During our stay 1912 a very few southern toads were heard and only one
record of eggs was made on Billy's Island, June 3, 1912. These were lost
like those of *Bufo quercicus* and were in similar situations. In the main, the
species doubtless is finished with egg-laying by the end of May, and it must
begin early for Mr. Harper reports "swarms of little toads appeared over the
paths, etc. about the middle of May, 1912."

In 1921 we have males croaking from April 23 to August 16, in 1922 from
June 19 to August 26. In 1921 we have mating records from April 23 to
July 29 or 30; in 1922 from July 2 to August 13. In 1921 we have ovulation
records from April 23 to July 3; in 1922 from June 22 to July 11. Throughout my notes I have the ovulation period given variously as follows: April 15
or earlier to August 1, August 13, August 17; April 24 to May 22; April 24
to August 13; April 24 or earlier to August 1 or August 15 or later; April 1
to August 15 or later.

In 1923 (p. 34) we write "From April 15 or earlier to September 1 six
forms breed." *Bufo terrestris* is given as one of the six. In one set of notes
before we knew *Pseudacris nigrita* and *Scaphiopus holbrookii* from this region
we made it the third breeder after *Acris gryllus* and *Rana sphenocephala.*
It may be the fourth or fifth breeder if not the third in the sequence. In 1924
Wright & Wright (p. 380) give ovulation "Season, April 15 or earlier to
August 13."

In the light of the fact that most mating and ovulations were at night
from April 22 onward and because of transformation data as early as April
27 or mid May this species may begin as early as March 1 to April 1 or
earlier.

Temperature and humidity. On April 23, 1921, we saw that toads would
breed at 58°–60° or lower, but whenever ovulation occurred we generally had
records of 60° or higher, usually at least 64°–75°, the average 71°. In 1922
most of our records of air temperatures at ovulation were 71°–79° but the

record runs farther into the summer. See Voice. As stated under voice a drenching rain proves the important item in starting ovulation. We observed that toads might breed at air temperatures of 58° or lower but 64°–75° or 60°–71° seems a fair approximation of the necessary minimum. Rain, however, is most important.

Egg-laying process. This species behaves in ovulation much as does *Bufo americanus*. On April 24 we made a few observations. The unvarnished journal notes are: When the female is not ovulating the male has the hind legs free and floating, but when female ovulates several inches of egg string the male brings his knees into the groin of the female and the heels almost touch the upper surface of the hind feet against the under side of the female's femur and near her cloacal opening. Female with hind legs stretched back, sometimes heels touching, sometimes not. Eggs rest in cup made by heels and feet of male. Male and female may remain in emission attitude 4 or 5 minutes or less. After the female crawls 1 foot or more, a minute or more may elapse before another emission. When a female has begun ovulation it it easy to pull the egg string out of the female. Water temperature where laying 71°, air in sun 94°. Surface of water at 11:30 a. m. 81°.

On June 7, 1921, we have the note that "Twice have *Bufo terrestris* females laid a complement of eggs without the attendant male."

EGGS

Attachment. In many transient pools the egg strings are strewn on the bottom or in some ponds in shallow water. More often the eggs are in strings attached or woven about grass, vegetation, twigs or other support in the water. In one pond we found them in a clear area and edge of a pond next the *Pontederia* zone amongst scattering *Sagittaria* and another water plant. These made a mat about which the eggs were woven. Sometimes they are fastened near the surface in deep pools or along lake edges.

Egg mass, egg description. In 1914 we wrote "Their characters if different in minute form from those of *B. l. americanus* can not now be stated. In general appearance, however, they were identical." Even in 1921 we made no detailed field notes on egg description but in 1922 on July 4 we have these rough characters outlined. "Pair caught at Starling Branch crossing laid between 1–7 a. m. today. Eggs seem to have only one jelly envelope. To-night about 6:00 found a mass of eggs in Anna's pond. In road to Folkston several masses found. The inner envelope of file revealed a day or more after laying, not apparent when fresh. This inner envelope averages 2.0 mm. It is near the outer envelope. No partitions between eggs. There is now a clear elliptical envelope or membrane around each egg. These do not touch the inner tube though. Possibly they are vitelline membranes. The outer envelope is 2.8 mm."

On July 11 we caught a mated pair. On July 14 we fixed it and on July 16 we counted the eggs in the left ovary of the female. There were 1,444 eggs. This female was rather a small one, not over medium size at the most. A total complement of 2,888 doubtless is small for this species.

Detailed laboratory studies by Mrs. Wright are as follows. "July 4, 1922, Starling Branch *Bufo terrestris* eggs. No inner envelope—no partitions—just one homogeneous tube. 8–11 eggs in 30 mm. Black with small grayish-white vegetative pole. Tube 2.8 mm. in diameter."

"Cannot find inner envelope or has inner tube swelled to meet outer tube. Finally found inner tube but not very well marked. Inner tube present but close to outer tube."

In another note we find "Tube inclined to be scalloped due to indentation between each two eggs. Axis of developing vitellus longitudinal with tube."

Or "vitelli 2.4–2.6 or 2.8 mm. apart. In others 1.8–2.0 mm. apart."

Other notes are: "vitelli 1.0, 1.2 or 1.4 mm., average 1.2, mean 1.2 mm.; inner tube 2.2–3.4 mm.; outer tube 2.6–4.6 mm. 6 eggs in 20 mm.; 7 eggs in 20 mm.; 7 eggs in 30 mm.; 8 eggs in 30 mm. and one 12 eggs in 30 mm."

Our final characterization in 1924 (p. 380) became the following: "Eggs in files. Files long (several feet in length or often a meter or more long); vitellus 1.0 to 1.4 mm.; tube diameter 2.6 to 4.6 mm. Inner tube present. 7 or 8 eggs in 30 mm. (1 3/16 inches); distinct space between eggs; no partition apparent; tube inclined to be slightly emarginate between the eggs; inner tube 2.2 to 3.4 mm.; outer tube 2.6 to 4.6 mm. Egg complement, 2,888."

Dangers. If the eggs are laid in shallow water 1 to 4 or 5 inches from the surface the danger of drying up in many ponds is grave to say nothing of the transitory localities the species picks in periods of downpours.

HATCHING PERIOD

On April 24, 1921, we found egg laying with water temperature 71°, surface water 81° at 11:30 a. m. On April 28 we make the note "*Bufo lentiginosus* eggs laid night of April 23–24 and morning of April 24 hatched a day or so ago. Collected April 28, 4:00 p. m. Temperature 82°." This implies 2 to 3 days for hatching. On June 22 found some eggs at Starling Branch crossing presumably laid June 19. These were about ready to hatch. They were in the open. But at Camp Pinckney in the shade on deeper water, turpentine water pits they were not hatched though we make the note they must have been laid June 19. These records would imply 3 or more days for hatching. Our data is scanty. Hatching apparently comes in 2–4 days.

TADPOLE

Color description from life (July 7, 1921). General color is black with scattered dots which are pale purplish vinaceous. Venter black with few scattered light purplish vinaceous spots but not clustered to make one continuous mass of color as on the belly of *B. quercicus.*

Tail. Upper crest spotted but not so strongly as in *Bufo quercicus.* Lower crest almost clear of spots. Lower edge of muscular part white or light chalcedony yellow.

General appearance. Body small (26 mm.) ovoid broader nearer vent than eyes. Dorsal aspect shows body decidedly tapers ahead of the eyes. Dorsal crest low, extends but slightly on to the body to a vertical just ahead of the buds of the hind legs. Dorsal and ventral crests about equal and about equal to the depth of the musculature. Tail short, tip rounded. Spiracle sinistral, directed mainly backward somewhat upwards, below the lateral axis. Eye above lateral axis. Eyes dorsal, close together, slightly nearer lateral outline than middorsal line. Anus median, opening in a level lower than the lower edge of the ventral crest. Muciferous crypts indistinct.

Mouth parts: Teeth 2/3.

Upper labium fringed with a continuous row of labial teeth, the papillae extending only each end of this fringe. The end of the second upper row does not extend beyond the end of the upper fringe. The median space between the two parts of the second row is contained 1.4–2.1 times the lateral row Horny beak about equal to or slightly less than the 3rd lower labial row of teeth or contained 1.75 times in the upper fringe, or about 1.5 times the first or second row of lower labial teeth, which are about equal. The third row of lower labial teeth may be contained 1.2–1.4 times in the length of the second or first lower lateral row. Rows of papillae at least two very prominent, sometimes 3–5 rows at corner of mouth. Lower loop of papillary border very prominent with at least 2 distinct rows of papillae. This loop sometimes extends slightly beneath the end of the third row of teeth. This loop decidedly lower in level than end of the third labial lower row.

Measurements. Length of body (5.0–9.8 mm.) in tail (9.0–15.0 mm.) 1.05–1.66, average 1.3. Width (5.2–7.0 mm.) of body in its own length 1.36–1.74, average 1.51. Depth (3.6–5.0 mm.) of body 1.22–1.6 in body width, average 1.36 (2.4–5.0 mm.) of body 1.86–2.25 in body length, average 2.07. Depth of tail in length of tail 2.4–4.5, average 3.27. Muscular part (1.4 2.2 mm.) 1.5–3.0 in depth of tail, average 2.11. Spiracle 1.0–2.0 nearer base of hind legs or vent region (3.6–6.0 mm.) than the tip of the snout (4.18–7.4 mm.), average 1.61. Spiracle 1.0–1.53 nearer eye (2.8–4.4 mm.) than base of hind legs or vent, average 1.26. Eye 1.0–1.57 nearer to tip of snout (2.6–3.8 mm.) than to spiracle (2.8–4.4 mm.), average 1.19. Nostril 1.1–1.8 nearer eye (1.0–1.8 mm.) than snout (1.6–2.6 mm.), average 1.48. Mouth (2.0–2.8 mm.) usually 1.2–1.6 larger than internasal space (1.6–2.4 mm.), average 1.36. Mouth contained 1.00–1.5 (average 1.17) in interorbital distance (2.0–3.4 mm.) Internasal space contained in interorbital space 1.1–2.1, average 1.56.

The dimensions of the largest tadpoles are:

	mm.		mm.
Total length	24	Spiracle to vent	4.5
Body length	9.8	Spiracle to eye	4.0
Body depth	5.0	Eye to snout	3.0
Body Width	7.0	Eye to nostril	1.4
Tail length	14.2	Nostril to snout	2.2
Tail depth	4.8	Mouth	2.8
Musculature of tail	1.6	Interorbital distance	3.4
Spiracle to snout	6.8	Internasal "	2.0

Measurements of 1912 specimens. The measurements of 20 specimens are as follows: Length of body contained 1.2–2 times in the tail, average 1.37,

mode 1.3. Width of the body in the length of the body 1.2–1.7, average
1.55. Nostrils .8–1.5 nearer the eye than the snout, average 1.2, mode 1.22,
one example 2.0. Eye lateral, usually much nearer to the snout than spiracle.
Distance between nostrils in interorbital distance .8–1.8 times, one example
2.0, average 1.25; in mouth 1.33–2.0, average 1.6. Spiracle 1.34–1.7, usually
1.4–1.6, nearer the base of the hind legs than tip of snout, average 1.47. Anus
median. Depth of the tail in its own length 3.8–6.0, average 4.6. Depth of
the muscular part of the tail in the depth of the tail 1.0–2.5, average 1.5.
Interorbital distance is contained in the mouth 1.1–2.0, average 1.4. Greatest
length 20.25 mm. Greatest length of the body 8.5 mm. Greatest length of
tail 12.75 mm. Greatest depth of tail 3.0 mm.

General remarks. In coloration, mouth parts and measurements these
are not unlike those of *Bufo americanus.*

LARVAL PERIOD

On June 22, 1922, we found eggs about ready to hatch in No. 2 turpentine
pit at Camp Pinckney. One July 25, at this same pit or 33 days later *Bufo*
tadpoles were transforming and transformed. We entered the swamp on
April 22, 1921, on April 23 and 24 eggs were laid and our first transformation
records are April 27 and May 22. The latter record is probably not from the
April 23 and 24 eggs or if so it gives a month for larval period. The next transformations come June 1, June 4, June 16. These if from April 23 and 24
eggs would give 38, 39, 41, 42 and 54, and 55 days. Doubtless 38–55 days
falls within the period though less time down to 30 days may be probable
on special occasions.

TRANSFORMATION

Period. In 1912 on June 12 in another more permanent pond a fine series
from tadpoles to transformations were taken. On June 24, still another
series of transformed frogs was taken.

In 1921 on April 27 around Long Pond's edges we found tadpoles, transformed toads and different sized young from 10 mm. to 24 mm. On May 7
in pools either side of the railroad found transforming young and different
stages of tadpoles. On May 15 many transformed young were travelling
on Billy's Island in the rain. On May 22 we secured more transformations.
On June 1 we note "toad tadpoles hopping around." On June 4 we make
three collections of transformed toads. On June 16 others were recorded and
transformations in July.

In 1922 we found southern toad toad tadpoles transformed at ponds 1
mile south of Trader's Hill and also at Trader's Hill Landing on June 23.
Four days later we find a few in Anna's Pond. On June 30, Saddlebag Pond
has transformed toads. A month later on July 24 and 25 at Camp Pinckney
transformed and transforming toads were in evidence.

This gives us transformation from April 27 to July 25 but eggs laid in
August must transform in September or even October.

Size. In 1912 the transformation sizes of 13 specimens range from 7.5–11.5
mm., average 9.75 mm., mode 9.5 mm. A series of June 24, 1912 was 6.5,

7, 7.5, 7.5, 7.5, 7.5, 7.5, 7.5, 8, 8, 8, and 8.5 mm. In 1921 our field notes seemed to imply 8–10 mm. in size, but access to two series reveals the following: Several taken April 27 are 6.5, 7, 7, 7, 7, 7.5, 7.5, 7.5, 7.5, 8, 8, 8, 8, 8, 8, 8, 8, 8.5, 8.5, 8.5, 8.5, 9, 9, 9, 9, 9, 9.5, 9.5, 9.5, 10, 10, 10, 10.5 mm.; or five of June 16 prove 8, 8, 8, 8.5, 9, 9.5 mm.

In 1922 on July 24 we secured a series of sizes as follows: 7, 7, 7.5, 7.5, 7.5, 7.5, 7.5, 7.5, 7.5, 7.5, 7.5, 7.5, 7.5, 8, 8, 8, 8, 8, 8, 8, 8, 8, 8, 8, 8, 8, 8, 8, 8.5, 8.5, 8.5, 8.5, 8.5, 8.5, 8.5, 8.5, 8.5, 8.5, 9 transfg, 9, 9, 9.5. One specimen appearing with this lot, is 12 mm. but it is far past transformation.

Apparently the range is about 6.5—10—10.5 mm., the mode 8 mm., average 8 mm.

GROWTH

If transformation comes at 6.5–11.5 mm., and males reach 84 mm. and females 92 mm., how long a period elapses from emergence from tadpole to the maximum sizes? Of if maturity comes at 42 mm. for male or 44 mm. for female, but better about 50 mm. or more for each, what is the interval between transformation and maturity?

Ninety-six specimens (U. S. National Museum material, 7 lots) taken in April by Dr. E. A. Mearns at Lake Kissimee seem to fall into the following groups: 37–47 mm.; 48–59 mm.; 59–68 mm.; 69–78 mm. Some other material in U. S. National Museum (158 specimens) falls into the following presumptive lots: 16–25 mm.; 25–35 mm.; 35–47 mm.; 48–59 mm.; 60–68 mm.; 69–78 mm.; 79–85 or 88 mm. On the basis of the 1912 Okefinokee material, the material seems to fall into groups 13–18 mm.; 27–29 mm.; 43– mm.; 48–59.5 mm.; 61.5–68 mm.; 70– mm. Our 1921 and 1922 material shapes as 6.5–10 mm.; 13–19 mm.; 21–28 mm.; 34–37 mm.; 44 mm.; 48–56.5 mm.; 58–66 mm.; 69–79.5 mm.; 81–86 mm.; 92 mm.

Apparently this species transforms at 6.5–10 or 11 mm.; at one year may be 13–25 mm.; at two years 25–35 mm.; three-year-olds 34–47 mm.; 48–59 or 60 mm. for four-year-olds; 59–66 mm. for five-year-olds; 69–78 or 79 mm. for six-year-olds; 79–86 or 88 mm. for seven-year-olds; 90 mm. eight years or more.

The first two years of presumptive growth may be interpreted wrongly. This species breeds over a long period and so it will be hard to arrive at presumptive growths without actual records of marked specimens, e.g., our 13–25 mm. may not be correct, for on June 16, 1921, we took transformation sizes from 8–9.5 mm. and three individuals 17, 21 and 28 mm. Should first year's growth be 17–28 mm. instead of 13–25 mm.? That we dare not say.

Transformation comes at 6.5–10 or 11 mm. When do the parotoids, cranial crests and tympana appear? We have examined our material of sizes from 11–35 mm., one 12.5 mm. specimen taken May 22, 1912, "apparently past transformation" has none of these three structures. A series of seven specimens taken May 31, 1921, and ranging from 13–16 mm. have not the tympana, crests or parotoid definitely outlined. In 1912 (May 15–June 24) fourteen different accessions of material from 11–16 mm. in length reveal none of these structures except two lots of 16 mm. One 16 mm. individual had them not and two had no crests nor tympana but the parotoid

were just outlined. All the accessions from 17 mm. onward had the parotoid
in different degrees of distinctness. From 11 to 22 mm. no tympana appear.
At 23 or 24 mm, the anterior half begins to appear as distinct but individuals
appear up to 24.5 mm. with no tympana. Some there are which do not have
it distinct until they reach 27.5–28 mm. To 21–23 mm. no cranial crests
appear but occasionally in this range crests are just outlined posteriorly.
From 23 to 24 mm. and onward the crests may appear as a groove or first
apparent posteriorly or as a fine row of tubercles. Occasionally a toad to
28 or 29 mm. may not have the crests outlined. At 34 or 35–37 mm. the
crests are beginning to thicken at their rear ends.

FOOD

Catesby makes the following notes "The Land Frog. The Back and
Upper part of this frog is gray, and thick spotted with dark brown spots; the
Belly dusky white, and faintly spotted: The Irides of the eyes red. They vary
somewhat in Colour, some being more gray, others inclining to brown. Their
Bodies are large, resembling more a Toad than a Frog, yet they do not crawl
as Toads do, but leap; they are seen most in wet weather, yet are very frequent in the higher lands, and appear in the hottest time of the Day: They
feed on Insects, particularly of one kind, which the following Accident seems
to confirm. As I was sitting in a sultry evening, with some company without
Doors, one of us let fall from a Pipe of Tobacco some light burning ashes,
which was immediately catched up and swallowed by a Frog of this kind.
This put us upon tempting him with a red hot Wood Coal, not less than the
End of one's Finger, which he also swallowed greedily; thus afterwards I
always found one or other of them easily deceived in this manner, as I imagine,
be taking it to be a *Cicindela*, or Fire-Fly, which on hot nights are very
numerous in Virginia and Carolina, where also these Frogs abound.—Catesby.
Vol. 11, p. 69.

Shaw (1802, p. 173) writes "This animal is common in Carolina and Virginia, feeding, like most others of this genus, on insects, and is said to be
particularly attracted by any luminous insects, as fire-flies, glow-worms,
etc., and will even seize and swallow a small, live wood coal of the size of the
end of the finger; mistaking it for some luminous insect, and seeming to receive no immediate injury in consequence." Harlan (1825, p. 345) has it
"preying on living insects only." In 1842, Holbrook (Vol. V, p. 9) says "It
feeds on various insects which it seizes only while alive and in motion."

ENEMIES

In 1912 these notes were made: The southern toad has a merciless set of
foes. The hog-nosed snake prefers them to all other diets and one snake may
have as many as two or three full grown toads in its stomach at one time. The
black snakes and garter snakes also are very partial to toads. In all instances
the head is swallowed first, and it is interesting to see how prominently the
head crests of *B. terrestris* stand out and how resistant they are to digestive
processes when the other forward parts of the body are well digested.

In 1921 we held the killifishes such as *Gambusia, Lucania* or *Fundulus* doubtless did little damage to the eggs. Possibly some newly hatched young might suffer. In some ponds turtles do considerable damage to tadpoles, or to adults as well. In some of the breeding congresses we have chanced on southern water snakes hunting for toads or frogs. At times we have caught them in the act of seizing a toad or frog or with the subject partially down. In 1922 on July 15 on our way out to Folkston we found a spreading adder. It began to hiss and spread. By pressing a stick on it it turned over on its back. By pressing farther it disarticulated its lower jaw and lolled out its tongue and finally disgorged a freshly caught southern toad.

AUTUMNAL DISAPPEARANCE

The Cornell parties which entered the swamp in December and January reported it in these months. In the U. S. National Museum collections there is scant if any material taken in October and November and first of December. In the same way our collection has little at these months. Doubtless from November to January is its most inactive period.

AFFINITIES

In 1912 we wrote "*Relationships.*—The American toads of the old *Bufo lentiginosus* series are yet in an unsatisfactory stage of analysis. At first Cope employed the cranial crests as one of the cardinal characters of differentiation. On this criterion *Bufo terrestris* and *Bufo americanus* can usually be separated, the former with posterior ends of the frontoparietal crests very much elevated and swollen and the latter with this region and whole crest low. Usually this character suffices to separate the two though we can find within these two a small degree of variability. The other two forms *B. fowleri* and *B. woodhousei* have the crests parallel or divergent, raised or low, merged at posterior ends or free and hence Miss Dickerson discards the character and ascribes the confusion within this assemblage almost solely to the reliance on this one character. If we rely on color we encounter an almost perfect *B. terrestris* duplicate (No. 6575) of the *B. fowleri* in the vertebral arrangement of the six pairs of dorsal spots as given by Miss Dickerson (p. 64). To be sure the writers' impressions of the color of *B. terrestris* and *B. fowleri* are that the former averages darker than the latter while the latter inclines towards the greenish or yellowish grey. The under-parts of *Bufo terrestris* are not always unspotted and Holbrook's figure shows the reverse condition. Our specimens are about evenly divided on the point, and rarely *B. fowleri* from N. J., L. I., and Woods Hole, Mass., are somewhat spotted though not as markedly so as in the northeastern Canadian specimens of *B. americanus* while some of the *B. americanus* of Ithaca may be practically if not solely unspotted. The head length is equally emphasized as a good distinction but since Cope's time most authors have not defined what they mean by head length in toad descriptions. Cope measured to the end of the frontoparietal crests and Miss Dickerson in her figure of terms employed gives the usual measurement to the caudal border of the tympanum. On the latter basis some *B. fowleri* would

have heads 3.5 in the length while obviously her 4 to 4.5 times in the body
refers to Cope's method of measurement. Some of *B. americanus* according
to Cope's method would be 4 in the body, but if measured to the tympanum
would be 3.5 in the length. Or a Texan *B. woodhousei* with head 4.6 in the
length by cranial crests test would be 3.5 by the tympanic rule, quite far
moved from "head five times in total length." The double file noted in the
egg strings of the European *Bufo vulgaris*, has been urged as distinctive of *B.
fowleri* while *B. americanus* never has such an arrangement. Rarely, *B.
americanus* eggs are in the double file and certainly *B. americanus* can and
does breed from April 20–August. The author has seen the eggs of *Bufo
fowleri* in two instances only and in each case they were more or less a double file.

"At the present, most beginners and some experts, some of which are with-
holding judgment, are unable to determine whether *B. fowleri* is distinct
enough to be considered a separate species whether it exists as a distinct form
at all or whether it needs an even finer refinement of descriptive characteristics.
At present the authors withhold judgment and merely show some of the
difficulties. *B. americanus* and *B. lentiginosus* seem quite distinct. Of *B.
fowleri* we say it probably exists as a separate form but needs description with
an abundant comparative series from Ontario to Texas, from which regions
our series has been taken but not in sufficient numbers to warrant a decision."

The foregoing paragraphs were written in 1913 but today the author is not
yet ready to speak any ill-considered conclusions on the *Bufo americanus–
fowleri–terrestris–woodhousii* complex. I have not worked on the life history
of *B. woodhousii*, have seen eggs of *Bufo fowleri* but four times and need more
personal experience with these two species. In its egg characters *Bufo
terrestris* has two jelly tubes like *B. americanus* but like *Bufo fowleri* may have
no partitions between the eggs. We have tadpoles of *Bufo americanus, Bufo
terrestris* and *Bufo fowleri* but feel hesitant to venture opinions on their degree
of relationship. On superficial morphological characters, in some respects,
Bufo terrestris appears as much related to *Bufo fowleri* as *Bufo americanus*.

Holbrook (1842, Vol. V, p. 10) reviews its history to 1842. We give his
"General Remarks. Catesby first described and gave a figure of this animal
under the name of Land-frog; and although his figure is badly executed, both
as to drawing and colouring (the elevation of the superciliary ridges not being
marked, and the eyes represented as red), it has been repeatedly copied by later
naturalists, as Foster, Shaw, etc. The name, however, Rana (Bufo) terrestris,
cannot be retained, as it is previously applied to another animal.

"Bosc, who from a long residence in Carolina, had a good opportunity of
examining this animal, refers it to the *Rana musica* of Linnaeus, in which he
is followed by Daudin, Merrem, and most naturalists. This cannot be correct,
for there are no toads, as far as has been hitherto ascertained, common to
North and South America; and Linnaeus, in the twelfth edition of the Systema
Naturae, gives Surinam, as the country of his *Rana musica*. Neither the
specific name, *terrestris*, nor *musicus* can then be applied to this animal, but
we must give it the one next in order under which it is found described—
Rana (bufo) lentiginosa of Shaw."

In 1849 (Appendix p. 15) Holbrook gives both *Bufo lentiginosus* Shaw and *Bufo erythronotus* Holbrook as of Georgia. In 1854 Girard (p. 56, p. 86) lists *Bufo americanus* LeConte, *Bufo lentiginosus* Holbrook with *Bufo erythronotus* as a synonym, *Bufo woodhousii* Girard, *Bufo cognatus* Say, etc. He was nearer the situation than LeConte in 1855 (1856, p. 430) who gives *B. musicus* Daudin (*B. lentiginosus* Holbrook), *Bufo americanus*, *B. erythronotus*. His comment that Girard is wrong in referring *B. erythronotus* to *Bufo lentiginosus* may be on a par with his placing *Bufo cognatus* in *Bufo muscicus*. DeKay (1842, p. 68) gives both *Bufo lentiginosus* and *Bufo erythronotus* each distinct, also *Bufo cognatus* as distinct and all three as extralimital to New York State. Only *Bufo americanus* does he credit to New York.

In 1858 Albert Gunther (p. 63) gives *Bufo lentiginosus* as consisting of two varieties "Var. A. *Bufo americanus* . . . . Bony ridges moderate, but swollen behind and "Var. B. *Bufo musicus* . . . . Bony ridge swollen behind.

In 1882 Boulenger (pp. 306–310) gives *Bufo lentiginosus* as having 5 subspecies, namely, Var. A. *americanus* (*quercicus, woodhousii*, etc.), Var. B. *musicus* (*lentiginosus*), Var. C. *frontosus*, Var. D. *cognatus*, Var. E. *fowleri*. His Var. B. *musicus* (*lentiginosus*) is with "Supraorbital ridges swollen behind, and produced beyond the angle of the postorbitals; subarticular tubercles generally simple; metatarsal tubercles moderate." Yarrow, 1882, (pp. 23, 164–167) gives the same five forms of *Bufo lentiginosus*. Cope (1886, pp. 515, 516) has *Bufo cognatus* separate from *Bufo lentiginosus* complex and describes *Bufo hemiophrys*. His *B. lentiginosus* he has as "B. l. fowleri . . . . Canadian and Hudsonian districts of eastern region." Bufo l. woodhouseii . . . Central region. Bufo l. americanus . . . eastern and Austroriparian regions." "Bufo l. lentiginosus . . . Austroriparian region."

In 1896 Rhoads (p. 396) in Tennessee took "*Bufo lentiginosus* (Shaw) Southern Toad. Specimens from Southern Tennessee approach nearly to those found in the Gulf States but the majority are intermediates . . . . On Roan Mt. he found *B. lentiginosus americanus* at 5,000–6,300 feet.

BIBLIOGRAPHY

1908   Allard, H. C. *Bufo fowleri* (Putnam) in Northern Georgia. Science N. S. Vol. 28, No. 723, Nov. 6, 1908, pp. 655, 656.

1791   Bartram, Wm. Travels through North and South Carolina, Georgia, East and West Florida. Phila, 1791, pp. 279, 280.

1882   Boulenger, G. A. Catalogue of the Batrachia Salientia S. Ecaudata ... British Museum 2nd edit. London, 1882, pp. 309, 310.

1907   Brimley, C. S. A Key to the Species of Frogs and Toads Liable to Occur in North Carolina. Journal Elisha Mitchell Sci. Soc., Dec. 1907, Vol. XXIII, p. 157.

1910   Brimley, C. S. Records of some Reptiles and Batrachians from the Southeastern United States. Proc. Biol. Soc. Wash., Mar. 23, 1910, Vol. XXIII, p. 11.

1922   Brimley, C. S. Herpetological Notes from North Carolina. Copeia No. 107, June 20, 1922, p. 48.

1923   ———. North Carolina Herpetology. Copeia, Jan. 20, 1923, No. 114, p. 4.

1926   ———. Revised Key and List of the Amphibians and Reptiles of North Carolina. Journal Elisha Mitchell Society, Vol. 42, Nos. 1 and 2, October, 1926, p. 80.

1886   Cope, E. D. Synonymic List of North American Species of Bufo and Rana, ... Am. Phil. Soc. Proc., 1886, Vol. 23, pp. 515, 516.

1889   ———. The Batrachia of North America. U. S. N. Mus. Bull. 24, 1889, p. 290.

1896   Cope, E. D. The Geographical Distribution of Batrachia and Reptilia in North America. The American Naturalist, Dec. 1896, Vol. 30, p. 1007.

1914   Deckert, R. F. List of Salientia from near Jacksonville, Florida. Copeia, Feb. 14, No. 3, p. 3.

1914   Deckert, R. F. Further Notes on the Salientia of Jacksonville, Florida. Copeia, August 29, 1914, No. 9, p. 2.

1921   Deckert, R. F. Amphibian Notes from Dade Co., Florida. Copeia, Mar. 15, 1921, No. 92, p. 21.

1922   Deckert, R. F. Notes on Dade Co. Salientia. Copeia, Nov. 20, 1922, No. 112, p. 88.

1842   DeKay, J. E. Natural History of New York, Part III, Albany, 1842, p. 68.

1906   Dickerson, M. C. The Frog Book, pp. 39, 45.

1890   Garman, H. Notes on Illinois Reptiles and Amphibians .... Bull. Ill. State Lab. Nat. Hist., Vol. III, Peoria 1896 Art X, Sept. 1890, pp. 189, 190.

1854   Girard, Charles. A List of the North American Bufonids with Diagnoses of New Species. Proc. Acad. Nat. Sciences Phila., Vol. VII, 1854, 1855. Phila. 1856, p. 86.

1827   Harlan, Richard. Genera of North American Reptilia and a Synopsis of the Species. Dec. 12, 1826. Journal Acad. Nat. Sci. Phila., Vol. V, Part II, 1827, pp. 344, 345.

1835   ————. Medical and Physical Researches, pp. 109, 110.

1843   Holbrook, J. E. North American Herpetology, 2nd Edition, Vol. V, pp. 7-12.

1848   ————. Reptiles. In Statistics of Georgia by George White, Savannah, 1849, Appendix p. 15.

1856   LeConte, John. Descriptive Catalogue of the Ranina of the United States. Proc. Acad. Nat. Sci. Phila., Vol. VII, 1854, 1855, 1856, p. 430. (Dec. 1855).

1895   Loennberg, E. Notes on Reptiles and Batrachians collected in Florida in 1892 and 1893. Proc. U. S. Nat. Mus., Vol. XVII, 1894, Wash. 1895, p. 338.

1924   Myers, G. S. Amphibians and Reptiles from Wilmington, N. C. Copeia, No. 131, June 30, 1924, p. 59.

1923   Nieden, Fr. Das Tierreich. Anura I, Berlin and Leipzig, pp. 124, 125.

1927   Pickens, A. L. Amphibians of Upper South Carolina. Copeia, Oct.-Dec. 1927. No. 165, Dec. 23, 1927, p. 109.

1895   Rhoads, S. N. Contributions to the Zoology of Tennessee. No. 1 Reptiles and Amphibians. Proc. Acad. Nat. Sci. Phila., Vol. 47 (1895), p. 396.

1924   Schmidt, K. P. A List of Amphibians and Reptiles. Collected near Charleston, S. C. Copeia, July 15, 1924, No. 132, p. 68.

1802   Shaw, George. General Zoology Amphibia Vol. III, Part I, 1802, p. 173.

1924   Viosca, Percy, Jr. An Ecological Study of the Cold Blooded Vertebrates of Southeastern Louisiana. Copeia, Feb. 1, 1923. No. 115, p. 37.

1923   ————. Distributional Problems of the Cold Blooded Vertebrates of the Gulf Coastal Plain. Ecology VII, pp. 307-314.

1827   Williams, J. L. A View of West Florida, p. 29.

1923   Wright, A. H. The Salientia of the Okefinokee Swamp, Georgia, Copeia, Feb. 1, 1923, No. 115, p. 34.

1926.   Wright, A. H. The Vertebrate Life of the Okefinokee Swamp in Relation to the Atlantic Coastal Plain. Ecology VII, No. 1, January 1926, pp. 82, 83.

1924   Wright, A. H. and A. A. Wright. A Key to the Eggs of Salientia East of the Mississippi River. The American Naturalist, Vol. LVIII, July-August, 1924, p. 380.

1883   Yarrow, H. C. Check List of North American Reptilia and Batrachia. U. S. Nat. Mus. Bull. No. 24, 1883, pp. 23.

Acris gryllus (LeConte)

(Pl. II, Fig. 1; V, Fig. 5; VI, Fig. 1; X, Fig. 11; XII, Fig. 6; XV, Fig. 7; XVII; XXIII; Text Fig. I, 9)

COMMON NAMES

Cricket-Frog. Savannah Cricket. Savanna Cricket. The Cricket Hylodes. Peeper. Rattler. Western Cricket Frog (*crepitans*). Savannah Cricket Frog. Cricket Toad. Western Cricket (*crepitans*).

RANGE

Check list. Florida to New York in the east; northward through the central valley from Louisiana and Texas to the Canadian Northwest Territories.

Supplementary records. Cope 1892 (p. 333) had them from the Staked Plains of Texas. Stone (1903, pp. 538–539) had them from Del Rio, Texas. Strecker (1908, p. 58) has it from Borachio, El Paso County, Texas.

In the western states Ellis (1913, p. 58) reports it at Wray, Colorado and in 1917 (p. 39) he reports it from Roswell, New Mexico.

In the extreme northeast Babcock in 1921 seriously questions the two previous records of its presence in New England.

In the north we have records from Baltrusol, N. J. and Passaic River Summit (A. C. Chandler 1909) to Hillsdale Michigan (T. L. Hankinson 1900) to Ames, Iowa, (Mr. and Mrs. (K. VanWinkle) E. L. Palmer 1924) to Emporia and Lawrence, Kansas (G. D. Hanna 1909). From Chapel Point, Maryland (Harper 1916) to Gloucester, North Carolina (Harper 1913), and Raleigh (Brimley, 1897) to Columbia, South Carolina (Corrington) to Caloosatcha River (J. C. Bradley 1911); we have it in our collections of the Atlantic Seaboard. From Georgia through Bay St. Louis, Miss., (1897) to Doucette, Texas (O. D. Ingalls (1909), it occurs in the Gulf States.

In 1917 we collected it from Petersburg, Va., May 31 and June 1 to Neuces River, Texas July 2, and the following intermediate localities: Dinwiddie, Va., June 1; Soudan, Va., June 3; Flatwood, Ala., June 9; LeRoy, Ala., June 12; Theodore, Ala., June 13; Biloxi, Miss., June 14; Dayton, Tex., June 22; New Braunfels, Tex., June 27. In countless places we recorded it between Virginia and Texas.

In 1925 we went out to New Orleans, La., with P. L. Viosca, Jr., who knows *A. gryllus* and *A. crepitans* better than any student of our Anurans. In Texas from Feb. 8, to June 30, 1925, Mrs. Wright and I collected *Acris gryllus* about San Antonio and at Helotes Creek, Texas. Southward we took it at Beeville, Texas, March 25 to May 1, 1925. Westward we found it 23 miles east of Del Rio, Texas, June 30, 1925.

In 1926 (p. 83) we termed "*Acris gryllus* N. Y.—Fla.—Tex." as a Lower Austral frog but it extends over into Upper Austral regions.

In Georgia, the State of which the Swamp is a part, from 1910–1911 Prof. J. C. Bradley secured it as follows: Sept.–Oct., 1910, Spring Creek, Decatur Co.; Mar. 5, 1911, Marietta; March 8, Wrens; Apr. 2, Gainesville; Apr. 22, Offerman, Satilla River; May 19, St. Simon Id., and June 7–23 Spring Creek, Decatur Co. In Cuthbert, Ga., March 29, 1921, F. Harper took this species.

Local Okefinokee records. In 1914 we wrote: "Our material consists of a series of tadpoles to transformation taken from May 28–June 15, 1912, and of 44 specimens of frogs of which 38 were secured between the above dates, 3 taken by Mr. Harper from May 2–23, 1912, and 3 on Dec. 22, 1913. This species was easily the commonest member of the *Hylidae* within the swamp. Most of our specimens came from Billy's Island, but representatives of the species were recorded or taken on Honey Island and its prairies, Floyd's Island and its prairies, Minne Islands, and at Mixon's Ferry and Hammock."

In 1921 we took it at Cypress Pond, Long Pond, Bullfrog Pond, Crosby Pond and other points on Billy's Island, Chesser Island, Black Jack Island, Honey Island and on prairies, Honey Island, Chase Prairie, and Black Jack strand; on Minne Lake River and a detour. We also recorded it in the Pocket, on Jones Island, Gallberry Island, Floyd's Island Prairie, Billy's Lake, and almost all over the swamp.

In 1922 we took it from Folkston to Jacksonville, Fla., from Folkston to Chesser Island, Okefinokee Swamp, at Camp Cornelia, Starling Branch, St Mary's River at many points and universally in the region surveyed. On the trip from Ithaca, N. Y. to Okefinokee Swamp June 3–14, 1922, we first heard *Acris* near Dyke Marsh, near New Alexandria, Va., and 12 miles north of Petersburg, Va., on June 7. Near Cheraw, S. C., June 8, we heard them at the same lake around which we heard *Hyla andersoni* and *Rana virgatipes*. At Mabee, June 9, *Acris* was calling at noon. On June 10 at night camp near Millen, Ga., they were calling and thus onward to Chesser Island, Okefinokee Swamp.

GENERAL APPEARANCE

Its original description (LeConte, 1825, p. 282) is "*Rana gryllus* (Savanna Cricket), above warty, colour various, with a triangular spot of darker on the top of the head between the eyes, and a paler line extending from the apex of this spot to the vent, hind part of the thighs yellowish or whitish, with one or two lines of dusky or brown."

Holbrook (1842, p. 131) gave its outstanding characters as "Head elongated, pointed, a triangular dusky spot between the orbits; body above cinerous with a green or sometimes red, vertebral line, and three oblong black spots, margined with white on the sides. Length 18 lines." The same year DeKay (1842, Part III, p. 70) gives the same characterization. O. P. Hay, 1892, calls its "Form frog-like," and W. P. Hay, (June 20, 1902, p. 128) so considers the form. To H. Garman (1892, pp. 341, 342) this frog is "small." This is a rather coarsely built frog, bearing a close resemblance in build to the *Ranidae*."

Morse (1902, p. 118) speaks of the *crepitans* form as "olive brown, with an inverted 'Y'-shaped green area; the median part of the 'Y' extends along the vertebral line, the forking taking place on the rump. Brown triangle between eyes. Sides marked with three oblong blotches. White line from eye to shoulder . . . Inner surfaces of thighs immaculate. Length 1 1/3 inch."

Or M. M. Ellis (1913, p. 58) characterizes it thus: "Head depressed and pointed, its length about 3 in the head and body; length of the hind leg to the heel reaching forward to the snout or beyond; male with a gular sac, size small, length under 1.5 inches."

COLORATION OF SPIRIT SPECIMENS (1912)

On the back the color may be grey, light brown, reddish brown, chestnut or almost black. Rarely green individuals were observed, but in general the browns predominated. The specimens taken on the open outskirts of the swamp were greyer while those from the interior of the swamp had shades of deep brown. All of the specimens over 17 mm. had the prominent black triangular patch between the eyes while almost all of those below 17 mm. to transformation size had no bars or marks at all on the upper surface which is a uniform light brown. The triangular interorbital mark has its apex pointed backward and is bordered by a lighter border which is continued along the

Plate XXIII

Cricket-frog (*Acris gryllus*)

1. Chase Prairie, Okefinokee Swamp, Ga. June 1, 1921.
2. 3. Tadpoles, Chesser Id., Ga. June 21, 1922. × 1.0.
4. Tadpoles with 4 legs, Starling Branch, Folkston, Ga. July 24, 1922. × 1.0.
5. 6. Transforming and transformed frogs, Chesser Id., Ga. July 8, 1922. Dorsal aspect. × 1.0.
7. Two males and two females, Billy Id., Ga. June 5, 1921. Ventral aspect. × 0.36.
8. Male croaking, First "Dreen," Chesser Id., Ga. July 25, 1922. Flashlight.
9. Male croaking, Coat-bet pond, Chesser Id., Ga. August 9, 1922. Flashlight.
10. Male croaking, Billy Id., Ga. May 16, 1921. Flashlight.
11. Eggs, Billy Id., Ga. May 16, 1921.
12. Tadpole with two legs, Starling Branch, Folkston, Ga.   July 14, 1922. Dorsal aspect. × 1.0.

1 2 3 7 6 5 4 8 9 10 11 12

back as a vertical line to the anus. This line is usually brown but may be white or green. One full grown (No. 6000) example deep reddish brown in color had no triangular spot, the usual recognition mark of the species. On the upper lip are three dark bars. Another leads from the eye across the angle of the mouth to the base of the shoulder. Separated from this by a prominent white line, another black bar passes over the tympanum from the eye to the shoulder. Back of the shoulder a dark oblique bar extends two-thirds of the distance to the hindlimbs. In the adults this mark is likely to remain longer and in young specimens more likely to appear sooner than the characteristic triangular spot, at least in the Okefinokee series. Along the back on either border of the vertebral line are two continuous or interrupted bars which extend almost to the hind-limbs. The hind-limbs are cross-barred, the femur, tibia, tarsus and foot all having them as in typically colored forms. In the fore-limbs the brachium seldom has any bars though the antebrachium may have them. In the Okefinokee series the most constant color character in transformed individuals to adults is the coloration of the posterior surface of the thighs. The typical pattern is upper part with body color with dark cross-bars. Then follows a series of four parallel longitudinal bands, the first three very prominent, white, brown, white. The fourth brown band may be obscured or absent. In all the specimens at least one white band shows though the others may be missing. The under-parts are whitish. Most of the younger individuals are almost entirely white, but in adults usually the under-surface of the hind legs is flecked with dark, in a few it becomes very cloudy. Very frequently the adults have the throat regions also with fine dark dots. Occasionally the thoracic region and rarely the belly are so marked. The males have yellowish on the throat. One of the party reported a live specimen with a greenish white venter.

STRUCTURAL CHARACTERS (WRITTEN IN 1912)

Above, the skin is usually more or less tubercular; some adults have the dorsal surface smooth as in the young; underneath, gular and thoracic regions usually smooth, rarely granular or areolate; normally areolation of the belly is quite distinctly marked off and in some specimens the granulations may form transverse ridges; thighs are also areolate; nostrils equidistant or slightly nearer snout than eye; tympanum indistinct; tympanic fold present, fold across the breast present in about three-fourths of the adults and absent usually in the young; inner and outer tubercle of foot quite prominent; subarticular tubercles moderate; discs small. The tongue is broad usually notched behind. In some the notch may be very slight, in others very prominent and the tongue is then cordate. In one the notch was very broad and was a shallow depression to each back corner. In several the tongue was round behind or abruptly truncate or obliquely truncate. In one the tongue was rounded but has a notch at either back corner. The vomerine teeth are usually two oval patches between or slightly behind the nares; sometimes the longitudinal axes are slightly inclined backward and sometimes not.

MEASUREMENTS
(1912–1914)

In 1914 the following measurements were made on the 1912 and 1913 material:

"The 44 specimens in length range from 12–24.5 mm., average 20.5 mm., mode, 21 mm., the head is 4.75–8.5 mm., average 6.8 mm., mode 7 mm., 2.5–3.5 in the combined length of head and body; length of head to canthus oris equal or slightly less than the breadth of the head at the same point, rarely more than the head; the width of the head 3.75–8 mm., average 6.5 mm., mode 7 mm.; snout 2–4.75 mm., an average 3.8 mm., mode, 4 mm., usually 1.5 greater than the diameter of the eye which ranges from 1.25–3.5 mm., average 2.6 mm., mode, 2.0 mm.; interorbital distance 1–2.5 mm., average 1.7 mm.; interorbital distance equals eyelid; femur 6–12.75 mm., average, 10 mm., mode 11 mm.; tibia 6.5–15.25 mm., average, 11.8 mm., mode 12 mm., in every case longer than the femur, usually 1.2 longer; body 1.8 longer than tibia; tarsus 4.5–8.5 mm., average 6.75, mode 7 mm., equal to the head in length; rest of foot 4.75–15.75 mm., average 9.8 mm., mode, 11 mm., longer than tarsus and averages slightly less than one-half the body (.47), the range however being from .25–.9 of the length of the body, *comparable to the two extremes of Cope's analysis ('89, p. 325) for A. g. crepitans and A. g. gryllus from north and south but here in one locality. Rest of foot is not longer than tibia but less:* anterior limb 19.5–43.5 mm., average 33.1 mm., averages 1.6 times the length of the body; hind-limb to heel usually extends to or beyond the end of the muzzle, rarely however, it reaches only to the eye."

(Recent Material)

Head to angle of mouth 1.3 (20 mm. ♂)—1.1 (20 mm. ♀)—1.07 (24 mm. ♂) —1.05 (24 mm. ♀)—1.33 (28 mm. ♀) in width of head; head to rear of tympanum .95–.85–1.0–.85–1.0 in width of head; head to angle of mouth 3.2–3.2–2.9–3.5–3.7 in length of body; head to rear of tympanum 2.3–2.4–2.6–2.8–2.8 in length of body; snout .7–.75–.74–1.1–.8 in first finger; snout 1.14–.85–.98–1.2–.8 in fourth finger; snout 1.14–1.15–.93–1.3–1.0 in first toe; eye 1.34–1.42–1.8–1.5–1.8 in snout; eye .54–.70–.66–.83–.71 in tympanum; eye .92–1.07–1.33–1.66–1.4 in first finger; tympanum 4.3–2.8–3.6–3.0–4.0 in intertympanic width; tympanum 2.5–2.0–2.7–1.8–2.5 in snout; internasal width .66–.66–.86–.71–.80 in upper eyelid width; interorbital width .83–.71–1.0–1.0–1.0 in upper eyelid width; interorbital width 1.25–1.7–1.15–1.4–1.25 in internasal width; interorbital width 2.5–2.0–2.7–3.0–5.0 in intertympanic width.

Forelimb. Forelimb 2.0–1.66–2.0–1.6–1.77 in length of body; forelimb 3.6–3.0–3.6–3.3–2.9 in hind limb; first finger 2.33–1.71–1.75–1.55–1.75 in third finger; second finger 2.0–1.47–1.52–1.55–1.75 in third finger; second finger .63–.88–.87–1\0–1.0 in first finger; third finger 1.04–1.04–1.02–1.03–1.0 in second toe; fourth finger 1.4–1.53–1.34–1.4–1.75 in third finger; fourth finger .6–.88–.77–.91–1.0 in first finger; internasal width .8–1.0–1.33–1.4–1.4 in first finger; internasal width 1.26–1.13–1.53–1.4–1.4 in second finger; internasal width 1.86–1.73–2.33–2.2–2.8 in third finger; internasal width 1.33–1.13–1.73–1.50–1.4 in fourth finger.

Hindlimb. length 1.8–1.75–1.8–1.56–1.6 in hind limb; tibia 1.63–1.63–1.66–1.7–1.6 in length; tibia 2.8–2.7–2.95–2.8–2.6 in hind limb; tibia .77–.92–.83–.64–.90 in fore limb; tibia 1.23–1.4–1.4–1.3–1.25 in hind foot with tarsus; first toe 1.45–1.2–1.44–1.33–1.4 in second toe; first toe 2.05–1.74–2.0–2.1–2.2 in third toe; first toe 3.1–2.6–2.6–2.7–2.72 in fourth toe; first toe 2.0–1.74–2.0–2.1–2.1 in fifth toe; second toe 1.4–1.5–1.4–1.5–1.55 in third toe; second toe 2.1–2.2–1.8–2.0–1.65 in fourth toe; second toe 1.4–1.5–1.4–1.5–1.5 in fifth toe; third toe 1.5–1.5–1.3–1.3–1.24 in fourth toe; third toe .97–1.0–1.0–1.0–.95 in fifth toe; fourth toe 1.00–.90–1.0–.9–1.0 in hind foot; fourth toe 1.04–1.08–1.1–1.07–1.28 in tibia; fourth toe .80–1.0–.92–.70–1.15 in fore limb; fifth toe 1.56–1.5–1.3–1.3–1.3 in fourth toe; internasal width 1.33–1.53–1.6–1.7–1.7 in first toe; internasal width 1.9–1.8–2.4–2.3–2.5 in second toe; internasal width 2.73–2.66–3.3–3.5–4.0 in third toe; internasal width 4.1–4.0–4.33–4.6–4.6 in fourth toe; internasal width 2.66–2.66–3.3–3.5–3.7 in fifth toe.

HABITAT

Several in their synonymies of this species refer to Wm. Bartram's Travels (1791, p. 278). Bartram's note follows: "There are yet an extreme diminutive species of frogs which inhabits the grassy verges of ponds in savannas: these are called savanna crickets, are of a dark ash or dusky colour, and have a very picked nose. At the times of very great rains in the autumn, when the savannas are in a manner inundated, they are to be seen in incredible multitudes clambering up the tall grass, weeds, etc. round the verges of the savannas bordering on the higher ground, and by an inattentive person might be taken for spiders or other insects. Their note is very feeble, not unlike the chattering of young birds, or crickets." This might apply equally to *Pseudacris ocularis* or Bartram's No. 5 frog. "a little grey speckled frog," be *Acris* as well.

LeConte, its first describer, did not remark in 1825 on its habitat but in 1855 (pp. 426, 427) wrote of *A. gryllus* that it was "Found in immense numbers in every piece of water in the Southern States, and *was* a few years ago commonly known by the name of Savannah Cricket."

Harlan (1835, p. 105) says it "Inhabits the Southern and Middle States; frequents the grass and verges of ponds." Holbrook (1842, Vol. IV, p. 132) finds "it frequents the borders of stagnant pools, and is often found on the leaves of aquatic plants, and rarely on the branches of such low shrubs as overhang or dip in the water." DeKay (1842, Part III, p. 70) has it "frequenting moist wooded places and border of ponds, and is often seen on aquatic plants . . ... It is never found on trees, and cannot adhere to the underside of smooth surfaces."

Abbott (1882, p. 710) contraverts that statement about adherence to under surface of objects. "In many instances they were found adhering to the under sides of projecting stones, roots of trees, and even to larger oak leaves. I find it stated by DeKay in Natural History of New York, that they cannot retain their hold upon the under sides of projecting objects; that the discs on their toes are not sufficiently large. This is an error; indeed, the specimens I have in a bottle, can retain their hold when the bottle is turned over."

Cope (1889, p. 329) maintains that "It keeps on the high grass in and around marshy places, seldom if ever ascending trees or bushes. When pursued it leaps with prodiguous agility, and hides under water."

H. Garman (1892, p. 342) holds "It is more terrestrial than our other Hylidae, and probably never resorts to shrubs and trees. It is usually found at the margins of streams or pools, into which it leaps when disturbed, but only to return to the shore a short distance from the observer."

"In South Florida (Loennberg, 1895 p. 338) along the borders of ponds and swamps, this frog is abundant though not commonly seen." At Turkey Lake, Indiana, C. Atkinson (1896, p. 258) finds them "Abundant along the shallow margins of the lake among marshes and lily pads."

In 1901, Oct. 18, at an artificial lagoon fed by Lake Mendota, Dane County, Wisconsin, P. H. Dernehl (1902, p. 75) took his series for his Place Modes of *Acris gryllus* at Madison, Wisconsin. "Along the banks of this artificial stream the frogs were extremely numerous, making it a comparatively small task to secure the one hundred specimens from which my tabulated results were obtained."

In 1908 Fowler found them in "pools of fresh tide water," in "swamps," "about ditches, especially in places where cattle have tramped about the mud"; also in "dry fields, roadsides and woods."

In Florida near Jacksonville R. F. Deckert (Copeia, 1913, No. 3, p. 3) finds this form "plentiful on edges of bayous." In 1915 (pp. 21, 22) he says that "*Acris gryllus* LeConte, the 'cricket frog' is one of the commonest frogs, great swarms of this species having been seen by the writer during the spring months about the edges of bayous, creeks and ponds."

On Long Island Boyle (1914, No. 7, p. 4) found "Many small ponds varying from a small pool to a fair sized pond, big and deep enough to swim in. Here as early as March 23, 1913, I found and collected several "cricket frogs." Helen Thompson Gaige (1914, No. 11, p. 4) found them "Abundant on the shores of ponds" in Richland County, Illinois.

In 1917 Hubbs (p. 99) finds them "abundant along the margins of ponds in the sand dunes between Miller, Indiana and Lake Michigan."

In Texas Strecker (1915, p. 40) finds "This tiny frog is distributed all over the State wherever there are lakes, ponds, springs or streams. I have found it even in the heart of well populated cities in little pools formed by rains." Pope (1919, p. 97) finds they are fairly abundant all along the banks and are calling vigorously at Houston, Texas.

In 1923 (p. 36) Viosca states that "*Acris gryllus* abounds along the creeks" of his Pine and Hardwood Uplands division or "Shortleaf Pine Hills."

After our 1912 trip we discussed this phase thus "This species of tree frog was easily the commonest form of this family in the swamp. It was never taken in trees or bushes. In the outskirts in the drier lands amongst the calico-bushes, blue-berries and other heaths it vied with the toads in abundance. Nevertheless, it did not appear wholly terrestrial. On Honey Island, Floyd's Island and Chase Prairies the full-grown adults as well as transformed examples were frequent on the water-leaves along the water-trails we followed. In the deep cypress forests between Billy's Lake and Minne Lake we noted them and all over the islands they were very common. Some of our best collecting courses were the cow and hog trails through the low shrubbery. Also in the various swampy cross-ways or trails from one island to another they occurred in the shallow water with the killifishes. Along the swampy tree and bush borders of Billy Island and in the wooded edges of Lee's clearing they foraged. In fact, they were as widespread as any Anuran of the swamp and seemed not to be wholly restricted to land or water. In the main they are shade lovers except in the open prairies, but here they can rest underneath the overlapping water-leaves."

In 1921 our first observation on habitat is April 23. "In the cleaner end of a cypress pond on the dead black leaves amongst *Polygonum, Hydrocotyle, Pontederia*, lots of *Acris*." Two days later we found *Acris* common and calling at 10:00 a.m. in a cypress pond (C.A.G. pond. *Hyla cinerea, Acris gryllus, Rana grylio* common). "Took *Lucania ommata* in the pond. There are bonnets (lilies) in the middle, some floating heart, plenty of pickerel weed, lizard's tail in bloom, water pennywort in bloom, a few southern tickseed in bloom (*Bidens*); red bamboo, buttonbush, Virginia willow, etc., around the edge."

In 1921 we found them in meadows and around ponds in North Carolina, in the open vegetation mats or wooded edges of cypress ponds, in moist pine barrens, occasionally in dry pine barrens, on water prairies, along open lake edges, on sphagnum strand—in fact, in almost every type of plant habitat which has any moisture at all.

FIRST APPEARANCE

This topic means very little with this species as the subsequent citations will show. Whether it be in its southern range or its extreme northern limits it is very early in the spring or at times appears in warm periods throughout the winter. Professor T. H. Morgan at Baltimore in 1891 (p. 754) reports *Acris gryllus* as the first frog to appear in the spring. O. P. Hay (1892, p. 462) says "this little chatterer appears very early in the spring." In Vigo County, Indiana, W. S. Blatchley (1891-1892, p. 27) finds that they "are active in certain localities even in midwinter, lively specimens having been taken on December 23, January 9 and February 16." In Houston, Texas, Pope (1919, p. 97) finds them active Feb. 8, 1918–Feb. 10. "This little frog was the first to appear in the spring and was abundant along the bayous all summer, . . ." In Doniphon County, Kansas, Jean M. Linsdale, makes these interesting observations: "On Feb. 2, 1924, several were found in the creek above the bridge. They were in the water above some old ice and below a top layer of new ice. All the frogs were stiff and floating and apparently they were dead. In the warm water of the springs and just below springs a few frogs of this species were found throughout the winter."

GENERAL HABITS

Metachrosis (variations in the individual).

LeConte (1855, p. 427) in describing the extreme variety "in color and in other marks" of *Acris crepitans* writes: "Whether all the variations above mentioned are permanent in the individuals where they have been observed or depend upon the will of the animal, I have not been able to determine precisely. In many instances, however, they are the voluntary changes which for some unknown reason this creature chooses to make in its appearance."

Cope (1889, p. 325) says that "In its habits the *Acris gryllus* is a lover of the muddy borders of the water, into which it leaps when alarmed. As it does not conceal itself among vegetation, like the *Hyla pickeringii*, it is much more easily caught than that species, and is more common in museums, though not less abundant. As the structure of the feet indicate, it is a good swimmer, and its powers of leaping are remarkable."

Abbott (1882, pp. 709, 710) gave close attention to the subject of their color and its changeableness. "While there are certain peculiarities of color that are persistent and characteristic of the species, these become of little prominence at times, so very great is the difference in the entire coloration of the animal. Furthermore, they change their hues with great rapidity, and during the course of a few moments will pass from an ashy paleness or clay color to an intense black, with the light dorsal stripe scarcely visible, or else either to a glowing red or brilliant metallic green. So very beautiful are these changes, and so different will any half dozen prove to be, that it is difficult to realize that the many before you are one and the same species. Of a series of six which I have long kept in confinement (October 20th to January 29th) in a bottle, one specimen was taken from a ledge of pale yellow clay. The "peeper" was of the same color, the post-orbital dark spot and light dorsal line being scarcely discernible. The uniform yellow tint, however, was relieved by minute round points of brilliant bronze. This individual, unlike its companions, did not alter in color for several weeks. The others were very changeable, and particularly so when exposed to direct sun-light. While I noted several instances to the contrary my impression is that usually the colors pale in direct sun-light, and deepen when the animals are in deep shade. This certainly is true of those I have in confinement, and agrees with my experience in searching for them during the past autumn. One fact with reference to the subject of their color is not in accordance, perhaps, with the above, but should not go unrecorded. The six individuals which I have in a bottle will, at times, present very different tints, although all are subjected to like surroundings. Of the six, two or three would be very dark, the others pale yellow. With some the dark triangular spot between the eyes would be very distinct, in the case of the others it could not be detected even in outline. It must be remembered, however, that these individuals were kept in most unnatural conditions, and had, at the time of this writing, been without food for one hundred days and at the same time remained as active as squirrels."

This species (Cope, 1889, p. 325) possesses the power of metachrosis or color changes in a high degree. The dorsal stripe and border of the interocular spot may be bright green, dirty white, or bright rusty; and the dorsal tubercles vary in color in the same way. The general tint varies from bright green to dull slate color. Under *A. g. crepitans* he remarks (p. 328) "In connection with metachrosis in this species I observed in a specimen lately dead that on the end of the muzzle, palpebrae, canthus rostralis, outer line of humerus, ends of sacral dispaphyses, where the derm was in a state of tension, that it assumed a bright green hue."

Dernehl (1902, p. 81) in writing "Color changes" says "The rapid color changes attributed to these frogs by various authors as Dr. Hay, Cope and LeConte were not observed in individuals which we had in confinement in the laboratory for some time, the only noticeable change being a fading or increase of the ground color, the bands of green or red remaining permanent."

Ditmars (1905, p. 192) notes "This species is subject to rapid and marked color changes under the influence of varying temperature and the mood of the individual. These changes affect the general color of the body and the bright band down the back."

Dickerson (1906, pp. 155, 156) holds that "the dark shades are taken on when the frogs are in dark situations and especially when the darkness is combined with a low temperature and moisture; the lighter coloration is assumed under the influences of bright light, high temperature and dryness."

Variations in color. LeConte (1825) in his original description called its "colour various." In 1826 he repeats the same.

Almost every author like Boulenger (1882, p. 336) holds its "Coloration very variable."

Cope (1889, pp. 324–331) gives the upper parts as mainly brown or gray with diverse dorsal stripes. H. Garman (1892, p. 342) finds the "Size and color are extremely variable. In most specimens from central and northern Illinois, the markings are all very obscure, and often the triangular spot between the eyes is so indistinct as to require close looking to detect it. Others of the marks described above may even be wanting, and in but few specimens are all the marks plainly visible. The greenish and reddish forms seem to be more abundant in southern Illinois. The skin of the more northern individuals is rougher, the warts often being elongate and ranged so as to form short ridges."

In another extreme of its range in south Florida, Loennberg (1895, p. 389) reports "All my specimens show the triangular black spot on the head. The median dorsal stripe is always reddish brown, and I have never seen it green. The posterior femoral stripes are very conspicuous. The light stripe from the orbit to the axilla is constant, but the other blotches are not always light bordered."

In 1902 (p. 128) W. P. Hay calls its "color variable and changeable." So also Dernehl (1902, p. 80) finds "The color of this species is extremely variable, usually the upper surface has a ground color of ashy gray with a faint greenish hue or brown. Dickerson (1906, p. 156) gives green, light red brown, clay colour, almost black, as dorsal colors.

Ellis (1913, p. 58) has the "color variable and changeable; generally brownish, greenish or reddish and somewhat clouded with dusky; . . ."

On April 23, 1921, a day or so after my arrival, the following hasty notes were made on color and environment. "*Acris*, captured a lot of them. Sometimes on a black soil, and hard to see except when they jump. Some brown all over back (except for dark marks) when on brown pine needles. Sometimes green all over except for the dark marks. Sometimes gray over drier sand. Amongst some of the light brown pine needles *Acris* reddish brown even on back of forelimbs and hind limbs." A month later on the island May 21, we record "one just captured as black as the blackish earth."

General habits. From C. C. Abbott (1882, pp. 707, 708) we have: "Abundant as is this batrachian, but little seems to be known of its habits, and certain misstatements concerning them have long been printed and have never, that I am aware, been either questioned or contradicted."

"During the month of April, 1881, I had excellent opportunities for observing these little creatures, and finding that but little had been recorded concerning them, availed myself of my chance and watched them closely for several weeks."

"While a network of ditches in a low meadow were being repaired or cleaned, I followed the workmen closely, ... the one striking feature of the locality, at this time, was the wonderful abundance of little "rattlers" (*Acris crepitans*), as I prefer to call them. . . . From the date of their earliest appearance until May 20, their numbers were incalculable. In every portion of the meadows at all wet, they were to be seen. Extremely active and very shy, they were difficult to catch provided you pursued a single individual, but by sweeping an ordinary dip net along the grass at the edge of any little pool, several were certainly to be caught . . . . About the 20th of May there was a very noticeable diminution of their numbers, and by the 10th of June not a specimen was to be found.

"The fact is, that their vigor culminates with the maturity of the ova and spermatozoa, and having spawned, they have no vital force remaining, and in the course of a few days after ovipositing, they die. Weeks then elapse when no representatives of this batrachian are to be found; indeed none exist, except the thousands of tadpoles.

". . . Their physiological activity culminates with the maturity of the ova and the labor of depositing it; this effected, they are worn out and in a very short time, die."

The article of which the above are excerpts is very interesting and in general instructive, but we believe this author falls in error in believing the adults die after breeding. Sometimes frogs of most species are found on breeding grounds dead. This is from vigor of breeding; such as violent matings, individual exhaustion after breeding etc., but a general rule of death does not obtain for any Anuran of Canada or the United States. We have captured *Acris* adults every month of the year and spent females aplenty. If there be any lessening in numbers it may be because of migrations, vegetation more concealing and the enemies of which he speaks.

O. P. Hay (1892, p. 462) finds: "This little frog is one of our commonest batrachians. During the summer season it may be seen in numbers along all of our streams. I doubt if it is often seen about the ponds or pools far from running water. It is not thoroughly aquatic but delights to spend its time amid the vegetation about the borders of the water. When alarmed it will leap into the water, but it often appears to become alarmed at its rashness and hastens to reach the land again. When followed up, however, it will go to the bottom and seek to conceal itself for awhile. Though belonging to the 'tree-frogs' it never ascends trees, and probably climbs only the shorter grasses and water plants." Blatchley (1891, p. 27) calls this species "the most abundant tailless batrachian in the country. Hundreds are to be seen along any small stream in spring and autumn. They appear less common in summer . . ."

" . . . It is my observation that it is to be found at all times during the summer."

Hurter (1893, p. 253) finds this form "the most common of all little frogs. It is found near pools and creeks, where it generally sits on the banks so as to resort to the water when alarmed. It can make jumps from three to four feet long."

Sherwood (1898, p. 18) holds "They are rarely found away from the borders of ponds, and their long leaps and swimming powers render capture very difficult."

Morse (1902, p. 118) finds that "So nearly does the color of the frog blend with that of its surroundings that it is detected with but the greatest difficulty. In the cricket frog we have virtually a tree-frog with terrestrial habits. The presence of the terminal suckers on the toes would seem to indicate a former arboreal mode of life. Common everywhere."

Ditmars (1905, p. 193) says "The animal is very difficult of capture since it possesses great leaping powers and quickness in diving. During periods of heavy dew these frogs may be found in high grass adjacent to marshes. Owing to its smallness and agility, it is rarely observed after its breeding season."

Of this species Fowler (1907, p. 102) writes "These little toads were found to be very abundant, though exceedingly difficult to see, on account of their small size and close resemblance to the aquatic vegetation in which they live. Their notes were a characteristic feature of these ponds all along the marshes most of the time, and also in the cedar-swamps. I have heard them in various places, more or less regularly, from spring all through the summer and on several occasions in Dr. Abbott's own meadows." (See Abbott 1882).

In 1918 Cope (1919, p. 97) writes of them at Houston, Texas, that "The frogs usually sit on the bank a few inches from the water. If danger approaches they plunge into the water and swim rapidly back to the bank unless too much alarmed, when they dive and hide in the mud. February 10 collected seven specimens in daylight. They are not nocturnal in habit but seem to be active both day and night."

Of the jumping records of *Acris* we record the following: On Apr. 23, 1921, we wrote "*Acris* can jump three or four feet sometines. . . . *Acris* usually jumps for several leaps before it disappears." On Apr. 25, 1921, we repeat that *Acris* males can jump 3 feet at times on water's surface." On May 17, we compared *Acris's* leap with our longest stride and wrote "*Acris* can leap at least my own pace." At another time some adult *Acris* puzzled me because they leaped into bushes 1–2 to 1 foot high." We queried as to the possibility of their being *Acris* one-year-old or *Pseudacris* but they were neither. On May 21, 1921, we note "*Acris* has been on the island hopping around on the ground and into small bushes from the ground and down to ground again. May be some of these have left the ponds."

Most writers assert that they never climb. On June 28, 1922, at Coat Bet Pond on Chesser Island, where flags were reaching above the water we found six or eight *Acris* crawled up on flag stems 2–3 inches above the water's surface. Sometimes they would leap off. Usually they stayed in place.

VOICE

Holbrook (1842, Vol. IV, p. 132) writes that "This is a merry little frog, constantly chirping like a cricket, even in confinement; . . ." Of some captives he says "Their chirp, at times, was incessant, and sprinkling them with water never failed to render them more lively and noisy." The last two expressions of "lively and noisy" DeKay repeats.

Charles C. Abbott (1882, p. 707) remarks that "One of the earliest indications of returning spring is the dear, bell-like note of the little batrachian, called by many the "Savannah cricket," known in New Jeresy as the "peeper" and scientifically designated *Acris crepitans* Baird." . . . "They were in full song, (April 1881) and when not disturbed, made more noise than all the frogs in the neighborhood together. They are quite timid, however, and on being approached were straight way 'mum.' Their vocal efforts seemed to increase until about May 1st . . .."

Of *Acris gryllus crepitans* Cope (1889, pp. 328, 329) notes that "The note of this species may be exactly imitated by striking two marbles together first slowly, than faster and faster, for a succession of about twenty or thirty beats. The noise can not be heard at a very great distance. Like *Hyla pickeringii* this species in confinement can readily be made to produce the note by imitating it, either with the voice or the clattering of two pebbles."

Hay (1892, p. 462) says "It is a cheerful little creature, and on warm days may constantly be heard executing its noisy song. This resembles closely the striking together rapidly of two pebbles, and, often, when their singing has been interrupted by the passer-by, it may be started again by clicking two stones sharply together."

H. Garman (1892, p. 342) writes of voice as follows: Its note is a rapidly repeated grating noise, thought to resemble the trilling of a cricket, whence the name cricket-frog."

Sherwood (1898, p. 18) writes "Very early in the spring and before the appearance of the 'peepers' (*Hyla pickeringii*), their rattling, broken cry may be hard. It is not sharp like that of *Hyla*, and would not be noticed unless one were near."

W. P. Hay (1902, p. 128) writes that "Both (subspecies) are found in abundance along the banks of streams and ponds whence their continuous metallic cry comes almost without intermission during the season of activity, particularly during hot, sunshiny days."

Morse (1904, p. 118) remarks that "The cricket-frog is well known to any one who frequents the riverside or the swamp—less, however, by its appearance than its note. If one can imagine a rattling of pebbles mingled with the screech of a violin string in a high note, he may have a suggestion of the cricket-frog's note. When given it is either a continuous chirp or given in sets of three each rising in pitch."

In 1905 Ditmars speaks of "its sharp, trilling cry, resembling in volume the call of the field cricket, . . . It "may be heard at various times."

Ruthven, Thompson & Thompson (1912, pp. 46, 47) report that "These frogs sing in chorus during the months of April and May and the isolated call may be heard all summer. The song resembles the chirping of a cricket, hence the common name, cricket frog." To Miss Dickerson (1906) the song "resembles the rattling call of the Swamp Tree Frog, but the notes are more rapidly given and are sharper in quality." She gives the pebble or marble figure. "The call has not great carrying power, either when given alone or when given in chorus."

Fowler (1907, pp. 102, 103) finds "Besides the rattling call a squeaky sound was heard occasionally, though only during the breeding season. . . . It may be stated that in my experience their call appears to be variable. . . . (two pebbles figure). . . . Perhaps the rattling of two castenets would be a better suggestion." Deckert (1915, p. 21) finds "Its rattling notes can be heard during the entire season, day and night" in Florida.

At Brevard, N. C., Dunn (1917, p. 621) from July 1 "Heard (them) nearly every night."

In 1920 Logier (1925, p. 92) found one specimen of this species at Point Pelee, Ontario. "On the afternoon of July 15th, while sketching beside this pond, my attention was caught by what to me was a new frog-note, and which sounded something like the tapping together of two pebbles. This call, which like the calls of our other diminutive frogs had considerable carrying power, was uttered intermittently, that is, the frog would call several times and then remain silent for a while. By following the sound I finally located the tiny producer, hiding among the rushes in the shallow water at the pond's margin. It dived when I attempted to capture it, but was dragged ashore in a net full of bottom trash. When landed it did not make for the water as frogs usually do, but took a few jumps further ashore as if in an effort to hide itself in among the shore vegetation."

Our records of calling in 1921 and 1922 extends from Apr. 21 into September or the whole period of our sojourn in the swamp.

Characterizations of its voice are quite numerous. For example, Overton's description is one of the most extended and best accounts: "The voice of a cricket frog is a combination of a rattle and a musical clink, but it is only about half as loud as that of a spring peeper. A chorus heard at a distance sounds like the jingling of small sleigh bells, for the musical element of its call travels farther than the rattle. A chorus heard close by sounds like the rattle of small pebbles poured upon a cement pavement.

"An individual frog sings for from thirty to forty-five seconds at a time. Its call has three phases. The first phase lasts for about five seconds and sounds like the clicks of a boy's marble dropped upon a cement pavement once or twice a second from a height of about six inches. The second phase sounds like the galloping of a small pony on a brick pavement, or like the clicks of a boy's marble dropped upon a pavement from a height of only an inch or two, and allowed to bounce twice each time. The third phase sounds like the regular cree-cree-creeing of a tree cricket, or like the rattle of a boy's marble that bounces rapidly when it is dropped at frequent intervals from a height of only half an inch. The time and rhythm of the sounds are about the same as that of the following syllables pronounced with the speed of ordinary reading;—"click, click, click, click, . . . click-e-ty, click-e-ty, click-e-ty, click-e-ty, click-e-ty, . . . cree, cree, cree, cree . . ."

"The cricket frog inflates a vocal sac under its chin during its call. It often sits quitely with its sac distended for many minutes between its calls. The violent efforts of its body in producing its sound make the frog resemble a small boy on his hands and knees blowing a fire with all his might. The vocal sac is bright yellow and when it is seen distended in the day time, it is so conspicuous that it reveals many a singer that otherwise would be almost invisible on a lily pad."

To us, on April 16, 1921, at Raleigh, N. C. "*Acris gryllus* calls sound like a rattle or some of the metal clickers." On April 25, 1921, in the Okefinokee Swamp, we repeat "*Acris* call is a rattle," just as C. M. Barber, 1923, speaks of the "rattle of Acris." On May 18 I have the following journal notes: "*Acris* call. Tick, tick, tick, tick and so on. Or *kick*, kick, kick, kick, . . . kick, kick . . . kick, kick, . . . kick, kick, . . . kick, kick, kick, kick, kick, kick. One *Acris* went on calling for 45 seconds. Another *kick, kick, kick, kick,* . . . kick, kick, . . . *kick, kick, kick.* Another 4 *kicks* pause, then 7 kicks in succession. Another called for 30 seconds straight." To F. Harper "its ordinary note is a simple rather strident *gik*, given either singly or in irregular but successive series.

Frequently one finds the males with inflated vocal sacs even when not calling. When calling the throat is never fully deflated. After a call it may be swollen to three-quarters the full capacity. Thus when the call is given the body sides are compressed and the vocal sac extended to its limit.

Our voice records for 1921 and 1922 follow:

1921

Apr. 15.   Raleigh, N. C.   Males calling.
"   17.   Raleigh, N. C.   Plenty calling in evening at Boone's Pond.
"   21.   Billy's Island, Okefinokee Swamp, Ga., Voice 5:00–12:00 P.M.
"   23.   Last night in early evening went after croaking *Acris*.
"   24.   Moonshine Pond.   In Pond heard no end of *Acris* 7:30 P.M.
"   25.   In Long Pond at 10:00 A.M. heard quite a few *Acris* calling in *Hyla cinerea* pond. In C. A. G. (*cinerea, Acris, grylio*) pond *Acris* common and calling.

Apr. 26. Calling at Billy's Lake.
" 27. Some *Acris* heard around Long Pond.
" 28. One heard.
" 30. 7:00–8:00 P.M. Air 58°, few *Acris* heard.
May 2. Several heard at Billy's Lake.
" 4. Several heard.
" 9. *Acris* in strong force 6:45 A.M. Air 64°.
" 10. This evening at 8:00 P.M., 72°, no end of *Acris* calling.
" 13. Swimming pool. Plenty of calling *Acris*. Afternoon.
" 14. *Acris* commonly calling at swimming hole and mating.
" 15. Temperature tonight only 66° and 67.° Only *Acris* calling. During day temperature 66°–69°.
May 16. In strong chorus. C.A.G. Pond.
" 18. Heard on the lake.
" 21. Few *Acris* calling occasionally in the ponds.
" 23. Minne Lake at noon. Several calling.
" 24. *Acris* still going. Air 77°F.
" 26. No end of *Acris* calling.
" 27. Common and in good voice.
" 30. Heard a few tonight.
" 31. *Acris*—several heard.
June 1. *Acris* common along canal.
" 2. One calling.
" 3. Plenty of *Acris* calling.
" 8. Mixon's Hammock. Hear *Acris*.
" 10. Minne Lake 10:55 A.M. hear several. Many in afternoon.
" 12. Several on prairie (Floyd's).
" 14. Floyd's Prairie 7:55 A.M. Several heard. 12:30 several heard.
" 20. Several calling at lake.
" 23. Long Pond some calling.
" 24. One heard.
" 25. Plenty calling aloud *Chorophilus* Pond.
" 28. One heard. A few occasionally calling.
" 30. One heard.
July 2. A few heard.
" 3. One heard.
" 4. An occasional *Acris gryllus* at Long Pond.
" 7. Several heard.
" 10. Two heard.
" 11. Last night great chorus.
" 12. Abundantly heard on trip to Chesser Island.
" 13. *Acris* common Chesser Island.
" 15. *Acris* abundant in cypress pond.
" 16. *Acris* very active.
" 17. *Acris* calling as lustily as *Hyla femoralis*.
" 18. Many heard.
" 24. One heard at noon (rain).
" 26. Last night quite a few *Acris*.
" 27. *Acris* commonly heard on prairie this afternoon.
" 28. *Acris* at Black Jack Island.
" 29. Several *Acris* heard Black Jack Island.
" 30. *Acris* calling.
Aug. 1–23. Heard down Suwannee River and along St. Mary's River from source to mouth by F. Harper and Marion Lee.
Aug. 23. *Acris* only anuran voice tonight.

1922

June 13. *Acris* heard on Chesser Island.
"   14. Common at Coat Bet Pond.
"   22. In great chorus in Coat Bet Pond and on the prairies.
"   27. Chorus of them tonight.
July 1. One heard in cypress bay.
"   2. Many heard calling and mating at Starling Branch.
"   3. Commonly heard.
"   4. Several heard.
"   5. Abundantly heard.
"   6. *Acris* frequently heard on prairie and about "houses."
"   7. Grand Prairie—many calling.
"   9. Common, active at Coat Bet Pond.
"   11. Several heard.
"   12. Calling moderately at Coat Bet Pond.
"   13. One heard.
"   18. In chorus at Coat Bet Pond.
"   19. Spanish Creek—several heard.
"   21. Several heard near Dinsmore, Florida.   Abundant at Coat Bet Pond.
"   22. Several heard at noon.
"   23. Few calling early.
"   25. Some calling after rain.
"   26. Several calling at Starling Branch.
"   27. Several calling near dark.
"   28. One or two calling.
"   31. One or two calling.
Aug.   1. Calling commonly along Dixie Highway near Waycross.
"   2. Calling on Billy's Island.
"   3. Several calling in grassy field.
"   4. Calling in considerable numbers 11:15 p.m.
"   5. 10:00 p.m.—Many calling.
"   6. Common on Billy's Lake.
"   7. One calling.
"   8. After today's rain all along Okefinokee Road *Acris* calling 8:00—11:00 p.m.
"   9. Trader's Hill Pond *Acris* calling 3:15 p.m. Calling lustily 8:00–11:00 p.m.
"   10. Abundantly calling Petty Pond 8:45–10:30 p.m.
"   11. Common from Folkston to Chesser Island but not at their height.
"   12. Several calling during day.
"   13. Commonly heard from St. Mary's, Ga.,-Chesser Island 7:00–10:30 p.m.
"   14. Several at night.
"   15. Common near Callahan, Florida.
"   18. Heard in pine barrens.
"   19. Commonly heard near Lake Sego.
"   21. One heard.
"   23. One heard.
"   28. *Acris* calling at Coat Bet Pond 9:00 a.m.
"   29. An occasional *Acris*.
"   30. *Acris* common on prairie and islet, commonly heard at night.
Sept. 1. Heard at night.
"   2. Several heard at night.
"   3. One or two heard on islet and others on prairie.
"   4. Two on camp on islet.

Considering 16 choruses from April 24–July 18, 1921, we have for nearby station records of maxima 81°–95° with exception of two 73°, usual range 81°–88°, average 81°, mode 86°, for the day before; and minima from 50°–73° (one to 46°), average 60°; for day of record, maxima of 81°–95°, average 89°, minima of 50°–73°, average 69°. Heavy rains preceded about half of the choruses. In last of April temperatures 84°–87° maxima and 50°–62° minima obtained the day of the records. In the first half of May maxima 81°–90°, minima 53°–67° prevailed. In the choruses of May 26 and 27 maxima 93°–95°, minima 65°–70° prevailed. In July 11–18 maxima 87°–94° obtained, minima 68°–73°. Minima thus mount from 50°–62°, 53°–67°, 65°–70°, 68°–73° in mid July. The mid July choruses were started by rains of two inches or more.

The actual records of air temperatures taken by us in 1921 when we heard *Acris* were about 10 instances from April 30–July 29. They range thus: 58°, 72°, 66° or 67°, 71°, 80°, 74°, 70°, 74°, 76°, 80°, 73°. In June and July each of these were preceded or accompanied by rain, clouds, storms, or threat of lowery weather. These average about 72°.

In 1922 on Chesser Island from June 14–22 we heard great choruses on the island and on the prairies and later in the later part of June. No minimum during our waking hours was below 71°–73°. Many days went up to 90° or higher, and much rain or cloudy weather was on. It seems that in mid summer rain is a potent factor. They will peep at 56° or lower. Somehow 65°–70° seems to be a preferable temperature for cheerful *Acris*. When minima get to 65° or 70° or higher and maxima reach 80° or 85° on into the 90°'s with some rain we have optimum conditions for great choruses.

MATING

Male (From life, June 25, 1921). Stripe down back and around triangle dark olive buff, throat raw sienna. All over the throat collections of dark dots which sometimes arrange in a reticulate fashion. Iris pale vinaceous drab on black. Light orange yellow rim around the pupil.

On one day, Apr. 23, I saw black, dark brown, reddish brown, light brown, green and gray specimens of *Acris*.

Female (From life, June 25, 1921). Of a mated pair: Clove brown above. Triangular spot between eye obscured by this dark color. Throat, breast and belly pale olive buff. More or less on under side of fore legs same color and so the spot below eye and along the upper and lower jaws, also the line from eye to arm insertion. Area back of arm insertion pallid vinaceous drab. Oblique bar on side clove brown with pale olive buff and olive ocher: Under side of hind legs clear with a little pigment. Brown long stripe on rear of femur snuff brown or dresden brown with clear unpigmented stripe below and above. Also another such brown stripe above the upper clear area. From vent around bases of hind legs to venter are pale olive buff papillae.

Structural differences. H. Garman (1892, p. 341) is one of the first to note that "The first finger of the male (is) but slightly swollen."

Many remark the difference in the throat of the two sexes. Ellis (1913, p. 58) holds "its voice being powerful because of the gular sac."

On Apr. 25, 1921, a pair were captured. Of it we record that "At night the *Acris* look all faded out including femoral stripes." "Male, orange yellow throat with white and dusky flecks. Forelimbs of male look slightly larger proportionally than those in the female. Often male may be green on back except for cords on back." On May 15, 1921 we write "The *Acris* males have the orange throat; this orange color extends to the brachium. Sometimes the skin on the brachium is papillose or raised up into little processes."

The measurements of 101 adults from Okefinokee Swamp, i.e., 55 males and 46 females yield the following results: males range from 15–24.5 mm., mode 18 mm., average 18 mm.; females, range from 15–24 mm., mode 21 mm.; average 19 mm. A study of the modes reveal that the males are at 18 mm. and the females at 21 mm. There are four doubtful external determinations of males from 15–17.5 mm. and of females four such determinations. At 15 mm., however, there are two certain males and one female; at 16 mm. 10 certain males and no females, at 17 mm., 8 certain males and 6 positive females. The range of 15–17 mm. is the uncertain overlap of transformation size with the beginning of maturing breeding frogs.

In a group of adult *Acris* collected from New Orleans by Dr. R. W. Shufeldt (U. S. N. Museum No. 13270) the 22 males ranged from 19–22 mm., the modes 20 and 22 mm., average 21 mm., the 30 females were from 16-26 mm., the modes 22 and 23 mm., average 22 mm. The modes and averages for males and females were higher than those of Okefinokee.

A collection made at Ames, Iowa, June 12, 1924, by Drs. E. L. and K. V. (Katherine VanWinkle) Palmer give a higher modal and average size. The twenty-two adults were taken from a breeding congress, 18 males and 4 females. The males range from 21–29 mm., mode 25 mm., average 25 mm., and the four females ranges from 27–29 mm., average 28 mm.

The measurements for 169 adults from various parts of *Acris's* range, i.e., 100 females and 69 males gives: females range from 16–33 mm., modes 22, 24, and 28 mm. average, 23.5 mm.; males range from 17–29 mm., modes 20, 22 and 25 mm., average, 22 mm.

Compared to this composite series the Okefinokee males have their range and mode 2 mm. lower, and their average 4 mm. lower; the females their range and mode 1 mm. lower and their average 2.25 lower.

Many queries arise: Do the 13.5, 14, 14.5, 15 mm. transforming individuals becomes sexually mature at once or are the debatable and positive 15–17.5 mm. ♂s from frogs which transformed at 9–12 mm.? Are all the adults from 15–24.5 mm. (the largest) one-year-olds when breeding or is less than a year needed for maturity?

At 15 mm. some males and females are not determinable externally. An analysis of a group of 30 frogs we took from Apr. 25–May 3 follows. These sex identifications are on external characters alone.

13 mm. not at transformation; 15 mm., possibly male; 15.5 mm., is it a female? 15.5 mm., is it a male? 16 mm. male two central plaits, throat yel-

lowish; 16 mm., sex not determined. Is it a female? 16 mm. looks a gravid female; 16 mm. probably male, heavily spotted from throat to fore abdomen but no plaits and little yellow on throat, yellow under hind legs, 16.5 mm. Is it a male or female? 17 mm. Is it male? Yellowish under hind legs; 17 mm. looks like female; 17 mm. looks like female; 17.5 mm. female, gravid, spotted throat and breast; 17.5 mm. sex not clear; 18 mm. male, throat heavily spotted, a single central plait; 18 mm. looks like female; 18 mm. female, spotted throat and fore abdomen; 18 mm. male, yellow throat and under hind legs; 18 mm. male, yellowish on throat, two lateral throat plaits, heavily spotted on throat, lightly so on abdomen, thumb possibly larger, under side of hind legs yellowish; 18.5 female, faintly specked on throat and pectoral region. A very rough individual; 19 mm. male some color on venter and throat, a median plait and a lateral plait on either side of throat, heavy spotting on chin and fore abdomen; 19 mm. female almost without specks on under parts; 20 mm. female, throat feebly punctate; 21 mm. female throat and pectoral region spotted; 21 mm. female throat and fore abdomen faintly spotted; 22 mm. female throat to fore abdomen faintly specked; 23 mm. female throat like rest of underparts; 23 mm. female throat, pectoral and fore abdomen heavily spotted.

The plaits on the throat may be one median plait or as often two central plaits. Occasionally beside one or both of these two will be a subsidiary one parallel with it. Sometimes under one ramus will be a parallel plait or one to each ramus. The throat may be very yellowish buffy. In alcohol it looks quite dark at times or may appear smoky or grayish with clear white papillate dots and fine punctures.

Some of the measurements of mated pairs are: 20.5 mm. ♂ × 24 mm. ♀; 18 mm. ♂ × 22.5 mm. ♀; 19 mm. ♂ × 19 mm. ♀; 18.5 mm. ♂ × 21.5 mm. ♀; 20 mm. ♂ × 24 mm. ♀.

Duration, night or day. On the evening of Apr. 24, 1921, we went to Moonshine Pond "Where we heard *Hyla femoralis* in the trees. In the pond we heard one *Hyla cinerea* calling. No end of *Acris* calling. Some *Rana sphenocephala* and plenty of *Bufo lentiginosus* began calling later. This at 7:30 P. M. Later captured on lily pads 5 calling males of *Hyla cinerea*. In same place took my first *Acris* pair in Okefinokee Swamp but they got away from me. In the pond were plenty of water lilies and water pennywort (*Hydrocotyle*)."

On the following day at 8:00 p. m. and later in another pond "on the lily pads and vegetation-carpet were untold numbers of *Acris gryllus*. The male often would keep the sac much inflated even though not croaking. Finally found a pair in axillary embrace. These were put into a bottle but they broke. At camp they were mated."

On May 14 in another pond at 8:00 p. m. "The *Acris* were calling loudly. We found among lizard's tail (*Saururus cernuus*) on the sphagnum surface-mat, a pair. They were resting quietly. Put them in a butter jar. The top of the jar had a small hole about which we had forgotten. When next we looked the pair had escaped. The next pair we saw amongst iris or sphagnum at the surface. Tried to catch them with both hands and failed. Later found another pair; when the electric flashlight went out they leaped away. They can leap two feet or more when mated. Finally caught the pair. Put them in a sack. This in a jar with hole plugged . . . . We took the pair of *Acris* out of butter jar and put them in a porcelain jar for two flashlight photographs. Later transferred them to photo jar without their breaking embrace."

On May 23, 1921, at a bayou of Billy's Lake we observed the odd behavior of two croaking males. Our journal note with no polishing is thus: "At noon along the edge under shade of some bushes was a small series of grass blades 5 inches high. A pair of *Acris* males, one directly behind the other about 3–2 inches. Each croaking male revealed his yellow throat very plainly in day time. Then it leaped on to the other. Then it leaped to one side and they were more or less back to back. At first I thought a mated pair must be in the water back of them because of water commotion, but it was each male stretching one leg out as far as he could behind. Then the second male attempted to embrace the other but merely leaped on to it. This process kept up for the 20 minutes we remained. Once one male crawled up the grass. The other followed. Once on a leaf-blade one could fairly see the leg stretched back. So also at other times. At times the leg would remain thus stretched out for some time, "frozen" so to speak. When another male not far away began croaking both croaked at same time. The process of play, by stretching, leaping on to each other or about each other was common to both of them."

On May 26, 1921, with air temperature 94° in partial shade 4:00 p. m. we found "gravid females in the pine barrens. About the ponds were no end of *Acris* calling. Saw two mated pairs. One at the base of a black gum on wet dead leaves at the edge of the pond and one pair on top of a grassy mat where many males were. Every mat had a male or two perched on it. The pair captured broke. At midnight they were not remated." On the next day, May 27, we have "The *Acris* pair of last night apparently have resumed mating since I caught them. The female has laid a few eggs."

At Southern Bullfrog Pond on the evening of June 3 "we found two mated pairs of *Acris*. Lost one. At *Chorophilus* Pond, the same evening were mainly *Acris*. Captured a pair there."

In 1922 we found a mated pair July 2 at Starling Branch crossing, between 8:30 p. m. and 12 midnight. "In a grassy overflow with *Bufo terrestris* and *Hyla femoralis* were plenty of *Acris*. Finally at 10:00 p. m. found a pair at the edge of the pond. Photographed them. Brought the pair to camp in a small bottle. They were caught in the bottle. The female and male broke. Stopper made it too confined and the female died."

Our experience at Dinwiddie, Va., June 1, 1917, may be apropos. "Toads, tree toads and bullfrogs around. . . . At the first ford about 6 miles beyond Dinwiddie, Va., near the road found several files of Fowler toad's eggs. . . . Found a mass of bullfrog eggs. . . . (tree toad eggs in another pond).

"After supper Munz (Professor P. A. Munz, Pomona College) and I went out for frogs. . . . In the *Acris* pool, long shallow, 1–4 inches deep (*Juncus* plentiful) we found plenty of *Acris*. After about one hour's collecting we found a mated pair in the water. The embrace is axillary . . . . Didn't find any of the eggs. The pond is a surface pond with trees on all sides but the east. . . . About 11:00 p. m. returned. Put extra males and female *Acris* in one compartment and started to put the pair in another part when we lost the female of the pair. A severe storm came up. Later Munz and I went out again. Soon found another pair. After capture they broke but soon resumed. When we put them in the can they separated. In the morning (June 2) no eggs from *Acris*. Munz and I went to the *Acris* pond and found the eggs." (See egg mass description). The mated pair never laid but three days after, June 4, 1917, one of the females laid eggs. These were our first identifications of *Acris* eggs in the field.

Amplexation. Normally *Acris* embraces are as in the *Hylidae* in general, i.e., axillary amplexation. The *Acris* pairs taken at Dinwiddie, Va., in 1917 were all axillary in type. On Apr. 25, 1921, a pair captured on a lily pad "was found in axillary fashion. When I put them into a bottle they broke. At camp they were mated axillary fashion. Then put them into a compartment of the fish can. The male then held the female with his forelimbs ahead of the forelimbs of the female and the hand of each forelimb came on to the pectoral region." The amplexation of all four pairs of *Acris* found the evening of May 14, 1921, were axillary with no departures. So also were the two pairs of May 26, the two pairs of June 3, and the pair of June 25, 1921.

OVULATION

Habitat. Abbott suggests blades of coarse grass. This expands in Sherwood to grass and weeds and in Ditmars to grass and reeds. John K. Strecker Jr., (1910, p. 80) places the "breeding localities" as "ponds and small streams." In 1906 Miss Dickerson (p. 156) has the eggs "attached to grass blades or leaves in the water."

In 1921 we took mated pairs in the open area of cypress ponds, in amongst the cypress of the edge of cypress ponds and bays, in cypress bays or glades, on sphagnum strands on prairies, in wooded streams or branches, and rarely in moist pine barrens. The open cypress ponds and prairies were the optimum habitats for ovulation.

Period. Abbott (1882, p. 707) gave this period as about May 1. Hay writes "Numerous specimens were found at Irvington on the 8th of March. The eggs are probably laid about this time, although I do not know anything about them." Brimley (1896, p. 561) says "This species (in North Carolina) breeds from April through most of the summer." Doubtless W. L. Sherwood (1898, p. 19) is following Abbott when he says "The eggs are laid early in May, in small bunches attached to grass or weeds. Development is prolonged." Following Abbott and Sherwood, Ditmars (1905, p. 193) writes "The eggs are deposited early in May in small bunches. They usually adhere to grass and reeds."

In 1906 Dickerson paraphrases the above data of period and asserts egg laying is in late April and early May.

In 1910 J. K. Strecker Jr., (1910, p. 80) gives "Apr. 10 to May 30" as the breeding period for *Acris gryllus crepitans* of Waco, Texas. Ruthven, Thompson and Thompson (1912, p. 47) hold "the eggs are laid in April and May."

In 1920 Wright (1920, p. 29) writes "The cricket frog is one of the first forms to appear in the spring, and according to several authors breeds in March, April and May or even later."

In 1921 on April 15, on St. Augustine School Grounds, Raleigh, N. C., we heard a few males calling at night 9:00 p. m. with temperature 68°. Then we thought that they and the meadow frogs were practically over breeding with a few stragglers in the ponds and wet meadows. But two nights later at Boone's Pond plenty were calling in the evening. This indicates Brimley's remark that they "breed from April through most of the summer" is nearer the truth for Raleigh.

In 1921 in the swamp from captive pairs we have May 15, May 16, May 27, June 4, June 25. In 1921 we took or recorded mated pairs: Apr. 24, Apr. 25, May 14, May 15, May 26, June 3, June 24. In 1922 we captured a pair July 2.

In 1921 we recorded great choruses Apr. 24, Apr. 25, May 9 and 10, May 13 and 14, May 16, May 26, May 27, June 3, June 25, July 11–18, July 27. In 1922 the choruses were June 14–22, June 27, July 2, July 5, July 7, July 9, July 18, July 21, Aug. 4–6, Aug. 9–11, Aug. 13, Aug. 15, Aug. 19, Aug. 30.

On the basis of spent females we find that in a group of 9 females captured Apr. 24–28, 1921, the night after we entered the swamp, 7 were gravid and 2 spent. Other female records for 1921 are June 16, gravid, July 2, gravid, July 29, gravid, June 3, spent, July 17, gravid, June 20, gravid, July 8, gravid.

We, therefore, see that on the basis of ovulation in camp we have records from May 15–June 25, on mated pairs evidence records from Apr. 24–July 2, on choruses from Apr. 17–Aug. 30, and on spent and gravid females records of spent females Apr. 24 and gravid females July 29. The ovulation period surely goes from Apr. 24–July 29 and if strong choruses help in the evidence from Apr. 15–Sept. 1. All our subsequent notes (1922–1926) summarize it as Apr. 15 or earlier to Sept. 1. Doubtless it lays beyond Sept. 1.

Temperature and humidity. In 1921, May 15, when the first pair laid in captivity the air temperature was 67°. Later the same day when another female laid we report "Today the temperature has been from 66°–69°. Still later, May 16, we record "The eggs during May 15 and May 16 to 9:00 a. m. had air conditions of 67°–71°F.

Humidity is the most important factor. The Apr. 24–25, 1921, period was preceded by heavy rain in surrounding stations. The May 13–16 was rainy and was followed by rain. The May 26–27 period had a few light rains around the swamp. On June 3–4 we had heavy rains. On June 24–25 rains prevailed. In 1922 on July 2 we had a rain at St. George of 2.00 inches. The air maxima and minima for stations around the swamp for these periods are:

Air Maxima		1921	Air Minima	
Range	Average		Range	Average
81–84	84	Apr. 24–25	50–62	54
73–88	82	May 13–16	59–67	65
90–95	94	May 26–27	63–70	68
82–86	84	June 3– 4	68–70	69
90–97	94	June 24–25	67–71	70
		1922		
90–98	94	July 2	68–72	70

It is apparent that air maxima vacillate backward and forward more than the air minima. In the above tabulation there is a steady climb of the range average of minima.

This table might permit of the interpretation that *Acris* might breed at 50° or 54° or 59° with rains prevalent. But the author believes 62°—72° or 62°—69° the optimum or prevalent influential minima in starting vigorous breeding from the last of April to July 1.

Egg-laying process. Of the first pair which laid May 15, 1921, we made these notes: "Surely the pair doesn't occupy one position but moves about with each oviposition. It could not have occupied one position above the stick for eggs to be placed on the stick as they are, i. e., for eggs to drop down from one position. These were never laid in one mass. Neither are they thus from the pair breaking up the mass from excessive activity in confined quarters." We did not observe the actual egg-laying but suspect they are somewhat of the *Hyla crucifer* type.

On June 4 we have the information that the "two mated pairs of *Acris* found June 3, 1921, laid eggs. One female at least. Believe she laid them without an embracing male." Three days later June 7 have a similar note "Female frogs laying without a male. On night of June 3, a female of a previous pair laid a complement without an attendant male. Previously another female *Acris* has thus done."

We suspect most of the eggs are normally laid at night. For example, a mated pair caught the night of June 24 were separated and the female had laid eggs before morning, and in the field most of the breeding activity comes at night.

EGGS

Egg mass, egg description. Abbott (1882, p. 707) is the first to speak of their eggs which "were deposited in little masses, attached to the blades of course grass."

Dr. K. V. (Katherine VanWinkle) Palmer who worked over our *Acris* collections and the 1917 transcontinental material found that in an Ames, (Iowa,) congress of *Acris* June 12, 1926, that some eggs tended to be in bunches or masses.

In 1917 at Dinwiddie, Va., we found this species breeding. Of it we write in 1920 (p. 29) as follows: "The writer recently found them breeding actively on June 1. They had chosen a shallow (1 to 4 inches deep) grassy meadow pool (Pl. X, fig. 1). The eggs were attached singly to sedge stems or were strewn singly on the bottom. In one or two instances three or four eggs were close together. Many of the eggs were in water not more than an inch in depth. Eggs of *Acris* hard. Found no more than ten eggs."

In 1921 our first record of eggs came the morning of May 15. "A general rainy morning. At 6:00 a. m. the mated pair of *Acris* hadn't laid. At 8:00 there were 74 eggs singly laid. At 8:00 the pair were still mated. At 9:00 when we returned the pair was broken. The eggs all rested on the bottom of the jar." On the afternoon of the same day "the female of my drinking cup (male of which leaped out) placed with the three males but she did not lay single eggs nor was she mated. Nevertheless she laid. Her eggs are in a single mass on the side of the small bottle in which she was and just above the water's level." Later the same day we wrote of the first complement thus: "There are two or three eggs fastened to the stick on its under side. The eggs are scattered all over the bottom of the jar."

Our field notes on eggs follow: Some *Acris gryllus* eggs were measured in the field under adverse circumstances May 16, 1921, "One vitellus was 1.0 mm.; outer envelope 3.8 mm. Another had vitellus, 1. 0 mm., inner envelope 1.8 mm. and outer envelope 4.0 mm." On May 27, we remark that eggs laid May 26–27 have "vitellus, 1.0 mm.; outer envelope 2.8–3.0 mm.; no inner envelope; egg vitellus creamish white; animal pole deep brown. Must be something wrong with measurements I made on the eggs of May 16."

On June 25, 1921 after a pair had laid eggs we examined the eggs in camp and made notes that the "vitelli were .9 mm., envelope 3.6–3.2 mm., upper pole 'brownish,' as we have used the term before in egg description (really nearer buffy olive), lower pole white. Envelope loose, full of trash on outer edge. Hard to determine where there are two envelopes."

On July 17, 1921, we for a period mistook singly laid eggs from the bottom of a pond for *Acris* eggs. They proved those of *Hyla gratiosa* which lays single eggs.

In 1922 on July 3 we artificially secured some eggs from a mated female which died. Her egg complement was 241 eggs. The eggs taken from the ovary took up water and the jelly envelope looked as if laid naturally. One jelly envelope appeared at first but later it very definitely became apparent that in these ovarian eggs there was a .9 mm. vitellus, *an inner envelope* 1.6–1.8 mm., and a 2.6–2.8 mm. outer envelope."

In Feb. 1923 (p. 34) we merely alluded to *Acris gryllus* eggs as "single submerged eggs." Laboratory measurements made by Mrs. Wright and myself yielded: eggs with vitelli .9–1.0 mm., average .98, mode 1.0 mm. and envelopes 2.4–3.6 mm., average 2.8 mm., mode 3.0 mm. In one egg an inner envelope seemed to be present and it was 1.8 mm. in diameter. In 1924 (p. 378) we summarized it thus: "Eggs deposited singly. Envelope single. No inner envelope or appearance as such, envelope firm, definite in outline 2.4 to 3.6 mm.; vitellus 0.9 to 1.0 mm. Egg complement 241." We are mindful of two difficulties, one the possibility of egg complement possibly being laid in a mass occasionally and also of the discovery that an inner envelope may eventually become the rule rather than the exception.

HATCHING PERIOD

The eggs laid May 15, 1921, between 6:00 and 8:00 a. m. were approaching hatching May 17 at 8:15 when preserved. Air minima of 61°, 64° and 65° and maxima of 73°, 84° and 76° obtained these three days. The other set of eggs laid May 15 hatched 12:00 (noon) May 19 or about four days later. The air mimina from May 15–May 19 ranged from 63°–65° and maxima from 73°–84°, or an average for all of 72°F.

MATURE TADPOLE

Color description from life (July 5, 1921). General coloration dark olive buff or old gold or olive lake or sulphine yellow. Belly especially on sides and on gill region light vinaceous fawn or shell pink or pale salmon color. Belly with ivory yellow or cartridge buff clusters of spots. These clustered spots almost cover the top of the body. The region back of the labial mouthparts has no light vinaceous fawn nor ivory yellow. The clusters of spots become almost continuous and look a patch of French gray or lilac gray on the throat region.

Tail. Tip of tail (upper and lower crests) conspicuously black (at times lost). Clusters of ivory yellow or cartridge buff spots on upper crest and upper part of musculature, less frequent on lower crest and lower musculature. These spots somewhat amongst black of tail tip. Tail crests almost transparent, certainly translucent almost clear of marks except under lens when the course of the blood vessels are marked by the body color (dark olive buff, etc.)

Iris ivory yellow above and below, behind and in front of pupil light coral red and black. Whole of iris more or less prettily marked with black interspersed with the two lighter colors mentioned.

General appearance. Tadpole medium (42.0 mm.) full and fairly deep bodied. Tail very long, tail tip very acuminate, with black flagellum. Tail proportionally the longest and most narrow (depth of tail in length of tail) of any of the Hylids in the U. S. Dorsal and ventral crests rather narrow, not equal to the tail musculature in depth. The dorsal crest extends on to the body to the vertical of the spiracle or just ahead of it but nearer spiracle than the eye. Spiracle sinistral, mainly directed backwards only slightly upwards, and it stands out from body in life almost on the lateral axis. Eye on lateral axis, eye hardly if visible at all from the venter (more like a Ranid tadpole) suborbital region oblique and vertical as in Hylids in general. Eye in dorsal aspect just inside the lateral outline. Anus dextral, opening on a level with the lower edge of the lower crest. Muciferous crypts not distinct.

Mouth parts: Teeth 2/2. Upper labium fringed with a continuous row of labial teeth; the papillary border does not extend above or inwards beyond the end of the labial fringe (unlike all our Hylidae of the U. S.). The end of the second row of upper labial teeth extend beyond the end of the upper fringe for 1/3 or sometimes about 1/2 of the length of the second upper labial row (in *H. crucifer* 1/4–1/6 the length of either lateral row). The median space between the second lateral upper labial rows of teeth long, contained 1.2–.75 times in either lateral row, i.e., rarely greater, often equal to and more often greater than either lateral row. The horny beak is contained in upper fringe 1.2–1.35 times or 1.35–1.5 times in the distance from one end of lateral row to the end of the other lateral row. There are practically no inner papillae. The first row of lower labial teeth about equal to horny beak or slightly larger. The second row of lower labium usually perceptibly longer than the first row, (the illustration is a little unusual in this respect).

Measurements. Length of body (9.6–13 mm.) in tail (26.6–42.2 mm.) 2.5–3.25, average 2.9. Width (5.5–9.0 mm.) of body in its own length 1.44–1.9, average 1.66. Depth (4.18–8.0 mm.) of body 1.0–1.3 in body depth, average 1.17. Depth of body 1.625–2.1 in length of body, average 2.0. Depth (4.2–7.8 mm.) of tail in length of tail 3.25–5.0, average 4.0. Muscular part (2.8–4.4 mm.) 1.2–2.15 in depth of tail, average 1.71. Spiracle 1.6–2.36 nearer base of hind legs or vent region (3.2–5.6 mm.) than the tip of the snout (7.0–10.0 mm.), average 1.92. Spiracle to eye usually equal to spiracle to base of hind legs or vent. Eye 1.0–1.66 nearer the tip of snout (3.0–4.2 mm.) than to spiracle (4.0–6.0 mm.), average 1.22. Nostril 1.0–1.33 nearer eye (1.4–2.4 mm.) than snout, (1.8–2.8 mm.). Mouth (1.8–2.4 mm.) usually 1–1.3 larger than internasal space, (1.4–2.6 mm.), average 1.06, rarely less than internasal space. Mouth contained 1.3–2.2 (average 1.71) in interorbital distance (3.0–4.6 mm.). Internasal space contained in interorbital space 1.33–2.2, average 1.7.

The dimensions of the largest tadpole are:

	mm.		mm.
Total length	42.2	Spiracle to vent	5.0
Body length	13.0	Spiracle to eye	5.2
Body depth	6.6	Eye to snout	4.2
Body width	8.2	Eye to nostril	2.2
Tail length	29.2	Nostril to snout	2.4
Tail depth	7.0	Mouth	2.0
Musculature of tail	4.0	Interorbital of distance	4.0
Spiracle to snout	10.0	Internasal distance	2.6

General remarks. Hay (1892, p. 462) "On the 16th of August . . . found numerous specimens of the tadpoles of this species. They were found hiding in the vegetation at the bottom of a small stream. They were in very different stages of development, some with body, the fore and the hind legs visible, others with only short hind legs." In Indiana, Hubbs (1917, p. 99) on Sept. 23 found "tadpoles of species . . . in the pond, as were also a few transforming individuals."

The first author to describe the mouth parts of the tadpole is O. P. Hay (1892, p. 462). He describes them as follows: "The arrangement of the horny denticles about the mouth of the larvae I found to be different from that of specimens of *Chorophilus triseriatus*. In both species there are two rows of horny denticles on the upper lip. On the lower lip, there are in *Chorophilus* three rows of denticles, but in *Acris* only two. Furthermore, in *Chorophilus* the denticles are finely serrated at their tips; in *Acris* this is not the case. The teeth of the latter genus are less numerous than in the former." No one else speaks of these mouth parts except Miss Dickerson (1906, p. 156) who uses Hay's characterization. Had the author of this article remembered this observation he would not have had so much difficulty in 1914, 1917 and 1921 before he finally identified the tadpoles.

In 1921 the first time we took adult *Acris* tadpoles with any degree of certainty was May 31. From that date to July 5 or 8 we still called them the black tipped tadpoles with some question as to their identity. For example, on July 2, we found "tadpoles with black tail tip. Are they *Acris* or something else? Not like normal coloration of *Acris* tadpoles." Even then the old error of considering *H. femoralis* tadpoles *Acris gryllus* still persisted with us and even to the date of this writing *Hyla femoralis* tadpoles from 1912–1921, crop up in our collection labeled *Acris gryllus*. It all arose because of a theory that the alternation of light and brown bands on tail musculature were transferred to the rear of the femur. Such alternation occurs in the tail musculature of a *Hyla femoralis* tadpole and on the rear of the thighs of *Acris gryllus*. Hence *Hyla femoralis* tadpoles were called *Acris gryllus* tadpoles for a long time. In fact, even though we were quite satisfied in 1922 we still vacillated per the following note: "July 13, took in an overflow a quantity of tadpoles. . . . A few had a black tip to the tail. Most of these, however, have lost the black tip. They have a triangle between the eyes and the banded arrangement on hind legs as do *Acris* adults. They are *Acris gryllus*. But what about the tadpoles recorded earlier as having a light and dark banded arrangement on the tail, an alternation of bands?" We now know that the tadpole with alternation of light and dark bands on the tail musculature is of *Hyla femoralis* and that the tadpole with a black tail tip is of *Acris gryllus*.

This tadpole puzzles us in more ways then one. Of it on July 8, 1921, we write "Found some tadpoles mature and with black tail tip. These are slim, long-tailed forms. The most conspicuous thing about them when alive is the *protruding spiracular tube*." The tadpole looked like a true frog tadpole and we were trying to link it up with *Ranas* whose life histories we did not know and that went on until the middle of the summer of 1922. Witness the following: "July 11 in a pond on the island between the first and second dreen we found in my seine one or two of these long-tailed black-tipped tadpoles. It was a cypress area, wooded, has *Polygala cymosa*, *Sabbatia decandra*, poison ivy, *Ilex myrtifolia*, *Pieris phillyreifolia*, *Leucothae*, *Clethra*. This tadpole does not have the crest far forward on the back. It has two rows of teeth above and two below. Can it be *Rana virgatipes* and that we missed that species at Billy's Lake in 1921? It looks more of a Ranid than a Hylid tadpole. It is not *Hyla squirella* nor *Hyla gratiosa*." In writing up the tadpoles of our 1912–1914 we described *Hyla femoralis* tadpole for *Acris gryllus*, but it did not appear in print but unfortunately in 1921 (p. 33) we wrote "The conspicuous character is the arrangement of coloration on the muscular part of the tail. There are four long bands—the first a brownish band from body to tip of tail; above this a cream white band, followed by another brown band to tail tip; and this surrounded by another short cream white band. There are two rows of teeth on the upper lip and three complete rows on the lower as in the case of some of the frogs." This tadpole described is of *Hyla femoralis* not *Acris gryllus*. It is one of the mistakes one assesses to pioneer work.

On Jan. 20, 1923 (p. 406) we corrected this description to "*Acris gryllus* —very long, black-tipped tails and projecting spiracular tube."

LARVAL PERIOD

Abbott (1882, p. 707) writes "I did not succeed in following the various stages of developmental growth from the egg to the matured animal, but was enabled to determine that it was more protracted than in the case of the common tree-toad (*Hyla versicolor*). The difference is, I believe, quite seven weeks."

Hay (1892, p. 462) believed they were breeding March 8 and he "recorded transformation Sept. 1. This would give 176 days or almost six months, rather a long period, though twenty-five days or a month in March could be given to hatching of the eggs."

When we believed *Hyla femoralis* tadpoles to be *Acris gryllus* we wrote (1920, p. 33) "The tadpole of the cricket frog develops in about the same length of time as that of the peeper. The tadpoles of the former (cricket frog) transform the same season the eggs are laid and seldom exceed 1 1/2 inches in length." We have had no opportunity of comparing *Acris gryllus* and *Hyla crucifer* tadpoles in the same locality. The above may be true and it may be false. At that time our evidence seemed to imply 60–80–90 days larval period.

In one pond in 1921 our first record of breeding comes May 26 and other breeding notes to June 3. Our first transformation came June 16, 17 and July 2, July 23. Manifestly the intervals of 13, 23 and 27 days do not seem reasonable but 59 days from May 26–July 23 or 50 days from June 3–July 23 seem nearer the truth. These June 16 and 17 transformations are from an earlier breeding so it may have been for the July 2 and July 23 transformations. In another pond we found great activity on Apr. 24 when a pair was recorded. The same pond had transformation June 3 and 4 and July 23. This gives conjectural periods of 41–90 days.

On Billy's Island we have several transformations July 23, 26, 27, also July 3–12 and June 15. Some breedings in these places May 13 and 12 and Apr. 24–28 give 32, 33, 48, 52, 59, 60, 66, 70, 70, 71, 75, 79, 86, 90, 90, 94 days of larval life, or an average of 67 days. Put in another way the first breeding evidence came Apr. 24, our first transformations were June 3, June 4 and June 16 or 40, 41 and 53 days but our entry Apr. 22 or 23 into the swamp precluded earlier records than Apr. 24 by us and these early *Acris* transformations were probably from earlier breedings than Apr. 24.

In 1922 we have evidences of 60, 68, 69, 71 and 78 days as possible larval periods. None of this evidence is positive. Fifty to ninety days seem within reason as the probable period.

TRANSFORMATION

Period. Abbott placed transformation in late August. Hay (1892, p. 462) says "The transformations occurred about Sept 1" in Indiana. Hubbs (1917, p. 99) found a few transforming Sept. 23 in Indiana.

In 1912 we found transformation likely from May 29–July 15 or later. In 1921 from June 3 to July 27, transformation was recorded. In 1922 we have transformation from June 22–Aug. 29. These transform from Apr. 1 or earlier to October 1 or later.

Size. We recorded in the field little regarding the size of *Acris* at transformation. On July 7, 1922, we observed that "it has the largest transformed size relatively (i.e., to adult size) of any of the Anura in the swamp." In 1920 (pp. 34 and 36) we have *Acris gryllus* transformation size one-half inch and the adult 1 3/4 inches. "The cricket-frog transforms from June 1 to July if the eggs be laid early, or in August if the eggs be laid in June. At transformation it averages a greater length than the swamp cricket frog, being 0.5 inch in length."

From Gainesville, Ga., as early as Apr. 2, 1911, J. C. Bradley secured transformed frogs 10 and 11.5 mm. long, and as late as Aug. 20, 1916, F. Harper took transformed frogs at Chapel Point, Maryland. These last are 10, 10 and 13 mm. in size. In 1920 we gave one-half inch as the transformation size. Our 1912 material yielded transformation sizes of 12 and 13 mm.

In 1921 on Apr. 28 we found one specimen 13.5 mm. but it was not at transformation. On June 3 we record one collection with a 13 mm. transformed individual and one 10 mm. with a stub of the tail. Another lot of 5 specimens are 13, 13, 13, 14, 14.5 mm. respectively are marked transformed but are doubtless slightly beyond. On June 14 we have one transformed at 12 mm. and another 10 mm. with a stub of the tail and a frog mouth. On June 17 we took one 14 mm. and past transformation. On July 12 we took three 13, 13.5, 14 mm. beyond transformation. Two transformed at 11.5 and 12 mm. and 3 with slight stub, these 11.5 and 13 mm. On July 23 we have three just transformed 12, 12, 13.5 mm. On July 2 we found in one place tadpoles of several sizes and transformations of 10, 12, 12.5 and 14 mm., and one beyond transformation 13.5 mm. On the 24th of July we found one transformed at 12.5 mm. and one 15 mm. almost transformed, 4 legs, with more frog-like than tadpole mouth. On July 26 we have a series of six transformed frogs, 11, 11, 11.5 (stub 5 mm.), 12, 12, 13 mm. On July 27–29 we have one specimen 13 mm., which is not at transformation. On the same date the two 11.0 and 11.5 mm. just transformed and five others 13, 13, 13.5, 13.5, 14.5 mm. are possibly just transformed. On July 29 we have one 11.5 mm. at transformation.

In 1922 on June 27 we took our smallest specimens of transformed frogs, one 9 mm. in length. On June 29, we have five specimens transformed; 10.0 (tail stub 3 mm.) 11, 11, 12, 12.5 (stub 7.5 mm.) mm. On July 12, at Starling Branch crossing we secured many mature and smaller tadpoles and transformations 8.5, 10, 10, 10.5, 11, 11, 12, 12.5 and 14 mm. These are dried up when measured. On July 14, are seven just beyond transformation 13,

13.5, 13.5, 13.5, 14, 14.5 and 14.5 mm. On July 18 on the prairies we secured three transformed frogs 12, 13, 13 (tail 6 mm.) mm. On July 28 we have transformed individuals 11, 11, 11, 11.5, 12, 12.5 mm. The last has forelegs just through the skin and the tail 21 mm. long. Finally on Aug. 4, 1922, we secured two transforming frogs 13.5 (stub 3 mm.) and 14 (stub 15 mm., almost transformed frog mouth) mm.

There are 51 specimens in 1912, 1921 and 1922 at transformation or just before. They range from 10–15 mm., 6 at 10 mm. and 2 at 13.5 mm., 1 at 14 mm., and 1 at 15 mm. The average is 13 mm. and so is the mode. Thirty-one of the 51 are 12 mm. or less. We also had 26 debatable stages on individuals possibly beyond transformation. These ranged from 13 mm.–14.5 mm., 8 at 13 mm., 8 at 13.5 mm., 4 at 14 mm., and 4 at 14.5 mm., or averaging 13.5 mm.

The transformation size usually ranges from 10–12.5, rarely to 15 mm. or rarely below 10 to 9 mm. Inasmuch as some tadpoles grow to large sizes before transformation the larval period must be variable. Furthermore, it is remarkable to have transformation at 14 or 15 mm. when one male has only a measurement of 15 mm., and several are clearly males at 17 if not 16 mm. In other words this species apparently at times almost transforms into mature breeding frogs.

General remarks. Abbott (1882, pp. 708, 709) in New Jersey records that "Late in August these tadpoles have become fully developed peepers. Even then they were very rare during that summer (I suppose this is always the case) but in September many were found in damp places, never in the water, but always near a running brook, or a spring. By the middle of September a marked increase in their numbers was noticed; but their haunts were different. I found very few in the meadows, but many in damp places, as spring holes, in the adjacent woodland, and particularly along a brook where the water flows rapidly over a rocky bed.

"It was here I closed my field studies of these batrachians. Early in October I found a number of these 'peepers' in a little ravine, through which the above mentioned brook passes. I noticed at this time, that these little creatures had a decided aversion to the water. Necessary as it was for them to keep their skins moist, they had no desire to become thoroughly wetted, and when by chance they made an unlucky jump and settled in the water, they straightway crawled out and took up a high and dry position on some projecting stone. If in the sunlight, so much the better. A bath seemed to chill them, and whenever I drove one into the water, I found that for several minutes after it emerged I could pick it up without difficulty; but in time it would regain its ordinary activity, and then quick indeed must be one's movements who would catch them with the hand alone."

In 1912 and in the first month of 1921 our mistaken field identification of the tadpole made our transformation evidence for these periods too confusing and uncertain to insert here.

In 1921, June 3, in one pond "Found on lily pads and other surface vegetation what I at first took for *Pseudacris ocularis*. The second specimen had a stump of a tail and a triangle between the eyes. It is *Acris* transforming and transformed. These *Acris* are about the size of an adult *Pseudacris ocularis*. Strangely enough we took a pair the female of which laid when these tadpoles were transforming. Transformation period must, therefore, be a long extended one. On June 14 we took transformed frogs at Minne Lake. On June 16 on Billy's Island in another cypress pond we found all stages to transformation. On the 17th more transformed individuals were taken. On July 3 we found many transforming on Honey Island Prairie. On July 12 more were taken on Billy's Island. On July 23 and July 27 others were recorded.

In 1922 we have several transformation notes: "On June 22 found tadpoles with large hind legs." On July 2 "on Grand Prairie and whole area from Lake Seagrove to Grand Prairie are *Acris* abundant. Found the species transforming, several on lily pads out from the edge of the islets ('houses, camp houses')." "July 13 at Starling Branch crossing we took in overflow crossing a quantity of tadpoles approaching transformation. A few had a black tip to the tail." At the same place "July 24 very few *Acris* tadpoles. One with 4 legs, long tail, the stage desired." In another pond "July 28 found plenty of transformed *Acris* and a few black tipped tadpoles." Of another place the same day we wrote "Still a few black tipped tadpoles in pond near the 2nd dreen."

In August we have a few notes: On Aug. 3–5 on Billy's Island in three different ponds they were transforming. On Aug. 17 at the edge of Starling Branch crossing "we found a transformed *Acris* on the ground." On Aug. 31 at two ponds "found several tadpoles with only two legs."

Our field notes above give in 1921 dates of transformation from June 3–July 27. In 1922 we have evidences of transformation from June 22 to Aug. 21 and F. Harper later, Aug. 29, found the houses (islands on prairies) "covered with transformed *Acris*."

In 1912 we secured very little on transformation in *Acris gryllus* of Okefinokee Swamp. Then we rite:

"In some overflow pools on Mixon's Hammock, June 16, 1912, we took several stages of this form. The pools were about a rod from the west end of Billy's Lake and had in it also toad and spring frog tadpoles, killifishes and pigmy sunfishes. Two of the series are at transformation and measure 12 mm. On May 31–June 2, 1912, on Honey Island Prairie where water is 4–5 feet deep we found them common at the surface either fully transformed or with tails yet visible. These measured 13 mm. These little creatures were resting on the lily pads of the open prairie or on the vegetation around the little islands. It is an interesting fact that in these transformed individuals (even in forms, just before the outpushing of the fore-limbs) the only adult marks are the conspicuous posterior femoral stripes and rarely the interorbital triangle. Several other individuals taken at the same time as the transformed individuals measured 16.75–19 mm., and another specimen taken on Floyd's Island June 25 measured 18 mm. The only mark these eight have in common is the same femoral coloration. A series of tadpoles taken June 16 represent stages just before outpushing of hind-limbs to transformation and no doubt the above period outlined for transformation, namely May 29–June 16 on this evidence might be pushed to July 15 or later. The breeding must come early in the spring with that of the spring frog or the development may be very rapid if the species waits until late April or first of May as some texts give it. Surely the transformation is not solely in late August or September, and it is barely possible that the period of final development is shorter than previously held."

GROWTH

In the Okefinokee region transformation, as we have seen, is from 9–12.5 mm., rarely to 15 mm. The 13 and 13.5 and 14, 14.5 and 15 mm. sizes are more often beyond transformation than at transformation but 9–15 mm. is its range. In the north in Maryland and Indiana we have transformations from 10–14 mm., e.g., Dr. B. W. Evermann at Lake Maxinkuckee, Indiana, took transformed individuals of sizes 11, 12, 13.5 and 14 mm. In Maryland Mr. M. K. Brady took it at 12.5 mm., and F. Harper at 10 and 13 mm.

Our Okefinokee males reached 24.5 mm. and the females 24 mm. The largest males for other parts of its range were 29 mm. and the females 33 mm. If *Hyla squirella* transforms at 11–14 mm. and at end of first year as frog reaches 17–24.5 mm., *Acris gryllus* a more active frog through the year ought from 9–15 mm. transformation size to reach in first year old stage 15–24.5 the largest we have or better to 22 mm. in males and 23 mm. in females. These first-year-olds would have a mode of 1.8 mm. for the males and 2.1 mm. for the females. In our study of 169 adults from non-Okefinokee localities we have a range considerably beyond 24.5 mm. our largest in the Okefinokee. Some of these reach 33 mm. (U.S.N.M. 3935). The lowest and highest modes for these males are 20 mm. and 25 mm. and for females 22, 24 and 28 mm. Possibly in the northern localities where transformation sizes are the same as for our smaller Okefinokee adults and where the growing season is not so long frogs from 23–29 mm. males or 26–33 mm. females may be two-year-olds.

We, therefore, postulate somewhat reasonably the following: transformation 9–12.5 mm. (rarely to 15 mm.); 1st year olds, 15–22 or 23 mm.; possible two-year olds, 22 or 23–29 to 33 mm.

AUTUMNAL DISAPPEARANCE

Abbott (1882, p. 710) in 1881 in New Jersey writes: "Sensitive as these 'peepers' are to changes of temperature, it is by no means the first frost that drives them into their winter quarters. In the autumn of the past year (1881) I found them last as late as Nov. 12th but even later (Dec. 27th) my son found one in the meadows which was as lively as a cricket. The frogs generally were singing this day. For more than two weeks prior to Nov. 12th there had been several white frosts, and the true frogs (Ranae) had all disappeared except such few as lingered in the warm waters of the larger springs."

In Illinois H. Garman (1892, p. 342) finds that "Examples nearly grown were taken November 17, 1888, under logs in the vicinity of a creek in Champaign County, where they were hibernating."

In June, 1896, C. S. Brimley (p. 501) makes the "cricket frog abundant, active all the year round except in the severest weather." Ruthven, Thompson & Thompson (1912, p. 46) finds "This species hibernates during the cold weather but soon becomes active again during warm periods." In Colorado M. M. Ellis and J. Henderon (1913) find it until Oct. 26. In Virginia, Nelson County, Dunn (1916, p. 22) finds one Nov. 26. Brimley has taken it at Bay St. Louis on Dec. 4 and at Raleigh on Dec. 12.

In 1913 and 1914 the Cornell party of Dec. 22, 1913–Jan. 1, 1914, found this species active and took several specimens. Doubtless this species is more or less active throughout the year in the Okefinokee Swamp.

FOOD

Holbrook (1842, Vol. IV, p. 132) gives this note: "It feeds on various kinds of insects, and makes immense leaps to secure its prey, or to escape its pursuers. It can easily be domesticated, and takes its food readily from the hand; I have kept several for months in a glass globe on a few sprigs of purslain (*Portulacca oleracea*), feeding them occasionally with flies."

Abbott (1882, p. 708) finds that "They fed ravenously at this time (breeding season) and even when confined in very cramped quarters, would devour any flies that came within reach." Later (p. 710) he states that "My impression is, that they do not require or partake of any food during their brief existence as matured 'peepers' in autumn (i.e., from completion of growth of their limbs in September to the commencement of their hibernation). My reason for this is based upon the fact that the specimens in a bottle, to which I referred, were placed in confinement on the 20th of October, 1881, and the date of writing, Jan. 29, 1882, a period of one hundred days has just elapsed. During this time these 'peepers' have had no food, have been quite as active as their limited quarters would permit, and yet have not lost weight to any important extent. One which I weighed on the day following its capture weighed forty-four grains and seventy-five days later had lost but one grain in weight. It is very different in spring; then they are voracious feeders and capture millions of minute insects. At this time their stomachs are always full; and while the size of the animal is not larger than in autumn, the weight is nearly twice as great."

To believe that they feed not from transformation to autumnal disappearance is foreign to the facts.

H. Garman (1892, p. 342) gives some definite items. "Its food consists of insects, and if the habits of the frogs led them more frequently into cultivated grounds they would doubtless do good service to agriculture in destroying aphides. Among other insects, *Chlorops*, crane flies, *Thyeocoris*, *Calocoris rapidus*, numerous pupae and wingless female Aphididae and Orthoptera have been determined from the contents of their stomachs."

ENEMIES

On 1912 specimens and collections we made the following observations: "It appears from stomach examinations that the enemies of *Acris gryllus* are as much aquatic as terrestrial. The snake which had eaten the cricket-frog was the aquatic southern riband snake (*Thamnophis s. sackeni*) and none of the numerous specimens of black or hog-nosed snakes has eaten it, strong negative evidence indicate that it is quite aquatic in nature. No doubt it proves one of the best sources of food for the herons, ibises and cranes."

In 1921 we have the following evidence. During a congress of *Acris* Apr. 25 in one pond *Thamnophis sackeni* was on the surface and ever present. On July 27 "on the prairie just north of Black Jack Island (F. Harper) came upon a seven-inch ribbon snake (*T. sackeni*), which had a grip on the hind leg of an *Acris*, . . ."

Other notes are on Apr. 28 we found fishermen who used *Acris* for "perch" bait. "Some think them better than crawfish." "Others used them for set-line bait." On May 6 we found "a cypress pond where I caught so many *Acris* earlier. They must have been leaving the pond before. This time there were few of them. The pond was almost dried up. Around little water remaining, in the center was a mud flat covered with dried and drying aquatic vegetation. Under this mat were young *Rana grylio*, *Acris*, etc. A pig was rooting up these frogs."

"Florida Grackles and a Great Blue Heron were walking around in the little center pool after *Elassoma*, water insects, frogs and tadpoles."

Abbott (1882, p. 708) in contrast to cricket frogs' ravenous appetite writes "On the other hand, they were the main food supply of certain fishes, all the snakes, the turtles and a few species of birds. I find that all of our snakes at this time (April and May) were more abundant in the meadows than elsewhere, and have no doubt (been) drawn thither for the purpose of feeding on these little batrachians. Even that lover of high, dry and dusty fields, the hog-nosed snake (*Heterodon platyrhinus*) was found to be stationed at intervals along the ditch banks, on the lookout for 'peepers'; the dissection of one of these snakes proved that it had fed upon these small frogs."

In 1917 Hubbs (p. 99) describes in considerable detail an interesting one-legged cricket frog "whether this monstrosity is the result of a mutation or of a very early injury can not be stated."

AFFINITIES

LeConte, its describer, called it *Rana gryllus*. Harlan (1835, pp. 104, 105) repeats his description, holds it erroneously supposed by Daudin to be the young of the *Hyla lateralis*, and gives its length as "one and one-half inches."

Harlan further describes (p. 105) another form *Rana dorsalis*. "*Char.*— *Above* fuscous, smooth, with a broad, green or reddish, longitudinal vertebral band, bifurcating anteriorly, and extending over each eye; *snout* above, pale or whitish; *beneath* white, *throat* and inner part of the thighs freckled; a white line on the side of the neck, extending from the eye to the scapula. Length of the body 8/10 of an inch; of the legs 1 1/2 inches. This measurement being taken from the largest of seven specimens. In habits Florida, Carolina and New Jersey. May prove a variety of *R. gryllus*. . . ."

Figured at p. 72 of this volume. This is very apparently *Acris gryllus* and was really first described by Harlan in 1826 (p. 340).

In 1841 Dumeril and Bibron (1841, pp. 507–509), place it and *Pseudacris nigrita* right after the genus *Litoria* as the two species of *Acris*. Specimens of each of these "deux tres-petites especes" they received from LeConte.

Holbrook's (1842, Vol. IV, p. 133) "General Remarks" about *Hylodes gryllus* are "The first notice of this animal is found in Bartram's Travels in Carolina and Florida; he calls it the Savannah Cricket, and gives a tolerable account of its manners. This animal forms a good connecting link between the genera *Rana* and *Hyla*, and seems to partake of the habits of both, for though it likes water at all times, yet it may be found on aquatic plants waiting for its prey; and it has the power of adhering to smooth surfaces like the Hylae, but much less perfectly, as it can never sustain itself on the under surfaces of leaves, etc."

"For the present I am disposed to arrange this animal with the Hylodes of Fitzinger: for 1. The extremities are slender, with the fingers and toes only slightly swelled at the tips; and 2. It cannot belong to the genus Rana, as it wants a bony sternum, etc."

"Dumeril and Bibron have established a new geuns *Acris*, for the reception of this animal and the *Cystignathus nigritus*; but I see no reason for removing it from that of Hylodes, especially as their genus is characterized by having the toes free." In 1849 (Appendix, p. 15) Holbrook still retains it in Hylodes. DeKay (1842, Part III, p. 70) "followed Dr. Holbrook in arranging it under Hylodes."

In 1855 to 1858 we have more activity in *Acris* species than at any other period unless it be the *gryllus-dorsalis* period of 1825–26. In 1855 Baird (pp. 59, 60) gives two forms as follows "*Acris crepitans*, Baird.—Brownish above. The median region of head and body above bright green; a dark triangle between the eyes. Three oblique blotches on the sides, nearly equidistant, the first behind the eye, the last on the flanks and running up the back; all usually margined with lighter. A narrow white line from the eye to the arm. Beneath yellowish white. Inferior face of thigh plain. Tibia a little more than half the length of the body; foot rather smaller. Head rather obtuse, scarcely longer than broad. Web of hind foot extending to the penultimate articulation of the 4th toe. Syn. *Hylodes gryllus* DeKay, N. Y. Zool. III, (1842) 70, Pl. XXII, f. 61. *Hab.* Northern States generally. "2. *Acris acheta* Baird.—Slender. Tibia two-thirds the length of body. Color above dark brown; blotched much as in *Acris gryllus*. Beneath white, closely mottled with brown on the body and on the inferior and inner faces of the limbs; where are also visible minute dots. Lower surface of body appears quite black. A narrow white line from eye to arm. *Hab.* Key West, Florida."

The first writer who attempts minutely to distinguish *Acris gryllus* and *Acris crepitans* is LeConte (Dec. 1855, pp. 426, 427) the first describer of the former. We will not copy his descriptions but he says of the latter (*A. crepitans*) that it "very much resembles the preceding (*A. gryllus*) but the head is shorter and blunter, the body likewise is not as slender or as graceful in form as in *A. gryllus* having a considerable resemblance to a toad. Varies extremely in color and in other marks. The only unvarying marks which I have been able to disover are the warts on the back, the dusky line from the axilla on the side (which sometimes almost vanishes), the darker angular spot above the anus (which at times is scarcely perceptible) and the white granules on the hinder and under parts of the thighs. . . ."

In 1858 (pp. 70, 71) Gunther places the genus "*Acris* Disk small. Toes broadly webbed; fingers free; tongue heart-shaped. North America." in the Polypedatidae. Interestingly enough he places *Acris pickeringii* in this genus and holds "This genus might belong to the family of Hylidae. Bibron and also Baird describe the diapophyses of the sacral diapophyses of the sacral vertebra as not dilated; but I ask naturalists having the opportunity of examining *fresh* specimens to direct their attention to this subject. The relation to *Pseudacris nigrita* is very great, which species also exhibits only slightly dilated processes."

In 1882 (pp. 336, 337) G. L. Boulenger gives three forms. "*Acris gryllus.*— United States: the typical form confined to the Austral riparian region, the var *crepitans* to the Eastern and Central regions."

"Var *crepitans*—Differs by a stouter habit, the head being shorter, and the tibio-tarsal articulation reaching hardly the tip of the snout. According to Mr. Cope (Check-list N. Amer. Rept.) this form should not be specifically separated from the preceding, but both are considered subspecies."

Var. *bufonia*. Resembles the preceding, but the head and back are covered with very large warts. Markings indistinct. Perhaps a species. ♀ New Orleans.

Cope (1889, pp. 324, 325) holds that "It is quite possible that it may become necessary at some future time to unite this genus with Hyla." . . . The northern and southern sections of this area produce forms which offer considerable differences, but which must be termed subspecies, on account of the existence in some localities of intermediate individuals. I have seen such from Illinois, Pennsylvania, Missouri, and elsewhere.

"These subspecies are as follows: Hinder foot less tarsus less than half of the length of the head and body; dermal tubercles larger; posterior femoral stripe less distinct—*Acris g. crepitans*. Hinder foot less tarsus longer than half head and body; dermal tubercles smaller; femoral stripe very distinct.— *Acris g. gryllus*.

"These subspecies are respectively of northern and southern distribution, the *A. g. gryllus* ranging from North Carolina to Florida and Louisiana."

"Specimens from the lower Mississippi are frequently of obscure colors, of rather larger size, and with large tubercles. I have not been able to distinguish them as forming a constant subspecies. Mr. Boulenger . . . refers such a specimen to a 'var. bufonia.' "

"As regards the transition of this subspecies and the *A. g. crepitans*, a number of specimens display intermediate proportions. Thus in some the posterior foot, minus the tarsus, is exactly half the length of the head and

body. In some lots from a single locality some specimens have the hind foot
one-half the length, while others fall a little below and still others fall a little
above this proportion.

"The distinctness of the posterior femoral brown stripe is subject to variation. . . ."

In 1892 Hay considers *Acris* "Closely allied to Hyla," and gives the two
subspecies as occurring in Indiana just as E. E. Ramsay (1901, p. 222), and
McAtee (1907, p. 15) do for Monroe County, Indiana. H. Garman (1892, pp.
342, 343) holds "LeConte's characterization of the two forms . . . the
best extant, but the only difference he presents which in so variable a species
is of a varietal importance, is the size (1.4 inches for variety *gryllus* and 1.2
for variety *crepitans*). None of the Illinois specimens examined are more
than 1.25 inches in length of body."

S. N. Rhoads (1896, pp. 396, 397) adds more to the *gryllus-crepitans* discussion "Examination of nearly forty specimens from widely separated
localities in Tennessee and Kentucky fails to reveal any constant distinctions
between *gryllus* and *crepitans*, if both forms are found in the State. Prof.
H. Garman considers the size of *gryllus* (1.4 in.) as given by LeConte as the
only reliable difference. This is much larger than any in my series, and as
the Samburg specimens are smaller and more slender than those from the
Cumberland plateau, the theory that the Southwestern frogs are larger
than Northeastern ones is contradicted. LeConte defines the habitat of
gryllus in the South Atlantic States, and that of *crepitans* in the remainder
of the eastern United States, but Prof. Cope's identication of the Smith-
sonian series allots specimens of both forms to both sides of the Allegheny
Mountains in such a way that faunal definitions lose their significance. Such
being the case I have lumped the entire Tennessee series under the original
specific name." W. P. Hay (1902, p. 128) holds *gryllus* and *crepitans* "of
very doubtful validity." Deckert (1915, p. 22) observes that "This species
looks and acts more like a water frog than a tree-toad, although belonging to
the latter family." In 1917 Dunn (p. 621) finds his material from the Northwest of North Carolina intermediate between *A. g. gryllus* and *A. g. crepitans*,
but in 1923 Brimley and Mabee (1925, p. 15) find in eastern North Carolina
both *Acris crepitans* and *Acris gryllus*.

Earlier than 1923 Percy Viosca, Jr., believed he could separate *Acris
gryllus* and *Acris crepitans*. In 1923 (p. 43) he discusses this matter thus:
"The puzzling status of the Genus *Acris*, as far as Louisiana is concerned, has
been positively cleared by these studies. There are two distinct species in
Louisiana, the upland species being, tentatively, *Acris gryllus*, and that of the
lowlands, *Acris crepitans*. Wherever their ranges overlap, they are found side
by side without interbreeding, each with its characteristic chorus and habits."

In 1925 we took one evening trip with him in February but the
author did not get enough experience in the one evening to warrant his attempting to tell them by song, habits and structural and color characters.
If any one can do it Mr. Viosca is the person with experience to do it. Furthermore, Mississippi Valley, Texan and southeastern forms crowd into

Louisiana. From New Orleans Boulenger described his "var. *bufonia.*" This region ought to have a diversity of *Acris* forms.

It is interesting that this form was described as a *Rana*. In the general appearance of its tadpole we considered it quite Ranid-like. In fact, for a time until we came to know *Rana virgatipes* tadpoles we wondered if these *Acris* tadpoles might be the young tadpole of Cope's frog. Gunther put *Acris gryllus* and *Acris pickeringii* (*Hyla crucifer*) in the same genus. Each lays single eggs with a single envelope though in each there are some evidences of an inner envelope and each has vitellus .9–1.0 or 1.1 mm.

Dumeril and Bibron established *Acris* for *Acris gryllus* and *Acris nigritus* (*Pseudacris nigrita*). Normally the various forms of *P. nigrita* lays eggs in masses not singly but Abbott generally and we rarely recorded masses for *Acris gryllus*. *Pseudacris ocularis* lay very similar single submerged eggs with a single envelope 1.2–2.0 mm., as in *Acris gryllus*. The *Pseudacris triseriata* or *P. nigritus triseriatus* tadpoles of western New York normally have teeth formulae of 2/2 like *Acris gryllus*. Holbrook placed *Acris gryllus* and *Pseudacris ocularis*, each in *Hylodes*.

In eggs it might be linked with *Pseudacris ocularis*, *Hyla crucifer*, *Hyla squirella* or *Hyla gratiosa*. In tadpoles it is in some ways apart from all the Hylids of the U. S. A. In other ways it falls close to *Hyla crucifer* or some species of *Pseudacris*. In transformation size it falls in with *Hyla squirella*, *Hyla andersoni* and *Hyla femoralis*. In tadpole coloration it is apart. *Acris* is sufficiently distinct to be retained yet awhile although it has characters in common with *Pseudacris* and *Hyla*. It is the most distinctive and commonest Hylid in U. S. A.

We have made no endeavor to separate *Acris gryllus* and *Acris crepitans*. They may be distinct. The only person who has given much attention to this question in recent times is Mr. Percy Viosca, Jr., who believes them distinct in appearance, habits, call, etc. Possibly he is right.

BIBLIOGRAPHY

1882 Abbott, C. C. Notes on the Habits of the Savannah Cricket Frog. Am. Naturalist XVI, 1882, pp. 707-711.

1896 Atkinson, C. Batrachia of Turkey Lake, Ind. Proc. Ind. Acad. Sci., 1895, Feb. 1896, p. 258.

1892 Blatchley, W. S. Notes on the Batrachians and Reptiles of Vigo County, Indiana. Journal Indiana Soc. Nat. Hist., XIV, 1891-1892, p. 27.

1882 Boulenger, G. A. Catalogue of the Batrachia Salientia —. British Museum, 2nd edit., London, 1882, pp. 336, 337.

1914 Boyle, H. S. Some Notes on the Cricket Frog on Long Island. Copeia, June 20, 1914 no. 7, p. 4.

1896 Brimley, C. S. Batrachia Found at Raleigh, N. C. Am. Nat. 30, 1896, p. 501.

1925 Brimley, C. S. and Mabee, W. B. Reptiles, Amphibians and Fishes Collected in Eastern North Carolina in the Autumn of 1923. Copeia, Feb. 16, 1925, No. 139, p. 15.

1889 Cope, E. D. The Batrachia of North America. Bull. U. S. Nat. Mus., No. 34, 1889, pp. 324-329.

1892 ———. The Batrachia and Reptilia of Northwestern Texas. Proc. Phila. Acad. Sci., Vol. 44, 1892, pp. 333.

1914 Deckert, R. F. List of Salientia from near Jacksonville, Florida. Copeia, Feb. 14, 1914, No. 3, p. 3.

1915 ———. Concluding Notes on the Salientia of Jacksonville, Florida. Copeia, July 27, 1915, No. 20, pp. 21-22.

1849 DeKay, James E. Zool. of N. Y., Part III, p. 70.

1902 Dernehl, P. H. Place-Modes of *Acris gryllus* for Madison, Wisc. Bull. Wisc. Nat. Hist. Soc., Vol. 2, n.s., No. 1, January 1902, pp. 75-82.

1906 Dickerson, M. C. The Frog Book. pp. 153-156.

1905 Ditmars, R. L. The Batrachians of the Vicinity of New York City. Guide Leaflet No. 20, Am. Mus. Journal Vol. 5, pp. 192, 193.

1841 Dumeril, A. M. C. and G. Bibron. Erpetology—Paris, Vol. 8, pp. 507-509.

1916 Dunn, E. R. Notes on Virginia Herpetology. Copeia, March 24, 1916, No. 28, p. 22.

1917 ———. Reptile and Amphibian Collections—North Carolina Mountains—. Am. Mus. Nat. Hist. Bull. No. 3, Art. 23, p. 621.

1913 Ellis, M. M. and Junius Henderson. The Amphibia and Reptilia of Colorado. Part I, Univ. Colo. Studies, Vol. X, No. 2, May 13, pp. 58, 59.

1915 ———. Part II, Vol. XV, No. 6, June 1915, p. 258.

1917 ———. Amphibians and Reptiles from the Pecos Valley. Copeia, Apr. 24, 1917, No. 43, p. 39.

1907 Fowler, H. The Amphibians and Reptiles of New Jersey. Annual Rept. N. Y. State Museum, 1906, 1907, pp. 99-104.

1914 Gaige, H. T. A List of Amphibians and Reptiles Observed in Richland County, Illinois, in May 1913. Copeia, Oct. 15, 1914, No. 11, p. 4.

1892 Garman, H. A Synopsis of the Reptiles and Amphibians of Illinois. Bull. Ill. State Lab. Nat. Hist., Vol. III, Art. XIII, 1892, pp. 340-343.

1858 Gunther, A. Catalogue of the Batrachia Salientia—British Museum, London, 1858, pp. 70, 71.

1826 Harlan, R. Journ. Acad. Na:. Sci., Vol. V, p. 340.

1835 ———. Medical and Physical Researches, Phila. pp. 104, 105.

1892 Hay, O. P. The Batrachians and Reptiles of the State of Indiana. Ind. Dept. Geol. Nat. Resources, 17th Annual Rept., 1891, Indianapolis, 1892, pp. 461-463.

1892 Hay, W. P. A List of the Batrachia and Reptilia of the District of Columbia and Vicinity. Proc. Biol. Soc. Wash., Vol. XV, June 20, 1902, p. 128.

1842 Holbrook, J. E. North American Herpetology, Vol. IV, 1842, pp. 131-133.

1849 ———. In George White's Statistics of Georgia 1849 Appendix.

1917 Hubbs, C. L. A One-Legged Cricket Frog. Copeia, Oct. 26, 1917, No. 50, p. 99.

1893 Hurter, Julius. Catalogue of Reptiles and Batrachians found in the Vicinity of St. Louis, Mo. Trans. Acad. Sci. St. Louis, Vol. VI, No. 11, Dec. 12, 1893, p. 253.

1825 Le Conte, John. Remarks on the American species of the Genera Hyla and Rana. Lyceum Nat. Hist. N. Y., Vol. I, May 16, 1825, pp. 278-282.

1855 ———. Desc. Cat. of the Ranina of the United States, Proc. Acad. Nat. Sci. 7, (1854, 1855), 1856, pp. 426, 427

1895 Loennberg, E. Notes on Reptiles and Batrachians Collected in Florida in 1892 and 1893. Proc. U. S. N. M., Vol. XVII, 1894, 1895, p. 338.

1925 Logier, E. B. Shelley. Notes on the Herpetology of Point Pelee, Ontario. The Canadian Field Naturalist, Vol. XXIX, No. 5, May, 1925, p. 92.

1907 McAtee, W. L. A List of Mammals, Reptiles and Batrachians of Monroe County, Indiana. Proc. Biol. Soc. Wash., Feb. 25, 1907, Vol. XX, p. 15.

1891 Morgan, T. H. Some Notes on the Breeding Habits and Embryology of Frogs. The American Naturalist, Aug. 1891, Vol. 25, pp. 753-760.

1904 Morse, Max. Batrachians and Reptiles of Ohio. Proc. Ohio State Acad. Sci., Vol. IV, Part 3, Special Paper No. 9, June 5, 1904, p. 118.

1914 Overton, F. The Frogs and Toads of Long Island. Mus. Brookl. Inst. Arts and Sciences, Science Bull. Vol. 2, No. 3, Nov. 3, 1914, pp. 30, 31.

1901 Ramsay, Earl E. The Cold Blooded Vertebrates of Winona Lake and Vicinity. Proc. Ind. Acad. Science, 1900, 1901, p. 222.

1895 Rhoads, S. N. Contributions to the Zoology of Tennessee, No. 1, Reptiles and Amphibians. Proc. Acad. Nat. Sci. Phila., 1895, 1896, pp. 396, 397.

1912 Ruthven, A. G. The Herpetology of Michigan. Mich. Geol. and Biol. Survey, Publ. 10, Biol. Ser. 3, 1912, pp. 45-47.

1898 Sherwood, W. L. The Frogs and Toads Found in the Vicinity of New York City. Proc. Linn. Soc. N. Y., 1897-1898, No. 10, pp. 18, 19.

1903 Stone, W. Proc. Acad. Nat. Sci. Phila., Vol. 55, Aug. 1903, pp. 538-539.

1910 Strecker, J. K., Jr. Notes on the Robber Frog (*Lithodytes latrans* Cope). Trans. Acad. Sci. St. Louis, 1910, Vol. 19, pp. 73-82.

1915 ———. Reptiles and Amphibians of Texas. Baylor Bulletin Vol. XVIII, No. 4, Aug. 1915, p. 49.

1923 Viosca, Percy, Jr. An Ecological Study of the Cold Blooded Vertebrates of Southeastern Louisiana. Copeia, Feb. 1, 1923, No. 115, p. 36, 43.

1920 Wright, A. H. Frogs: Their Natural History and Utilization. Rept. U. S. Com. Fisheries 1919, Appendix IV, Doc. 888, 1920.

1923a ———. The Tadpoles of the Frogs of Okefinokee Swamp, Georgia. The Anat. Record Vol. 24, No. 6, Jan. 20, 1923, p. 406.

1923b ———. The Salientia of the Okefinokee Swamp, Georgia. Copeia, Feb. 1, 1923, No. 115, p. 34.

1926   Wright, A. H. The Vertebrate Life of Okefinokee Swamp in Relation to the Atlantic Coastal Plain. Ecology, Jan. 1926, Vol. VII, No. 1, p. 83.

1924   Wright, A. H. and A. A. Wright. A Key to the Eggs of the Salientia East of the Mississippi River. The American Naturalist, Vol. LVIII, July-August, 1924, p. 378.

Pseudacris nigrita (LeConte)

(Pl I. Fig. 9)

COMMON NAMES

Swamp Cricket Frog. Swamp Tree Frog. Swamp Chorus Frog. Swamp Tree-toad. Striped Tree-frog. Rough Chorus Frog. Black spotted Tree Frog.

RANGE

Check list. "Type locality not given. Range: South Carolina to Mississippi." Stejneger & Barbour 1923, p. 28.

Supplementary records. C. S. Brimley (1910) has "*Chorophilus nigritus* Rough Chorus Frog" from Bay St. Louis, Mississippi, Feb. 10, 1898, 1." At Jacksonville, Fla., R. F. Deckert (1914, No. 3) found "*Chorophilus nigritus* LeConte, common during the winter months." Fowler (1917, p. 39) records it at Brickells Hammock and Mersa Isle near Miami, Fla., in February and March 1916. Löding (1922, p. 17) records it in Mobile County, Ala. In South Carolina at Greenville A. L. Pickens (1927, p. 109) secured several specimens. Holbrook (1842 Vol. IV, p. 108) gave its distribution as Georgia and Carolina. LeConte observed it in the former State, and I have seen it in the latter. LeConte (1855, p. 427) holds it "Inhabits Georgia and South Carolina . . . " Our records and others like Cope send it into Florida. O. C. Van Hyning at Gainesville, Florida has sent me several times representatives of this species.

Local Okefinokee records. Our records are wholy outside the swamp along its eastern border and at Fargo, Ga. On June 15, 1922, M. D. Pirnie and the author took two specimens two miles east of Chesser Island. The next was taken south of Spanish Creek near Folkston-Moniac road July 15, 1922. Three days later we took one at Murray Bay northeast of Chesser School and Starling Branch. On August 16, 1922 we secured one at one to one and a fifth miles south of Hilliard, Florida. In 1921, August 5, F. Harper recorded it at Fargo, Ga., on the southwestern edge of the swamp. In 1909 September 11, Professor J. C. Bradley collected a *Pseudacris* which at the time we identified as *Chorophilus occidentalis*. It looked to be *P. nigrita* and comes from near the Okefinokee Swamp. This same collector secured two *P. nigrita* at Tifton, Ga., September 8, 1910.

GENERAL APPEARANCE

On May 16, 1825 Captain John LeConte characterizes this form as follows "6 *Rana nigrita*; above black, speckled with small white warts; middle of the back cinereous with an interrupted stripe of black, upper lips with a white line; beneath granulate whitish; sides golden; legs barred with whitish, hind part of the thighs brown; hind legs very long." If, for example, a specimen be faded out one of the outstanding characters will be the last one of long legs in LeConte's preliminary "indication" or description.

Thirty years later (1855, p. 427) this author describes it at length— "*Chorophilus nigrita* . . . . Body elongated rather narrow, above with numerous small warts. . . . Tympanum distinct, black or of the color of the body. . . . Beneath . . . (in dead specimens appearing granulate). . . .; thighs and tibiae granulated, more or less covered with small warts. A very slightly perceptible web between the second and third and between the third and fourth toes, the fourth and fifth are closely united at the base. Fingers and toes with small dilations at their tips. . . ."

In 1841 (p. 509) Dumeril at Bibron gives it "Caracteres. Deux groupes de dents vomériennes affectant une forme en chevron. Tympan assez distinct. Une tres-courte membrane a la racine des orteils."

In 1862 Holbrook (Vol. IV, p. 107) gives "The head is elongated, . . . the snout rather pointed. The nostrils are lateral, and nearer the snout than the orbits. The eyes are large and prominent . . . . The mouth is rather large, and the palate is armed with two thick groups of minute teeth, placed between the posterior nares and disposed a little 'en chevron'. . . . The body is slender . . . . The anterior extremities are slender . . . ; there are four long and delicate fingers. The posterior extremities are very long . . .; there are five toes, not palmated."

DeKay (1842, Part III, p. 65) in his Extra-limital forms of New York gives "*Cystignathus nigritus* (Id. Holbrook Vol. 3, pl. 19; and Vol. 4, pl. 26, 2nd Ed.) small, olive brown; an interrupted black vertebral line, with blackish blotches along the sides; legs barred; upper lip white. Length 1½ inches. Carolina, Georgia."

In 1858 A. Gunther (p. 97) gives its color as "Blackish ash, with three or five darker, sometimes interrupted longitudinal bands; a black streak passing through the eye above the tympanum; upper lip with a whitish streak. a. Adult. Georgia. From Mr. Cumming's Collection. b. Adult. Great Bear Lake. Presented by Sir J. Richardson." Of course, this last refers to *P. septentrionalis.*

A. L. Pickens (1927, p. 109) records that "Specimens from A. L. Pickens, Greenville (S.C.) are indefinably intergraded with some other forms. To me some appear to have inclination toward *P. triseriata*, others, perhaps toward *P. feriarum.* The more typical form seems to appear in the lower Piedmont."

COLORATION OF SPIRIT SPECIMENS

LeConte's first extended description of its color comes in 1885 (p. 427):— Color above dark slate with more or less of oblong or oval or round, sometimes very numerous black spots, which often form stripes. Upper lip white-which color often extends to the insertion to the arm. Irids golden . . . . A broad black band extends from the nose through the eyes and along the sides to beyond the middle of the body. Beneath whitish, sometimes tinged with yellow with a few black spots irregularly assembled in groups, cancellately reticualate . . ., arms and legs spotted and barred with black . . . . Chin often dusky.

(We will not undertake to describe coloration in spirits. See coloration from life under mating).

STRUCTURAL CHARACTERS
(See General Appearance)

Cope (1889) held that the skin was warty, above the head acuminate, the width entering the total three times; heel reaching anterior to orbit; size larger. All these characters are contrasted with *C. feriarum* and *C. triseriatus*. Hay in 1892 follows the same general characterization of *C. nigritus nigritus*.

Baird (1854, p. 60) when he separates *Chorophilus nigritus* from *Helocaetes triseriatus*, *H. clarkii* and *H. feriarum* he said it was "smooth above, granulated beneath. Extremities of limbs simple not dilated at tip. Hands free; feet with a slight basal web, which is entirely wanting between the two other toes. Tongue orbicular; emarginate behind. Teeth posterior to the nares. Tympanum distinct. Transverse apophyses of sacral vertebrae dilated into triangular pallets."

MEASUREMENTS
(Recent Material)

Head to angle of mouth 1.15 (25 mm.♂)–1.0, (28 mm.♀) in width of head; head to rear of tympanum 1.0–.9 in width of head; head to angle of mouth 3.37–3.1 in length of body; head to rear of tympanum 2.95–2.8 in length of body; snout .52–.87 in first finger; snout .74–.87 in fourth finger; snout .60–.76 in first toe; eye 1.50–1.2 in snout; eye .60–.54 in tympanum; eye .8–.87 in first finger; tympanum 3.4–3.4 in intertympanic width; tympanum 2.5–1.84 in snout; internasal width .80–.83 in upper eyelid width; interorbital width .80–.83 in upper eyelid width; interorbital width 1.0–1.2 in internasal width; interorbital width 2.8–3.4 in intertympanic width.

Forelimb. Fore limb—1.92–2.0 in length of body; fore limb 3.0–3.0 in hind limb; first finger 2.0–1.75 in third finger; second finger 1.7–1.4 in third finger; second finger .85–.8 in first finger; third finger .70–.71 in second toe; fourth finger 1.4–1.75 in third finger; fourth finger .70–1.0 in first finger; internasal width 1.1–1.33 in first finger; internasal width 1.27–1.66 in second finger; internasal width 2.18–2.33 in third finger; internasal width 1.5–1.33 in fourth finger.

Hindlimb. Length 1.56–1.5 in hind limb; tibia 2.0–2.0 in length; tibia 3.1–3.0 in hind limb; tibia 1.03–1.0 in fore limb; tibia .9–.95 in hind foot without tarsus; first toe 1.21–1.4 in second toe; first toe 2.57–2.4 in third toe; first toe 2.71–3.6 in fourth toe; first toe 2.64–2.6 in fifth toe; second toe 2.1–1.9 in third toe; second toe 2.2–2.6 in fourth toe; second toe 2.1–1.8 in fifth toe; third toe 1.05–1.35 in fourth toe; third toe 1.02–.95 in fifth toe; fourth toe 1.5–1.0 in hind foot; fourth toe 1.65–1.06 in tibia; fourth toe 1.71–1.06 in fore limb; fifth toe 1.02–1.44 in fourth toe; internasal width 1.27–1.13 in first toe; internasal width 1.5–1.66 in second toe; internasal width 3.27–3.17 in third toe; internasal width 3.45–3.33 in fourth toe; internasal width 3.36–3.0 in fifth toe.

HABITAT

Its original describer, LeConte (1855, p. 427), gives it as an inhabitant "in ditches and ponds." Deckert (1915, p. 22) found it "in great numbers about ditches and bayous." In 1917 Fowler (p. 39) secured it in a hammock.

In 1921 (Aug. 5) F. Harper just outside the swamp at Fargo, Georgia, noted that "After considerable search one of the frogs was located in a thick clump of sedge, its body half submerged."

In 1922 on June 15 near Chesser Schoolhouse in forenoon, (U. S. Geol. Sheet, Folkston sheet) "under chips, small boards and logs found 3 *Pseudacris* in dry pine barrens, associated with *Bufo quercicus*. Area beneath boards and cones more or less dry." On July 2, we "went to night hawk nest area (*Pseudacris nigrita* spot). At 6:00 p. m. heard no *P. nigrita*. Heard one or two *P. ocularis* in the grass."

On July 15, 1928, "on high sandy ridge south of Spanish Creek, Folkston, Georgia. *Quercus catesbaei, Quercus cinerea, Gaylussacia dumosa* and a very much serrated poison ivy (*Rhus*). Miles and I were looking at the *Rhus* carefully and gingerly. He saw something jump amongst it. Thought it a grasshopper but he soon found it to be a frog. It was *P. nigrita*. The frog was first on a dead twig of a fallen branch. It would leap amongst dead leaves, amongst some grass-like grasses and amongst the ivy."

On August 16, 1928, "In making a detour on to the Dixie Highway about 1.2–1.3 miles south of Hilliard, Florida, we came to the road opposite a wet pine woods. In one little temporary pond in a tussock of grass beside the small pool was a *Pseudacris nigrita* calling."

FIRST APPEARANCE

We suspected its presence long before 1921–1922 but not until 1921 did we find it. This led us to believe it a very early spring or late winter breeder. Deckert (1914 and 1915) "found (it) in the winter and early spring." Our first record of June 15, 1922, is of no consequence in this category. Students and friends (Dr. A. A. Allen and others) of the author have described from Florida in February and early spring swamp cricket frogs which must be this species though slightly rougher than our specimens (see Cope's *C. verrucosus*). C. S. Brimley received it February 10, 1898, Bay St. Louis, Miss. O. C. Van Hyning has secured for me croaking *P. nigrita* at Gainesville, Fla. in February and early spring.

GENERAL HABITS

Metachrosis. Miss Dickerson (1906, p. 157) wrote that the combined (*triseriata-feriarum-nigrita*) group was "Changeable from a colour so dark that it is nearly black, to flesh colour. When light, the colouration may be bluish or ash grey, fawn colour, or even salmon or red in tone.'' This applies quite well to *P. nigrita* in its restricted sense except that we have not recorded any salmon-red individuals yet, though they are possible.

On August 5, 1921, F. Harper came on one live frog which "was blackish-olive, whitish below, and had a greenish-white maxillary streak. After a couple of days of captivity in a can, its black back had changed to olive, coarsely spotted with black."

Variations in color. Back: Black, speckled with small white warts; middle of back cinereous with an interrupted stripe of black.—LeConte 1825, Harlan 1825 and 1835.

Back olive brown, with a tinge of yellow, and an interrupted black vertebral line—Holbrook 1842.

Color above dark slate, with more or less of oblong, oval or round sometimes very numerous black spots, which often form stripes.—LeConte 1855.

Gray or greenish-black, with usually three longitudinal rows of black, light-edged, roundish spots. Occasionally these spots fuse into bands. . . . A narrow black band starts at the tip of the snout, runs through the eye, covers the tympanum and ends at the shoulder or beyond—Deckert 1915.

Blackish ash above, with three interrupted black longitudinal bands; loreal and temporal regions black—Boulenger 1882. Color above leaden, with three longitudinal rows of darker, light-edged spots, extending one on each side, and one on the median line. These spots may be united into a band on one or on both sides or on the middle line. Cope 1889.

Blackish ash, with three or five darker, sometimes interrupted longitudinal bands; a black streak passing through the eye above the tympanum —Gunther 1858.

Belly. Beneath granulate whitish.—LeConte 1825.

Beneath whitish granulated.—Holbrook 1842.

Abdomen yellowish-white.—Holbrook 1842.

Beneath whitish, sometimes tinged with yellow with a few black spots assembled in groups cancellately reticulate.—LeConte 1855.

Beneath white immaculate.—Boulenger 1882.

Inferior surfaces yellowish.—Cope 1889.

The under surfaces are greenish-yellow.—Deckert 1915.

General habits. To Deckert (1915, p. 23) this is a shy species, extremely difficult to catch. Holbrook (1842, Vol. IV, p. 108) holds "But little is known of the habits of *Cystignathus nigritus*; but, from the form of the posterior extremities and the arrangement of the toes, it would seem to be a land animal, and closely allied with the *Cystignathus ornatus*." In general we suspect it accords closely in habits with *P. triseriata* and *P. feriarum.* From remarks and observations of O. C. Van Hyning at Gainesville, Florida, this is quite likely true.

VOICE

"Its call is similar to that of the cricket 'frog,' but much louder, and the crepitations are slower." (Deckert 1915, p. 23). In 1921 at Fargo, Ga., F. Harper "During downpours on the afternoon of August 5, . . . began to hear several frogs calling in a field grown with grasses and sedges and flooded with rain. The notes consisted of a shrill, metallic, staccato trill, frequently repeated: i-i-i-ik, i-i-i-ik, i-i-i-ik. They were indistinguishable from those of representatives of this genus in the Athabaska region (*septentrionalis*) and in the District of Columbia (*feriarum*)." (We are not including notes of our experiences with *triseriata*, *feriarum*, etc. forms in New York, Pennsylvania, Canada, Texas and other places nor are Hay's, Dickerson's or other characterizations included. Their notes pertain largely to northern forms and they felt, possibly rightly, that *triseriata*, *feriarum* and *nigrita* were all forms of *P. nigrita*. There are those who also would put *P. septentrionalis* in the *nigrita* group).

In 1922 we found it June 15 but not calling. On July 15 we took another "near where we thought we heard it when we were after *Hyla squirella* at night." Then on August 16 near Hilliard one was heard after a very intense rainy spell of miry detours. To me this form which was finally captured "sounded like our New York *Pseudacris*." To F. Harper it sounded like a metallic, staccato trill, five notes, ic, ic, ic, ic, ic. All our records in July and August are clearly sporadic croakings long after breeding and after heavy rainfall.

MATING

Coloration. (The colors given are from life June 15, 1922, but not from sexed specimens. Specimens, 17 mm. long).

Back drab gray, smoke gray, darb or grayish olive. From snout down middle of back is one row of more or less connected dusky drab or deep brownish drab spots. Stripe along jaw pale rose purple or pale salmon color or cartridge buff with some seafoam green.

The row of continuous spots down back at half way point becomes two rows of separate spots. On each side is one more row of separate spots. Dark area from snout through eye, back of eye and extending along the side to groin. Cross bars of legs same color as spots of back and light thin bars between the spots of legs like background of the back. Under parts white. Iris black with brownish vinaceous dots. At times iris has considerable of glass green.

Structural differences. A male (August 16, 1922) of 25 mm. has the throat darker than the rest of under parts or rather more yellowish (in spirits). On the throat are four longitudinal plaints. Possibly the thumb is somewhat enlarged.

OVULATION

Of the form *P. nigrita*, in its restricted sense, we have no observations except negative evidence. In 1921 we were within the swamp from April 25 onward but it was not until August we found it. In 1922 we were on an island near the eastern edge from June 14 to September 1 or later and found a few specimens on the mainland, none calling except one in August. The breeding must have been early and most tadpoles transformed before June 15. Deckert found them active and calling in winter and early spring.

EGGS

(Not described).   Doubtless like those of Hay's (Indiana), Morgan's (Maryland), Wright's (New York) swamp cricket frog observations and those of several other observers.   We also have *Pseudacris* eggs from Texas and tadpoles from several diverse parts but no eggs of *P. nigrita* as such are on record.

TADPOLES

(Wherein these differ from Texas, Indiana, Maryland, New York and Louisiana tadpoles has never been observed or recorded by any South Carolina to Mississippi naturalist or visitor to those parts).

LARVAL PERIOD

In the northern regions kindred species take 67 days (Hay's), 60-70 days (Wright) or about two months as larvae.   In 1922 we found none on June 14 on our arrival nor any thereafter.   Most of the breeding must have been over before April.

TRANSFORMATION

In general it must take place before June 1.   In the North the bulk of larvae of the related species are transformed by June 15 or by the end of June, and it must come earlier in Georgia.   The northern forms transform at about 9-12 or 13 mm.

GROWTH

Possibly with transformation presumably from 9-12 or 13 mm. the frogs taken June 15, 1922, which were 17 mm. are one-year-olds.   Those taken July 15 and 18 and August 16, 1922, were 22, 23 and 25 mm.   Are they two-year-olds and does the species breed at two-year-old stage or do some even enter breeding after one year?   We know not.

ENEMIES

This species cannot help being one of the abundant foods of snakes and numerous foes in early spring through no definite records appear.

AUTUMNAL DISAPPEARANCE

Our latest records are: August records in 1921 and 1922, September 8, 1910, and September 11, 1919.

AFFINITIES

LeConte (1825, p. 282) placed *Rana nigrita* right after *"Rana gryllus* (Savannah cricket)."   Harlan (1825, p. 341; 1835, p. 105) repeats LeConte's "indication" of a fuller description.   Dumeril and Bibron (1841, Vol. 8, p. 509) places it in their new genus *Acris* with the "palmure des pied trescourte" as contrasted with "bein developpée" in *Acris gryllus*.

In his Catalogue of Reptilia and Batrachia Holbrook (1849, Appendix p. 15) still uses *Cystignathus*.

LeConte (1855, p. 627) writes "This species has been placed by Dr. Holbrook in the genus *Cystignathus*, to which it cannot possibly be referred, as it has the vocal vesicle under the chin and not at the corners of the mouth. M. Dumeril has called it an *Acris*. That genus has the toes properly and strongly webbed."

In 1858 Gunther (p. 97) places it in Fitzinger's genus *Pseudacris*. Four years before Baird (1854, p. 60) established *Helocaetes* for *H. feriarum*, *H. triseriatus* and *H. clarkii*, and *Chorophilus* for *C. nigritus*. *Chorophilus* he held was "Distinguished from *Acris* by expansion of apophyses; from *Litoria* by the emarginate tongue, less membrane of toes, and more posterior palatine teeth; from *Hylodes* in having a membrane at base of toes, etc." *Helocaetes* was different "from *Chorophilus* in more anterior position of vomerine teeth, etc."

From 1882 (Boulenger) onward until 1917 (the first edition of the Check List of Stejneger and Barbour) *Chorophilus* has remained. Until 1892 *C. triseriatus*, *C. feriarum*, *C. nigritus* traveled as separate species but at that date O. P Hay put them all under *C. nigritus* as subspecies and Miss Dickerson followed his treatment. The authors of the Check List, through they separate them, were not satisfied with the status of the species or forms of *Pseudacris* nor is any one today. *P. ocularis* is distinct. *P. ornata* is distinct. Is *P. occidentalis* a good form, or near if not *P. ornata*? Are *P. nigrita*, *P. triseriata*, *P. feriarum* and *P. septentrionalis* all one? We have worked out one life history in Southern Texas, one in Pennsylvania and one in New York. About two more life histories ought to give enough ammunition to determine this question. We have hastily glanced over the U. S. National Museum *Pseudacris* material but more fresh material is needed.

In 1889 Cope said he described another form *C. verrucosus* from Florida. Possibly it is a good separable from but *Pseudacris* in Florida and Texas tend to become more warty, as do often *Acris*. Cope held *C. nigritus* to have longer hind legs, tubercular upper surface peculiar and swollen gular region wanting in Northern frog, i.e., *C. feriarum*.

In 1923 Noble on the basis of a "huge series" (336 specimens) of *P. ocularis* collected by Mr. J. A. Weber, some *P. occidentalis* and comparative *P. septentrionalis* material concluded that *Pseudacris* has no characters distinguishing it from *Hyla* and it must be referred to *Hyla*. He may be right but we are still following Stejneger and Barbour's Check List (1923) in retaining *Pseudacris* until it is carefully and thoroughly worked out. For example, we have lived with *P. ocularis* in 1914, 1921, 1922, 1928. It is a distinct species. We lived with *P. ornata* in 1925. It is a distinct form from the *P. triseriata*, *P. nigrita*, *P. feriarum*, *P. septentrionalis* group. Life history notes of this complex have been published by Hay, Morgan and others. We have worked them out in Texas and two different places in New York and collected tadpoles from New York to Texas. This complex is the crux of the question, not *P. ocularis*. Until the puzzling forms are worked out (*P triseriata*, *P. feriarum*, *P. septentrionalis*, and *P. nigrita*, *P. verricosus*) are carefully studied in situ and in laboratory it is better to keep the genus *Pseudacris*. Subsequent investigations may prove realignment desirable.

BIBLIOGRAPHY

1854   Baird, S. F.   Descriptions of New Genera and Species of North American Frogs.
        Proc. Acad. Nat. Sci. Phila. Vol. VII, p. 60.
1914   Deckert, R. F. Copeia, Feb. 14, 1914, No. 3.
1915   ———. Copeia, July 27, 1915, No. 20, pp. 22, 23.
1842   DeKay, James E. Zoology of New York, Part III, Albany, 1842, p. 65.
1841   Dumeril, A. M. C. et G. Bibron. Erpetologie Generale, Vol. VIII, 1841, p. 509.
1917   Fowler, H. W. Copeia, Apr. 24, 1917, No. 43, p. 39 (wrongly labelled p. 27).
1858   Gunther, A. Catalogue of the Batrachia-Salientia in the Collection of the British
        Museum, London, 1858.
1825   Harlan, R. Journ. Acad. Nat. Sci. Phila. Vol. V, Part II, Phila., 1827, p. 341.
1835   ———. Medical and Physical Researches Phila. 1835, p. 105.
1892   Hay, O. P. The Batrachians and Reptiles of the State of Indiana. Indiana Dept.
        of Geol. and Nat. Resources. 17th Ann'l, Report. 1891. Indianapolis, 1892, pp.
        409-602.
1842   Holbrook, J. E. North American Herpetology, Vol. IV, 1842, pp. 107, 108.
1849   Holbrook, J. E. Catalogue of Reptilia, Amphibia and Fish of Georgia. In White,
        G. Statistics of the State of Georgia, Savannah, 1849 (Appendix, p. 15).
1825   LeConte, John. Annals Lyceum of Nat. Hist. N. Y. Vol. V, Part 2, N. Y. 1825,
        p. 282.
1856   LeConte, John. Descriptive Catalogue of the Ranina of the United States. Proc.
        Acad. Nat. Sciences Vol. VII (1864, 1855) Phila. 1856, p. 427.
1922   Löding, H. P. A Preliminary Catalogue of Alabama Amphibians and Reptiles.
        Geol. Survey Ala. Mus. Paper No. 5, Ala. Mus. Nat. History, University Ala-
        bama 1922.
1923   Noble, G. K. The Generic and Genetic Relation of Pseudacris, the Swamp Tree
        Frogs. Am. Mus. Novitates No. 70, Apr. 23, 1923, pp. 1-6.
1927   Pickens, A. L. Amphibians of Upper South Carolina. Copeia No. 165, Oct.-Dec.
        1927 (Dec. 23), p. 109.

Pseudacris occidentalis (Baird and Girard)

(Account written in 1929)

SMOOTH CHORUS FROG

In 1909 in September Professor J. C. Bradley took a frog which we then identified as *Chorophilus occidentalis*. Not until 1912 did we see *Pseudacris* alive in Georgia and Florida first hand in the field and the identification is uncertain and doubtless incorrect. Cope (1889) pronounces two specimens taken by W. J. Taylor at Allapaha, Georgia, as *C. occidentalis*. This locality is in the upper Suwannee drainage. We have not yet critically examined these two specimens.

Holbrook in his own region (South Carolina) recognized in 1842 three species: *Cystignathus ornatus*, *Cystignathus nigrita* and *Hylodes ocularis*—the three distinct groups of today. In 1849 he gives the same three species. LeConte (1855), another resident of these parts (in Georgia at Riceboro whence Cope's *C. occidentalis* material largely came) gives three species (of the three types): *Chorophilus nigrita*, *Chorophilus ornatus* and *Hylodes ocularis*. Apparently LeConte did not honor or recognize *C. occidentalis* at Riceboro, Georgia. Cope when distinguishing *C. occidentalis* makes it the eastern representative of *C. ornatus* which he has from Texas.

But Boulenger in 1882 does not help matters by recognizing both *C. ornatus* and *C. copii* (*C. occidentalis*) in the same region. Sometimes it is hard to believe that both Holbrook and LeConte are so lacking in taxonomic sense and that old museum material from LeConte can be acclaimed new or *C. occidentalis* by Cope and Boulenger. Rather what these cataloguers have called *C. occidentalis* in the Southeast is doubtless what the resident naturalists, Holbrook and LeConte, called *C. ornatus*. The only collector and resident in recent years who has lived in the Southeast long enough to collect and observe three forms of *Pseudacris* is R. F. Deckert (1913-1915). In 1913 he found *C. nigritus, C. ocularis* and *C. occidentalis*, the latter "plentiful, in scattered companies." In 1915 he gave us the only detailed first hand account since the description of *C. occidentalis*.

His whole account is worthy of repetition. His descriptions and accounts read like our experiences with *P. ornatus* in Helotes and Beeville, Texas, in 1925. His notes are:

"*Chorophilus occidentalis*, B. & G. is a beautiful species, rarely seen except in early spring. At this time, however, it occurs in great numbers in the large, shallow bayous, where it stands almost straight upright, on some twigs or weeds, with its large throat pouch distended, giving vent to its piercing call. This call is very loud, similar in pitch to that of *Hyla pickeringi*, but much shorter, and at a distance sounds like the ring of a steel chisel, when struck with a hammer.

"This is the largest species of the genus *Chorophilus*, attaining a length of 1 1/2 inches, from snout to vent. It is stout of body, the head is pointed, the arms and legs rather short and stout. The toes are very slightly webbed, the disks on fingers and toes scarcely noticeable. The subarticular tubercles are very prominent.

"The structure of this species indicates terrestrial, possibly subterraneous habits. I have dug specimens out of the sweet potato hills in my garden.

"The smooth, shiny upper surfaces are rich reddish brown or fawn colored, like specimens of our northern Wood frog. There is a black band on each side, beginning at the nostril, running through the eye, over the tympanum to the shoulder. The edge of the upper jaw is silvery white. The groin is rich yellow or orange, with large elongate or round black spots. The undersides are white, faintly spotted with brown at the throat, flesh colored posteriorly. On the back there may be two broad, dark brown parallel bands. The arms and legs are banded more or less distinctly with brown." This was the only one of Deckert's Jacksonville Anuran species we missed. We did not arrive early enough to find it in activity.

The *P. occidentalis-P. ornata* difficulty can be easily settled with new material taken from South Carolina to Texas. *Pseudacris* does not have nine species in U. S. A. Too many personal equations enter the problem with scanty material. And *Litoria occidentalis* Baird and Girard may be a Riceboro (Georgia) form as Cope believed but is it not *C. ornatus* of LeConte, its collector, and a familiar student of *C. ornatus* at Riceboro, Georgia? He never said Riceboro, Ga., had both *C. ornatus* and *C. occidentalis*. To populate South Carolina to Florida with 5 species of *Pseudacris* is overcrowding and the placing of the so-called San Francisco *Litoria occidentalis* (1853) in the Southeast was not apparently honored by LeConte two and one-half years later (December 1855,) in his Descriptive Catalogue of the Ranina of the United States. LeConte himself collected Baird & Girard's *L. occidentalis* types in 1850, yet five years later he omits, forgets or disregards them. Still in fairness it must be said he does not mention the other three species of that paper: *Bufo halophila*, *Hyla regilla* or *Rana LeContei*.

In the Amphibians and Reptiles of Arkansas Hurter and Strecker record *Chorophilus occidentalis* from "Hot Springs (Combs)". Strecker knows *Pseudacris ornatus* and has contributed as much or more to its habits than any one living but the *Pseudacris occidentalis* is doubtful.

In December 1927 Mrs. Wright and I superficially examined the *Pseudacris ornata*, *P. occidentalis* material of the U. S. National Museum. The material of the latter species is generally rather old. A few tentative notes we made were that No. 5905 *C. occidentalis* of Cope's identifications is *P. ornata*. Some specimens from Florida labelled *P. occidentalis* are *P. ocularis* without vitta. Some *P. occidentalis* collected by Hurter in Mississippi look to be *P. ornatus*. Another specimen collected by J. Hurter from Waco, Texas, was labelled *Lithodytes latrans* and proved to be *Pseudacris ornata*. This is a little of the apparent mixed condition of *Pseudacris* with little good comparable museum material. No hope comes except from considerable collecting and field familiarity with the forms themselves. We have not yet begun a critical study of *P. ornata-P. occidentalis* nor the *P. nigrita* complex but immediately plan such a study.

Since the above was written we remembered that C. S. Brimley (1910, p. 11) secured "*Chorophilus occidentalis* from Bay St. Louis, Mississippi, February and April 1898, 5." and *Chorophilus ornatus* "Hastings, Florida, June 1901, 1; Green Cove Springs, Florida, July, 1898, 5." He is the only person to receive each from the Southeast.

Pseudacris ocularis (Holbrook)

(Pl. I, Fig. 7; IV, Fig. 6; V, Fig. 6; VI, Fig. 4; X, Fig. 8; XII, Fig. 8; XV, Fig. 8; XVII; XXIV, Text Fig. 1, 6)

COMMON NAMES

Swamp Tree Frog. Swamp Cricket Frog. Little Chorus Frog. Tree Frog.

RANGE

Check list. "Type Locality: South Carolina and Georgia. Range: Southeastern United States"—Stejneger & Barbour Check List (1923, p. 28).

Supplemental records (or detailed account of records). Outside of the Okefinokee parties from 1912-1922, the one student of Amphibia who has actually known this species first hand and best is R. F. Deckert. Subsequently, Mr. Jay A. Weber and others secured material for Dr. Noble and more recently Mr. Vernon Bailey has taken it in Florida for the U. S. National Museum. In 1911 and 1912 R. F. Deckert (Copeia, 1914, p. 3) found it "abundant and everywhere" ten miles south of Jacksonville. In 1915 the same author (1915, p. 23) reports them "very numerous near Jacksonville" . . . . In 1920 he

PLATE XXIV

Black chorus frog (*Pseudacris ocularis*)

1. Saddlebag pond, Trail Ridge, Folkston, Ga. July 9, 1922.
2. Male croaking on trunk of black gum, Billy Id., Ga. May 20, 1921. Flashlight.
3. Male croaking on bush, Chesser Id., Ga. July 26, 1922. Flashlight.
4. 5. Mature tadpoles, Saddlebag pond, Trail Ridge, Folkston, Ga. June 30, 1922. × 1.0.
6. Tadpole with two legs, Saddlebag pond, Trail Ridge, Folkston, Ga. June 30, 1922. × 1.0.
7. Tadpole with four legs, Trail Ridge, Folkston, Ga. June 30, 1922. × 1.0.
8. Tadpole with short tail, Chesser Id., Ga. July 6, 1922. × 1.0.
9. Transformed frog, Saddlebag pond, Trail Ridge, Folkston, Ga. June 30, 1922. × 1.0.
10. Male croaking on twig four feet above water, Billy Id., Ga. June 24, 1921. Flashlight.
11. Habitat of *Pseudacris ocularis*, in grass and small bushes of foreground. Trees and bushes of Siren Run in background, Billy Id., Ga. May 27, 1921.
12. Male croaking on grass blade, close to the water, Billy Id., Ga. July 6, 1921. Flashlight.

(Copeia, 1921, p. 22) finds it quite numerous in Dade County. In May, 1922, he recorded (Copeia, 1922, p. 88) it again in Dade County. In 1923 Noble (1923, p. 3) had specimens from Lee Co., Florida, Arlington, Florida, near Jacksonville, Florida, Hampton Co., S. C. and Wilmington, S. C. Noble did not intend Wilmington, South Carolina, for G. S. Myers (1924, p. 59) records "I know of no other specimen being recorded from the State (N. C.). It is the one mentioned by Noble (Am. Mus. Novitates, 70, p. 3) from Wilmington." Wright (1926, p. 82) gives *Pseudacris ocularis* as a Sabalian species from South Carolina to Florida. Inasmuch as Wilmington, N. C. is Sabalian country it is not surprising to find it recorded there. Its range seems to be from N. C. to Dade and Lee Counties in Southern Florida. The last record is Brimley's (1926, p. 82). He records the "Little Chorus Frog (*Pseudacris ocularis*) from "(Pitt, Craven, New Hanover)" counties.

The earlier material is somewhat as follows: Holbrook (1828 or 1842) has specimens of *Hylodes ocularis* from S. C. or Georgia. Several years later he (1849, App. p. 15) records this species from Georgia. LeConte (1855, p. 429) says *Hyla ocularis* "inhabits Georgia." In 1875 Cope (1875, p. 30) dubs it *Chorophilus angulatus*. Boulenger (1882, pp. 333, 334) probably had no material at hand. Cope (1887, pp. 348-349) had not Girard's specimens from Charleston, S. C. and relied on Baird's manuscript notes. Until 1911-1928 it was not at all common in collections.

Local Okefinokee records. In 1912 we wrote "In all we have ten specimens from the swamp, one taken May 28, 1912, one May 30–July 15, 1912, two June 21–22, 1912, three June 24, 1912, two July 1–15, 1912, and one after July 15, 1912."

In 1921 on Sunday, July 3, we took a handcar trip to Honey and Black Jack Islands. It was a misty day at first, then sunny, and rained all the afternoon. The temperature was from 71°–76°. On the sphagnaceous strand of Honey Island heard these creatures, near Black Jack Island, and on Honey Island in mid afternoon, in Cypress bay between the Pocket and Jones Island, and all along the trestle between Jones Island and Billy's Island. Later and earlier on Billy's Island we found them in several locations. On Floyd's Island and Chesser's Island we also heard and saw them.

In 1922 we secured them on Chesser Island, near old Suwannee Canal, along road to Folkston, in ponds near Trader's Hill, near an overgrown sphagnum bog outside the swamp along the road from Folkston, Ga., to Jacksonville, Fla.

GENERAL APPEARANCE

Holbrook speaks "of this beautiful little animal, as the smallest of the frog kind with which I am acquanited . . . ." Its general characters he gives as follows: "Head long; snout pointed; upper jaw white, which colour is continued to the anterior extremity, above this a black band runs over the shoulder and terminates on the flanks; body short, chestnut-brown or bronzed; abdomen yellowish-white." DeKay (1842, Part III) gives "*Hylodes ocularis*. (Holbrook, Vol. 3, pl. 14; and Vol. 4, pl. 35, 2d Ed.) Very small; Reddish brown; a black band from near the end of the snout, runs through the eyes and along the flanks.   Length three-quarters of an inch.   *South Carolina* and *Georgia*." LeConte, 1855, calls it "The smallest of all known Ranina.   From the small size of this and the preceding species, the web between the third and fourth toe is not very perceptible."   Boulenger (1882) calls it "extremely small."   Cope (1887, p. 348) says that "its most striking features will be found in the large size of the eyes, the acuteness of the head, the small tongue, etc.   The tibia is longer than in any of the genus."   To Deckert (1915, p. 23) "This is the smallest of the North American frogs, rarely exceeding 2/8 inch from snout to vent.   The head is pointed, the eyes large, the limbs and body slender.   The disks on the fingers and toes are small but distinct.   The skin of the back is covered with very fine warts, that of the belly finely granulated.   Evidently Miss Dickerson (1906, p. 162) did not have the species at hand.   Of it she writes "This species is said to be the smallest among North American Hylas.   Its unusual characteristics seem to be the pointed paw, the long legs, and the light line along the outer edge of the tibia."

C. S. Brimley's (1926, p. 82) revised key summarizes or distinguishes the little chorus frog as having "snout truncate in side view, adult about two-thirds of an inch in the length of head and body."

These are the brownies of frogdom in the United States.   They are usually uniform gray, brown or greenish on the back, with a vitta from eye backward as a stripe of variable length.   The snout is pointed, projecting.   They certainly at first acquaintance impress one as the possible young of some *Hyla*.   We thus puzzled and most authors who have seen them alive have gone through the same stage, particularly if they are green like so many transformed Hylas.

COLORATION OF SPIRIT SPECIMENS (1912)

The original color notes of Holbrook which have been constantly repeated are: "the pupil black, and the iris grey, with a tinge of red.   The upper lip is white, and this color is continued in a line to the axilla; above this is a black blotch which begins very narrow and becomes broad under the orbit, passes over the shoulder, and there terminates.   The chin and throat is yellowish-white.   The body—uniform chestnut-brown or bronze-coloured above and yellowish-white below.   The anterior extremities—brown above and clouded white below;—The posterior extremities—reddish brown above, barred with dusky, and obscure white below; . . . ." LeConte (1855, p. 429) describes it as "Above brown or bronzed or silvery grey, very finely specked with dusky or darker, a tolerably wide band of black proceeds from the tip of the nose to the middle or beyond the middle of the sides, this is bordered beneath with white.   Chin and under side of the thighs speckled with black.   Legs speckled like the back and more or less spotted and barred with dusky, fingers and toes all furnished with small disks."

Cope in 1887 gives its general color as dark chestnut above, gives a median dorsal stripe which bifurcates behind and says it can be distinguished from other *Pseudacris* by its chestnut color   Deckert (1915, p. 23) who has seen many characterizes it as follows: "The color is yellow, reddish brown or chestnut. The upper jaw is margined with white. There are three longitudinal dark brown dorsal bands, one from tip of the snout to above the vent, usually bifurcate posteriorly, and one on each side of this, starting behind the eye. Underneath, it is pale yellow. The males throat is dark brown, and can be distended to the size of a large pea. The arms and legs are distinctly cross-banded." Deckert thus is one of the first to describe the male and adds yellow to the general color.

Weber (Noble 1923, p. 4) finds them green in life. Noble (1923, p. 5) finds the lighter phase of more frequent occurrence and without mid-dorsal line of dark brown while the less frequent type "dark phase has three longitudinal stripes of dark brown on the back, very similar in form to *P. triseriata.*"

Color has been too strongly emphasized in this group. From just chestnut or bronze in Holbrook we have had silver grey, yellow and finally green added to general descriptions of its color. Cope emphasized the chestnut as distinctive. All the above colors may be recorded, though the author has seen fewer green specimens than of any other phase. The Florida collectors (see Deckert, Noble) often mention the mid-dorsal stripe but we have very few with it. Yet a recent collection from Florida made by Mr. Gerritt S. Miller have the general type without dorsal stripes and only the lateral stripes as in Holbrook's figure, but examples appear with mid-dorsal stripe or supplemental ones on either side of it.

Some rough notes we made on this collection of 8 males made by G. S. Miller Jr. and C. R. Aschemeier are: "The vocal sac of the male, even when collapsed, sometimes appears to cover almost half of venter of body, the rear of it may reach caudad to the pectoral region (line connecting one arm insertion with the other).

U.S.N.M. No. 71038. Has no dorsal stripe but has dark dots on back and tibia sometimes assembling in somewhat larger ill-defined spots. The entire vertical parts with dots like those of the back, but much wider spaced. Sometimes this dark punctate arrangement becomes very pronounced.

U.S.N.M. No. 71036. No dorsal stripes.

U.S.N.M. No. 71039. No dorsal stripe. If anything, these males from Gainesville seem to be more tuberculate on the venter than do those of the Okefinokee.

U.S.N.M. No. 71040. Has the venter from somewhat caudad of pectoral line more tuberculate than almost any other hylid in the U.S.A., but not on hind legs. Hind legs big proportionally. Color fawn brown on back. No dorsal stripes.

U.S.N.M. No. 71041. No dorsal stripes.

U.S.N.M. No. 71034. No dorsal stripes.

U.S.N.M. No. 71035. Darker back. No dorsal stripes.

U.S.N.M. No. 71037. Has suggestion of indistinct stripe down mid dorsum and on either side of it is a dorsolateral stripe toward the rear. The eye vittae go just back of axillae. There is a prominent dark stripe on the front of the tibia. This coloration suggests the typical *Pseudacris* coloration. there is a dark spot on the top of the snout. None, however, have a triangle between the eyes.

STRUCTURAL CHARACTERS (WRITTEN IN 1912)

Upper parts smooth; the under parts also smooth, except for the ventral parts back of the ventral fold, the upper breast and belly and under side of the thigh granulate; nostril lateral and much nearer the tip than the eye; snout pointed and projecting; lower jaw narrow; cleft of the mouth deep, to the vertical of the tympanum; in most of the specimens a prominent breast fold present; in all, tongue entire and in most broad; in the smaller forms where lower jaw is sometimes narrower, tongue is sometimes narrow; tympanum .5–.3 of the eye; disks moderate on the feet; disks more prominent on the fingers; first finger shorter than the second; second and fourth fingers about equal; third finger longest; subarticular tubercle small; a metacarpal tubercle present; fingers free; metatarsal tubercles external and internal small; subarticular plantar tubercles indistinct; fourth toe much longer than 3rd or 5th which are about equal; 2nd slightly larger than the first; toes hardly half webbed; in some of the larger specimens there is present an indistinct fold from eye over tympanum to the arm insertion.

MEASUREMENTS
(1912–1914)

In 1912 the measurements of the ten individuals were "from 12–15.5 mm., average 12.5 mm.; the head is 3.5–6 mm., average 4.5 mm., more than the width of the head (like Boulenger's *C. copii*); head contained in the length 2.3–3.4 times, average 2.75, mode 2.9; the width of the head, 3–4.5 mm., average 3.75 mm., 3–4.3 times in the length of the body; about the same or narrower than Cope's 3–3.5 for *C. occidentalis*; snout 1.5–2.75 mm., average 1.36, from 1–2 times the eye rarely 1 times and usually about 1.5 times the eye; the eye is from 1–2 mm.; interorbital distance which is .5–2.25 mm., average 1.5 mm., equal to or greater than the eyelid which is .75–1.5 mm., average 1 mm. The femur is 5.25–8 mm., average 6.5 usually less than the tibia, occasionally equals tibia; tibia 5.75–8 mm., average 6.8 mm., usually continued 1.75–2 times in the length of the body; tarsus 3.5–5.25 mm., average 4.4 more than the width of the head and usually equal to the length of the head; rest of the leg 4–6.25 mm., average 4.9 mm., equal to or slightly more than the tarsus; anterior limb from axilla 5.25–7.75 mm., average 6.4 mm., about equal to femur; posterior limb 19–23.5 mm., average 20.4 mm., usually 1.5–1.6 times the length of the body; usually the heel of the hind limb reaches snout, occasionally half way between the eye and the tip of the snout.

(Recent Material)

Head to angle of mouth 1.0 (17.5 mm. ♀) in width of head; head to rear of tympanum .91 in width of head; head to angle of mouth 3.5 in length of body; head to rear of tympanum 3.18 in length of body. Snout, 0.5

in first finger; snout, .75 in fourth finger; snout, .66 in first toe; eye, 1.8 in snout; eye, .5 in tympanum; eye, .85 in first finger; tympanum, 5.0 in inter-tympanic width; tympanum, 3.3 in snout; internasal width, .5 in upper eyelid width; interorbital width, .5 in upper eyelid width; interorbital width, 1.0 in internasal width; interorbital width 2.25 in intertympanic width;

Forelimb: Forelimb, 2.5 in length of body; forelimb, 3.3 in hind limb; first finger, 2.0 in third finger; second finger 1.5 in third finger; second finger, .75 in third finger; third finger, .83 in second toe; fourth finger, 1.33 in third finger; fourth finger, .90 in first toe; internasal width, .75 in first finger; internasal width, 1.0 in second finger; internasal width, 1.5 in third finger; internasal width, 1.125 in fourth finger;

Hindlimb: length, 1.3 in hind limb; tibia, 2.2 in length; tibia, 2.9 in hind limb; tibia, .875 in forelimb; tibia, .85 in hind foot; first toe, 1.25 in second toe; first toe, 2.0 in third toe; first toe, 2.75 in fourth toe; first toe, 2.1 in fifth toe; second toe, 1.6 in third toe; second toe, 2.2 in fourth toe; second toe, 1.68 in fifth toe; third toe, 1.375 in fourth toe; third toe, 1.05 in fifth toe; fourth toe, 1.23 in hind foot; fourth toe, 1.4 in tibia; fourth toe, 1.2 in fore limb; fifth toe, 1.3 in fourth toe; internasal width, 1.0 in first toe; internasal width, 1.25 in second toe; internasal width, 2.0 in third toe; internasal width, 2.75 in fourth toe; internasal width, 2.1 in fifth toe.

HABITAT

Holbrook (1842, p. 138) refers to this species as "choosing the same damp places for its abode (as *Acris gryllus*) and is not infrequently found on the leaves of such low shrubs as inhabit the same localities, as the myrtle (*Myrica cerifera*); . . . ." ". . . this animal is not infrequently found on low bushes, or leaps upon them when pursued, ..." . . . . "They are all found near water, or in darkest places, like to Ranoida, but are never observed sitting half immersed in it, though they will conceal themselves by diving to the bottom when pursued."

Deckert (1915, p. 23) writes "During the spring months, they abound on the marginal vegetation of the 'bayous," . . . ." In 1922 he (1922, p. 88) reports them "heard at Homestead and in rain-ditches along the road to a little beyond Royal Palm Hammock," in Miami district. Mr. Jay A. Weber (Noble 1923, pp. 4, 5) gives his experiences with them as follows: "The tiny frogs were a brilliant light green in life, similar to, but even brighter than *H. cinerea*. They were observed most abundantly at Rocky Lake. A narrow belt of reeds along the water's edge had been tramped down by cattle, and it was here the frogs in association with *Acris* were found. They were extremely agile and I found it impossible to get near enough to catch them by hand. As one approached them they would hop among the crushed, but still living reeds, where their green coloration caused them to disappear immediately. Never did they seek a hiding place in the holes or shallow puddles in the manner of *Acris*. The deep water of the lake was full of fish and I noticed that neither *Acris* nor this species ever hopped into the deep water. At last, after constructing a club from the base of a cat-tail stalk, I succeeded in approaching close enough to secure specimens. The species is the rarest of the riparian frogs in the region that I visited and its extreme agility and protective coloration make it the hardest, by far, to catch."

In 1912 we have these notes of this species in Okefinokee Swamp. "These forms were taken generally in rather moist situations. One of the special places was a narrow marshy crossway between two islands with associated killifishes and young Centrarchidae. On May 28, 1912, at the end of the lumber railroad and near Mixon's Ferry we found some *Chorophilus* hopping about in the vegetation with oak toads as associates. On May 10 on Honey Island Prairie, a different sort of place, there were some small frogs which we considered *Chorophilus* but of them we made no collections. The bulk of the specimens were secured in some small ponds on Billy's Island or in the damp dark localities among the heath cover."

On May 16, 1921, "picked up *Pseudacris ocularis* in the grass, in amongst pipewort (Eriocaulon)." The next day on Billy's Island we went out to Crosby Pond. In the grass, sedge and *Eriocaulon* cover, also some heaths, took *Pseudacris ocularis*." The following day, May 18, "at 4:40 P.M. went to Crosby Pond. *Pseudacris ocularis* may start up from sphagnum edge of Cypress Pond where sphagnum is no more than an inch above solid ground and in the piney wood's side outside the gum border of a pond. May start this form up from the ground. It will leap 1–1 1/2 feet at times. Laid on *Eriocaulon*, small *Sarracenia minor*, sedge and saw palmettos. Took a dozen of them." On June 8 "we went to Siren Run which is getting very dry. In one moist place amongst pipeworts (*Eriocaulon*) found a few *Pseudacris ocularis*."

On June 25 we found them common in one pond "Many in bamboo (*Smilax*) vines, on bushes some 4–5 feet up. Others on level of water. All the way from open pond through fringe of gum trees to the outer edge of the pond, in amongst fallen pine tops, in amongst trash, where water is shallow and covered with drift particles, etc."

On July 15, 1921, on a trip to Chesser Island we found them abundant on the outer edges of cypress ponds outside the swamp, on the outer edge of the marginal cypress bay. Most of them we "caught in the grass near the edge of ponds."

In 1922 we found them from Trader's Hill to Chesser Island in similar habitats to those of 1921, e.g., on June 17 "in grassy and sedgy area we found several on the edge of pine barrens on outer edge of cypress bay or branch and also one mile south of Canal near swamp's edge."

FIRST APPEARANCE

At the very first of our 1912 trip we found them (May 28). In 1921 we entered the swamp the last week in April, one month earlier than above. At once the boys brought in 3 frogs (April 24) and they were females, which implies the species was well out. No doubt resident naturialists will find earlier dates of appearance for this species as for all frogs of the Okefinokee. The earliest record I can find is Deckert's (1921, p. 22) note for Miami region.

"This is the smallest of North American Salientia and was found to be quite numerous in a dried-up ditch with black muck bottom at Little River, Feb. 23. A dozen specimens were taken and liberated later on at 19th Street, Miami, in a small hammock. It is the only member of the genus observed here so far." So, too, G. S. Miller Jr. and C. R. Aschemeier took adult males (U.S.N.M. 71034-41) at Gainesville, Florida, April 3, 1926, and O. C. Van Hyning has taken it from February onward at the same place.

GENERAL HABITS

Metachrosis. On May 21, 1921, "It is curious that I put all sixteen frogs in a pan and put it in the desk beside two books. All those on the north side were of the reddish brown phase. Those on the south side of a gray phase. The first were beside the deeper reddish binding of Jordan—Evermann's Fishes of North America and the gray ones near Smith's Fishes of N. C., reddish lighter manuscript holders or covers." On the evening of May 21, 1921, during a great chorus of this species they impressed us as much faded out at night.

Variation in color. Others have recorded individuals: chestnut brown, bronzed (Holbrook); brown, bronze or silvery grey (LeConte); dark chestnut (Cope); yellow, reddish brown, chestnut (Deckert); green (Weber).

In 1912 we secured the following colors: gray, greenish, light yellowish olive, dull citrine, chestnut bay. In 1921 we took individuals: brown, reddish brown, gray, amber brown, hazel, tawny, buckthorn brown, light grayish olive, light olive gray, deep olive gray, cinnamon.

On May 17 we had diverse colorings in a lot of sixteen in one pan. "Some were tawny, hazel or amber brown on upper surfaces, others buckthorn brown. One is light grayish olive or light olive gray; another deep olive gray. The stripe on the upper jaw was almost cream, chalcedony yellow or glass green. Belly chamois, cream buff, or calomel buff. Iris, cinnamon."

General habits. Holbrook, its describer (1842, p. 138) says this species "is closely allied to the *Hylodes gryllus* in its habits, choosing the same damp places for its abode, ..." Under this species he notes "The members of this genus, like those of the last, are all diurnal in their habits, or seek their food by daylight. They all delight in the heat of the sun, and the brighter its rays, the more merry and noisy are they."

In 1921 we first met them in numbers May 16 on Billy's Island "In the grassy pipewort cover they, when disturbed, could jump 1-1½ feet away like an *Acris*. The *Pseudacris ocularis* would jump into small bushes. Were very hard to catch. Of six I saw I caught only two. One I thought I had killed. His tongue hung out yet he jumped. The jump apparently remains to the last. The adult *Acris* will leap into the bushes ½-1 foot high. Are these last year's *Acris*? This is only a guess, a possibility." We soon satisfied ourselves they were different. On May 21 we "found *Pseudacris ocularis* hopping over water like a young bullfrog, usually over a dense mat of grass in water."

VOICE

We took these creatures as early as 1912 but have no clear recollection or notes to indicate we distinguished their notes in that year. Apparently the first person to recognize their notes was R. F. Deckert (1915, pp. 23, 24) who reports "males giving vent to their faint calls, which sound more like the chirping of insects than the calls of frogs."

Our first acquaintance with a chorus came the evening of May 20, 1921. My journal reads thus: "Then went down to the pond east of the negro quarters and it sounded as if bedlam had broken loose. I heard a cricket-like note everywhere and concluded it was *Pseudacris ocularis*. Have heard isolated calls of this note during the day and at night for several days, but it was dismissed as a possible insect yet my identification has not satisfied me. Later the boys came. I had found *Pseudacris ocularis* to be the author of the cricket-like note. One frog was on a grassy mat; one on a log; another calling from a pine bush at edge of water; another on the side of the bole of a tree. They do not like the electric spotlight. One on pine bush after a time worked up into the leaves or crawled up the branch. We flashed one on the side of a black gum. Its throat pouch was transparent and we could see through it and discern the bark behind. This one, one of the boys discovered without flashlight, merely by the aid of moonlight. Many are in the grass and are hard to see. We timed the croaks. One gave 49, 52, 55, 58 cheeps in a minute; another 45, 48, 50, 52, 54, 56, 58, 59, 61, 2, 5, 7 calls a minute; another 30, 32, 34, 36, 38 a minute. We found that they averaged in general about 32 calls a minute with silent intervals averaging one second to one and seven-eighths or two seconds. In some cases as few as 20 per minute were recorded. Some would be regular; some irregular. Its note is penetrating and can be heard 150-200 feet away. It is high pitched, insect-like. In some respects it is little like the notes of other *Pseudacris*, yet in other respects it reminds one of the other species of the *triseriata-feriarum-nigrita* group. It is an amusing little creature as it squeezes its slender body and throws out its large sac one-half the size of the body. It may be perched obliquely on the side of a bole of a tree, lengthwise of brush clump or more often cross-wise of a branch. It may not be on a bush at all when calling. However, one characterizes it be it as a chirp, trill, cheep, squeak, or as high, shrill, insect-like, it surely is a loud piercing call for so little a mite of frog flesh."

In late May, 1921, when following *Pseudacris ocularis* vigorously we concluded from our experiences with it that above a certain required minimum temperature plays less role in croaking of frogs than humidity. When the temperature at night became the warmest they might not call if the air had been dry at that period.

"On July 3, 1921 we made a trip by lever car to Honey Island, Honey Island Prairie, and almost to Black Jack Island. Railroad to within 1 mile of Black Jack. It rained at lunch and afterwards. On our return we heard *Pseudacris* all over the prairie and in sphagnum of wet thickets especially. On Honey Island we stopped and caught a few *Pseudacris*. All along trestle between Jones and Billy's Island we stopped and caught a few *Pseudacris* calling. Never heard such a frog din. Same on Jones Island. Later on Billy's Island no end of *Pseudacris* in the hammock near Newt Pond."

Our journal notes of calling are:

1921

April 25. Two or three frogs brought into camp.

May 16–18. Common in Cypress Pond edge.

" 20. In *Chorophilus* (*Pseudacris*) Pond at 4 P.M. no end of *Pseudacris* calling by day. In chorus in evening.

" 21. No end of *Chorophilus* calling at 8 P.M. Air 70°. Were calling vigorously in afternoon.

" 22. Several heard in mid afternoon. Hear them at night at Newt Pond.

" 24. In moist pine barrens near edge of cypress bay heard two at 4 P.M., bright sun. Tonight at 10 P.M., air 77°, a few calling.

" 26. A few *Pseudacris* calling in *Chorophilus* Pond and other places.

" 27. Temperature up to 91°. Few calling in mid afternoon. Several heard at night.

" 31. Hear one or two *Pseudacris ocularis* at 11:30 P.M.

June 2. One calling, several seen this day.

" 3. No *Pseudacris* calling at *Chorophilus* tonight, 75°. One heard in hammock tonight back of camp.

" 4. Heard none calling except one in grassy field near camp.

" 5. In evening went to Long Pond trestle. Heard plenty of *Pseudacris ocularis*, air 71°.

" 14. Heard one or two *Pseudacris ocularis* about 8 A.M., Floyd's Island.

" 21. Heard one *Pseudacris* at *Bufo* Pond at 10 A.M.

" 23. Heard a few.

" 24. After rain common at *Chorophilus* Pond.

" 25. Common, plenty at Newt Pond. Several calling at *Chorophilus* Pond. Hear one at 10:30 A.M., Long Pond.

" 28. One heard on Jones Island.

" 29. Several heard early in morning about 5.

" 30. Several heard in outer edge of pond, not middle, 3 P.M.

July 1. Quite a few calling by Indian Mound ponds.

" 3. Heard in Honey Island Strand near Black Jack Island and on Honey Island all in early afternoon. Later in the Pocket. Commonly heard between Jones Island and Billy's Island.

" 4. Plenty at Long Pond.

" 6. *Pseudacris* heard 75–80 yards away.

" 7. Photographed croakers tonight and last night.

" 11. A few heard along Suwannee Canal at 6 P.M.

" 12. Common, heard 1–3 P.M. along canal.

" 15. Saw and heard plenty of *Pseudacris* on Chesser Island.

" 15. Hear *Pseudacris* around Bay Pond. We saw and heard plenty on the mainland and on the Island.

" 16. Immense chorus but hard to hear because of choruses of *Hyla gratiosa*, *Bufo quercicus*, etc. Much laying.

" 17. There are fewer calling tonight, yet they are abundant.

" 18. One or two heard Chesser Island.

" 27. Cloudly. This afternoon, Billy Island, heard a few *Pseudacris ocularis*. A few in the woods. One calling near camp.

" 28. Several heard in piney woods. Rainy. In middle of island where some gallberry bushes (*Ilex glabra*) with temperature water are, hear *Pseudacris*. Strong chorus tonight.

"　29.　Black Jack Island. Down pour near our camp in temporary pool. One of the greatest choruses of *Chorophilus ocularis* I ever heard.

Aug.　9.　One or more heard along St. Mary's river.

"　11.　Many heard along River.

"　17.　Several heard at Camp Pinckney, Ga.

1922

June 14.　A few were calling in Coat Bet Pond, Chesser Island at 8–9 and possibly later.

"　19.　Heard a few in one or two places on our return from Folkston.

"　21.　Heard one or two beside path from landing into Chesser Island.

"　23.　A few calling near the ponds 1 mile south of Trader's Hill, Ga.

"　26.　Heard some in cypress around an open cypress pond.

"　27.　Heard a few near Anna's Pond, Starling Branch, Colerain and several other places.

July　2.　8:30 P.M.–12 midnight. Heard many in different places on our way from Chesser Island to Starling Branch.

"　3.　Heard several in pond ½ mile west of Trader's Hill. Choruses in many similar places. Associated with *Bufo quercicus*.

"　11.　Heard several at first and second crossings.

Aug.　8.　Along Chesser Island Road and Old Okefinokee Road heard quite a few 8–11 P.M. Temperature 79°.

"　11.　Folkston–Chesser Island: Many immense choruses in wet grassy places 8–12 P.M.

"　13.　Commonly heard from St. Mary, Ga.–Chesser Island.

In 1921 and 1922 the prevailing temperatures when we heard the species in chorus frequently were from 70°–79°. An average of 50 temperatures taken when the species was calling gives 74°. The most common range was from 71°–76°. The big choruses almost invariably came after a big rain. Then the wet grassy places teemed with little *Pseudacris ocularis*. In 1921 on May 20 we had an immense chorus, they were calling during the day. The temperatures were 70°–72° and the activity came after a rain. On June 24 and 25 after a rain they were common. Temperatures of 70°–76°, 72°, 73°, 76° and much higher in mid-day prevailed. On July 15 a strong thunder storm began. On this day and the following day *Pseudacris ocularis* without end began. Temperatures from 73°, 76° and upward obtained. On July 29 we were caught in a down pour on Black Jack Island. We were encamped in the moist pine barrens. All about strongest chorus of *Pseudacros ocularis* we ever heard. Temperature about 73°.

In 1922 we had similar experiences. Humidity is first needed to send them into breeding. The temperatures most prevalent are from 70° to 79°.

MATING

Coloration. In 1921 "April 25 Dave Lee brought in some *Chorophilus*-like forms." On April 28 we have these notes about these first specimens of 1921 (our first since 1912). "Three dead several hours. Maybe they are young *Hyla femoralis* (they were not). Back from tip of snout brown with fine close set series of grayish white spots giving creature a grayish back. Band from tip of snout through eye over arm insertion half way or 2/3 way to groin.

Band under eye to angle of eye pinkish bronze continued as broken series or row of spots to arm insertion. Belly cream or yellowish with scattered black dots widely spaced. Yellowish cream spots also scattered over belly and on sides below black side stripe. Dark band on back of fore arm." Examination of these prove them females. In spirits they are now (seven years later) with the lateral stripe obscurely or slightly revealed.

"On August 18, 1922, at Hilliard, Fla., (.7 mi. south beside Dixie Highway found a little *Pseudacris ocularis* which is cinnamon or ochraceous tawny in color." This proves an adult male with plaited throat.

Structural differences. In 1912 we discussed this matter very briefly thus "There are three males in the lot of ten, and each has indications of a prominent gular pouch. These pouches are in a collapsed state and the wrinkles are mainly in the lower throat region. All three have the breast fold prominent; two are chestnut or bay and one olive or greenish. In one the throat is very dark in color; in the others as light as the other ventral parts. There is no decided enlargements of the fingers. Many of the males from 11.5 mm. onward may have a plait parallel to lower jaw margin and somewhat mesad of it. Then there is likely to be a collection of irregular folds in mid-ventral throat instead of pectoral region. Sometimes it looks like a little triangle in the mid-region of lower throat."

Some of the males from 11.5 mm. onward may have a plait parallel to the lower jaw margin and somewhat mesad of it. There is sometimes one or more often two mesal longitudinal plaits rarely three mesal plaits. Then there is likely to be a collection of irregular folds in mid ventral throat ahead of pectoral region. Sometimes it looks like a little triangle in the mid-region of lower throat. Sometimes two transverse plaits, rarely one, appear in alcoholic males just ahead of pectoral fold.

Females have more tendency to have the lateral stripe prominent and the dorsal band and intermediate dorsal oblique stripes to groin., i.e., 5 stripes. Rarely a male has them but males more often have the lateral band absent. In 1921 on June 23, we found a 14.5 mm. ♂; on July 7, a 13 mm. ♂, 14.5 mm. ♂, and 16 mm. ♀ ; on July 8 a 13.2 mm. ♂, 15 mm. ♂; on July 13-17, a 14 mm. ♂, 14.8 mm. ♂, 15 mm. ♂, 17 mm. ♀ ; on July 17 we took three pairs; 13.4 mm. ♂, 14 mm. ♂, 14 mm. ♂; 15.5 mm. ♀, 16 mm. ♀, 16 mm. ♀.

The measurements of one lot of 14 adult males are: three, 11.5 mm.; five 12 mm.; five 13 mm.; one 13.5 mm. The measurements of a group of four ripe females are: 12 mm., 13 mm., 13.5 mm., 17.5 mm. Some of the freshest material (U.S.N.M. 71034–41) are 8 frogs collected by Mr. Gerritt S. Miller Jr. and C. R. Aschemeier, Apr. 3, 1926, at Gainesville, Florida. They are all males with inflated throat sacs preserved in not entirely collapsed state. They measure: two 14 mm., three 14.5 mm., two 15 mm., one 15.5 mm.

Thus we have externally apparent males from 11.5–15.5 mm., and females 12–17.5 mm. The males have two nodes 13 mm. and 14.5 mm., possibly 1st-year-olds and 2nd-year-old frogs. Surely this species begins breeding when one year old if not sooner. The average of 35 adult males is 13 mm., also its greater mode, the average of nine females is 15 mm.

Duration, night or day. Pairs mated in laboratory the night of May 26, 1921, were in embrace next day without ovulation. They were captured at night and mated at night.

Amplexation (Normal, abnormal). The first amplexation came May 26, 1921. Several males and females were captured in the evening. "Put all *Pseudacris* together. Soon two pairs were mated, one pair of male and female. . . . Typical axillary embrace. They kept thus until we reached camp and were flash-lighted without disturbing their amplexation."

On May 21, 1921 "Caught a lot of *Pseudacris* males in the pond in the afternoon. Two males amplexated. It was an axillary embrace." On May 26, 1921 "put many *Pseudacris* together. Soon two pairs mated—One was a female with two males embracing, one male holding the female axillary fashion and other male holding the mating male axillary fashion. They kept thus until camp was reached and were flash-lighted."

OVULATION

Habitat. The search for this life history was long and at times discouraging. On May 26, 1921 "we went for oak toads and *Pseudacris*. In pond here the *Pseudacris* are gone from damp grassy sedgy places. Have they reached the pond? Found only one in this area where for ten days they were common." "*Pseudacris* often in little islands of grass mats where grass extends 1–2 inches above water. Principally on little leaf islands with a black gum or so and one or two overhanging bushes; on wet old leaves of former years, also along edges of pond north and east side in grass or on leaves around black gum trees. On one grassy log a male was calling; a foot or less away was a female and not far from her another female. Apparently the females are beginning to approach the water. Have seen a few females in the water. Put all the males and females together. Soon two were mated." The following morning, May 27, 1921, we noted: "No eggs as yet." On June 4 we went to *Chorophilus* pond for habitat pictures. On mossy logs were *Pseudacris*. Looked faithfully for a pair but did not find them."

On June 25, 1921, "found a big congress. Are they finished breeding or at height of breeding or what? Am afraid this form is so tiny it has slipped by me."

Not until July 16, 1921, did we find mated pairs in the field. From laboratory mated pairs no eggs had come. "While searching for coatbets (*Hyla gratiosa*) I found a pair of *Pseudacris ocularis* on a mossy log amongst *Woodwardia* fern. Tried for it and missed it. Later it leaped to a fern stem where we caught it. In a stand of ferns next to a tree with hurrah bushes (*Leucothoë racemosa*) were two pairs. Later Harper caught a pair but alas lost the male! One or two more females were taken and several males. The pairs laid by the next morning."

Period. On the basis of mating we have mated pairs from May 26 to July 16 in 1921. On the basis of calling we have records from May 16 to 20— August 18 and some of the August records are of immense choruses in mid August. In 1912 a female taken June 16 was unspent. In 1921 three females taken April 24 were spent; on May 23 three or four females were found un-spent, and numerous ripe females and pairs were taken July 16. This implies ovulation from April 24–July 16.

On the basis of tadpoles we have mature and transforming tadpoles by June 28–July 1, 1922, July 8 and July 19, just when we recorded heavy egg-laying the year before. This implies egg-laying in May or last of April.

In 1923 (1923, p. 34) we gave this species as one of five which started to breed from "May 15 on to June 1st." In our notes we variously have it "May 25–   ," "May 26–July 18," "May 16–August 13" and in 1924 (1924, p. 378) it appears May 16–August 21. This last period about represents our knowledge of it in 1924 if we do not consider spent and unspent females and transforming tadpoles. These latter send the ovulation at least to April 24 if not before. April 24-August 21 are the extremes of our evidence. This species being a *Pseudacris* we might suspect it of appearing early but we dare not prophesy breeding before March and possibly it may extend through September to October 1.

Temperature and humidity (See voice discussion). The only record of positive ovulation came from July 15 and 16, 1921 when temperatures from 73° and 76° obtained. This record comes after a hard rain. We have mating records from 72° upwards. As determined under the topic of voice, ovulation probably comes primarily after downpours when temperatures are usually 70°–79°.

Egg-laying process. In localities they choose even more shallow places than *Hyla crucifer*, but were the author to show the eggs fastened to a stick I doubt if few in America could tell them from *Hyla crucifer* eggs laid in cap-tivity. We got the same captive complements as in this species. They lay in somewhat similar places, have more or less similar individual eggs. We will not be surprised to discover they lay their eggs in a similar way. In fact, we suspect they belong nearer *Hyla crucifer* than near the other *Pseudacris* species or *Hyla gratiosa, Hyla squirella, Hyla andersonii* in egg-laying method.

EGGS

Attachment, dangers. One specimen, a female (No. 7114), the specimen where the lateral stripe breaks into mottlings, has large ripe eggs, which are astonishingly large for the size of the frog. This specimen is only 15.5 mm. long yet its eggs are .8–1.0 mm. in diameter. A slight examination of the egg content shows 50 for either side is high and a complement of 100 eggs is the lowest record for any North American Salientia. This female was taken on Mixon's Hammock June 16, 1912, in some overflow pools with spring frog and toad tadpoles and with transforming cricket frogs. The middle of June is much later than the breeding period for the larger northern *Chorophilus* which are amongst the first to breed. These small males 12–13 mm. with gular pouches apparent and this ripe female 15.5 mm. with ripe ova, very strongly discredit any belief that these creatures are young forms of a larger form. (Above note of 1912.)

In 1921 these pairs of July 16–17 were captured in water from 3–12 inches in depth. Their eggs hatch quickly and probably would not have been caught by quick drying had they been laid naturally. Many eggs in small pools might be caught except that ovulation usually comes at rainy periods.

The eggs laid the night of July 16–17, 1921, were mainly attached to sticks. "The three pairs were put into containers; two pairs in the photographic jar; the other pair in a round collecting bottle, all the equipment we had available. Into each we put one or two sticks. The eggs are strewn along on the sticks as in *Hyla crucifer*. Two masses of the three complements were somewhat like normal *Pseudacris* masses (like *P. triseriata-feriarum-nigrita* group) of western New York and Texas forms. The eggs themselves look like those of *Hyla crucifer*. The vitellus is brown above and creamish or yellowish on lower pole. Ten of the eggs are floating. Quite a few single eggs on the bottom of the jars. Must lay submerged eggs attached to grass, fern and other herbaceous stems.

The next morning in this pond "in water 3–6 inches deep with dip net discovered eggs which seemed *Pseudacris ocularis* eggs (like those in camp). These eggs are harder than those of *Acris*."

Egg mass, egg description (See general account of eggs). The first eggs laid in camp July 16–17, 1921, were roughly measured. "The vitelli measured from .6–.8 mm.; the outer envelope from 1.4–1.8 mm. With my lens I could see no inner envelope. Egg reminds me of that of *Hyla crucifer*. Vitellus brown and cream color."

In 1923 (1923a, p. 406) we gave their "eggs laid singly." In 1923 (1923b, p. 34) we write "*Pseudacris ocularis* emit single eggs on the bottoms of ponds and on vegetation." In 1924 we (1924, p. 376) place the eggs in the category "envelope single. Envelope 1.2 to 2.0 mm. Vitellus 0.6–0.8 mm. Egg complement, 100.—*Pseudacris ocularis*."

Mrs. Wright's laboratory notes on 17–20 eggs are: Egg vitellus .8 mm. or less; vitellus .6–.8 mm.; vitellus mode .8 mm., average .75 mm.; vitellus brown above, cream below; no inner envelope; envelope 1.2 –1.8 mm. in diameter; envelope average 1.36, mode 1.4 mm.

HATCHING PERIOD

On the night of July 16 from 8–10 P.M. we found 3 or 4 mated pairs in a pond on Chesser Island. Each pair laid eggs that evening. On July 18, we have the note "The *Chorophilus* eggs laid night of July 16–17 hatching by 3 P.M. of the 18th. Fast work." This means a maximum of 42 hours if laid soon after 10 P.M. or if not laid until 4 or 5 A.M. July 17, a maximum period of 35 or 36 hours. These were in ordinary collecting bottles and petri dishes. The temperatures for those days for surrounding stations were: minima 68°–70°, average 72°; maxima 87°–92°, average 90°. The maxima probably were very effective in the petri dishes.

MATURE TADPOLE

Color description from life (June 30, July 8, 1922). Dorsal color citrine drab or deep olive. Over the dorsum of the body are definitely scattered *distinct black spots.* Lower belly a block of orient pink or orange pink. Sometimes this is broken into a mottled arrangement when the gill region and sides are reached. Area around the mouth and an extension backward on each side martius yellow. Heavily speckled on under side of developing hind legs or femur when two legged stage is well started.

Tail. Lower edge of muscular part for the basal one-half a line of martius yellow. The upper edge a rim of muscular part apricot buff to apricot orange or rufous to ferruginous. This color extends on to the top of the body and gives it the same color dorsally as upper musculature. The middle of the muscular part is with a prominent sharply defined band of chestnut brown or black at the basal half or two-fifths of the tail and hazel or cinnamon rufous onward to tip. This dark middle stripe extends onto the body in transforming individuals, becomes the dark stripe either side of the median dorsal stripe. From mature tadpole to transformation the three-striped (light, dark light) arrangement obtains, the lower stripe being least conspicuous. The rim of the tail crests is with large blotches. The interval between the crest rim and the musculature is translucent and without spots or dots.

Iris black, citrine drab or deep olive finely speckled with empire yellow or bittersweet orange.

In alcohol the broad brown tail band follows on to body to back of the eye. Above brown band is a clear white edge which extends on to the body and around the edge and then forward. Below brown band is a light band.

General appearance. Tadpole quite small (23 mm.) full and deep bodied (in general appearance somewhat like *H. crucifer*). Tail quite long, tail tip sharply acute or even acuminate. The dorsal and ventral crests about equal. The dorsal crest not deeper than tail musculature and extending on to the body to the vertical halfway between eye and the spiracle. Spiracles sinistral, directed backwards and upwards, far below, lateral axis, the spiracular opening prominent elliptical round. Eye on the lateral axis, dorsal aspect on the outline and therefore visible in the ventral aspect as well. Anus dextral, opening on a level with the lower edge of the ventral crest. Muciferous crypts not distinct.

Mouth parts: Teeth 2/3. Upper labium fringed with a continuous row of labial teeth; the papillae extend above and inwards beyond the end of the labial fringe for about 2/9–1/4 of the length of the upper fringe. The horny beak is contained in upper fringe 2.0 times in the upper fringe. The median space between the second lateral upper labial rows of teeth long, 3–4 times the length of either lateral row. Inner papillae sparse or absent on upper labium and opposite the anus or horny beak. At ends of the second lower labial teeth row two or three rows. Sometimes on sides two rows of labial papillae from upper fringe down. The papillae do not extend under second row to the end of the third row of labial teeth as in *H. crucifer*. The second row of papillae across the lower labial border is about equal to the second row of labial teeth. The third labial row of teeth is short, 1/4–1/3 the length of the first or second row of lower labial teeth. The first and second rows about equal and about two times the horny beak in length, upper fringe somewhat angulate in the middle.

Measurements. Length of body (7.8–9.0 mm.) in tail (12–14.4 mm.) 1.33 –2.0, average 1.58. Width (4.0–4.8 mm.) of body in its own length 1.3–2.1, average 1.65. Depth (3.8–5.0 mm.) of body 1.0–1.4 in body width, average 1.17. Depth of body 1.72–2.2 in length of body, average 1.90. Depth (3.2– 4.0 mm.) of tail in length of tail 3.1–4.4, average 3.58. Muscular part (2.0– 2.2 mm.) 1.7–2.2 in depth of tail, average 1.88. Spiracle 1.7–2.1 nearer base of hind legs or vent region (2.8–3.8 mm.) then the tip of the snout (4.8–6.8 mm.), average 1.675. Spiracle to eye (3.0–3.4 mm.) equals spiracle to base of hind legs or vent. Eye to tip of snout (2.6–3.8 mm.) about equal to eye to spiracle. Nostril 1.25–2.0 nearer eye (1.2–1.6 mm.) than snout (2.1–2.4 mm.), average 1.5. Mouth (2.0–2.8 mm.) usually equals internasal space (2.0–2.8 mm.) Mouth contained 1.5–1.9 (average 1.66) in interorbital distance (3.0 –4.2 mm.). Internasal space contained in interorbital space 1.3–2.1, average 1.63.

The dimensions of the largest tadpole are:

	mm.		mm.
Total length	23.0	Spiracle to vent	3.8
Body length	8.8	Spiracle to eye	3.0
Body depth	5.0	Eye to snout	3.0
Body width	5.2	Eye to nostril	1.2
Tail length	14.2	Nostril to snout	2.2
Tail depth	3.2	Mouth	2.2
Musculature of tail	2.0	Interorbital distance	3.4
Spiracle to snout	6.8	Internasal distance	2.2

General remarks. In 1923 (1923, p. 406) we characterized the tadpole thus "Eggs laid singly. . . . *Pseudacris ocularis* scattered distinct black dots on body, black band on musculature of tail, clear intervals between musculature and rims of the crest." In 1928 we summarized it thus "*Musculature with a distinct brown lateral band with light area below*; crests usually clear with fine scattered fleckings, sometimes with fleckings gathered near outer rim; one or two rows of papillae below the hind lower labial row of teeth; nostril to eye in nostril to snout 1.25 –2.0; depth of tail in tail length 2.9–4.4, average 3.4, 3.55; spiracle 1.15–2.1 nearer vent than snout, average 1.5–1.875; median space between second upper labial row 2 1/2 or 3–7 in either lateral portion; horny beak in upper fringe, 15.–2.0. (Characters above shared with *Pseudacris* of Raleigh). The characters given for *Pseudacris ocularis* are: "Dorsal crest to vertical midway between spiracle and eye; spiracle equi-distant from eye and vent; spiracle 1.7–2.1, average (1.875) near vent than snout, mouth and internasal space equal; one row of papillae below and third lower row of teeth; third lower labial row of teeth .33 of the first lower row; *dorsum of body in life with definite* scattered black spots; musculature with three bands, apricot buff (light), chestnut brown (dark) martius yellow (light); first and second lower labial rows 2.0 greater than the horny beak; horny beak in upper fringe, 2.0; median space between second upper labial row of upper labial teeth 3–4 in either lateral portion. Eggs single."

LARVAL PERIOD

We never raised this species from egg to transformation. Too many investigations were going at once to get them past the adult tadpole stage and such laboratory tadpoles reared for identification could give us little real idea of the larval period. The earliest we know the species to have bred is April 24; the earliest we have taken tadpoles transforming is June 30. I believe the difference between those two dates or 67 days is an average period for the species. The first stray choruses, or mating we have observed came in the latter half of May and the bulk of our transformation records is the first of July. This presumptive evidence would give about 45 to 60 days for larval period. Forty-five to seventy days may represent the larval period. More evidence is needed.

TRANSFORMATION

Period. On June 30, 1922, in Saddle-bag Pond (near Chesser Island School U. S. Geol. Moniac Quad.) "found these tadpoles transforming in *Woodwardias* (ferns) around the edge of this cypress pond. Also in open pond, slightly so. Transformed ones have median stripe most conspicuous, the stripe of the tail continues on the body as a stripe either side of the median stripe and the stripe through the eye least conspicuous. The ground color of the adults is more or less prominent in the dorsal of the tadpoles. There is a prominent black band on the muscular part of tail. Very strongly defined black band, this is with light band below and a less conspicuous one above for 3/16–1/8 of an inch. This last extends on to the body." From this same pond tadpoles taken July 6 transformed July 8.

On July 18, 1922, "around the west edge of Murray Bay in the more or less flooded area (at times not now) of gums and pines found many transformed *Pseudacris ocularis*. They were difficult to catch because of minute size, fear of crushing them and their marvellous ability to jump. In grassy edges these transformed frogs and adults are also present."

On August 18, 1922, "at Hilliard, Florida, beside the Dixie Highway found little *Pseudacris ocularis* which is cinnamon or ochraceous tawny in color."

Size. On July 2, 1922, we took six transforming and transformed frogs of the following lengths and characters: Two, 9 mm. transformed; one, 9 mm. and only 2 mm. stub; one 11 mm. and 2.5 mm. stub; one, 9 mm. plus 1.05 mm. tail, frog-like appearance; one 9 mm. plus 1.25 mm. tail, tadpole appearance,—9–11 mm. in transformation size. Twenty to twenty-five tadpoles taken at the same place and many with prominent hind legs have body 10 mm. I believe the 11 mm. transforming specimen abnormally large for this species.

Two taken July 8, 1922, were: one fully transformed 8 mm.; one 8.5 mm. (with tail 1.35 mm.). On July 19 in another place we found five transformed and transforming individuals and 19 mature tadpoles. The five were: three, 8.5 mm.; two, 9 mm.

On July 18, 1922, in Murray Bay found 29 transformed *Pseudacris ocularis*; two, 7 mm.; seven, 7.5 mm.; nine, 8 mm.; six, 8.5 mm.; five 9 mm.

All in all the size seems to range from 7–9 mm., one specimen 11 mm. probably being abnormally large. Of 41 specimens two are 7 mm.; seven 7.5 mm.; ten 8 mm.; ten 8.5 mm. and twelve 9 mm.; 8 to 9 mm. being the average and modal size.

GROWTH

At transformation these pygmies are 7–9 mm. in length. On July 18, 1922, we took 29 transformed frogs from 7–9 mm. and five adults: two males 11.5 mm.; one male 12 mm.; one male 13 mm.; one female 13 mm.—two size forms 7–9 mm. and 11.5–13 mm., the latter doubtless one year old. We have some isolated specimens of males 13.5 mm. In 1912 the males were 12–13 mm. one female 15.5 mm.

Cope gives .62 of an inch for total length. Our female 17.5 mm. is .70 of an inch and may represent an approximation of the maximum, though I am positive I have seen larger specimens.

In 1921 on May 16, four 12 mm., four 13 mm., and one 11.5 mm. males and three females, 12 mm., 13.5 mm., and 17.5 mm. were taken. On June 23, one male 14.5 mm. was taken. On July 7, we have 13 mm. ♂, 14 mm. ♂, 16 mm. ♂. On July 8, 13.2 mm. ♂ and 15 mm. ♂. On July 13–17 we took 14 mm. ♂, 14.8 mm. ♂, 15 mm. ♂, 17 mm. ♀. On July 17, one more set of 3 pairs give 13.4, 14, 15 mm. ♂s and 15.5, 16, 16 mm. ♀s. Miller's group (U.S.N.M. 7(034–41) of eight males 14–15.5 mm. look comparable to the 17.5 mm. female above and our 1912 female of 15.5 mm. or the 1921 14 mm.–17 mm. material.

The evidence seems to point to 7–9 mm. for transformation; 11.5–13.5 for 1st-year-olds; 14–17.5 mm. for second-year-olds. Possibly 11.5–17.5 mm. all represent first-year-olds.

FOOD

We have made no study of this phase nor has any other naturalist. The food of these brownies of our frog species would be very interesting to study; must be minute insects, spiders, etc. Those who wish to work with the smaller insect forms ought to find this species a good collector for entomologists.

ENEMIES

On May 17, 1921 on Billy's Island we found a fine *Thamnophis sackenii* (Ribbon Snake) where little chorus frogs were in grassy, sedgy, pipewort, heath cover. This species must be a common prey for many snakes of the ponds, bays and moist pine barrens and for other animals as well.

AUTUMNAL APPEARANCE

We know nothing of the activities of this species beyond the first of September. Doubtless it is active most of the year except for mid-winter.

AFFINITIES

Holbrook remarks that *Hylodes ocularis* "is closely allied to *Hylodes gryllus* in its habits, choosing the same damp places for its abode, — and like *Hylodes gryllus*, too, it has the power of adhering to smooth surfaces, though not so perfectly so as the *Hylae*." It is quite arboreal at times on boles of trees, etc., far more arboreal than Acris.

Holbrook (1843, p. 38) remarks: "I have chosen the specific name *ocularis* for this animal, from the black spot along the eye; and this has been done the more willingly, as it is possible this animal may in the end prove to be the *Hyla ocularis* of Bosc and Daudin, which LeConte thinks, however, is most probably only a variety of the *Hyla squirella*; and yet, as this animal is not infrequently found on low bushes, or leaps upon them when pursued, it is not possible that Bosc might have supposed it to be a real Hyla. Should it then turn out to be the *Hyla ocularis* of Bosc, an additional synonym will be saved; but if it is an undescribed animal, which I believe, then the demonination *Hylodes ocularis* is well enough, as it belongs to another genus."

LeConte (1855, p. 429) places it in *Hyla ocularis* following *Hyla pickeringii* in his account. He credits it to Daudin. "From the small size of this and the preceding species, (*Hyla pickeringii*) the web between the third and fourth toes is not very perceptible." LeConte in this article recognizes *ocularis* as of *Hyla*, *ornata* and *nigrita* as of *Chorophilus*.. A year before he recognized *Chorophilus* with *nigritus*, *Helocaetes* with *feriarum*, *triseriata* and *clarkii*.

In some ways were it not for the tadpole coloration, the single eggs, self color and some structural characters one might be led to consider *P. ocularis* apart from the other *Pseudacris* which are of larger size, more spotted backs and with egg masses. *Pseudacris septentrionalis*, *P. triseriata*, *P. nigrita*, *P. feriarum* generally so far as known and from my own experience tend toward the laying of egg masses rather than single eggs. Our life history material on *Pseudacris ornata* is too fragmentary for positive assertion on this point.

Miss M. C. Dickerson (1906, p. 157) writes: "The *Chorophilus* material is confusing and insufficient to settle any problems. . . . However, the whole subject is in need of investigation and is open to revision." In 1923, Noble, her successor, wrote on the Generic and Genetic Relations of Pseudacris, The Swamp Cricket Frogs "basing his conclusions largely on a detailed consideration of *Pseudacris ocularis*. His conclusions are that "The species of *Pseudacris* must be referred to *Hyla*, although all species are distinguishable from American *Hylas* on external characters."

In egg characters it seems to fall nearer *Hyla crucifer* in size of eggs, envelopes and vitelli where LeConte apparently placed it in Hyla. In other ways it is not far removed from *Acris gryllus* with which Holbrook placed it as of *Hylodes*. Possibly *Acris* lays masses at times (single usually) like other *Pseudacris* species.

In tadpole coloration *Pseudacris ocularis* has the brown lateral band of the other *Pseudacris* species. In tadpole pattern it is nearer *Hyla crucifer* than *Acris gryllus*. In labial teeth it has a formula 2/3 not 2/2 as in *Acris gryllus* regularly and sometimes in *Hyla crucifer*. The latter however is also 2/3 and some *Pseudacris* tadpoles (other species) may have 2/2.

In adult coloration it approaches more nearly in some individuals (five stripes) the *Pseudacris* type rather than that of *Hyla crucifer* or *Acris gryllus* but unlike most individuals of *Pseudacris* species it is usually self color on the back. The author has seen in the field many fine *Pseudacris* from New York to Brownsville, Texas, and this species in many ways seems the most distinct species of the group unless it be *Pseudacris ornata*. Each has been poorly understood. *Pseudacris ocularis* proves a common form wherever found. So, too, *Pseudacris ornata* doubtless will prove not so rare. Had the average person lived and played with this species from 1912-1922, as some of us have, he might conclude *Pseudacris ocularis* the most distinct and possible aberrant species of the group both in diminutive size, in self color (others sometimes are though not always so), in singly-laid eggs and other impressions one gets from the species. With only *Pseudacris ocularis* and *Pseudacris ornata* at hand one would question whether to put them together if he had not been schooled in the history of the group. Furthermore, though the present author has worked out the life history of three or four species of *Pseudacris* in twenty years he dare positively assert that "The species of *Pseudacris must* be referred to *Hyla*. . . ." In the same paper we have "Future work may show that *P. septentrionalis*, *P. triseriata* and *P. feriarum* are closely allied and possess characters in common, distinguishing them from the more Hyla-like species of the genus." Stejneger and Barbour in adopting their course in retaining *Pseudacris* until this central core of *Pseudacris* are carefully worked out—life histories, field impressions, anatomy and all—take the more conservative course. All the collections in the U. S. A. will not clear it up like actual field experience with each form. I would not be surprised, however, if some, if not all of *Pseudacris* might be eventually referred to *Hyla* as Noble suggests, but why hurriedly consign them all on the detailed study of one possible outlying species. Nevertheless *Pseudacris ocularis* is as near *Hyla crucifer* as any hylid. It is Sabalian in distribution and *Hyla crucifer* more northern in general. Or it may be a good *Pseudacris* coincidental within the range of other *Pseudacris*. Apparently *Pseudacris* is largely an upper Austral group (except possibly for *P. septentrionalis*).

BIBLIOGRAPHY

1882   Boulenger, G. A. Catalogue of Batrachia Salientia S. Ecaudata in . . . B. M. 2nd edit. London 1882, pp. 333, 334.
1926   Brimley, C. S. Journal Elisha Mitchell Soc., Vol. 41, Nos. 3 & 4, Apr. 26, p. 82.
1875   Cope, E. D. Check List—List Batr. & Rept. N. Am., 1875, p. 30.
1913   Deckert, R. F. Copeia, Feb. 14, 1914, No. 3, p. 3.
1915   ———. Copeia, July 27, 1915, No. 20, p. 23.
1921   ———. Copeia, Mar. 15, 1921, No. 92. p. 22.
1922   ———. Copeia Nov. 20, 1922, No. 112, p. 88.
1906   Dickerson, M. C. The Frog Book p. 162.
1838-42. Holbrook, J. E. North American Herpetology, 1st ed. II, 79, pl. XIV, 1838; 2nd ed. IV, pl. 35, 1842.

———— ————. Cat. Reptiles of Georgia. In White, Geo. Statistics of Georgia, Savannah, 1849. Appendix p. 15.
1855 LeConte, John Proc. Acad. Nat. Sci. Phila., Dec. 1855, p. 429.
1924 Myers, G. S. Copeia, June 30, 1924, No. 131, pp. 59, 60.
1923 Noble, G. K. Am. Mus. Novitates Apr. 23, 1923, No. 70.
1923 Stejneger, L. & T. Barbour. A Check List of North American Amphibians and Reptiles. 2nd Edition, Cambridge, 1923, p. 28.
1923 Wright, A. H. Copeia, Feb. 1, 1923, No. 115, p. 34.
1923 Wright, A. H. and A. A. Wright. The Anatomical Record Jan 30, 1923, Vol. 24, No. 6, p. 406.
1924 Wright, A. H. & A. A. Wright. The American Naturalist, July-August, 1924. Vol. LVIII, p. 379.

Pseudacris ornata (Holbrook)

(Pl. I Fig. 8)

ORNATE CHORUS FROG. ORNATE TREE FROG.

Holbrook in 1842 credits this form to South Carolina and DeKay followed him in giving South Carolina as its range. In 1849 Holbrook gives Georgia as also a part of its range. LeConte 1855 (doubtless on Riceborough evidence) says it "inhabits Georgia, very common in the pine barren ponds."

Gunther (1858, p. 29) gives *Cystignathus ornatus* with "Body and head short as in *Hyla viridis*; skin smooth; tympanum distinct; tongue nearly circular; vomerine teeth in two rounded groups behind the inner nostrils. Dovecolour above with oblong spots of dark brown, margined with yellow.

a. Adult. Georgia. From Mr. Cuming's Collection. Differs in having the back uniform olive-colour; sides with three black spots, viz., a streak from the eye to the shoulder, an oval spot in the middle of the sides and one or two smaller ones on the loin."

(See discussion under *P. occidentalis*). We did not take *Pseudacris ornata* in the swamp in May-June 1912, nor in April-Aug. 1921 nor in June-August 1922. We have seen it at Helotes and Beeville, Texas in 1925. C. S. Brimley (see *P. occidentalis*) received it from Green Cove Springs, (1898) and Hastings (1901) Florida. In 1930 and 1931 we have received it in February or early spring from O. C. Van Hyning of Gainesville, Florida.

Hyla andersonii Baird

(Pl. II, Fig. 3; X Fig. 1; XII, Fig. 3; XV Fig. 1; XVII; XXV)

COMMON NAMES

Anderson Tree Frog. Anderson's Tree Frog. Anderson's Hyla. Anderson Tree Toad. Green and Yellow Tree-toad.

(This species and *Rana areolata* are two species the author has studied the least. Noble and Noble, 1923, have treated most of the essential features of this species. It is included here to make comparisons, and to add our impressions of it at Lakehurst and North Carolina and as a captive in 1906-1908. It is also a possible Okefinokee anuran.)

RANGE

Check list. "Type Locality: Anderson, South Carolina.

Range. White cedar swamps in Southern New Jersey". Stejneger and Barbour, 1923, p. 29.

Supplementary records. The Check List (above) appeared about coincident with the publication of the extended studies of Noble and Noble (1923). In view of their detailed observations the present writer will not attenpt a long account of this species except to summarize some topics so that this species (a possible hypothetical species of the Okefinokee Swamp region) may have the same form treatment as the others.

The writer, unlike some of the Philadelphia or American Museum groups, has not had the continued experience with this species some of these gentlemen have. Nevertheless, he has seen and recorded this species in North Carolina and New Jersey near the two extremities of its range. After Baird's description (1854, pp. 60, 61) all the records from 1854-1904 are from the Philadelphia (and its environs) group of naturalists (Leidy, Cope, Peters, Abbott, Moore, Stone, Fowler, Rehn, Klein, etc.). From 1898 onward the New York group (W. T. Davis, James Chapin, W. D. Miller, C. L. Camp, K. P. Schmidt, G. K. Noble, G. S. Myers and R. Sackett), led by W. T. Davis have followed the trail until its habits are well enough known for life-history studies. Early in that search James Chapin was associated with W. T. Davis and our first acquaintance of this species alive came through two specimens "sent July 21, 1906, to Dr. Burt G. Wilder from James Chapin, these he collected at Lakehurst, N. J." We mention this because Fuertes (who recently died) painted one of these frogs—one of his only amphibian paintings (now in possession of Professor H. D. Reed). Besides from 1906 specimens of these gentlemen, came Miss Dickerson's excellent plate of a female (Dickerson 1906, Plate VII).

It is interesting that the first two, W. T. Davis and James Chapin (who first began 1904-1906 studying this form) should be the first to record it from North Carolina (1920) and we (1922) who received first live specimens (1906) from them, should independently (1922) record this species in North Carolina 35-50 miles southwest of Southern Pines, their locality of 1920. Our record is midway between Rockingham, N. C. and Cheraw, S. C. on the North Carolina side of the State Line at Everett's Pond. Southern Pines country is partially of the same river drainage (Pedee River). If any one wishes to record it in South Carolina he can follow the Pedee down from Everett's Pond and no doubt easily find it.

The record from Anderson, S. C., has always bothered the writer. In 1917 we went through Anderson and had no opportunity to collect at this place. Anderson is twice as far from the coast as Southern Pines, N. C. or Cheraw, S. C. is from the coast. Possibly the species extends that far inland along the Savannah River. No life zone map can show all the river valley extensions inland. Anderson's tree frog is a lower Austral (Austroriparian, Upper Coastal, etc.) form, and Anderson, S. C. is in Upper Austral (Carolinian, Piedmont, etc.) country. If such terminology be employed it may be well to remember that C. S. Brimley and F. Sherman, Jr. (1908) send the lower Austral line from Raleigh to Charlotte, N. C. or farther west. In this event possibly Anderson's tree frog is not from Anderson.

Of its northernmost range, W. DeW. Miller (1906, p. 68) writes: "About eight years ago James Chapin and I found this beautiful Tree Frog at the Runyon Pond two miles south of Sayreville, Middlesex County. Since that time I have found it at several other localities in the same region—one mile south of Old Bridge, about one mile southeast of Browntown and at Freneau near Mattewan. These localities are all in the sandy pine barren 'island' north of the Pine Barrens proper. Thus this species extends northward to within three miles or less of the lower Raritan River, its range coinciding at this point with that of the Carolina Chickadee."

Of its range northward, W. T. Davis, two years later (1908, p. 49) writes, "In addition to the notes on this species printed in the American Naturalist, it may be added that it occurs still further north than Lakehurst and Farmingdale, and has been heard by the writer at Jamesburg on the South River. Messrs. Miller, Chapin, and Skinner have found the frog at Runyon, also on the South River. It no doubt occurs as far north as the Raritan."

If we call it a pine barren's form we must remember it is not recorded on Long Island nor westward of Anderson, S. C., in Georgia, Alabama, etc. If it be termed a sphagnaceous tree frog why is it not in the Dismal Swamp, Great Alligator Dismal Swamp (N. C.) or Okefinokee Swamp? On the basis of associated species *Scaphiopus holbrookii* extends into New England and southward to Florida and Texas. *Acris gryllus* is not comparable in the southern states and if not found in pine barren bogs in New Jersey, it is abundant in such places and many other localities in the South. Even yet in spite of the fact that *Hyla andersonii* outstrips it northward (See W. D. Miller), *Rana virgatipes* seems its nearest associated species, though *Rana virgatipes* outstrips it southward to Okefinokee Swamp.

In northward range *Rana sphenocephala* if recognized as distinct doubtless about coincides in its northern extension with *H. andersonii*. Though not yet recorded from New Jersey (1925) some meadow frogs from Lakehurst southward look much like *Rana sphenocephala*.

After my experiences with *Rana virgatipes* in New Jersey, North Carolina and Georgia the writer instinctively expects and looks for *H. andersonii* wherever he hears *Rana virgatipes*. True in Dismal Swamp, Craven Lakes, Wilmington and in Okefinokee Swamp they are not yet recorded, but they will doubtless be recorded near these places with intensive search. To know the notes of frogs gives the best clue to possible new records for "rare" frogs.

GENERAL APPEARANCE

Cope (1887, p. 365) held it "in proportions and general appearance similar to the *Hyla arborea* of Europe." In its stout body it differs from the more slender Hylas, *H. cinerea* and *H. cinerea evittata*. By its lateral band, it has its dorsal color more sharply defined from venter than in any other species of our Hylids. Brimley (1907, p. 158) gave the "plum colored line along the sides of body with yellow spots below it" as its distinct mark.

COLORATION OF SPIRIT SPECIMENS

Fowler (1908, p. 111) in describing Viereck's specimen writes "After having been in alcohol several years it has changed to a plumbeous or slate-gray color above with paler or whitish borders to brownish of sides and dark lateral stripes. The limbs through plumbeous above are only so to carpus and tarsus, which are a pale brownish like entire under surfaces of limbs. Throat, breast and belly pale or whitish." Leidy's specimen in alcohol faded to "dull brownish above and whitish below." (Fowler, p. 110). The author quotes at above length because a *Hyla evittata* or *Hyla squirella* might be confused with an old specimen of *Hyla andersonii*. In one collection a group of *Hyla squirella* was confused with *Hyla andersonii*, but the light upper lip of *Hyla squirella* finally separated them. So also alcoholic specimens without vitta and line revealed are hard to separate from *Hyla cinerea evittata*. One specimen twenty years in alcohol has a light line like *Hyla cinerea* but not a straight line as in *Hyla cinerea*. Usually some indication of the vitta before and behind eye is revealed. One specimen preserved in 1906 is vinaceous drab or purple, drab or livid brown on upper parts and throat region. Another of same year is greenish glaucous blue or Niagara green.

STRUCTURAL CHARACTERS

This phase has had much attention and needs no repetition here.

MEASUREMENTS

(Recent Material)

We have no 20 and 28 mm. specimens. Our measurements of one male 36 mm., and two females 36 and 44 mm. respectively give little idea of the range of relative measurements.

Head to angle of mouth 1.16 (36 mm. ♂) −1.2 (44 mm. ♀) in width of head; head to rear of tympanum 1.07 (36 mm. ♂) −1.2 (44 mm. ♀) in width of head; head to angle of mouth 3.0–3.5 in length of body; head to rear of tympanum 2.77–3.3 in length of body; snout .92–.94 in first finger; eye .92–1.0 in first toe; eye 144–1.33 in snout; eye .8–.66 in tympanum; eye 1.3–1.44 in first finger; tympanum 3.3–5.2 in intertympanic width; tympanum 18.6–2.6 in snout; internasal width 1.0–1.125 in upper eyelid width; interorbital width .80–.88 in upper eyelid width; interorbital width .80–.9 in internasal width; interorbital width 2.4–2.9 in intertympanic width.

Forelimb. Forelimb 1.8–2.0 in length of body; forelimb 2.7–2.0 in hind limb; first finger 1.5–2.76 in third finger; second finger 1.3–1.25 in third finger; second finger .85–7.5 in first finger; third finger .77–.85 in second toe; fourth finger 1.1–1.25 in third finger; fourth finger .75–.75 in first finger; internasal width 1.5–1.5 in first finger; internasal width 1.75–2.0 in second finger; internasal width 2.25–2.5 in third finger; internasal width 2.0–1.41 in fourth finger.

Hindlimb. Length 1.5–1.41 in hindlimb; tibia 2.0 (44 mm.) in length; tibia 3.0 in hindlimb; tibia 1.1 in forelimb; tibia .90 in hind foot; first toe 1.16–1.7 in second toe; first toe 1.66–2.6 in third toe; first toe 2.16–3.5 in fourth toe; first toe 1.8–2.7 in fifth toe; second toe 1.43–1.52 in third toe; second toe 1.85–2.06 in fourth toe; second toe 1.56–1.6 in fifth toe; third toe 1.3–1.34 in fourth toe; third toe 1.1–1.04 in fifth toe; fourth toe 1.27–.97 in hind foot without tarsus; fourth toe 1.38–1.25 in tibia; internasal width 1.5–1.25 in first toe; internasal width 1.75–2.12 in second toe; internasal width 2.5–3.25 in third toe; internasal width 3.25–4.4 in fourth toe; internasal width 2.75–3.4 in fifth toe.

HABITAT

(See Voice discussion for habitat notes)

In 1908 Mr. Davis (pp. 49, 50) presents some good habitat notes which we quote in toto. "On the evening of July 19, 1907, I went hunting *Hyla andersonii* at Lakehurst. The first one that I heard was in a small red maple and about eight feet from the ground. This was quite high up, for they usually climb only five or six feet from the ground. I could not reach the little frog, nor could I bend the sapling that hung over a marshy place. I therefore shook it suddenly, which caused the frog to jump into a still smaller maple. This I could bend over, and it sat looking at me until I captured it with my hand.

"Of quite a different disposition was the next one I found. It also was in a small maple, but when it saw me and I tried to capture it with my two insect nets, it immediately jumped and as it was getting quite dark by that time, I was unable to locate it on the ground among the undergrowth. A little later I heard it singing again, and so went back to find that it had climbed up a huckleberry bush that was covered with a considerable growth of *Smilax glauca*. The leaves of the vine made it quite difficult to locate the frog, which must have been near, for when I drew close it hopped on to a lower part of the bush, and though I tried to capture it with my two nets, I was unsuccessful. This frog was a most persistent singer, and so in a short time I went back to the same bush up which it had climbed after being so rudely dislodged. After much looking and with the aid of the moon, I located the frog on the flat side of a *Smilax* leaf and brought the two nets together with the result that I found the frog in one of them.

"The next evening I found one in a cedar tree in a swamp. When I got around the tree through the bushes to where the frog had been, I found that it had gone to the side of the tree that I had just left. As I approached slowly it would jump from tree to tree, and from limb to limb, every now and then stopping to sing when it heard the calls of its rivals, two of which were in the same small swamp. In this way I slowly pursued the frog, being much interested in its well-founded fear and its inability to keep quiet. It never climbed over six feet from the ground so that I easily captured it when I desired."

In 1928 Dr. & Mrs. A. B. Klots located ten individuals and their notes on position are apropos.

"The exact positions of ten individuals were located, of which seven were captured. High-bush Blueberry tangles festooned with Green Briars made further investigations in this line impossible. The individuals are here referred to by number.

"Numbers 1, 2, 3, 4 and 5 were in one group, within 50 feet of the main 'pike' from May's Landing to Hammonton. The ground was covered quite evenly with Blueberry bushes from a foot to 18 inches high. Scattered Pitch Pines up to 12 inches in diameter stood from 10 to 30 feet apart. The ground was at most damp, and the only water nearby was a shallow pool about 30 feet away which probably dries up in the summer. Near the bases of the pines stood taller Blueberry bushes, up to three feet in height. No. 1 was sitting on the main stem of a small Blueberry bush, 18 inches from the ground and six inches from the tip of the bush. A Pine stood $1\frac{1}{2}$ feet away. No. 2 was on the leaf of a Blueberry bush, $2\frac{1}{2}$ feet from the ground and $1\frac{1}{2}$ feet from a Pine trunk. No. 3 was on a little twiglet growing out from the trunk of a pine $3\frac{1}{2}$ feet from the ground. No. 4 was on the ground at the base of a Pine. No. 5 was one foot from the ground, where the twig of a Blueberry bush lay against the trunk of a Pine. All of the specimens in this group showed a strong preference for the near vicinity of a Pine.

"Nos. 6, 7 and 8 were in a thicket of small Red Maples and high Blueberry bushes in a creek 'bottom'. No. 6 was on the main stem of a Blueberry bush about four feet from the ground. No. 7 was similarly located. No. 8 was about six feet from the ground in a small Red Maple.

"Nos. 9 and 10 were in a thick tangle of high Blueberry bushes and *Smilax*. Both were near the tops of Blueberry bushes at least nine feet from the ground. For fifty feet around none of the vegetation was any lower, so it seems that these individuals climbed higher than is usual for the species in order to be out in the open.

"Not all of the individuals were as tame as is generally noted for *andersonii*. A number of individuals would not continue singing when the observer turned the light on them or approached nearer than fifteen or twenty feet, and so could not be located. A silent *andersonii* in a thick tangle of Blueberry bushes could give points on hiding to a very small needle in a very large haystack. No females were taken."

FIRST APPEARANCE

The records of earliest spring appearance are the following: "a specimen of *Hyla andersonii* obtained at Clementon, N. J., May 12, 1901, by Mr. Henry L. Viereck"; (Stone, 1901, p. 342). Several down to Noble and Noble (May 14) have recorded them in May. The reason adduced by Stone for its scarcity also explains why earlier records in spring and later records in fall are not available. Stone held (before Davis proved it abundant) that "though probably of restricted distribution the species would no doubt prove more abundant if specially sought for, the comparative remoteness of the New Jersey barrens, where most of the specimens are found, and the retiring habits of the animal both tending to make its detection difficult". (Stone, 1901, p. 342). Of course, this species appears earlier than May 12.

GENERAL HABITS

Metachrosis. This species is not recorded as capable of a wide range of color variation. Miss Dickerson (1906, p. 133) records that her lone female specimen might pale or deepen in its green or take on a tinge of brown. Noble and Noble (1923, pp. 432, 433) on the basis of their experience with four or more pairs and others seen or taken noticed that light, excitement or humidity might change their color. The first and last factors are most analyzable and their results accord in the main with most species. The writer suspects that time will reveal as marked variation in general color in this species as in *Hyla cinerea*. *Hyla andersonii* seems truly more constant than *Hyla squirella* but once upon a time green *Hyla squirella* were pronounced unknown. Outright statements concerning color are dangerous. For example two males of *Hyla andersonii* were received July 21, 1906. Each had a similar green backed livery. One we fixed at once in alcohol. Today it is a shade of dark green. The other was kept until November 27, 1908, when it was fixed in 5% formol. It is now in alcohol and is purplish drab.

Variations in color. (See *Hyla cinerea*).

General habits. Davis (1907, p. 49) writes that "The adult *Hyla andersonii* is amusingly active at night and jumps about the lower limbs of the trees and on the bushes with much agility. They seem rarely to climb over five or six feet from the ground. They sit upright and look pert, and if interrupted in the midst of their song they leave their bubbles blown up until such a time as the intruder goes away or stands still. In the day time they are usually quiet and for the most part hide in the deep moss and leaves lying on the ground."

Miss M. C. Dickerson (1906, pp. 132, 133) had this species under observation in captivity and for a long time:

"The creature has a very gentle and alert expression. It is in fact, one of the most alert and timid of our tree frogs. In captivity it is seldom content until it finds some moist hiding-place in moss and ferns or under wet decaying pieces of wood. When such a place is found, the *Hyla* backs into it with the burrowing movements common among the Salientia. Here, with flattened body and closed eyes, it remains sleeping away the days and nights. The sleeping position is interesting, in that the long delicately-colored toes are lifted to the green of the sides, the rest pressed close to the body just above the shoulder.

"This *Hyla* is relatively sturdy. The tree frog found June 1, 1888, was still alive and well in January, 1889. How much longer it lived is not recorded. The specimen caught in September, 1904, is in plump condition now in June, 1905.

"This specimen photographed moulted the skin February 10th. For several hours before the moult the skin was very dry and lustreless, and the frog kept rubbing one hand and then the other over the head and eyes, as if in discomfort. The skin was thin and white. It was shed in one piece and swallowed as it was shed, in just the manner described for the similar process for the toad and frog.

"This Hyla differs conspicuously from *Hyla versicolor* and *Hyla regilla*, in fact from most of its nearest relatives in North America, by the fact that it has apparently but a limited power to change colour. The green may pale or deepen, it may even take on a tinge of brown; the lavender tints of hand and foot may be extremely light, or so dark that they become a deep purplish brown. But when we compare this with the radical and rapid changes in *Hyla regilla* and others, the limitation is very evident. As far as observed, the pattern of dress is never obscured.

"*Hyla andersonii* is an agile climber, but ascends largely by clasping the hands and feet around the support. The adhesive power of the disks is relatively not great, and the under surface of the body does not seem to aid them as much in climbing as it does many tree frogs. On a relatively smooth vertical surface up which *Hyla cinerea, versicolor, pickeringii, regilla*, and many others will climb rapidly and with confidence, Anderson's *Hyla* holds itself with great difficulty, even for the space of a few seconds."

VOICE

The records of capture and voice characterizations make up much of the literature of this species. The call has been and is the clue to its whereabouts. Like each of the Hylas its voice is specific and distinct. But voice characterizations whether by syllables, figures of speech (similes, metaphores), musical notation, human imitations or other means are dubious evidence from which to draw conclusions. For example, John E. Peters (1889, pp. 58, 59) "On June 1, 1888 (he) found a specimen of *Hyla andersonii* Baird in a wet place on the border of a pine barren at May's Landing, N. J. It was quite lively when caught, but it soon became sluggish in confinement. Its voice was shrill and light, comparatively speaking; and it consisted of a repetition of the smae note three or four times in regular succession, in a sort of 'peep, peep, peep, peep,' as nearly as I can give it. The specimen was sent alive to Dr. C. C. Abbott, of Trenton, N. J. who says in his 'Catalogue of the Vertebrate Animals of New Jersey' (Geology of N. J., Cook 1868, p. 805) that it is 'a Southern species, a single specimen of which was found in Camden County in 1863' by Dr. J. Leidy. . . . The specimen is still alive (Jan. 1889), and may be seen by applying to George Pine, Esq., Trenton, N. J."

A year later the Dr. C. C. Abbott above (1890, p. 189) wrote as follows: "The specimen of this beautiful batrachian referred to by Dr. Peters in the January Naturalist is still in excellent health (Feb. 1890), and occasionally utters its characteristic cry, which should not be described by the word 'peep' for it suggests a similarity to the cry of the Pickering's Hyla, which shrilly 'peeps'. The *andersonii* utters a single note, better described by the syllable 'keck', which it usually repeats three or four times. It is not a frog-like note at all, but much resembles the call of the Virginia rail (*Rallus virginianus*). If the collector follows up any 'peeper' in the marshes, he will not discover additional specimens of *Hyla andersonii*."

Of the same individual H. W. Fowler (1908, p. 111) writes "Dr. Abbott tells me that the example Peters sent him from May's Landing alive uttered a sound more like a clatter, or sharp click, something like that made by the Virginia rail. The vocal vesicle resembled that of *Hyla versicolor*. It appeared to take in a big breath and produced about 6 clicks as the air escaped." Thus it appears the doctors (M. D.) do not agree. No one reports how George Pine might have characterized this individual frog. Furthermore, there are many people who have characterized in my presence *Hyla crucifer, Pseudacris triseriata, Pseudacris nigrita, Acris gryllus* as "peep"ers although the writer might not do the same. If one used the "keck" characterization of Abbott and Harper's *kek* for *Hyla femoralis* one might infer close relationship. The latter, however, characterizes the call of *Hyla andersonii* as "quak". The calls are different as both Harper and I know from experience. From the diverse characterizations of the call of *Hyla andersonii* Noble and Noble (1927, p. 426) write "One would gather from the literature that the Anderson Tree Frog had a variety of calls", but they proceed to state it has one call thereby implying quite rightly that the different renditions of its call are for one call not many. But the abnormal calls of the tree toad recorded by Wright are assigned by them to Overton's "turkey root" call. One call is that call but others are not. Herein is revealed the difficulty of one person interpreting the call evidence of another. Overton, Harper and the writer have been abroad at night together, so by direct identification we know what the other means by each syllabic or simile characterization, but I would hate to have to identify a frog without this aid though hearing is one of my best means of identification. No two have characterized more frogs nor better than Overton and Harper, yet their characterizations are not the way I always hear them.

In 1894, J. Percy Moore (1894, pp. 1045, 1046) writes of its voice and habits thus: "About the middle of June, 1889, Mr. Louis M. Glackens and the writer were engaged in general biological studies along the Atsion and Batsta Creeks in Atlantic and Burlington Counties, New Jersey. On the night of June 17th we stopped at Pleasant Mills. Shortly before sundown a thunder storm arose, just previous to and during which the frogs became very noisy in a swampy thicket near by.

"The note was an unfamiliar one and invited investigation, which resulted in the capture of two specimens of this handsome and rare species. The shrill quack-ack, which at the time was compared to the note of a frightened guinea fowl, and which is not unlike the call of a rail, was constant and seemed to come from every tree, but during our progress through the voices immediately around us, for a radius of about 25 feet, were silent. This circumstance, and the oncoming darkness made it difficult to secure specimens, although frogs were so abundant. The two secured were found perched on the lower side of branches of pines with dilated and vibrating throats, though at the moment they were silent; and it was noted that they emitted an odor which was likened to that of raw green peas. . . . The following morning we could find no trace of them, but later in the day heard another chorus in the middle of a dense swampy thicket. Since then Mr. H. F. Moore and myself have repeatedly visited the locality in quest of the Hyla and its eggs, but entirely without success."

W. T. Davis who has done more than any other individual to introduce this species to naturalists writes of it in 1905 (p. 795) as follows: "At Lakehurst, New Jersey, especially in the latter part of May and in June, there are heard at evening coming from the white cedar swamps, many voices that resemble the familiar quacking of ducks. If one will take the trouble to wade into one of these swamps at twilight and approach the singer cautiously, it will be discovered that he is a male *Hyla andersonii*. He pipes and sings 'aquack-aquack-aquack' many times, or until his bubble of air gives out. This is the time, when he is singing, to take a step forward. Even when the observer is very near and evidently plainly in view, he cannot resist the temptation to sing, for he hears his rivals all about calling loudly. The notes are not all alike in sound, and some individuals remind one of the 'potrack-potrack' of the farm and guinea fowl. The Hyla will be found seated on the lower limb of some tree, or among the top branches of a huckeberry bush. I have heard this frog singing at mid-day when the sun was shining brightly, especially after a shower. Also solitary individuals may be heard in the swamps much later in the year, and they do not appear to wander as far from the water as does *Hyla versicolor*". In 1907 (1907, pp. 49, 50) Davis recorded them calling in August. "On the warm cloudy evening of August 10th *Hyla andersonii* was heard near some pools a short distance north of the village of Farmingdale, N. J."

. In 1916 T. Barbour (1916 pp. 6, 7) and his brother F. K. Barbour, of their observations speak thus: "At dusk we have usually taken our supper, and then waited for darkness to come on and for the Hylas to begin to sing, and have had good luck taking Hylas by the following method: One of us with an electric flashlight would start for the nearest singing Hyla, while the other usually waited some distance away. As soon as the Hyla stopped singing, the person who was not trying to approach would imitate the call of the frog, and this would start it singing again vigorously, and while it was singing the collector bearing the light would approach as quickly as possible, standing still as soon as the singing ceased. This process was kept up until finally the light flashed on the vibrating white throat of the singing Hyla, and its capture then became a perfectly simple matter, as long as they stared stupidly at the brilliant light.

". . .This year (1915), however, we did not get down to Lakehurst until the 8th of July, when we found the Hylas singing in goodly numbers in the white cedars about the lake. . . . A large number of individuals kept on singing so vigorously until at least the 20th of July. I might add that the singing begins with dark, though an occasional voice may be heard upon a lowery afternoon, and the greatest concert takes place before ten o'clock. At about this time, the number of singing individuals is noticeably less."

Thus from 1889-1918 the "calling" season appears from records to be from May to August 10.

Noble and Noble (1923, pp. 426, 429) recorded that: "*H. andersonii* has only one call and that is given with fully inflated pouch. It is a series of ten to twenty, or even more, resonant nasal quănks. If one tries to shout the word quank while holding the nostrils closed, a sound is produced not unlike the note made by this frog. The call sounds somewhat different from a distance, especially when several frogs are calling at once. Then the notes tend to run together, each note having two syllables, a-quănk, a-quănk".

"1. *H. andersonii* begins calling in early May from concealment on the ground.

2. In the middle of May and throughout June and July the males call chiefly from bushes or from trees.

3. At various intervals throughout May and June (and some years in July) when the rains have flooded the bogs and changed the ditches into small sphagnum-choked streams, the males leave their calling stations and make their way to the nearest of these small streams. This migration occurs about midnight. The males begin calling again from their new positions near the sphagnaceous streams. . . ."

They heard Anderson tree frogs from May 13-14 to July 23.

On June 8, 1922, on our way to Okefinokee Swamp we camped in the evening on the north side of Everett's Pond, N. C. near the South Carolina-North Carolina line. The instant it became dark "We heard plenty of *Acris gryllus*, *Bufo fowleri*, *Rana catesbeiana*, a few *Rana clamitans*, *Hyla cinerea* in chorus, *Hyla versicolor*, quite a few. In the wooded sections or streams following into the lake in dense thickets, *Smilax*-briar entwined, were *Rana virgatipes* croaking quite general. Fine! Several in different places. Later Harper went above his tent and heard a strange note some 20 rods away. The note was lower than that of *Hyla cinerea*, much more rapid than it, possibly like it in form, yet not. In some ways it seems quite different from *Hyla cinerea*. Captured this one nearest the tent. Another individual heard near a negro cabin. We could not get it because we strangers did not wish to disturb them. We heard another near the cabin. This at a distance sounded quite different from *Hyla cinerea* down by the lake.

Later in the evening Miles Pirnie heard one opposite our camp. All the frogs heard were in or near the lake. These *H. andersonii* were in a stream or branch with sweet gum, tangle of oaks, bamboo briars (*Smilax*), *Magnolia glauca*, maple, black gum and red maple.

Harper speaks of the calling of these Hylas thus: "I heard the note of *H. andersonii* at a distance of 200 yards and suspected almost at once what it was. Trailed it and after a long wait located it in some tall bushes in the edge of a branch swamp. Its note bears a general resemblance to that of *H. cinerea* but goes about twice as rapidly, is about half as loud and sounds more like quak, quak, then quonk. It carried fairly well at 200 yards and about 300 yards would probably be the limit. . . . Did not see it croak. Its periods are infrequent and irregular, 2 minutes interval. Perhaps 15 or 20 or 25 notes given in one period."

On June 28–29, Mrs. Wright and I heard these *Hyla andersonii* in the wooded edge of Mr. P. H. Emlie's lake at Lakehurst, N. J. Some of the principal trees and shrubs where the males were numerous were: *Magnolia virginiana, Acer rubrum, Vaccinium corymbosum, Vaccinium atrococcum, Azalea viscosa, Chamaecyparis thuyoides, Nyssa sylvatica, Ilex glabra, Clethra alnifolium, Viburnum nudum* and *Rhus vernix*. Again on May 23, 1924, we heard a few, though as on the former occasion our attention was mainly directed to *Rana virgatipes* tadpoles and transformed frogs.

In June 1928 (15th–28th) Alexander Barrett Klots and Elsie Broughton Klots made these detailed notes on several frogs found at Weymouth in Atlantic Co., N. J.

"Many attempts have been made to reproduce the quality of the song in print, with results differing for practically every observer. Thus the call has been variously recorded as "peep," "keck," "quak" (Harper), "quack-ack" like a frightened guinea fowl, and "quank." To the writer the call seemed a nasal "quack," almost verging on a "quank" but without the strong "n" sound of the latter. The call was never disyllabic.

"The note is repeated at about half-second intervals for sometimes fully 30 seconds. When the frogs are in full song an interval of about two minutes intervenes between outbursts. We had no difficulty in starting the frogs calling again at distances of from fifty to three feet, after they had been silent for a minute of two. One individual was recorded as having called 74 times in one period of song.

"The frogs definitely associate together for singing, whether because of the presence of females or for companionship. The latter probably plays a considerable share in the performance, as is evidenced by the quick response to an imitation of the call. Five such singing groups were definitely located. Of these the first contained seven individuals, the second contained three, the third contained eight, the fourth contained three and the fifth, which was just across an uncrossable creek, contained at least six. Only once was a single individual noted in song alone, and that was a frog which called three times in a spot a half-mile distant from any others and was never heard from again.

"The locations of the groups were fixed, and during our stay did not change a particle. Night after night a group would be in exactly the same area, though the individuals composing it shifted position a bit.

"The time of singing was remarkably constant. On every night but one the chorus started between ten and fifteen minutes before sundown. On the one exception, a clear dry night with a bright moon, the first songs were not heard until twenty minutes after sundown.

"The carrying power of the song was excellent. A chorus was plainly heard as an entity over 800 paces away, with two patches of woods and a brushy swamp intervening. The wind was negligible. Individual voices were distinguishable 754 paces away down a straight road, with a light wind blowing from the observers toward the frogs."

1

2

3

4

5 6 7 8 9

MATING

Male.—(From life). Upper parts (dorsum, upper lip, angle of mouth and dorsal surfaces of limbs) cress green to a light cress green, in sides lighter to deep chrysolite green. Stripe along side, behind vent, along limbs, upper jaw cartridge buff, ivory yellow or marguerite yellow or seafoam yellow. Area back of and along side of vent vinaceous drab, purple drab becoming over tympanum dark purplish drab. A little of same color scattered on throat. Tops of forefeet and hind feet deep brownish drab except for first two digits which have the cadmium yellow spots on the top. Fore part of under side of antebrachium and under part of brachium with cadmium yellow—deep chrome or orange spots, also a little area in axilla; also groin and most of fore and hind part of femur, whole undersides of tibia and inner side of foot. All these orange or deep chrome spots on a raw sienna or mars yellow background. Iris more or less vinaceous drab or purple drab with vinaceous tawny spots. Under parts white except for dark purplish drab of throat.

Female.—(From life). Throat white, grayish or with slight purplish drab tinge. Green patch below angle of mouth usually white edged, usually absent in males.

Structural differences. The differences in color already noted, and larger females than males are the perceptible differences. Noble and Noble (1923, p. 433) note that the male has minute asperities on inner and upper side of thumb. They gave average length from vent to snout of ten females as 40.9 mm. (extremes 44 and 38 mm.), of fifteen breeding males as 36.7 mm. (extremes 35–38 mm.). The females, as in most of our Hylas, are larger. Although some authors have spoken of them as "about 2 inches in body length, I have seen none over 47 mm. in length. The range of males seems to be from 30 mm.–41 mm. in body length; of females 38–47 mm. No doubt sexual males below 30 mm. and females somewhat below 38 mm. will be found.

Duration, night or day. Amplexation. All the records of mating by Barbour, Davis and Noble and Noble were for the evening. In each case apparently the pair broke after laying. In no instance are abnormal embraces recorded or mentioned. All doubtless are axillary or supra-axillary. The last authors speak of "a normal supra-axillary amplexus" and describe the amplexus.

OVULATION

Habitat and period. Barbour (1916, pp. 6, 7) the first to record a mated pair and secure eggs writes "Up to this year (1915) I have known nothing regarding the breeding habits or the time of egg-laying of these Hylas, but have assumed that it was in May, as Davis reported them singing very plentifully at that time. This year, however, we did not get down to Lakehrust until the 8th of July, when we found the Hylas in goodly numbers in the white cedars about the lake. After capturing a number of singing males (I had never taken a female before), my light flashed by the merest chance upon a pair of Hylas sitting well up in a pine tree, in embrace. This, and another taken, in a similar situation, were the only females secured, although we took several males from the low oak scrub about a small fresh water pool in the pine barrens. All of our catch was placed in a large mouthed jar and brought home to Rumson alive. The next morning a number of gelatinous egg-masses were found in the bottom of the jar. Since they were pretty well smashed up from the struggles which the Hylas made trying to escape, it was impossible to distinguish whether the egg-masses were laid in a characteristic form. We were both surprised to find these eggs, as we had not supposed that this Hyla laid so late in the year; yet we had always wondered why such a large number of individuals kept on singing so vigorously until at least the 20th of July."

Davis and Chapin secured ovulation June 13 and 14, 1922. Noble and Noble recorded ovulation May 20–21 and June 4–5, 1922. For the species, ovulation records then obtain for May 20–21, 1922, June 4–5, 1922, June 13–14, 1922 and July 8, 1915, or from May 20 to July 8. If a few tadpoles transform in late June, as we observed in 1923 at Lakehurst, possibly breeding may some years begin as early as May 1. Doubtless with this species, as with most frogs and certainly southeastern United States frogs, humidity (rains) is the important external factor in onset of breeding. In this species, as in all our southern frogs, it is a long season breeder or protracted breeder as Noble has called it. But exposure and protracted breeding classifications are local at the most, e.g., *Scaphiopus holbrookii* and all Scaphiopi may be very protracted and generally are. *Rana pipiens* may or may not be long extended in breeding season. Most southern and southwestern forms have long breeding seasons.

Thus far the eggs laid in nature have been laid in sphagnaceous streams or puddles near by. Once upon a time we were ready to call *Rana virgatipes* a Sphagnum Frog on the basis of Lakehurst experience but it is not wholly so. So, too, *H. andersonii* may be more widespread in its place of ovulation. One wonders whether in Cheraw, Anderson and Southern Pines it is limited to sphagnum. We did not casually record sphagnum at Cheraw but we did not search for it. In a similar way we suspected they may reach higher than 6–8 feet in the trees when not ovulating.

Egg-laying process. Noble and Noble (1923, pp. 433-439) gave detailed attention to the interesting egg oviposition, making observations on two pairs in the field and two in the laboratory. It is too explicit for me to paraphrase and too extended to quote in toto.

EGGS

Noble and Noble (1923, p. 439, 440) distinguish the eggs thus:
"1. Single, not adhering to one another, usually scattered among the water weed.
2. Attached to sphagnum (rarely debris) or free and rest on bottom.
3. Found on bottom of small, non-stagnant pools, or in slow-moving streams of the pine barrens.

Before cleavage the cap of the animal pole is usually dark brown, the other two-thirds of the egg, creamy white. . . ." *Hyla andersonii* as they discover like many other North American frog's eggs change in pigmentation soon after they are laid. To continue with the description. "The egg is surrounded by the vitelline membrane and by the two gelatinous membranes of the usual type. The gelatinous capsules vary enormously according to their age and treatment. The following measurements are taken from a series preserved in formalin. They agree well in size with some living specimens. Diameter of Ovum—1.2–1.4 mm. Diameter of Inner Capsule—1.9–2.0 mm. Diameter of Outer Capsule—3.5–4.0 mm. The vitelline membrane may be best demonstrated after maturation when the animal pole is slightly flattened leaving a space between membrane and ovum.

"In nature, *H. andersonii* was estimated to lay eight hundred to one thousand eggs. None of our laboratory animals laid more than eight hundred eggs."

HATCHING PERIOD

Noble and Noble (1923, p. 441) had eggs hatch in laboratory in four days and believed it would take longer in nature. In South Carolina or North Carolina it might even happen in less than four days. In New Jersey it might be longer or shorter.

MATURE TADPOLE

Color description from life (May 23, 1924). General coloration of body olive, brownish olive, or dark olive. Back with scattered black spots. Gill region with a sheen of ochraceous salmon or vinaceous tawny or vinaceous salmon. Interspersed with this color is some black. The mental region is clear of color. Below eye blotched with black, bronze (or one of three gill region colors) and green yellow. Over the belly in younger specimens is a full block of ochraceous salmon or vinaceous cinnamon. In older specimens green-yellow or citron yellow or sometimes seafoam yellow across the belly or on the gill region.

Tail. Starting from the base of the tail there is a longitudinal irregular blackish band along the musculature of the tail one-half of an inch or more from the tip of the tail. This band is more or less interrupted, not a clearly defined band as in *Hyla femoralis* or in *Pseudacris ocularis* or other *Pseudacris* species. Below the band is a clear area of warm buff or cream color or cartridge buff or seafoam yellow. In some specimens there is a similarly colored area 1/8–1/4 inch long above the dark band. The very lower edge of the musculature is with a fine purplish line. Just above this edge are a few scattered collections of black dots. Upper and lower crests heavily clouded with blackish dots which in places assemble in clusters. In younger tadpoles quite a prominent irregular margin of blackish on the crests and the musculature band of black more regular and not so interrupted.

Eye with pupil rim prominent ochraceous salmon or vinaceous tawny or vinaceous cinnamon. Rest of pupil spotted with this color and black. All in all it is a prominently colored eye.

General appearance. Tadpole (35 mm.) full and deep-bodied. Tail medium to fairly long, tail tip acuminate or sharply acute. The dorsal and ventral crests about equal. The dorsal crest is less than the depth of the musculature and extends onto the body to the vertical midway between hind legs and the spiracle. Spiracle sinistral directed upwards and backwards, far below lateral axis, the spiracular opening plainly visible and elliptical or round. Eye just touches or is below the lateral axis, is in dorsal aspect on the lateral outline and in consequence visible from the venter. Anus dextral, opening at or only slightly above the lower edge of the ventral crest. Muciferous crypts not distinct.

Mouth parts: Teeth 2/3. Upper labium fringed with a continuous row of labial teeth; the papillae extend above and inwards beyond the end of the upper fringe for about 2/7–1/4 of the length of the upper fringe. The end of the second upper labial row may be even or beyond the end of the fringe. The horny beak is contained in upper fringe 1.5–1.7 times. Median space between the lateral second upper labial row 1.25–2 in the length of either lateral row. The lateral row is contained about 2 1/2 in the upper fringe. The inner papillae extend beneath the third lower labial row of teeth giving a two-rowed appearance of papillae below it like *Hyla cinerea*. The third row of labial teeth is short (in one specimen subdivided) and is 2/9–1.3 times (usually 2/5, rarely as small as 1/8) in the length of the first or second rows. The first and second rows about equal or 1 1/2 greater than the horny beaks.

Measurements. Length of body (10.0–12.0 mm.) in tail (11.5–23.0 mm.) 1.1–2.0, average 1.67. Width (6.0–7.2 mm.) of body in its own length 1.5–1.85, average 1.65. Depth (5.0–6.5 mm.) of body 1.0–1.85 mm. in body width, average 1.2. Depth of body 1.61–2.18 in body length, average 1.86. Depth (5.0–7.0 mm.) of tail in length of tail 2.5–3.5, average 3.0. Muscular part (2.0–3.0 mm.) 1.9–2.5 in depth of tail, average 2.1. Spiracle 1.0–1.5 nearer base of hind legs or vent region (5.0–7.0 mm.) than the tip of the snout (6.0–9.0 mm.), average 1.22. Spiracle 1.25–2.3 nearer eye (2.5–4.8 mm.) than base of hind legs or vent, average 1.86. Eye 1.0–1.6 nearer to spiracle (2.5–3.5 mm.) than to tip of snout (3.0–4.2 mm.), average 1.25. Nostril 1.2–2.1 nearer eye (1.2–2.5 mm.) than snout (2.5–3.0 mm.), average 1.5. Internasal space (2.2–3.2 mm.) usually .75–1.6 larger than mouth (2.0–3.0 mm), average 1.25. Mouth contained 1.33–2.5 (average 1.85) in interorbital distance (4.0–5.5 mm.). Internasal space contained in interorbital distance 1.33–2.2, average 1.8.

The dimensions of the largest tadpole are:

	mm.		mm.
Total length	35	Spiracle to vent	6.0
Body length	12	Spiracle to eye	4.8
Body depth	5.5	Eye to snout	4.2
Body width	7.2	Eye to nostril	2.5
Tail length	23.0	Nostril to snout	3.0
Tail depth	6.3	Mouth	3.0
Musculature of tail	3.0	Interorbital distance	5.0
Spiracle to snout	9.0	Internasal distance	2.8

General remarks. The first author to discover and to describe the tadpoles is W. T. Davis (1907, pp. 49, 50). "It was observed in June at Lakehurst that the males of *Hyla andersonii* were attracted to a few small pools in particular, several of which were only a yard or two in diameter. On July 21st, with Mr. James Chapin, I made search of these pools for the tadpoles, and was fortunate in finding a number in one pool, although they appeared to be absent from another and similar locality about a mile distant where the adult frogs had been and were still most numerous. The tadpoles collected were in all stages from a few millimeters long to those just leaving the water as little frogs. The mature tadpoles are from 35 to 40 mm. long and of the usual tadpole color, that is, of the color of the muddy bottom of a pool. The under parts are lighter and show a golden sheen, which sometimes extends up the sides. The small hind legs show early on the ends of the toes the disks that are so conspicuous in the mature Hyla. The tail is spotted, and there is usually a dark irregular marginal band. The maculations sometimes become irregular blotches as on the tails of the tadpoles of *Hyla versicolor.*"

Noble and Noble (1923, pp. 443–448) give a detailed account of the tadpole of this species with illustrations of labial mouth parts and the mature tadpole.

LARVAL PERIOD

We found the larvae in several pools, grassy, sedgy, sphagnaceous along a dense woody border below Mr. P. H. Emlie's lake at Lakehurst. The following trees and shrubs were in the wooded edge where numerous *H. andersonii* were calling and taken. The tadpoles also were in the more or less open shrubby areas where *Vaccinium* and *Magnolia* (small) were common. A few pools were connected with streamlets and water ditches.

The tadpoles we took June 29 began transforming July 2. This species actively croaks in May in other years. These tadpoles doubtless were at least from eggs hatched in the first half or middle of May. My determination is from comparative experience with *Hyla squirella, Hyla femoralis, Hyla cinerea, Hyla gratiosa, Hyla arenicolor* and *Hyla crucifer*. At the time at Lakehurst we concluded 50–75 days a probable larval period. Noble and Noble found transformation July 23. If these transforming frogs were from eggs of May 20 or June 4, we have 49–64 days for larval period. Transforming frogs of July 1 and 2 apparently from earlier seasonal oviposition might take 10 or more days longer.

TRANSFORMATION

Period. Messrs. Davis and Chapin found this species transforming from tadpoles to frogs July 21, 1906 (Davis, 1907, pp. 49, 50). On June 29 the author and Mrs. Wright found a few tadpoles with two legs well developed and by July 2–4 they began to transform and travel about my screened porch. The last transformed July 15. The bulk of these tadpoles at Lakehurst must have transformed by July 15–30. Noble and Noble found them transformed July 23, 1923. The eggs taken by Barbour (1916, pp. 6, 7) July 8 doubtless would not have changed to froglets until August 25 or September 1. Judging from choruses we heard June 26–30, 1923, and previous observations by others the transformation doubtless extended from June 29–September 1 with the majority changed into frogs before August 1.

Size. "When the tail is nearly absorbed, and they leave the water, they are about 25 mm. long and of a dull olive green. They grow lighter, that is, brighter green in hue with the disappearance of the tail until the little frogs which in length of body are 15 mm., resemble the mature individuals. The white that margins the green of the back and extremities is not so conspicuous as in the adults, and the saffron of the under parts is wanting in those that I have examined." (Davis, 1907, p. 50).

In color the transformed frog looks much like that of *Hyla femoralis* or of *Hyla squirella*. The dark vitta does not extend along the side but is a purplish area before and back of the eye just before the tail is entirely absorbed. Not until the four legs were acquired did our froglets have green appearing on the back.

The range in body length of one collection of 10 individuals is 11.5–13.0 mm.; average 12.0 mm.; mode 12.0 mm. Our transformation sizes, therefore, prove slightly smaller than those of Mr. Davis. The two records combined give a range of 11–15 mm. for transformation size.

GROWTH

This species begins as little froglets at 11.5–15 mm. in body length. Dr. Barbour has material, 13 specimens (M. C. L. Nos. 3218, 3577–79, 3551–60) from Lakehurst most of which was taken by himself and F. K. Barbour. These measure 35 ♂, 36 ♂, 36 ♂, 37 ♂, 37 ♂, 37 ♂, 38 ♂, 38 ♂, 38 ♂, 38 ♂, 38.5 ♂ mm., 38.5 ♂, 40.5 ♂; and one female 44 ♂ mm. This gives a range of males from 35–40.5 mm. The Nobles (A. M. N. H. Nos. 16960–83) had males 35–38 mm. and females 38–44 mm. From comparative experience they may prove 3 years old, but our collections and collections in general have so little material between 15 mm. and 35 mm. that it is useless to attempt an approximation of this question. Possibly some adults of second year from 26 or 27–33 or 34 mm. may breed.

FOOD

Noble and Noble (1923, pp. 448, 449) record that "The stomachs of ten males which were captured during June while calling from bushes or low trees contained the following food: 5 grasshoppers (two species); 2 beetles, 3 ants (two species), 1 dipterous insect, 2 dipterous pupae (tabaniid?), and some unidentifiable insect remains. None of the specimens taken in embrace contained food in their stomachs, but only a few pairs were killed immediately after oviposition." Dr. Burt Green Wilder made extended notes on food and food prehension in this species. He kept a male (sent by Dr. James P. Chapin) from July 21, 1906 to November 21, 1908, when the creature was killed. It, therefore, lived in captivity over two years. Unfortunately his notes are not to be found. This is the same specimen L. A. Fuertes painted.

ENEMIES

There are plenty of water snakes in the neighborhood which might prey on the adults when in ponds, and on journeys to and from breeding places. In some localities the associated *Chrysemys picta, Clemmys guttata, Chelydra serpentina* and other turtles do damage to tadpoles. In general the associated fish, such as *Acantharchus, Enneacanthus, Mesogonistius* and *Umbra* doubtlessly prove of little consequence in the economy of the tadpoles. The eggs are laid in shallow places where the fish are not so common.

AUTUMNAL DISAPPEARANCE

The last date of appearance is September 5, 1904, (Davis, 1904, p. 893). "Mr. J. A. G. Rehn has reports of one seen August 16th, 1907, at Stafford's Forge, in Ocean County. It was probably driven from the woods by a forest fire" (Fowler, 1908, p. 193). Of course, it must retire into winter retreat much later.

AFFINITIES

Cope likened it to *Hyla arborea* as did Boulenger (1882).

Cope (1862, p. 155) in speaking of the first specimen he ever saw alive and from which this color description from life comes writes that,

"I am indebted to Dr. Jos. Leidy for a beautiful specimen of this frog. It was found in a cedar swamp, near the town of Jackson, in New Jersey, sixteen miles east of Philadelphia. Without careful examination of the specimen, he supposed it to be the viridis of the Southern States, from its great resemblance to that species, and presented it as such, at the meeting of the Academy the same evening (Vid. Proc. Acad. for July, p. 305). At the same time Baltimore was given as its northern limit upon the authority of Dr. Uhler of that place. As Dr. Holbrook gives lat. 33° as the most northern habitat known to him, it would be interesting to receive specimens from Baltimore, as there is a possibility of the supposed viridis being the andersonii.'

At this time Cope (1862, p. 154) and later (1889, p. 365) likened it to *Hyla arborea* as did Boulenger (1882).

Barbour (1914, p. 239) has compared it with *Hyla pulchrilineata* (Santa Domingo) the form Boulenger (1882) places just before *Hyla andersonii* in his Catalogue. Noble & Noble (1923) assert that "*Hyla andersonii* is not closely related to *H. arborea* nor to *H. pulchrilineata.*" "The relationships of *Hyla andersonii* are to be sought in Chinese forms and probably in *H. immaculata* Bott (Boettger)". It may not be related to *Hyla arborea*. It is interesting to attempt to link it with a Chinese form, but somehow the author is inclined to believe we must search for an American forebear. "*Hyla andersonii* has been derived from a group of Hylas which laid surface eggs, its method of oviposition being a modification of their method." The present writer who has seen in nature and laboratory as well the eggs of almost all the Hylids of the U. S. A. would not unhesitantly say this is the case though he is inclined toward it.

In general coloration it falls in the group of *Hyla cinerea, Hyla cinerea evittata, Hyla gratiosa* (sometimes clear green), *Hyla squirella* (sometimes clear green). Several of these species in males may have green from fore arm forward on either side of the throat. In some individuals almost to symphysis of the jaw. In *Hyla andersonii* it is more definite (white edged usually in the female). (See extended discussion under Variation in color *Hyla cinerea*). In general, the upper parts of *Hyla andersonii* are uniform. Sometimes though numerous *Hyla cinerea* without white or yellow dots or spots on back may be collected but usually they have them. *Hyla gratiosa* usually has its characteristic dorsal spots but occasionally it may be green with a few dorsal yellow or white spots. Am sure I saw one *Hyla andersonii* male with a dorsal yellow spot or so but haven't the specimen now to prove it. Too great emphasis cannot be laid on any one character of coloration in Hylas in establishing or eliminating relationships. LeConte (1825) questioned Daudin's green *Hyla squirella* description and illustration but green they will become at times. The above *Hyla* species are also sexually dimorphic as well as *Hyla andersonii*.

If *Hyla cinerea* with lip and lateral white or yellow stripe with thin purplish line below appear with light line different in extent, purple below absent or present, light line on upper lip only, or without lateral stripe at all (*evittata*) it can also intensify the purplish below the white line to get the effect in *Hyla andersonii*. In a somewhat similar way *Hyla squirella* and *Hyla andersonii* might be linked hypothetically. It is, however, hypothesis and is so involved the writer handles it warily. Voice is uncertain in evaluation of relationships. Each person might hear it differently, use musical notation, syllables, lines and other forms of characterizations. Too many personal equations are involved unless one person heard all forms to be considered. In egg deposition its eggs are single placed (several emitted at one time) but more or less singly placed in dropping to the bottom. Its method of laying eggs is very interesting. This might lead one to suspect that when some local naturalists of the South can devote some time to *Hyla squirella, Hyla gratiosa* and other species some of these may have a similar method of deposition. To be certain it must be field and laboratory determined and well checked which most itinerant naturalists have not the time to do thoroughly. Noble and Noble describe the egg minutely. Without the egg in hand, the writer hardly can say whether it is of *Hyla squirella* affinity (two envelopes) or *Hyla gratiosa* (single envelope) or *Hyla cinerea* (two envelopes). In some way *Hyla cinerea* with both surface film and strewn eggs in submerged bladderworts, etc., may be the nearer form though *Hyla gratiosa* and *Hyla squirella* have singly strewn eggs.

In general coloration the tadpoles look like *Hyla femoralis*. The first tadpoles of *Hyla andersonii* that the writer saw at Lakehurst reminded him very decidedly of *Hyla femoralis*. Knowing this form was not in Lakehurst we naturally placed them in *Hyla andersonii*. By accident they proved the very pools in which Noble and Noble worked so hard the previous year. Superficially I took them to be near *Hyla femoralis*. Closer inspection made the resemblance less apparent. They do not superficially and clearly fall into the group with heavily spotted and somewhat scarlet suffused tails (*H. arenicolor, H. femoralis, H. versicolor*). Neither do they superficially fall into the greenish tadpoles of *H. gratiosa, Hyla cinerea* group. Examinations of their mouth parts apparently put them near this group (short third lower labial tooth row and other characters).

This topic could be expanded at will. The value of certain criteria in determining its possible relationship to *Hyla arborea*, or to *Hyla pulchrilineata* are not for me to discuss. If we let license run riot we might call it a northern representative of *H. gratiosa*, or an offshoot from *Hyla squirella* as a radiation center or a *Hyla cinerea* derivative just as *Hyla c. evittata* apparently is. The writer is still searching for slow coming material before he indulges in that joyous privilege of final pronouncements on questions of relationships.

Though not exactly pertinent to the topic of affinities possibly the follow-notes from life may be interesting. In camp 1922 at Chesser Island we had a male *Hyla andersonii* (from North Carolina) and males of *Hyla cinerea, Hyla femoralis, Hyla versicolor* and *Hyla squirella*. Our rough journal notes reveal the following notes made at one sitting under similar conditions with fresh material.

Back. Hyla andersonii, cress green; *Hyla cinerea*, rear greenish-yellow; head viridine; *Hyla femoralis*, brownish drab. *Hyla versicolor*, rear pale smoke gray; rest grayish olive to vetiver green; *Hyla squirella*, buffy brown or isabella color or old gold; rear, yellowish citrine or apple green.

Degree of white on venter. Hyla andersonii, whitish on venter; *Hyla cinerea; Hyla versicolor; Hyla femoralis; Hyla squirella*, least whitish on venter.

Degree of orange. Hyla squirella, most orange below; throat, under side of fore feet, fore limbs, hind limbs and hind feet fore and aft. *Hyla andersonii*, front and rear of hind limbs when revealed; under side of foot; *Hyla versicolor*, groin; front and rear of femur shows it slightly.

Green on throat of males: Hyla andersonii, Hyla cinerea, (*Hyla gratiosa*).

Iris. Somewhat of same color as back: *Hyla cinerea, Hyla versicolor, Hyla squirella, Hyla femoralis.* Somewhat like vitta: *Hyla andersonii*.

Vitta. Hyla cinerea, Hyla versicolor, no vitta nor stripe through the eye; *Hyla femoralis, Hyla squirella*, line in front of eye obscure or absent; *Hyla andersonii*, vitta prominent.

BIBLIOGRAPHY

1868 Abbott, C. C. Geology of New Jersey by G. H. Cook. Appendix E, p. 805.
1890 ———. The American Naturalist February 1890, Vol. XXIV, No. 278, p. 189.
1854 Baird, S. F. Proc. Acad. Nat. Sci. Phila., April 1854, pp. 60, 61.
1916 Barbour, T. Copeia, Jan. 24, 1916, No. 26, pp. 6, 7.
1907 Brimley, C. S. Journ. Elisha Mitchell So. XXIII, p. 158.
1863 Cope, E. D. Proc. Acad. Nat. Science Phila. Vol. 14, March 25, 1862, pp. 154, 155.
1887 Cope, E. D. The Batrachia of North America, U. S. Nat. Mus. Bull. 32. Washington, 1887, p. 365.
1904 Davis, W. T. Proc. Nat. Sci. Assoc., Staten Island, Oct. 15, 1904, Vol. IX, No. 8, p. 26.
1904 ———. American Naturalist Nov.-Dec., 1904, Vol. XXXVIII, p. 893.
1905 ———. American Naturalist Nov. 1905, Vol. XXXIX, No. 467, p. 765.
1907 American Naturalist Jan. 1907, Vol. XLI, No. 481, pp. 49, 50.
1908 ———. Proc. Staten Island Assoc. Arts and Sciences, Feb.-May 1908, Vol. II, Part II, pp. 49-50.

1922 ————. Journ. N. Y. Ento. Soc. Mar. 1922, Vol. XXX, No. 1, p. 74.
1906 Dickerson, M. C. The Frog Book, pp. 131-133.
1908 Fowler, H. W. Annual Rept. N. J. S. Mus. 1906, Part I, 1907, pp. 108-112.
1908 ————. Annual Rept. N. J. S. Mus. 1907, Part III, p. 193.
1930 Klots, A. B. Copeia Oct.-Dec. 1929, Jan. 16, 1930, No. 173, pp. 108-111.
1916 Miller, W. DeW. Copeia, Aug. 24, 1916, No. 34, p. 68.
1894 Moore, J. Percy. American Naturalist Dec. 1894, XXVIII, No. 336, pp. 1045, 1046.
1923 Noble, G. K. and R. C. Noble, The Anderson Tree Frog. Zoologica, Aug. 20, 1923.
1889 Peters, John E. American Naturalist Jan. 1889, Vol. XXIII. No. 265, pp. 58, 59. Smith, W. H.
1923 Stejneger, L. and Barbour, T. A Check List of North American Amphibians and Reptiles. Second Edition, Cambridge 1923, p. 29.
1901 Stone, W. Proc. Acad. Nat. Sci. Phila., June 1901, Vol. 53, p. 342.
1906 ————. American Naturalist Mar. 1906, Vol. XL, No. 471, p. 163.

Hyla cinerea (Schneider)

(Pl. II, Fig. 5; V, Fig. 1; VII, Figs. 1, 4; X, Fig. 2; XII, Fig. 4; XV, Fig. 2; XVII; XXVI; Text Fig. 1, 12)

COMMON NAMES

Green Tree Frog. Carolina Tree Frog. Cinereous Frog. Bell Frog. Fried Bacon Frog. Cow-bell Frog. Bull Frog. Tree Frog (Holbrook). Green Tree Toad. Carolina Hyla. Banded Hyla (*semifasciata*). Hallowell's Tree Frog.

RANGE

Check list. Type Locality: "Inhabits Carolina." Range: Virginia to Florida, west to Texas, and northward up the Mississippi Valley to southern Illinois." Stejneger & Barbour Check List 1923, p. 30.

Supplementary records. In 1926 (Wright '26, pp. 82, 83) held *Hyla cinerea* to be a Lower Austral species from southern New Jersey to Texas. In 1917 our route from Washington southward to Texas was through Upper Austral or Piedmont country. We did not see or hear this species until Flatwood (Wilco Co.) Alabama, was reached. We next took them at Pass Christian, Miss., June 14, at Devers and Berwick, Louisiana, June 18 and 19, between Beaumont and Neches River, Texas, June 21, or from Alabama to Texas. In Texas in 1925 we found them south of Beeville and almost to Corpus Christi. Pope (1919, pp. 95, 96) recorded it at Houston, Tex. In North Carolina Brimley records it in Dare and Lenoir Counties. In 1922 we found it as far west as Richmond County south of Rockingham, N. C. In 1924 George S. Myers (1924, p. 60) reports it from Wilmington, N. C. The following month, 1924, Schmidt reports it from Charleston, S. C. In 1922 from near Columbia, S. C., June 9, through Millen, Ga., June 10, and Screven, Ga., June 11, and Waycross, June 12, to Okefinokee, June 13, we recorded this species. All in all, the records distinctly make it a Lower Austral form.

Local Okefinokee records. We recorded it from the following Okefinokee localities: Billy's, Black Jack, Chesser, Floyd's, Honey Islands, the Pocket, Craven's and Mixon Hammocks, Billy's and Minne Lakes, Chase and Grand Prairies, Suwannee Canal, Suwannee and St. Mary's River, Starling Branch and numerous localities around the swamp. It was widespread in this region and a very common frog.

GENERAL APPEARANCE

DeKay (1842 Part III p. 72) held this extra limital frog to be "Bright green, with a yellow line on each side from the snout to the posterior extremities. Length 1¾ inches. From Lat. 30° N. to Mississippi."

In 1906 Dickerson (p. 127) wrote "The Green Tree Frog is perhaps the most beautiful tree frog of North America. Its slender form and smooth fine coat of green and gold certainly give it an air of distinction. It is more slender than any other North American tree frog. The slenderness is accentuated also by the lengthwise stripes of metallic white or yellow."

In 1915 Deckert (p. 3) described it as "an aristocratic looking tree toad, with its long, slender figure of the brightest green, edged on each side with a band of pale gold or silvery white. Its size is larger than any of the preceding species (*H. pickeringii*, *H. squirella* and *H. femoralis*) often reaching 2½ inches from snout to vent."

It is a very slim, smooth, green frog. It may have side stripe, pointed head and shallow face (*H. cinerea*) or have no stripe, broader head and deeper face (*H. c. evittata*). It is relatively the longest legged *Hyla* of the swamp. Specimens of *Hyla versicolor*, *Hyla gratiosa* and *Hyla cinerea* at 56 mm. have hindlimbs respectively 70 mm., 73 mm., and 89 mm. in length.

COLORATION OF SPIRIT SPECIMENS (1912)

Color in spirits olive brown, olive green, brownish; in life all of the specimens were grass green or yellowish green. The same color occurs on the dorsal surfaces of the fore- and hindlimbs and forward from the arm on to either side of the throat. Sometimes this narrow area of green is absent but usually it reaches along either ramus as a narrow band seldom reaching the symphysis of the lower jaw. In three examples (Nos. 6524, 6535, 6532), the green extends across the throat while in the others the throat is clear. The characteristic straw or yellowish band on the sides of the body is more or less variable. In most it starts on the snout but few have it beginning beneath the eye as Holbrook records. Usually where the tympanic fold crosses it the band may be narrower, broken or missing for a short distance. In the majority the band reaches to the groin although several have it ending midway between the fore- and hind-limbs. The band usually reaches its greatest width on the side of the body. Often it is a narrow line on the sides, in one (No. 6511) it is almost absent and very thin being only .5 mm. long beneath the tympanum and .5 mm. long back of the tympanic fold. This is a very close approach to the condition of *Hyla evittata*.

A similarly covered line occurs along the posterior edge of the forearm and carpus, along the posterior margin of the tibia, and tarsus and anterior margin of the tibia; rarely one or all of these bands may give way to green body colors, the anterior tibial band being most frequently lost and the tarsal carpal and forearm bands are seldom lost.

Most of the 23 adults have few to 25 small irregularly arranged cream or orange yellow spots on the green back. In a few they become quite conspicuous; others have the back absolutely free of them.　The short tranverse light line above the anus usually but not always present.　The ventral surface of the body is white or yellowish white.

STRUCTURAL CHARACTERS (WRITTEN IN 1912)

Upper surfaces quite smooth or minutely granulated; slightly granulate on the throat; most of the gular sac, the breast and its fold, under sides of the arm and legs smooth; belly and posterior ventral surface of the thigh strongly granulate.　Third finger longest; fourth toe longest and with two phalanges free; a tympanic fold from tympanum to base of arm; vomerine teeth between inner choanae at equal intervals from them and from each other; in two not transverse but oblique in position and in one (No. 6530) a continuous ridge not divided into two; tongue roundish or elliptical slightly notched; nostrils decidedly nearer tip of snout than eye.

MEASUREMENTS
(Recent Material)

Head to angle of mouth 1.0 (20 mm.)—1.25 (28 mm.)—1.05 (36 mm. ♂)—1.18 (44 mm. ♂)— 1.2 (44 mm. ♀)—1.05 (56 mm. ♂)— 1.11 (56 mm. ♀) in width of head; head to rear of tympanum 1.0–1.0–.95–1.0–.92–1.03–1.0–1.0 in width of head; head to angle of mouth 2.85–3.5–3.8–4.0–3.66–3.3–3.3 in length of body; head to rear of tympanum 2.85–2.8–3.4–3.14–3.14–3.1–3.0 in length of body; snout .66–.70–.8–.92–.86–.72–.65 in first finger; snout .83–1.0–1.2–1.23–1.06–1.05–1.0 in fourth finger; snout .66–.70–1.0–.77–.66–.77–.8 in first toe; eye 1.0–1.66–1.25–1.3–1.875–1.5–1.66 in snout; eye .5–.83–.75–.50–.625–.66–.75 in tympanum; eye .66–1.16–1.0–1.2–1.61–1.08–1.08 in first finger; tympanum 4.0–4.2–3.0–4.4–4.8–3.75–3.33 in intertympanic width; tympanum 2.0–2.0–1.66–2.4–3.0–2.25–2.2 in snout; internasal width 1.0–1.5–.83–.75–1.0–.90–1.1 in upper eyelid width; interorbital width .60–.85–.71–.75–.77–.81–.71 in upper eyelid width; interorbital width .60–.57–.8–1.0–.77–.91–.50 in internasal width; interorbital width 2.3–2.4–2.5–2.75–2.6–2.7–2.14 in intertympanic width.

Forelimb: Forelimb 2.1–1.8–2.05–1.9–1.83–2.43–2.24 in length of body; forelimb 3.0–3.03–2.8–2.74–2.62–3.6–3.2 in hind limb; first finger 1.75–1.57–1.75–1.5–1.38–1.7–1.77 in third finger; second finger 1.4–1.22–1.4–1.28–1.2–1.3–1.27 in third finger; second finger .8–.77–.8–.875–.86–.76–.70 on first finger; third finger .85–1.09–.92–.83–.88–1.0–.95 in second toe; fourth finger 1.4–1.1–1.16–1.12–1.12–1.15–1.15 in third finger; fourth finger .8–.7–.66–.75–.81–.7–.65 in first finger; internasal width 1.33–1.75–1.33–1.5–1.85–1.3–1.4 in first finger; internasal width 1.66–2.25–1.66–1.75–2.1–1.7–2.0 in second finger; internasal width 2.33–2.75–2.33–2.25–2.5–2.2–2.5 in third finger; internasal width 1.66–2.6–2.0–2.0–2.3–1.9–2.2 in fourth finger.

Hindlimb: length 1.42–1.76–1.41–1.43–1.43–1.5–1.43 in hind limb; tibia 2.0–1.64–1.94–1.91–1.76–1.93–1.86 in length; tibia 2.85–2.76–1.94–2.73–2.52–2.9–2.66 in hind limb; tibia .95–.9–.94–1.0–.96–.80–.83 in forelimb; tibia .7–

.7–.62–.78–.72–.8–.70 in hind foot; first toe 1.5–1.71–1.3–1.5–1.6–1.57–1.37 in second toe; first toe 3.0–2.4–1.8–2.4–2.5–2.14–2.0 in third toe; first toe 3.75–2.85–2.4–3.2–2.85–2.37 in fourth toe; first toe 2.75–2.28–1.7–2.2–2.2–2.0–1.875 in fifth toe; second toe 2.0–1.41–1.38–1.6–1.56–1.36–1.45 in third toe; second toe 2.5–1.66–1.84–2.13–2.0–1.8–1.72 in fourth toe; second toe 1.85–2.28–1.7–1.6–1.375–1.27–1.45 in fifth toe; third toe 1.25–1.17–1.33–1.33–1.28–1.33–1.2 in fourth toe; third toe .91–.94–.94–.91–.88–.93–.93 in fifth toe; fourth toe .93–1.15–1.12–1.12–1.12–1.15–1.1 in hind foot; fourth toe 1.33–1.7–1.54–1.43–1.56–1.45–1.57 in tibia; fourth toe 1.3–1.55–1.46–1.43–1.5–1.15–1.3 in forelimb; fifth toe 1.36–1.25–1.41–1.45–1.45–1.42–1.26 in fourth toe; internasal width 1.33–1.75–1.66–1.25–1.4–1.4–1.77 in first toe; internasal width 2.0–3.0–2.16–1.875–2.28–2.2–2.4 in second toe; internasal width 4.0–4.25–3.0–3.0–3.5–3.0–3.55 in third toe; internasal width 6.0–5.0–4.0–4.0–4.5–4.0–4.25 in fourth toe; internasal width 3.66–4.0–2.83–2.75–3.1–2.8–3.4 in fifth toe.

HABITAT

LeConte (1825, pp. 279) gives its habitat as follows: "Inhabits in great numbers in Carolina and Georgia, particularly on water plants, such as *Pontederia cordata*, the Nymphaea, and others, that generally grow in ditches, and on the margins of rice fields." Holbrook (1842, Vol. IV, p. 120) records that "These animals are found on trees, but most commonly about the broad-leaved plants, as the *Pontederia cordata*, Nymphaea, etc; they are also very numerous in fields of Indian corn (*Zea mais*), where they conceal themselves from their enemies by passing in between the broad green leaves of the plant, the colour of which is so nearly their own, that it is not easy to find them." In 1856 LeConte (p. 428) records that "In the spring it is found in rice fields in astonishing quantities."

Deckert (1914, No. 3, p. 3) "found (them) in scattered bands, among water hyacinths on creeks." In 1915 Deckert (p. 4) "occasionally met with (it) on corn fields, its chief haunts, however, seem to be the shores of the creeks, where it occurs in scattered companies on the water hyacinths and bulrushes."

In Louisiana Viosca (1923, p. 39) finds that the denser areas in the fresh water marshes adjacent to the wooded swamps "furnish the ideal habitat for *Hyla cinerea* and *Rano sphenocephala.* . . ."

In 1912 we made the following notes about their habitat in the Okefinokee Swamp: This tree frog is very common in the Okefinokee Swamp. We found them in the large bay and cypress trees along the watercourses and about Billy's Island. In some of the swampy edges of the islands and about Lee's clearing they also occurred. On Honey Island Prairie the trees seemed to teem with them during the evening chorus. The following day in the forenoon when the sun was very hot they were frequently taken and more often seen on the lily-pads and other aquatic plants at the surface of the prairie. Some were secured on the bushes and trees near our camp, on low heaths and rarely near or on the ground.

In 1921 we found them commonly in cypress ponds, cypress bays, in hammocks near the cypress bays or near the edge of the island, along the edge of water courses and on the prairies. On June 4 we found a pair in the "lumber camp quarters near a house corner on the south end of the easternmost street in a temporary pool. Probably from houses near by. Boys tell about finding them in or around the rain barrels." Our first specimen in 1921, April 22, we found in a rain barrel.

In several instances we have records of them from ivy covered porches where they reside some times. On July 22, 1921, at Hampton Mizell's residence, Hopkins, Georgia, on his porch were two *Hyla cinerea*, one of which we saw calling.

In 1922 we heard them quite commonly on the prairies, and in some cypress ponds. We occasionally heard them in branches (like Starling Branch) and in the water pits beneath the oaks and trees at Camp Pinckney, St. Mary's River. At night the frogs may be on the bushes and stems above the water or more frequently at the water's level. During the day they rest mainly on the stems above the water. For example, at Camp Pinckney in the afternoon of June 27, 1922, "took *Hyla cinerea* in Pond No. 2 on a vertical wild rice stem, the frog some 3 feet above the water." Eight days later, July 5, at Camp Pinckney, "over Pond No. 3 on wide leaved grass-like plants were some 7 or 8 *Hyla cinerea* perched 1–3 feet above the water." Or two months later at the same place August 11, 1922 "on grass stems found 3 males 2 feet above the water."

FIRST APPEARANCE

The earliest note of activity in the South I have observed is Pope's (1919, p. 95) record for "February 13, 1918. Caught a young one in the grass close to the bayou. Found it actively hopping after dark, habits evidently nocturnal. In the course of the next two months I collected three others, two young and one adult 5 cm. in length. The latter was sitting on the top of a stub close to a bayou fast asleep in the day time." In 1897 W. C. Kendall took this species on Feb. 14, at Beecher Pt., Florida and on March 16 secured more at the same place.

The earliest record the author has of this species is along the Medina River south of San Antonio, Texas. Here in company with Miss Ellen D. Schultz, Mrs. Wright, Messrs. Roy D. Quillen and R. D. Camp we found February 15, 1925, this species buried in the moist sawdust or humus or fine dust of decaying logs. With it in these logs we dug out a brown snake (*Potamophis striatula*) DeKay's snake (*Storeria dekayi*), variable swift (*Sceloporus variabilis*), spiny swift (*Sceloporus spinosus*), ground lizard (*Leiolopisma laterale*), short-lined skunk (*Eumeces brevilineatus*) *Bufo valliceps*, and *Tantilla nigriceps* and countless invertebrates.

GENERAL HABITS

Metachrosis. "As to coloration, this tree frog has great ability to change from light to dark. The colour may be nearly black, or it may be so light a greenish yellow that the stripes can scarcely be distinguished. There is some variation in colour pattern; that is, the light bands on the legs may be narrowed or obsolete, the light band on the side may extend no farther than half-way instead of quite to the posterior end of the body, and the dark bands bordering the light ones may be distinct or wholly lacking. . . . This *Hyla* sometimes has a few small orange, black-rimmed spots on the back." (Dickerson, 1906, p. 127).

There is a great variation in color. In general at night yellowish green or light greens are prevalent. During the day I have noticed pairs where the male, the more exposed, was olive green or slaty and the less exposed female was a lighter green than the male. Certainly the more exposed frogs of the daytime are not always darker. The very palest *Hyla cinerea* I ever saw was on the exposed edge of a cypress head, at mid-day.

The same conditions do not always produce the same coloration. In one case we had many *Hyla cinerea* in a botany drum. All were light green except three, one of which was almost black, another olive green, a dark green, and the third yellowish green.

Variation in color. In 1825 LeConte (p. 279) wrote "The description of this animal should be corrected by saying, that the lateral line, from which the name is derived, is most commonly silvery, in some few instances yellow."

In 1856 Hallowell (pp. 307, 308) held that "in lateralis (*viridis* Hollb.) the lateral stripe extends as far as the anus, and there is a white band running the whole length of the tibia, both anteriorly and posteriorly. The anterior band is absent in *semifasciata*." Hallowell's *H. semifasciata* was supposedly larger than the true *H. cinerea* and had the lateral band ending half way along the side.

In 1890 and 1892, H. Garman recognized these two varieties as *Hyla cinerea cinerea* and *Hyla cinerea semifasciata*. In 1899 G. S. Miller, Jr., examined the *Hyla cinerea* material from the vicinity of Washington and recognized in addition to the *cinerea cinerea* and *cinerea semifasciata* a new frog *Hyla evittata* "like *Hyla cinerea* (Daudin) but with broader, deeper muzzle and normally unstriped body and legs." "As to the constancy of the color differences between the two forms" (*cinerea* and *evittata*) he writes:

"I have handled about two dozen living and freshly killed specimens of *Hyla evittata*, and have probably seen nearly as many more at a distance of only a few feet. Among these one had a faintly developed stripe at the angle of the jaw. Of the twenty-two alcoholic specimens collected by Mr. Hay and now in the National Museum, eight have traces of the body stripe, which, however, in no instance is margined with black, or as sharply defined as those southern specimens in which the stripe is shortened and narrowed. Of sixty-one specimens of *Hyla cinerea* (seven received alive from H. H. and C. S. Brimley taken at Bay St. Louis, Miss., and the others preserved in alcohol in the U. S. National Museum) there is considerable variation in the leg stripes, though varying in length and breadth, is conspicuously developed, definite in outline, and usually margined with black. In the two abnormal individuals (one from Bay St. Louis, Miss., the other from New Orleans, La.) the leg stripes are absent, and the body stripes reduced to mere traces near the angle of the jaw. When forwarding the unstriped specimen from

Mississippi, the Messrs. Brimley wrote that it was the only one of the kind observed among the large numbers that have passed through their hands. Such individuals as these are readily distinguished from the faintly striped specimens of *Hyla evittata* by the form of the muzzle."

In 1910 C. S. Brimley writes that "A single specimen resembling *cinerea* but lacking the yellow line on the side, also came from here" (Bay St. Louis, Miss.). He probably alludes to Miller's specimen. In 1915, Grönberger writes of *H. evittata* as follows: "Efforts will shortly be made to secure specimens of *Hyla evittata* Miller which are said to be very numerous in the ponds between Mr. Palmer's farm and the Potomac River, and also to establish whether *Hyla cinerea* coexists with or is not, as some claim specifically identical with *Hyla evittata*."

In 1924 (p. 60), G. S. Myers discusses some of his material from the Wilmington (N. C.) country thus: "In the 14 adults, six showed partial or total lack of the yellow band along the jaw, side and tibia. Two were altogether without these markings, appearing very like *H. evittata* Miller. The head shape was typical of *cinerea*, as observed in other specimens from Florida and Louisiana. In the opinion of some, the blunt head of *evittata*, described and figured by Miss Dickerson (Frog Book, pp. 128-130, Pl. LII) is not a good character, and *evittata* is simply the unbanded form of *cinerea*.

"With this view I cannot at present agree. Numerous times several of the *cinerea* were in full cry in the terrarium and their call was very different from that described by Miller for *evittata*. . . ."

In 1910 Brimley (p. 11) speaks of a "Hyla (sp.) Bay St. Louis, Mississippi, in January and February, 1901, several specimens of a tree frog with the sharply defined side line of *cinerea* but with dark spots on the back like *squirella* were received from this place. My notes state that they were apparently a little stouter than *cinerea* and grayer in color."

On June 14, 1917, several of us (Professors H. H. Knight, P. A. Munz, G. B. Upton and others) encountered this same mixture of characters. At the time the writer had forgotten Brimley's experience but it immediately came to mind when the variations began to appear. The rough journal note runs thus: "At noon we stopped in a low woods near one of the bays between Pass Christian and Bay St. Louis. On the saw palmetto leaves we found no end of *Hyla cinerea* and *Hyla squirella* in all color phases. Believe *Hyla andersonii* not so different. These creatures were on the saw palmetto leaves or in the bases between two stems. In one place found two specimens, one a brown phase and one a green phase. Some have a yellowish or orange color on the posterior faces of thighs. Others have purplish. Some have a yellowish line on lip and a few besides have faint yellowish line on side. Many have a purplish area from nostril to femur along the side like *Hyla andersonii* only not so distinct. Adult *H. cinerea* were often on the face of the leaf and on upper side. Others were on the underside of the leaf. Sometimes in one clump of 4 or 5 plants as many as 6 or 8 specimens were found. Often a fine correspondence of brown specimens and brown leaves or green frogs with green blades. In one clump one yellowish green on back, another dark greenish

1

2

3

4

6

5

7

8

and a third purplish brown. One captured by H. H. Knight had quite a purplish area from nostril to femur. Some of the *Hyla cinerea* have a narrow purplish line above and below the white, cream colored, or straw colored lateral band. Is this the cradle of Southeastern tree frogs? There were un-spotted *H. evittata, Hyla squirella, H. cinerea,* olive or green or possibly brownish with or without lateral bands, with or without dark borders to band, also specimens very suggestive of how *Hyla andersonii* form might possibly be derived." Alas this most interesting series, one the of largest we ever collected, dried up and was lost before we ever studied it critically. Only 14 clear *Hyla cinerea* of this series remain. The interesting specimens are lost.

In 1922 on our way to Okefinokee Swamp we heard from our camp on the Alexandria (Henshaw Sparrow station) heights what the writer took to be *Hyla cinerea.* I suspected they were *Hyla evittata* and Mr. Harper recognized them as such from his previous collection of them. They impressed me as *Hyla cinerea* in call and the author has always inclined to the belief that *Hyla evittata* is *Hyla cinerea* but it is not yet settled. To call it *Hyla cinerea evittata* as Dunn (1918, p. 21) and Stejneger and Barbour (1923, p. 30) have is about all that we can do until the life history is worked out by some one who knows *Hyla cinerea* intimately. These forms from Virginia northward tend to predominate in *evittata* coloration; those from North Carolina southward to Texas are regularly striped with occasional *evittata* forms.

The lateral stripe present or absent is not in the southern forms a sex char-acter. In our 1921 material three of our records are of females 57 mm., 55 mm., and 56 mm. in length and two males 58 mm. and 55 mm. All these five have a jaw stripe. In a male and a female the lateral stripe is missing on each side. In one specimen, male, the stripe is present on one side and missing on the other side. In one female lateral stripe missing on one side. On this side jaw stripe only 7 mm. long from beneath eye to angle of mouth. On the opposite side the lateral stripe is just a little beyond shoulder. In the other female no stripe on one side and hardly none of the other side.

The head characters are supposed to be diagnostic but broader noses and deeper faces occur with the narrow noses, nearer nostrils and shallow faces. We have before us an *evittata* female with deep face, wider separated nostrils, broader, blunter nose and a male of the same length vittate, pointed nose, shallow face and nostrils nearer together. At transformation the stripe may sometimes be absent; in fact at times it may be more absent than present.

General habits. In 1842 (Vol. IV, p. 121) Holbrook remarked that "At certain seasons they may be seen on the ground on their way to pools of water; they are exceedingly active, leaping at times eight to ten feet."

"The Green Tree Frog is most interesting when kept in captivity. It lives high among the ferns and vines of its moss-garden, and is especially fond of flies. It will see a fly at a distance of three or four feet, and will catch it, making but one leap over the intervening distance. It is said that this tree frog can leap a distance of eight to ten feet. When the call is given, the throat pouch is inflated and the body over the lungs swells and relaxes forcibly." (Dickerson 1906, p. 127).

In 1915 Deckert (p. 4) held that "Although (it was) a powerful leaper, it is easily caught when once located, as it is not at all shy." Pope (1919, p. 96) held "from the frequency of its call this *Hyla* seems to be fairly abundant (at Houston, Tex.), but its secretive habits and protective coloration make it very hard to find."

VOICE

In Daudin (1803, p. 29) we find that this species "croaks without ceasing tchit-tchit-tchit-tchit." J. LeConte (1825, p. 279) records that "They are very noisy, particularly at night, their voice somewhat resembles the sound of a bell." LeConte (1856, p. 428) said it "is commonly known as the bell-frog, its notes resembling the sound of small bells. It is frequently called *fried bacon frog*, as its voice seems to some ears to repeat these words." Holbrook (1842, Vol. IV, pp. 120, 121) holds "they remain quiet and motionless during the heat of the day, but in the morning or evening, or before a shower, they emerge from their hiding places and become very brisk and noisy. Their noise proceeds from a single note, which, at a little distance, is not unlike the sound of a small bell; and there seems in general to be one leader of their orchestra, and when he raises his note, hundreds take it up from all parts of the cornfield, and when he stops, the concert is at an end, until he again begins."

Harrison Garman (1892, pp. 347, 348) holds "Its note resembles the tone of a cow-bell heard at a distance. Where abundant about water, the frogs are very noisy just after dusk, the chorus being broken, however, by longer and shorter intervals of silence. A single note is first heard, and as if that were a signal, it is taken up and repeated by a dozen noisy throats till the air is resonant with sound. After a time it ceases as suddenly as it began, to be again resumed after a period of quiet."

In 1915 Deckert (p. 4) says "Its call sounds like: Grab, grab, grabit, grabit, etc., uttered in a shrill, loud voice, and has a startling resemblance to the human voice. One would never think the call came from a frog."

In 1919 Pope (pp. 95, 95) "throughout the month of May and into June. . . heard this frog quite often, calling from the trees at all times of day, but most frequently late in the afternoon. The call has been compared to a cow-bell, which it resembles in tone, but the manner of delivery suggests a cuckoo. It usually consists of fifteen or twenty notes given in rather rapid succession, but too distinctly to be called a trill. The cadence becomes slower after the first, and the last few notes are often given with some hesitation. From the frequency of the calls this Hyla seems to be fairly abundant. . . ."

In 1912 when we first made the acquaintance of this form in the Okefinokee we wrote "In the daytime when the weather is sultry or especially in the evenings of late May or early June some of their immense choruses are not easily to be forgotten. Sometimes a chorus starts suddenly, quickly reaches its crest and ends abruptly to be resumed later after a shorter or longer sharply defined interval. Along some of the water-courses like Billy's Lake one lone frog nearby will begin, then stop, but ere he has finished, another just ahead of the speeding boat has taken up the task. Thus, the chorus may travel along the margin of a lake for considerable distances. Usually these experiences came in the later afternoon (after 3:00 p. m.)"

Five years elapsed before we heard them again. At Flatwood, Ala., after 6:30 p. m. "in a drying-up swampy pond heard a chorus which sounded like a cow-bell at a distance. To one member of the party it sounded like an exhaust running into an oil well pipe. Took one with flashlight. It was *Hyla cinerea*. It was on some bushes and its sides and throat looked like a pink ball."

In 1921 we made the following notes: On Billy's Lake at night May 11, "the *Hyla cinerea* of a place would sing, then stop, and the wave of sound pass on down the lake. The frogs were mainly in the bushes along the edges and hard to find in a casual way. We had to get out of the boat and search. We found one two feet from water on a horizontal branch. It was literally covered with gnats, mosquitoes, etc. After much manoeuvering, we finally had it focused. After we had waited some time for it to croak, we discovered the frog gone. About 11:00 p. m. the *Hyla cinerea* stopped. Temperature 71°. Falling temperature and cooling rain anticipated."

On May 14 at 8:00 p. m. went to the C. A. G. (*Hyla cinerea, Acris gryllus, Rana grylio*) pond. When I approached the pond heard no end of *Hyla cinerea* calling everywhere. On one iris blade found a male one foot above the water. Nearby on another iris blade was a second male. In amongst a mat of pickerel weed (*Pontederia*) and lizard's-tail (*Saururus*) found a male at the surface and croaking; in a bush three feet above water another male; in a cypress tree four feet above water another; on a lily pad still another. No females seen. When one catches them with throat inflated they give a funny squeak as if the balloon had burst.

When the chorus is in full swing the males are easy to capture, not hard to observe or photograph by flashlight. On April 25, 1921, we went to one pond "where many *Hyla cinerea* were on lily pads. Several were also in the bushes. One of these allowed me to stroke it with a flashlight and did not move. Finally it merely scrambled farther down the branch on which it was resting." At other times it will leap from the branch to another lower branch and will land in the water. In the latter case it scurries along on the water to some vegetation for a new perch.

This is easily one of the most characteristic anuran voices of the swamp. We have heard it from mid April to September. Its call is loud, the frogs are numerous and the voice period is long. It is one of the rain signals for the residents who call it "rain frog."

Mr. F. Harper makes the following notes on its voice: "The calls are given at the rate of about 75 per minute: *quonk, quonk, quonk, quonk*, etc. Meanwhile there is an alternate inflation and deflation of throat and body. The note comes at the maximum inflation of the throat sac, which is then fully half the size of the body. Between croaks the throat does not fully collapse, there remaining a little balloon-like expansion in the middle. After starting off with the ordinary note described above, a frog will often redouble its speed and at the same time add a rolling quality to the note: *crronk-crronk-crronk-crronk*, etc. The throat sac is then only slightly deflated between croaks. When two individuals are calling together, but not in unison, there is an interesting antiphonal effect, as of a double note: *bo-babe, bo-babe, bo-babe*, etc. Probably both the calling periods and the intervals between them are irregular in length. On one occasion the former appeared to last 1¼ minutes, and the latter about 2 minutes. When one frog pipes up, after an interval of general silence, all the others in the vicinity generally chime in almost immediately, as if having just awaited such a signal to start the chorus. As a matter of fact, a spirit of competition probably enters here, each male being desirous of announcing his location to any nearby female that may be ready to mate.

A resume of the croaking records for 1921 and 1922 is:

1921

April	24.	Heard one in Long Pond 7:30 p. m. Males on bonnets croaking in evening in another pond.
April	25.	One heard at 10:00 a. m. Few heard in afternoon.
April	27.	Many heard at night.
April	30.	Cold tonight. Air 58°. No *Hyla cinerea* calling.
May	3.	Tonight at 8:00 the temperature is 56°F. The last few days have been so cool that the *Hyla cinerea* beginning choruses are closed.
May	9.	Billy's Lake, a few calling at 8:30 p. m. Temperature 73°.
May	10.	Croaking at night the Southern bull frog pond.
May	11.	"Wave" chorus at Billy's Lake stopped about 11:00 p. m. Temperature fell to 71° and a cooling rain anticipated. It came.
May	13.	Few heard in afternoon.
May	14.	In a *Pontederia* and *Saururus* pond heard tonight no end of *Hyla cinerea*.
May	16.	At 7:00 p. m. heard an immense and intense chorus along Billy's Lake in all the ponds and bays. "We flashed a *Hyla cinerea* calling. They are easy subjects."
May	19.	At times plenty of *Hyla cinerea* calling.
May	20.	Common at night.
May	21.	*Hyla cinerea* going strong at 7:00 p. m. Air 70°. Few calling in mid afternoon.
May	22.	Wonderful chorus east of Billy's Lake. Great racket in Moonshine Pond 9:00 p. m.
May	24.	"Strong tonight" at 10:00 p. m. Air 77°F. No end of them calling.
May	26.	In many ponds the dominant note. Starting up at 5:00 p. m.
May	27.	Going 8–11:00 p. m. and later.
May	30.	Out tonight. Heard *H. cinerea* calling commonly.
June	3.	A few calling
June	4.	One or two calling.
June	5.	Many heard in various places at night.
June	7.	Air 71°. Many heard at Moonshine Pond.
June	8.	A number calling about dusk. Air 70°.
June	15.	Tonight at times quite a chorus in some of the cypress ponds. Air 80°F.
June	19.	Every night for a week *Hyla cinerea* has been active.
June	21.	Last night a chorus.
June	23.	Ponds alive with croaking *H. cinerea* after the evening's rain of 2 or more inches.
June	24.	*Hyla cinerea* abundant.
June	25.	Strong tonight. "Today heard several and once or twice in hot day *H. cinerea* burst into chorus. Is a storm coming?"

June 28. A large chorus.
June 29. Commonly heard in one pond.
July 3. A few calling from 5:00 p. m. onward.
July 4. Some yet calling at Long Pond.
July 6. A few heard.
July 9. A few early in evening and a moderate chorus later.
July 11. Some calling. Later a great chorus on prairie.
July 17. A few heard at night.
July 23. Singing at 8:00 a. m. At night calling loudly.
July 24. Large chorus.
July 26. Last night a chorus.
July 27. Many heard on prairie.
July 29. Several calling.
July 30. *Hyla cinerea* calling.
August 1-12. Heard almost every night.
August 23. Heard in forenoon.

1922

June 8. *Hyla cinerea* in chorus at Everett's Pond, N. C. (near Cheraw, S.C.)
June 10. Near Millen, Ga., heard a chorus.
June 12. Heard one 6–7:30 p. m.
June 14–22. Great choruses on prairies.
June 28. One heard.
June 29. Plenty calling on Suwannee Canal and on prairies.
July 2. Calling loudly at Chesser Id. landing.
July 3. Heard a few last night.
July 5. Calling on prairie.
July 7. Chorus at Lake Seagrove 8:00 p. m.
July 12. Heard at Coat Bet Pond.
July 23. A few *H. cinerea* on prairies.
July 25. "Not so many calling on prairies as I would suppose after the hard rain."
July 26. Heard a great breeding chorus of *Hyla cinerea* near Starling Branch.
July 27. One heard on Chesser Island.
July 29. One heard 9:00 p. m.
August 1. Several calling.
August 2. Several calling.
August 6. Commonly heard on Billy's Lake at night.
August 7. Several calling Chesser Island.
August 8. A very few *H. cinerea* calling 8–11:30 p. m. after rain. Temperature 79°.
August 11. Large chorus Camp Pinckney.
August 13. Several heard on trip to St. Mary's, Chesser Id., 7–10:30 p. m.
August 15. 7:00 p. m. *H. cinerea* calling. Callahan, Florida.

When the choruses of *Hyla cinerea* began after dusk, 70°-82° or 84°F. temperature prevailed. For example, in 1921 this species was heard for several days in last of April but when in early evening 58°F. was recorded on April 30 none were heard. From this date for several days in May the minima ranged from 44°-54° until May 8. No *Hyla cinerea* were calling. But on May 9 the early evening temperatures reached to 73° and the green tree frogs began again. Thereafter 68°-80° temperatures generally prevailed when calling occurred. But the great choruses came when the storms threatened, were imminent, or after heavy downpours. Humidity is doubtless more important than temperature in inducing calling or choruses.

MATING

Male (From life, April 26, 1921). In dark olive green male there are twenty orange spots scattered over the back, lighter in green of sides below lateral stripe; stripe (cream colored) extends almost to hind legs. Obscure on snout ahead of eye. Cream colored or white stripe on back of forearm. Iris bronzy. Pupils horizontal.

Same on back of lower leg and along hind end of foot. Throat from angle to mouth to slightly back of chin green. Chin proper yellowish cream. Back of these two areas, yellowish cream and green, is the wrinkled pink area of the throat proper.

One light colored male with stripe straw-colored, only an inch behind insertion of arm area black above and below the stripe. (Non Ridgway.)

(From life, May 18, 1921). Back may be apple green, dark green olive, greenish olive, deep slaty olive to almost black, the stripe on side light dull green yellow or clear dull yellow. In one male stripe not beyond tympanum and suggestive of *H. evittata.* The vent, forearm stripe, foot stripe and heel are white. One dark male had the foot stripe fainter. Iris russet vinaceous.

Female (From life, April 26, 1921). With no pink chin, green extends in on sides of throat for slight distance. Straw colored stripe to insertion of hind legs prominent, also stripe under eye and around stripe. Under parts from groin to chin the same cream color. (Non Ridgway).

(From life, May 18, 1921.) Back may be from apple green to deep slaty olive. Stripe pale chalcedony yellow.

Structural differences. In the pair of May 10, 1921, the female was much longer. On June 4, 1921, the mated pair captured the day before was colored at 11:00 a. m. as follows: Female, yellow green; male deep slaty olive. Another female in the jar was also deep slaty olive.

In 1912 we analyzed the differences thus: In the series of 23 adults, without exception the six females are the largest being 56, 57, 58.5, 59, 59, 60 mm., average 58 mm.; while the 15 males range from 46–55 mm., average 51 mm. Of course, the females can be told because of the absence of the vocal sac which in the males is not especially colored. In one or two of the females the throat was quite greenish across the whole width. The breast fold is not so prominent and the throat region not wrinkled area (in spirits). A firm and full appearance in the inguinal region reveals the ripe females at once though the waist is almost as in the males,—slender even when the eggs are ripe. In the male enlarged thumbs or nuptial excrescences seem to be absent.

A survey of our 1921 and 1922 material with comparisons with our 1912 Okefinokee specimens and other material from other parts of the range of this species reveals two gravid females of 41 mm., two females at 44 mm. and one at 45 mm. One would expect the male external characters to appear slightly smaller. One 35 mm. specimen has a slightly wrinkled throat. One specimen of 37 mm. has the throat wrinkled and is a male. Of three 38 mm. specimens one is doubtfully male externally; another has the throat wrinkled but not prominently and is a distinct male. Two specimens 39 and 42 mm. appear to be males. From 44 mm. onward we have many males. The evidence if summarized is: 28 females from 41-63 mm. in length, average 53 mm., mode 57; 53 males from 37–59 mm. in length, average 50 mm., mode 55 mm. The males and females may begin breeding rarely at the end of their second year but the rate of growth and ripening of gonads point to the beginning of the third year and third spring after transformation as the first ovulation for the individual frogs.

Duration, day or night. The first record we have is on the evening of May 10, 1921. "This evening at 8:00 p. m. (Temperature 72°) went to new pond southwest of boys' swimming hole in Billy's Lake. Here were no end of *Acris gryllus* and *Rana grylio* in all stages. Easy to capture them at night except the adult *R. grylio* but even these can be taken. The pond is cypress-lined. Moon shows just above them. Beautiful picture though some might think of the moccasins, alligators, etc. when wading around at night. Heard a *Hyla cinerea* nearby. Began to search. It stopped. Later thought I saw it. Seized it and it proved a ripe female, not croaker. This female was in a cypress 4 feet above the water. Went away. Later the croaker started again. On the flat side of an iris leaf three feet from the captured female was the male. Was the female approaching the croaker? Put both in a jar. Came back to camp. The male and female are mated at 9:00 p. m." On the morning of May 11 the pair were broken and no eggs laid.

On the night of July 3, 1921, after a heavy rain we found two mated pairs of *Hyla cinerea* not in their accustomed place of ovulation. In the water between the furrows of sweet potatoes found one of the pairs. The other was in another cultivated field between furrows of cane or corn. *Bufo quercicus* and *Hyla femoralis* pairs were also in numbers.

On July 7, another pair was found in a temporary open grassy pool near the lumber company's wood pile, quite an aberrant place for ovulation. Equally so was the temporary pool in the street of the Billy Island Lumber Camp where on June 4, 1921, a pair was found.

As to duration of embrace we have little evidence. Normally they lay the same night a pair is captured. The pair of May 10 were broken the morning of May 11. On the night of May 14 these were mated again and then alternately broke and embraced for several days after without ovulation.

Amplexation (Normal, abnormal). The pair mated May 10, 1921, had an axillary embrace. "The bent toe pads of two fingers (outer ones) of the male show slightly." On May 11 they broke. On the night of May 14 "The male held the female with his forelegs in front of the female's forelegs. One arm came to the middle line of the female's throat and the other arm came to the corner of her mouth. Later the male embraced normally."

On May 14, 1921, brought in many males. Put them together and two were soon mated in an axillary fashion. The embrace was not strong for they broke when we tried to flashlight them.

On May 18, 1921, "at 9:30 p. m. in Long Pond on moss edge, not in pond proper we found a mated pair of *Hyla cinerea*. Apparently the females are often met at the very pond's edge. They broke. Put them in photo jar.

Later they resumed." The embrace was a normal axillary amplexation as it was with the mated pair of June 4, 1921, the two pairs of July 3, 1921, and the pair of July 7, 1921.

OVULATION

Habitat. Under voice we have noted this species in the bushes in the verdant edges of Billy's Lake and in a cypress pond (C.A.G.) with its mats of sphagnum, *Hydrocotyle, Iris, Pontederia, Saururus, Castalia, Nymphoides,* etc. On May 19, 1921, we made these comparative notes on habitat from one cypress pond: "*Rana clamata* along outer edges in *Decodon,* some *Pontederia* and entirely on east side of Long Pond. *Rana grylio* in middle. *Acris gryllus* widespread. *Hyla femoralis* mainly on either northern or southern end. *Hyla cinerea* out in the middle and around edges also but *Hyla femoralis* as yet around edges." They also breed commonly on the prairies, sometimes in the cypress bays and at times in transient pools or inundated cultivated fields of the islands or mainland.

Period. In 1915, at Jacksonville, Florida, Deckert (p. 4) reported that "This species seems to have no special breeding season, and is never heard in the early spring, when the majority of the other frogs and toads congregate at the shallow bayous." Pope (1919, p. 96) of Houston, wrote "I could get no light on its breeding habits."

From the evidence of mated pairs in 1921 we might call May 10–July 7 the maximum period. In 1921 we recorded eggs May 18, May 23, June 4, July 3 or from May 18–July 3.

In 1923 Wright (1923, p. 34) held that "From May 15th to June 1st five more (species) start (ovulation). ... *Hyla cinerea* ..." In 1924 Wright and Wright (1924, p. 378) give the "Season, May 19 to August 21" as the period of ovulation. Another note represents breeding as beginning May 10 and still another notation has the period from May 18–July 30.

In 1912 we evaluated our evidence as follows: "We suspected this species must be breeding during the period of the greatest choruses which we recorded May 30–June 4. Of the 12 adults taken between May 30–July 15, 1912, only two were females (taken respectively June 3 and June 6). Only the first of these two was gravid, the other was spent. Of the ten adults secured after July 15, four proved ripe females. Then, the remains of another frog taken June 15, 1912, from the stomach of a black-snake proved to be a ripe female. Thus we have outlined a period of ripe females from June 3–July 15 or later. The species may breed from the last of May through June and July."

A summary of our material on the basis of spent and unspent females for years not of 1912 is as follows: On April 28, 1921, the only two females caught respectively 55 mm. and 57 mm. are spent. On May 15, 1921, we took three females, two 55 mm. and 56 mm. spent, and one 57 mm., gravid. In June, 1911, at Spring Creek, Decatur Co., Ga., Professor J. C. Bradley took two females 44 and 59 mm. respectively, each gravid. On June 5, 1921, we secured a ripe female 59 mm. long. The day before another unspent female 57 mm. On June 21, 1917, at Devers, Texas, we captured a gravid female. On June 30, 1921, a female 56 mm. was not quite ripe. On July 3, 1921, we have two spent females.

This evidence of 1911, 1917, and 1921 yields the facts that breeding began before April 28 and reached at least to July 3. The gravid females recorded above for the period after July 15, 1912, send the ovulation far into July. From spent and unspent females evidence, mating pairs, actual eggs recorded and early and late choruses this species may lay at least from mid April to mid August or later.

Temperature and humidity. In the six or seven instances of ovulation or mating in 1921, we have a rain of .88–2.80 inches before or .84–1.00 the day of the record. On the day before the record the maxima ranged from 75°–91°, the minima 60°–74°; on the day of the record, maxima 80°–91°; minima 62°–70°. Close study of these temperatures shows 65°–76° minima prevalent when ovulation occurred.

On May 16, 1921, when we had an immense chorus we made the note "The humidity, previous rain and threatening rain must be more of a factor than temperature."

Egg-laying process. In 1912 if the presumptive egg packets (June 1, 1912) of 5–30 eggs were *H. cinerea* these must be moving about as in *Hyla versicolor*, *Hyla femoralis* and some others. Then we held that each female if she lays packets of only five each would have about 70–100 packets to lay or if in masses of 30 each about 10–16 different ovipositions. In 1921 on May 23 when we found them in the field sometimes the packets seemed distinct and other times not so much so. The eggs might be more or less strewn on the vegetation or at other times be in packets. Then we noted on the spot that all the complement apparently is not laid at the same place or time; there is some moving about. Possibly its method may be somewhat akin to that described by Noble and Noble for *Hyla andersonii* where it strews its eggs on the sphagnum.

The eggs laid May 18, 1921, were not hatched May 24, 1921. They eventually spoiled. Doubtless this means they were laid by the female when not mated. On July 9, 1921, we also recorded that the eggs laid by the pair of July 4 did not hatch. Here also they were doubtless laid when not paired. If each case represents infertility from male it may be the captivity, restricted quarters where there is little opportunity to move about.

EGGS

Attachment, egg mass. The first eggs laid by the pair of May 18, 1921, were deposited in our photographic jar and give no idea of the mass form in the field. In the illustration they appear as a flocculent mass of eggs.

In 1912 we made these notes on the eggs of this species: "On June 1, 1912, Dave Lee found some amphibian spawn in some pools of their clearing. These pools were near the swampy thicket around the edge of the cultivated corn and chufa's fields and were decidedly transient in nature. The eggs were in masses on the surface of the water more or less like tree toad (*Hyla versicolor*) eggs. In each mass were 5–30 eggs. These packets were easily discernible because of the excessive amount of air bubbles in them. In a few instances the masses were slightly beneath the surface an inch or more and the eggs matted together in semi-ball-like fashion. Usually, however, the film form of the tree toad complement obtains with this species. In addition the color of the eggs (brown animal pole and cream or yellowish white vegetative pole) makes the resemblance more marked. A comparison of the eggs taken in the field with the ovarian eggs of *Hyla carolinensis* satisfies the authors that the identification is correct but it is yet circumstantial or presumptive." Now we know the presumptive evidence would be just as strong or stronger for these masses being those of *H. femoralis*, yet we cannot forget that in these transient pools of these same cultivated fields we found two mated pairs of *Hyla cinerea*. Doubtless they could not lay normal masses in shallow water as they do in deeper cypress ponds, prairies or lakes.

On May 23, 1921, "from 2:30–5 p. m. we spent on Billy's Lake in a 'bonnet' (waterlily) area where Billy's Lake turns into the run for Suwannee Canal. Here we have heard a wonderful *Hyla cinerea* chorus. On the edge of a yellow waterlily (*Nuphar*) leaf where a part of the edge was submerged was a mass of *H. cinerea* eggs, 25 in all; in a water pocket where the petiole stem enters the midrib of the leaf was another packet of 10 eggs. The first packet I saw was on a bladderwort (*Utricularia*) stem. Another was wound around a *Nuphar* petiole. In one bladderwort the eggs were amongst the leaves and 3–4 inches below the surface. Hard to distinguish the eggs and bladders at times. Another mass attached to bladderwort leaves or floats. A little farther on a mass amongst algae."

The later records of 1921 are not presumptive. We had the camp eggs laid May 18–19 to compare with these field-laid eggs of May 22–23.

Egg description. Our field notes are as follows: Measurements of the eggs laid in camp May 18–19, 1921, are: ".8 mm. vitellus; 2.8 mm. inner envelope; 3.6–4.0 mm. outer envelope. The animal pole is blackish, very slightly brownish; the vegetative pole about as white as many frog's (*Rana*) eggs." On June 4, 1921, the following notes are made: "Eggs of *Hyla cinerea* are as follows: vitellus 1.0–1.2 mm.; inner envelope 2.2 mm. or 2.4 mm. Animal pole black or brownish black, darker than in *Hyla femoralis*, animal pole almost white or cream color sometimes a slight yellowish tinge but not so much as in *Hyla femoralis*. Outer envelope a part apparently of jelly material and poorly defined."

Mrs. Wright's laboratory examinations give the following measurements: vitellus .8 mm.–1.6 mm. for 29 specimens, mode 1.2 mm., average 1.15 mm.; inner envelope 2.0–3.4 mm., mode 2.4 mm., average 2.55 mm., outer envelope, 3.2–5.0 mm., mode 4.0 mm., average 3.8 mm.

In 1912 the count of the ripe eggs in one female gives 343 and in some of the others where slightly more occur the complement certainly does not exceed 500. In comparison with some of the other tree frogs it is a relatively small complement for a frog 50–60 mm. long. Of course, the form is very slender of body.

Dangers. The presumptive eggs discovered June 1, 1912, in the edge of the cleared fields were in a pool with 2 inches of water. On June 4, the pool was a mere moist depression with no water. No doubt the percentage of loss from such a cause is great but not so much so in this species as in *Hyla femoralis, Bufo quercicus, Gastrophryne carolinensis.* *Hyla cinerea* normally lays in deeper water than these three species.

HATCHING PERIOD

The eggs discovered June 1, 1912, in a pool with 2 inches of water were hatched June 4, or three days later. The eggs laid by a pair after midnight on the night of June 4–5, 1921, hatched June 7 by 6:00 a. m., or about two days after ovulation. These were in a shallow basin and the air temperatures were: maxima 82°–89°, minima 66°–70°.

MATURE TADPOLE

Color description from life (July 26, 1921). Top of body generally citrine or olive green or oil green, sometimes a bright spinach green or forest green. Stripe on side of head from snout to eye sulphur yellow and ivory yellow. Belly solid cartridge buff or ivory yellow. Breast and lower throat light vinaceous fawn. Mental region and upper throat dusky slate-blue with scattered spinach green spots. Sides of the body in branchial region and under eye spotted dusky and slate blue or slate-blue, light vinaceous fawn, cartridge buff, sulphur yellow.

General color of tail sulphine yellow to citrine. Amongst brown and far down tail sulphur yellow to light green yellow edges to crests or between crests. Base of muscular part of tail with some light vinaceous-fawn spots along the middle of it for 1 centimeter or more. In almost mature tadpoles not black spots on the crests. About time hind legs begin to grow upper and lower crests with prominent blackish spots. Fine spinach green flecks over tail except near the edges of the tail crests. In the younger tadpoles without blackish spots the black is in specks all over the tail and these faintly appear on the tail crests as dark edges.

Iris light cadmium to buffy yellow with dusky in front and behind the pupil.

General appearance. Tadpole medium (40 mm.) full and deep bodied. Tail acuminate, tip acuminate, sometimes acute. Tail long. The dorsal and ventral crests about equal and about equal to musculature in depth. The dorsal crest extending on to the body to the vertical about midway between the eye and spiracle. Spiracle sinistral, directed upwards and backwards, far below lateral axis, the spiracular opening very visible as a round or elliptical opening. Eye on lateral axis, in dorsal aspect on the lateral outline and in consequence visible from the venter. Anus dextral, or only slightly above the lower edge of the ventral crest. Muciferous crypts not distinct. As they approach transformation the whole tail becomes spotted with conspicuously dark and light spots.

Mouth parts: Teeth 2/3. Upper labium fringed with a continuous row of labial teeth; the papillae extend above and inwards beyond the end of the fringe for about 1/4 to 2/9 of the length of the upper fringe. The end of the second row is usually even with the end of the upper fringe. The horny beak is contained in the upper fringe 2–2.3. Median space between the lateral second upper labial row 3 or 4 times in the length of the lateral row. The latter row about 2 1/2 in the upper fringe. Inner papillae extend beneath the third lower labial row of teeth often giving a two rowed appearance below it like *H. andersonii, H. femoralis, H. versicolor* or *H. squirella*. The third lower row of teeth, however, is not like this group but shorter like *H. gratiosa* or *H. crucifer*. In one specimen it was absent, with the papillae below also absent. This third row is contained 2/5–1/6 in the length of the first or second row of lower labial teeth. The first and second rows (lower labial) are equal or 1 1/3 greater in length than horny beaks. Sometimes fringes are united by their ends as in *H. gratiosa*.

Measurements. Length of body (11–15 mm.) in tail (16–25 mm.) 1.25–2.0, average 1.6. Width (6–7.5 mm.) of body in its own length 1.8–2.2, average 1.9. Depth of body (6.0–7.0 mm.) equals body width. Depth of body 1.69–2.5 in body length, average 1.95. Depth (7.0–8.0) of tail in length of tail 2.0–3.125, average 2.75. Muscular part (4.0) 1.75–2.4 in depth of tail, average 1.925. Spiracle 1.15–1.6 nearer base of hind legs or vent region (5.0–7.0 mm.) than the tip of the snout (8.0–9.0 mm.), average 1.375. Spiracle 1.4–2.3 nearer eye (3.0–3.5 mm.) than base of hind legs or vent, average 1.85. Eye 1.1–1.65 nearer spiracle (3.0–3.5 mm.) than to tip of snout (3.5–5.0 mm.), average 1.38. Nostril 1.0–1.5 nearer eye (1.8–2.5 mm.) than snout (2.0–3.5 mm.), average 1.35. Mouth (2.0–3.5 mm.) 1.–1.4 in internasal space (3.0–4.0 mm.), average 1.25. Mouth contained 1.6–2.0 (average 1.83) in interorbital distance (5.0–6.0 mm.). Internasal space contained in interorbital space 1.25–1.8, average 1.48.

The dimensions of the largest tadpole are:

	mm.		mm.
Total length	40	Spiracle to vent	7.0
Body length	15	Spiracle to eye	3.0
Body depth	6	Eye to snout	5.0
Body width	7.0	Eye to nostril	2.5
Tail length	25.0	Nostril to snout	3.5
Tail depth	8.0	Mouth	3.0
Musculature of tail	4.0	Interorbital distance	6.0
Spiracle to snout	9.0	Internasal distance	4.0

General remarks. In 1923 Wright (1923, p. 406) gives this characterization: "*Hyla cinerea*—greenish tadpoles, yellowish tails." When they are young they have a little light cross band across the body reminding one of the pattern in small *Rana heckscheri* tadpoles. Before we knew this Rana's tadpoles well we had superficially identified its young tadpoles as *Hyla cinerea* tadpoles.

In 1922 by living on Chesser Island we secured less of this species and *Rana grylio* but 1921 we used to secure these two tadpoles in considerable numbers in the floating islands of vegetation along the edge of Billy's Island. We would haul the vegetation into the boat. Tadpoles of these two frogs *Hyla cinerea* and *Rana grylio* were the commonest anurans. In 1922 we had great difficulty in separating young *Rana grylio* tadpoles from mature *Hyla cinerea* tadpoles.

In 1922 the mature tadpoles were mainly taken in July and in 1922 we recorded them July 24 and August 11. This seems to imply ovulation mainly after the first of May.

LARVAL PERIOD

In 1921 fully grown tadpoles were captured in July. The first eggs we recorded were May 18, 1921, and the first mated pair May 10, 1921. The first recorded transformation in 1921 is July 12. This might imply 55 to 63 days for larval life.

TRANSFORMATION

Period. In 1921 most of the tadpoles of July 25 implied transformation August 1 and later, although six were actually at transformation. In 1922 mature tadpoles were recorded as late as July 24 and August 11. This implies transformation in August or as late as September 1. Surely eggs laid July 3, 1921, could not transform short of the last of August or September 1. Our latest date of transformation is October, 1915. This must be from eggs laid by August breeders. In 1912 we recorded one July 2 from Minne Lake. Our range of dates is from July 2 to October. July and early August doubtless are the crest of transformation.

Size. Our data are meager. In 1912 one transformed frog measured 12 mm. One taken October, 1915, was only 11.5 mm. The lone specimen of 1921, July 12, is 15 mm. In Long Pond, Billy's Island, July 25, 1921, we took six transforming frogs, 16, 16, 16, 16, 16, 17 mm. respectively. One or two tadpoles (July 25, 1921) which were almost at transformation measured 16 mm. On July 26, 1921, in a smaller place we found a tadpole a very few days from transforming and 17 mm. in body length. Possibly 11.5 mm.–17 mm. fairly outlines the transformation size.

GROWTH

In October, 1915, we recorded a 11.5 mm. transformed specimen and October 9, 1906 a set of three 25, 27, 30 mm. respectively, two size groups. Several isolated transformed records of 12, 15, 16, 17 mm. respectively were made. In one set from Florida we have a 14 mm. and 20 and 26 mm. specimen—two groups. Another set has 23, 24, 24 mm. specimens and a 33 mm. individual, possibly two groups. From Pass Christian, Miss., June 14, 1917, we have the following at 36, 38, 39, 41, 41, 42, 45, 45, 46, 46, 47, 48, 48, 48 mm. respectively. On July 15, 1916, we have some more specimens from the same size group: 35, 36, 36, 37, 38, 38, 38, 39 mm. respectively. On July 14, 1915, four specimens are at hand, one 38 mm. and three 44, 45 and 47 mm. re-

spectively are recorded.   This evidence thus far might be interpreted in two
ways: 1st years old 20–27 mm., or 20–30 mm., 2nd years old 27–39 mm. or
30–42 mm.; 3rd year olds 41–46 mm. or 44 mm.   Beginning with the larger
sized series, we have the following evidence.   On July 15, 1922, we took 45
mm. and 55 mm. specimens, apparently two groups, 3rd and 4th year olds.
In June, 1911, we have 44, 44, 46, 48 mm. specimens and 55 and 59 mm.
specimens, two groups, again distinct groups.   But on June 2–6, 1912, we
have a flowing series of 47, 48, 50, 50, 52, 54, 54, 56, 58 mm. specimens.   We
might interpret them all of one year 47–58 mm., or in the light of other material break the third year olds either at 49 or 55 mm.   We have nine collections where none of the individuals are below 50, 51, 52 or 53 mm. and
these reach to 63.   In this group 55 mm. is the mode with 57 mm. and 52 mm.
next in order of frequency.   In the lower group 45 mm. and 48 mm. are the
modal points.   In the 30–39 mm. ranges 38 mm. is the modal point.

If modal points be used the age groups are 11.5 mm.–17 mm. transformation; 20–30 mm., 1 year olds, 24 mm. mode; 33 mm.–42 mm., 2 year olds,
38 mm. mode; 45 mm.–50 mm., 3 year olds, 48 mm. mode; 51–59 mm., 4
year olds, 55 mm. mode; 63 mm., 5 year olds.   On the basis of absent measurements and other data we might interpret the groups thus: of these 103
frogs 11.5–17 mm. at transformation, 17–27 mm. one year olds; 27–39 mm.
as two year olds, no 40 mm. specimen; 41–48 mm. three year olds, no 49 mm.
specimen; 50–60 mm. four year olds, no 61 or 62 mm. specimens; 63 mm.,
five year old.

FOOD

Holbrook (1842, Vol. IV, p. 121) reported that "They feed on various insects, especially the common fly, which they seize with great adroitness,
leaping a foot or more to secure it."

Dr. Vernon R. Haber has examined all our material.   In his paper on
"The Food of the Carolina Tree Frog, *Hyla cinerea* Schneider" he summarizes the food as follows:

"The Carolina tree frog, *Hyla cinerea* Schneider, habitually is arboreal,
at least non-aquatic, excepting during mating and hibernating periods.

"The younger forms rapidly adapt themselves to a type of diet which is
characteristic of the adults of the same species, as is revealed in table 2.

"Habitually frogs of this species feed upon characteristically non-aquatic
forms until they are absolutely obliged to resort to water for breeding purposes.   They may take a few aquatic forms while en route to and from the
breeding places, for most of the aquatic forms could have been taken above
the water surface, as explained in the text.   It is doubtful that frogs of this
species feed while mating.

"It is not likely that these frogs while in the water for mating purposes
had taken terrestrial forms which had fallen into the water, for if such had
been the case, it seems that they also would have taken a larger percentage of
aquatic forms which habitually swim about upon or near the water surface.

"The diet of this species of frog includes such destructive forms as those
listed in table 1.   Of the five families of destructive Orthoptera, representa-

tives of all but one, the Phasmidae or walking sticks, were recovered. Of the 68 per cent which recently had eaten insects, one-third had taken Orthoptera, and slightly more than one-fifth had taken to Heteroptera.

92 per cent had taken arthropods.

68 per cent had eaten insects.

24 per cent had devoured Orthoptera, of which cockroaches were found in 11 per cent, Acrididae in 8 per cent, Gryllidae in 3 per cent, Mantidae and Locustidae each in 1 per cent.

24 per cent had but a short time previous secured Coleoptera, of which 5 per cent had eaten Cerambycidae, 4 per cent had taken Curculionidae, 3 per cent had devoured Cistelidae; Lampyridae, Coccinellidae and Scarabaeidae each had been swallowed by 2 per cent, while representatives of the following were included in the diet of 1 per cent each; Anthribidae, Carabidae, Chrysomelidae, Cicindelidae, Lathridiidae and Staphylinidae.

21 per cent lately had gotten Lepidoptera, 7 per cent yielded caterpillar remains.

15 per cent had devoured Hymenoptera. Ants were taken from 12 per cent and Scoliidae from 1 per cent.

13 per cent had obtained true bugs, of which but 8 per cent were further recognized. From the digestive tracts of 2 per cent each came Neptidae and Pentatomidae, which each of the following were yielded by but 1 per cent respectively; Belastomatidae, Corixidae, Pyrrhocoridae and Scutellaridae.

7 per cent had taken Odonata.

6 per cent had eaten Diptera.

3 per cent had obtained Homoptera.

Aphidae coming from 2 per cent, Jassidae from 1 per cent.

2 per cent had included Physopoda or Thysanoptera.

1 per cent gave up each of the following: Euplexoptera, Neuroptera and Trichoptera.

51 per cent a short time before they were captured had eaten harmful insects, and several had taken several of such insects.

31 per cent recently had gotten insects which are of useful or harmful economic importance.

15 per cent had taken insects which are of beneficial economic importance.

7 per cent recently had eaten insects which are of negligible economic value.

24 per cent positively had taken spiders, of which 6 per cent could be further identified, 2 per cent had taken Lycosidae, 2 per cent had Salticidae, 1 per cent had taken Filistatidae, and 1 per cent had taken Argiopidae; this latter 1 per cent had eaten three argiopids all of which were easily identified to the species. The remaining 18 per cent contained bits of legs, chelicerae and other portions of the bodies of spiders which could not be further identified.

4 per cent had gotten ectoparasitic mites of insects.

2 per cent had included Phalangidae.

1 per cent respectively yielded each of the following: Myriapoda, Phyllopoda and Pseudoscorpionida.

55 per cent arthropod remains which could not be further identified beyond reasonable doubt.

36 per cent were gluttonous, see ‡ of all tables and interpretative notes.

35 per cent had swallowed epidermis.

41 per cent were nematode infested, usually from the duodenum posteriorly; in 1 per cent nematodes were found in the stomach. Most of the nema-

todes which were found in the alimentary tracts were *Cosmocerella haberi* Steiner. Three other new species of nematodes were found in the bodies of these frogs. They are to treated at greater length in an appropriate journal elsewhere at some future date. (See Steiner, G., Some Nemas from the Alimentary Tract of the Carolina Tree Frog (Hyla carolinensis Pennant) Journ. Parasitology, Sept. 24, 1924, Vol. XI, pp. 1–32).

7 per cent of these frogs were Opalina infested.

"In their feeding habits frogs of this species have tendencies which are of beneficial economic importance. Rather frequently complaints are registered concerning the presence of certain insect enemies of florists in greenhouses, etc. Doubtless several dozens of the species of smaller tree frogs which are common to a locality, if kept in such places would materially aid in keeping down plant-lice, certain kinds of moths, beetles, mites, ants, cockroaches, crickets, sow-bugs, diplopods, centipedes, etc. By means of adhesive discs upon the tips of their phalanges, frogs of this species are able to adhere to the smoothest kinds of vegetation and even to glass. They would damage few if any of the most delicate of plants as they leap to and fro among the foliage and ordinarily they absolutely would not damage any part of a plant by directly feeding upon its tissues."

ENEMIES

In 1912 this tree frog was found in the stomach contents of only one species of snake, the black snake. One had taken four of them, head first and the long slender legs were the only undigested remains. One of the four is a ripe female and doubtless this individual with the other three were captured while bound for the breeding ponds or while in them. The wonder is that this bright common morsel is not more frequently captured, for the pine woods tree frog (*H. femoralis*) was taken by four different species of snakes.

In 1921 one of the Lee boys told me they caught "trout" (*Micropterus salmoides*) with *Hyla cinerea* as bait. Doubtless on the prairies and along the water courses when the *Hyla cinerea* descend to the waterlily level largemouth bass and other fish feed on them as do water snakes and ribbon snakes.

On May 11, 1921, along the edge of Billy's Lake we thought that we observed gnats, mosquitoes, etc., and other Diptera all over these frogs. All the specimens we collected (however) according to the Cornell Department of Entomology are of one kind, a harmless species (*Oscinis longipes*). These frogs are convenient resting places, like the immediate vegetation in which these flies were equally abundant. No doubt harmful Diptera prey on the frogs.

One of the reputable lumber foreman told us about the following episode which with variations has been told of more than one species of *Bufo*. While smoking he was seated on a log in the cypress bay. After a time he flipped his cigarette and the lighted stub landed near a green tree frog. It seized the stub in its mouth and went through interesting antics to eject it.

AUTUMNAL DISAPPEARANCE

From none of the Cornell Expeditions of December and January have we received this species. Our latest residence in the swamp has been in August

PLATE XXVII

Pine wood's tree-frog (*Hyla femoralis*)

1. Male croaking, Billy Id., Ga. May 16, 1921. Flashlight.
2. Male resting on bit of bark, Billy Id., Ga. May 16, 1921.
3. Male croaking in cornfield, Billy Id., Ga. June 4, 1921. Flashlight.
4. Tadpole, Anna's Pond, Folkston, Ga. June 27, 1922. Lateral aspect.
5. Two males, Billy Id., Ga. May 18, 1921. Lateral aspect. × 0.33.
6. Transformed frog, Billy Id., Ga. July 25, 1921. Lateral aspect. × 0.33.
7. Eggs, stained, Chesser Id., Ga. July 4, 1922. × 1.3.
8. Female and male, Chesser Id., Ga. July 3, 1922. Ventral aspect. × 1.0.
9. Eggs, stained, showing loose jelly envelopes, Chesser Id., Ga. July 27, 1922.

1

2

3

4

5

6

7

8

9

and September when the species was active. On October 9, 1906, Mr. A. G. Hammar secured three one year olds at Jennings, La., and we have another record of transformation in October, 1915.

AFFINITIES

Holbrook (1842, Vol. IV, pp. 121, 122) reviews this in detail. According to him Linnaeus held it a form of *Rana arborea* and credited it to Europe as well as America (*Rana arborea* var. B.) Laurenti called it a variety of the European *Hyla viridis*. Gmelin considered it a variety of *Rana arborea*. Schneider called it a variety of *Calamita arborea*. Daudin pronounced it a distinct form as does Holbrook, 1842, and LeConte 1856. The latter writes (1856, p. 428) "Our American animal has but little resemblance to the European, especially in form."

Like *Hyla gratiosa*, *Hyla femoralis*, *Hyla versicolor*, *Hyla cinerea* has indefinite outer envelopes. In egg deposition it may be between *Hyla gratiosa* and *Hyla andersonii* group and the surface surface film group of *Hyla versicolor* and *Hyla femoralis*. In some ways we incline to a closer relationship with the former group. In tadpole mouth parts we placed it with the *Hyla gratiosa*, *Hyla andersonii* group with their short 3rd lower labial tooth row in contrast to the long 3rd lower labial row of teeth in *Hyla squirella*, *Hyla femoralis*, and *Hyla versicolor*. In tadpole coloration and general appearance it is more suggestive of *Hyla gratiosa* although the crests are quite different. Of the American Hylas it seems all in all nearer *Hyla andersonii* and *Hyla gratiosa* and somewhat approaching *Hyla squirella*.

BIBLIOGRAPHY

1907 Brimley, C. S. Journ. Elisha Mitchell Soc., Dec. 1907, Vol. XXIII, No. 4, pp. 158, 159.
1910 ———. Proc. Biol. Soc. Wash., Mar. 23, 1910, Vol. XXIII, p. 11.
1803 Daudin. Histoire Naturelle, Generale et Particuliere des Reptiles, Vol. VIII, p. 29.
1914 Deckert, R. F. Copeia No. 3, Feb. 14, 1914, p. 3.
1915 ———. Copeia No. 18, May 15, 1915, p. 4.
1842 DeKay, J. E. Natural History of New York. Zoology of New York, Vol. III, Part III, p. 72.
1906 Dickerson, M. C. Frog Book, N. Y., p. 127.
1918 Dunn, E. R. Copeia, Jan 25, 1918, No. 53, p. 21.
1890-92 Garman, H. Bull. Ill. State Lab. Nat. Hist., Vol. III, pp. 189, 346-348.
1915 Grönberger, S. M. Copeia, Nov. 19, 1915, No. 24, p. 55.
1926 Haber, Vernon R. Journal of Comparative Psychology, Apr. 1926, Vol. VI, No. 2, pp. 214-216.
1856 Hallowell, E. Proc. Acad. of Nat. Sci. Phila., 1856, pp. 307, 308.
1825 LeConte, J. Annals Lyc. Nat. Hist. N. Y. Vol. I, Part Second, 1825, p. 279.
1856 ———. Proc. Acad. Nat. Sci. Phila., 1856, p. 428.
1899 Miller, G. S., Jr. Proc. Biol. Soc. Wash., Sept. 28, 1899, Vol. XIII, pp. 75-78.
1924 Myers, G. S. Copeia, No. 131, June 30, 1924, p. 60.
1919 Pope, Philip H. Copeia, No. 76, Dec. 31, 1919, pp. 95, 96.
1924 Schmidt, Karl P. Copeia, No. 132, July 15, 1924, p. 68.
1923 Stejneger, L. and T. Barbour. A Check List of North American Amphibians and Reptiles. 2nd Edition, Cambridge, 1923, p. 30.
1923 Viosca, Percy, Jr. Copeia, Feb. 1, 1923, No. 115, p. 39.
1923 Wright, A. H. The Anatomical Record. Jan. 20, 1923, Vol. 24, No. 6, p. 406.
1923 ———. Copeia No. 115, Feb. 1, 1923, p. 34.
1923 ———. Ecology VII, No. 1, January 1926, pp. 82, 83.
1924 Wright, A. H. and Wright, A. A. American Naturalist, Vol. LVIII, July-August 1924, p. 378.

Hyla femoralis Latreille

(Pl. II, Fig. 8; V, Fig. 2; VII, Fig. 3; X, Fig. 4; XII, Fig. 13; XV, Fig. 3; XVII; XXVII; XXVIII; Text Fig. I, 17)

COMMON NAMES

Pine Woods Tree Frog. Pine Woods Tree Toad. Pine Tree Toad. Pine Tree Frog. "Scraper Frog." Femoral Hyla.

RANGE

Check list. "Type Locality: Carolina. Range: Carolinas to Florida and west to Texas." Stejneger and Barbour Check List 1923, p. 30.

Supplementary records. In 1926 (Wright, 1926, p. 82) we considered *Hyla femoralis* as one of the eleven Okefinokee frogs "which occur mainly in the Sabalian region or Gulf strip of the Lower Austral region." Its restricted range in North Carolina (Brimley, 1907, pp. 159) in Craven and New Hanover Counties and near Wilmington (Myers, 1924, p. 60) N. C., in South Carolina at Mt. Pleasant (Schmidt, 1924, p. 68) and Goose Creek and Cope's record for Georgia (Cope, 1889, p. 372) from Riceborough around to Nashville and Allapaha directly west to Waycross, Ga., also confirms this interpretation.

In 1922 on June 8 we did not hear it near Cheraw, S. C., when *Hyla cinerea, H. andersonii, Rana virgatipes, Bufo fowleri, Hyla versicolor* were calling, nor at Columbia, S. C., June 9, nor at Millen Sta., June 10 (*Hyla squirella, Hyla cinerea, Hyla gratiosa, Hyla versicolor* calling). On June 11 from the Altamaha near Jesup through Screven to Waycross and from Waycross to Folkston we heard them in the piney flatwoods. In February, 1911, J. C. Bradley took the species at Waynesville, Ga.

In 1917 our route led through Raleigh, Spartansburg, Atlanta, Montgomery to Mobile, Alabama. Not until we reached the Tombigbee river below Jackson in Washington County did we record our first specimens of this species. Then we came into Sabalian influences. In 1923 Viosca (1923, p. 36) records it from the Longleaf Pine Hills of Louisiana.

Little is known about this species and writers have assumed it not so abundant as others. Brimley (1910, p. 12) speaks of it as "apparently less common than *cinerea* and *squirella*." In the piney woods we have more notes on it than any other Hylid (except *Acris*) it was so abundant. Like *Hyla gratiosa* at times it betakes itself into the high pines and is hard to get, and like *Hyla gratiosa* is a decidedly Sabalian or Gulf strip species.

Local Okefinokee records. In 1912 we took it in the following Okefinokee localities: Billy Island, Mixon's Hammock, Honey Island, Prairie-heads. In 1921 on Billy, Chesser, Floyd, Craven, Black-Jack Islands, the Pocket, Craven Hammock, Billy's Bay, Honey Island Prairie, Suwannee Canal, St. Mary's and Suwannee Rivers. In 1922 we secured it at Trader's Hill, Camp Pinckney, Folkston, Starling Branch, St. Mary's, Chesser Island and other places in Georgia and at Callahan, Florida. It is essentially a pine barrens species.

GENERAL APPEARANCE

Cope (1889, p. 371) writes: "Body short, rather broad, and the entire appearance as to pattern of color and shape not very dissimilar from Hyla versicolor, from which, however, it is readily distinguishable by the femoral yellow spots; the dark postocular vitta, the absence of light spots under the eyes."

Brimley (1907, p. 158) characterizes it as follows: "Back . . . markings do not form an X-shaped mark. Back of thigh with yellow spots or variegations. No light spot below eye. No yellow spots on sides."

Deckert (1915, p. 3) who has studied southeastern frogs more intimately than most observers says this species "resembles our own gray tree frog, with its rough skin and star-shaped dark patch on the back, but is smaller and more slender."

We would consider this species a small species. Cope considers 35 mm. above the average size and his largest is 39 mm. LeConte a century ago gave 1 1/2–1 3/4 inches as the adult range and it has been repeated for this little understood form. It may reach 45 mm., as he says, but of the 140 specimens from 20 mm. upwards we have none over 40 mm., the average, 30 mm.

COLORATION OF SPIRIT SPECIMENS (1912)

In spirits the upper parts are usually some shades of dark brown, rarely light brown; in life the color of all our specimens was invariably gray or rarely grayish brown. The under parts are white. The blotch between the eyes is constant but seldom triangular. From either cephalic corner it sends a bar to the anterior end of the upper eyelid. From the two caudal corners of this interorbital spot two branches extend obliquely backwards to another median spot just back of the shoulder region on the anterior back. In two specimens these branches are connected with the anterior dorsal spot but not with the interorbital spot (just as in Holbrook's figure, Vol. 4, fig. 3) as most texts usually represent it. Obliquely backward from the anterior dorsal spot runs a dark bar to the middle of each side. Frequently between these last two bars there are two more which extend backwards from the anterior dorsal spot along the posterior back. Sometimes one or both of these bars is disconnected with the anterior dorsal spot or almost absent. Several isolated irregular spots sometimes take their place or represent the more regular bars.

From the tip of the snout a dark line extends to the eye. From the eye to the ear it is a band with two dark borders. Back of the ear the lower border ceases and the upper one passes over the shoulder to the middle of the side. Whenever this lower border extends farther back it is more or less broken. In all cases it more or less demarcates the separation of the brown or gray of the back from the white of the belly. Beneath this line there may be some of the dorsal color but very little. When this line breaks up back of the middle of the side, it often produces a mottling, reticulation or vermiculation along the groin. In some specimens the line may be faint or almost absent on the snout or back of the shoulder. In most of the larger specimens there is a dark line along the posterior edge of the forearm and anterior edge of the foreleg.

Most of the specimens have the transverse bars of the fore and hind limbs rather indistinct. Some have the whole throat to the white breast fold dotted. others have just the chin dotted or only its sides. In the males the whole throat area is much darker and the chin much the lighter. The posterior edge of the thigh has the dorsal body color with three to ten distinct circular or elliptical yellowish or yellowish white spots unlike the thigh reticulations in *Hyla versicolor*. Sometimes in the larger forms the spots are fewer and irregular, cordate or comma-shaped due to the fusion of spots.

STRUCTURAL CHARACTERS (WRITTEN IN 1912)

Upper surface more or less smooth, occasionally with scattered granulations; belly, under surface of thigh and breast strongly areolate, the throat granulate (smooth in one), the pectoral or breast fold smooth or slightly granulate, rarely strongly granulate. Third finger longest; fourth finger slightly longer than the second; fourth toe longest and with two phalanges free; the web does extend as a margin *to the disc of the longest toe but is not so wide as in Hyla versicolor;* tympanic fold present, rarely almost absent; vomerine teeth between the posterior nares; tongue usually slightly notched as Cope figures ('89, Fig. 94, 4) but 5 specimens have no notch, two being rounded and three truncate; two of the notched specimens had the right lobe much smaller; nostrils nearer tip of the snout than the eye.

MEASUREMENTS
(Recent Material)

Head to angle of mouth 1.14 (20 mm.)–1.25 (28 mm. ♂)–1.1 (28 mm. ♀)–1.2 (36 mm.♂)–1.31 (36 mm.♀)–1.47 (40 mm.♀) in width of head; head to rear of tympanum 1.06–1.0–1.0–1.09–1.09–1.11 in width of head; head to angle of mouth 2.85–3.5–3.1–3.6–3.8–3.7 in length of body; head to rear of tympanum 2.6–2.8–2.8–3.27–3.13–3.0 in length of body; snout .625–.88–.80–.70–.66–.91 in first finger; snout .875–1.10–1.1–1.1–1.0–1.08 in fourth finger; snout .625–.66–.70–.80–.66–.83 in first toe; eye 1.33–1.5–1.66–1.25–1.5–1.33 in snout; eye .66–.66–.83–.71–.62–.55 in tympanum; eye .83–1.33–1.33–.875–1.33–1.21 in first finger; tympanum 3.5–4.5–3.4–4,0–4.4–4.8 in intertympanic width; tympanum 2.0–2.25–2.0–1.6–2.4–2.4 in snout; internasal width 1.0–1.0–1.0–.83–1.16–1.2 in upper eyelid width; interorbital width .8–.66–.71–.57–.75–.625 in internasal width; interorbital width 2.8–3.0–2.4–2.8–2.75–3.0 in intertympanic width.

Forelimb: forelimb 1.66–2.0–1.86–2.1–2.1–1.81 in length of body; forelimb 2.5–3.2–2.73–3.1–3.18–2.7 in hind limb; first finger 1.6–1.62–1.5–2.0–1.87–1.36 in third finger; second finger 1.33–1.44–1.2–1.4–1.5–1.25 in third finger; second finger .63–.88–.80–.70–.80–.91 in first finger; third finger .75–.77–.66–.85–.80–.93 in second toe; fourth finger 1.14–1.3–1.1–1.27–1.25–1.15 in third finger; fourth finger .71–.60–.63–.72–.66–.77 in first toe; internasal width 1.25–2.0–1.6–1.16–1.33–2.2 in first finger. internasal width 1.5–2.25–2.0–1.66–1.66–2.4 in second finger; internasal width 2.0–3.25–2.4–2.33–2.5–3.0 in third finger; internasal width 1.75–2.5–2.2–1.83–2.0–2.6 in fourth finger.

Hindlimb. length 1.5–1.5–1.46–1.5–1.5–1.5 in hind limb; tibia 1.8–1.9–
1.8–2.1–2.05–1.9 in length; tibia 2.7–2.9–2.64–3.1–3.08–2.8 in hind limb; tibia
1.1–.90–.96–1.0–.97–1.05 in forelimb; tibia .68–.70–.64–.70–.80–.76 in hind
foot; first toe 1.2–1.6–1.14–1.5–1.5–1.4 in second toe; first toe 2.4–2.66–1.7–
2.25–2.37–2.0 in third toe; first toe 2.8–3.33–2.85–2.9–3.0–3.0 in fourth toe;
first toe 2.2–2.66–1.71–2.12–2.37–1.9 in fifth toe; second toe 2.0–1.6–4.5–
1.5–1.58–1.4 in third toe; second toe 2.33–2.0–2.5–1.9–1.5–1.58–1.4 in third
toe; second toe 2.33–2.0–2.5–1.9–2.0–2.14 in fourth toe; second toe 1.8–1.6–
1.5–1.4–1.58–1.35 in fifth toe; third toe 1.16–1.25–1.66–1.27–1.26–1.5 in
fourth toe; third toe .93–1.0–1.0–.94–1.0–.95 in fifth toe; fourth toe 1.07–1.15–
1.0–1.05–1.16–1.07 in hind foot; fourth toe 1.57–1.45–1.55–1.5–1.46–1.4 in
tibia; fourth toe 1.7–1.3–1.5–1.5–1.41–1.47 in fore limb; fifth toe 1.2–1.25–
1.66–1.34–1.26–1.6 in fourth toe; internasal width 1.2–1.5–1.4–1.33–1.33–2.0 in
first toe; internasal width 1.5–2.5–1.6–2.0–2.0–2.8 in second toe; internasal
width 3.0–4.0–2.4–3.0–3.16–4.0 in third toe; internasal width 3.5–5.0–4.0–
3.8–4.0–6.0 in fourth toe; internasal width 2.75–4.0–2.2–2.83–3.16–3.8 in
fifth toe.

HABITAT

Holbrook (1842, Vol. IV, p. 128) writes: "This little animal lives in the
deep forests of Carolina and Georgia; it chooses trees for its residence, and is
sometimes found thirty feet from the ground, feeding on such insects as choose
the same localities." In 1855 LeConte (p. 429) notes that they are not about
dwellings like *Hyla squirella*. Deckert (1914, p. 3) in his "List of Salientia from
near Jacksonville, Florida," (1911–1912) says "*Hyla femoralis* Latreille, (is)
common on pine trees, but not easily caught." In 1915 (p. 3) the same author
adds: "*Hyla femoralis* Latreille is called the Pine tree toad, from its habit of
frequenting the tops of pine trees almost exclusively during the summer
months."

In 1925 Viosca in discussing the Florida Parishes or uplands of Louisiana
comments that "To the east of the Shortleaf Pine area are the Longleaf Pine
Hills with gentle slopes, and intertwined by winding creeks. Here we have a
limited representation of practically all species found in the uplands generally
and in addition, some species which may be said to be characteristic. *Hyla
femoralis* is the typical tree frog of this section."

At Leroy, Ala., June 12, 1917, Dr. H. H. Knight while sweeping bushes
and lower branches of trees with an insect net for Caspids caught two young
Hyla femoralis.

In 1912 we make the following notes on habitat: "On the outskirts of the
swamp we found this form in the cut-over lands. Here they were taken on
the small shrubs and on the ground. On the lily-covered prairies south of
Honey Island they were not infrequently found as was *Hyla cinerea*. A few
were observed on the lily pads or in bushes of the little islets of this area.
Many of the specimens from Billy's Island were taken from the various buildings of the Lee family and particularly from the sides of the old cabin camp
of our party or in the small shrubs or trees nearby. Holbrook's observations
that it (Vol. 4, p. 128) differs from *H. squirella* "for it is never found near

outhouses or about fences and in old fields" must consequently not be taken too literally, though the conditions on Billy's Island even in Lee's clearing are yet essentially forest-like in their nature.

In 1921 we have made the following notes on habitat. On April 27 we have "This morning four *Hyla femoralis* are dead. Two inches of rain water in their can. Apparently they like water in general less than some other forms and are rather delicate." On May 9 "Harry Chesser brought us a *Hyla femoralis* which he caught on a cypress tree in a cypress bay. Surely it is not restricted to pines." On May 7 we have a *Hyla femoralis* from the hammock.

FIRST APPEARANCE

In 1921 we entered the swamp April 21. At once the boys began to bring us pinewood's tree frogs. One specimen of April 25 was a spent female which shows the specimen must have been abroad some time before. The earliest seasonal record we have is a specimen taken February 19,1911, by Professor J. C. Bradley at Waynesville, Ga.

GENERAL HABITS

Metachrosis. In 1826 (p. 342) Harlan holds "its colors various: a variety with the back chiefly occupied with a large irregular blotch; *legs* barred." In 1855 LeConte (p. 428) notes that "The darker marks in the head and back are sometimes evanescent but the yellow spots on the hind part of the thighs are always more or less distinctly visible. The chin is cancellately reticulate, sometimes speckled with dusky, sometimes altogether of that color. The color of the body above varies at the will of the animal."

Deckert (1915, p. 3) writes that "Its usual color is dark reddish-brown or chestnut, but it can readily change from fleshy pink or pale gray to any shade of brown, gray or green."

In 1921 a little 20 mm. *Hyla femoralis* has these colors (Non-Ridgway) April 26: "Back greenish gray with dusky. Black line from snout through eye over tympanum past angle of mouth half way to unguinal region. Upper margin silvery or yellowish silvery; lower margin of black vitta yellow. There is some pinkish bronze on rear end of vitta. Bright silvery or yellowish stripe on back of hind foot, fainter on back of tibia. Yellow over vent and on to femur posterior half way to knee. Only three rear orange yellow spots on each femur."

On April 27, 1921 we have the note "James Lee says that he found on rail fence some which are whiter than those he finds in the rain barrels which have boards or cover over the top." One rain barrel specimen we watched for several days before May 2. On May 4 we observed that it "had remained several days. It is as dark as the wood over it." On the following day, May 5, it was still in the barrel.

Two weeks later, May 19, "on the way back from a trip to Crosby Pond at 6:00 p. m. near the remains of an old cypress pond in piney woods saw a female *Hyla femoralis* hopping along into saw palmetto. It was as whitish gray as any *Hyla versicolor* I ever saw. The spot in middle of back showed beautifully, also spot between the eyes. This female I took out to look at it. It leaped away on to gray sand. Has a hard time seeing it, it matched the gray sand so well. In one minute since its capture it had darkened considerably. In denser cover 9 inches high with small saw palmetto, *Vaccinium myrsinites*, calico bush, *Gaylussacia frondosa*, etc., found a half grown *H. femoralis*. It was green on its back (very suggestive in size, color and appearance or marks of *Hyla squirella*, which strangely enough we don't get here). A little later lost another *Hyla femoralis* in same place as the green one. Anent the half grown green specimen on May 21 we have the note: "In the compartment of *Hyla femoralis*, most of the specimens, in fact all (including one little half grown one green when captured) are vandyke brown or moss brown." "A captive female in jar June 19 is pale light mouse gray on back with no markings revealed." On July 18, Harper makes the note: "*Hyla femoralis* on green palmetto frond in sun in p.b. about 4:00 p. m., bleached out, much as at night; bending the neck back, to rival *Chorophilus*."

General habits. In 1921 we acquired the following notes on their daytime, non-breeding habits and resting.

On April 23, the boys found two on the rail fence at 2:30 p. m. The next day they brought three more from the same fence. On April 26, the boys found some more *Hyla femoralis* in the rain barrels along the railroad and near the company's wood pile. "In a pine near camp about 15 or 20 feet up on the end fork of large branch is a *Hyla femoralis* male. It doubtless is the one we have heard ever since we have been here." On April 27 the boys brought in another male from the rain barrels along the railroad. The rain barrels too are used in putting out the trees when they start to burn.

VOICE

LeConte, 1855, seems to be the first to note that it differed from *H. squirella* in voice. No one since has remarked about its voice until Deckert (1915, pp. 3, 4) writes that "The noise resulting from the calls of the males on these occasions, is deafening. This call cannot be reproduced on paper, being a rapid succession of harsh, rattling notes, higher in pitch than the call of *H. squirella*, and kept up all night. During the dry season this tree toad occasionally calls from the tops of the pine trees, one answering the other."

In 1921 the first general calling of *Hyla femoralis* came May 14. Then the author "Went to Billy's Lake Landing. Worked eastward. Heard plenty of *Hyla femoralis* in trees. They are approaching or are on the edge of cypress ponds. Some are yet high in the trees. They are calling at intervals all over the piney woods, particularly near the edges of cypress bays. One call, an interval, one very faint call, interval. . . ."

On May 16 "When a threatening storm passed over *Hyla femoralis* from the trees were almost in chorus. Around cypress ponds several calling. One was on a projecting piece of pine bark on the tree and within reach, about six feet from the ground. Harper saw it croak. Afterwards the throat pulsated all the time." Harper notes that it "let me come up in plain sight, within a couple of yards and croaked for me on its bark slab-perch. Throat kept distended while its sides, or rather whole body, vibrate. *Kek, kek* about 20 times, usually ending in *krak, krak*. Surely a cracked voice." Later in the evening we visited this croaker but "it was gone and not on the bit of projecting bark. Soon we understood. In two or three trees low down we heard *Hyla femoralis*. Their notes are speeded up, more extended and continuous than when high in the pines. One we found on the moss. The instant we entered (another) pond we heard a queer note and it was from the trunk of a bay tree right near us. It proved to be a male *Hyla femoralis*. All around us they were calling. One was in a bush 3 feet above ground. Another on moist ground at edge of pond in amongst six foot sedges. When a male croaks it is the lower throat which swells out, not the chin region as well. Brought back three *Hyla femoralis*."

On May 21 "After the rain we started for the turpentine still. In piney woods heard and saw *Hyla femoralis* all afternoon but isolated calls. When a warm shower came they leaped into chorus. Sounds like a peculiar *Cicada* note in chorus, only once in a while is the frog-like character revealed when a frog ends its call with the last two or three squeaks. This gives it away. The chorus is one continuous stridulating din and goes down the piney woods like a wave. Rain is not over. They are at it yet (5:30 p. m.)."

During a congress when several species are breeding in the same pond the machine gun calls of *Hyla femoralis* make it difficult to hear or time other calls. Once when we were timing the intervals in *Gastrophyne's* calls *Hyla femoralis* calls would break in frequently. In 1921 and 1922 we recorded several instances where their calls drowned out the calls of *Hyla gratiosa, Hyla squirella, Bufo quercicus* and *Pseudacris ocularis*. We tried the experiment of half closing our ears to close out the *Hyla femoralis* calls. The other sounds came out very distinctly in the attempt. The breeding evening congress call is the diurnal *Kek* speeded up, as many as 6 or 7 coming in a second. We have counted 60 or 70 or more calls in rapid succession without deflation.

1921

April	24.	Heard *Hyla femoralis* in trees 7:30 p. m. Long Pond.
April	25.	Near Long Pond one or two calling.
April	27.	In the trees *H. femoralis* are calling in isolated cases but more than heretofore. Day overcast. 67°. At 9:30 heard a few in trees. Air 76°.
April	28.	About three heard.
April	30.	Tonight air cold. Temperatures range from 50–70°. Little humidity, brisk. Over in Long Pond and elsewhere we hear no *Hyla femoralis*. As yet we have not heard them at night.
May	3.	Tonight at 8:00 air 56°. The last few days have been so cool that we have heard no *Hyla femoralis*.
May	9.	Occasionally during day (air up to 84° or higher) hear *Hyla femoralis*.
May	11.	Temperature 70°F. at 6:30 a. m. Feels like rain. Hear several *Hyla femoralis*.
May	12.	Considerable rain. One *Hyla femoralis* heard.
May	14.	At 7:00 p. m. several *Hyla femoralis* calling. During day several calling from pine trees.

May 15. Rains from east all day. *Hyla femoralis* calling at night. Temperature, today 66–69°; tonight 66–67°. During day once in a while *Hyla femoralis* calls.

May 16. Storm threatening, brought almost a chorus in pine trees today. Very active at night.

May 17. Heard *Hyla femoralis* several times but not very active.

May 18. Chorus at 9:30 p. m.

May 19. Several calling around edges of ponds.

May 20. One calling. We have heard this species soon after camp was established. Several calling in woods.

May 21. No end of *Hyla femoralis* calling at night. Air 70°.

May 24. Tonight very few calling 10:00 p. m. Air 77°. A dry non-humid day.

May 27. Hear *Hyla femoralis* about camp. Air 78°, 1:20 p. m.

May 28. Hear one at 8:00 a. m. Air 82°.

May 30. Hear several 7:00 a. m.

June 1. On Jones Island hear *Hyla femoralis*. Common near canal.

June 2. Two heard.

June 3. None calling on Island. Common on Billy Island Bay.

June 4. Hear 7:20 a. m., pinewood tree frog in trees. Sky overcast. Air 73°.

June 5. No end of *Hyla femoralis* calling and abroad.

June 12. One heard in hammock.

June 13. One or two heard.

June 14. One heard. Air 71°.

June 16. Heard 7:00 a. m., one.

June 18. One heard 6:15 p. m.

June 20. From time to time heard quite a few. Air 75°.

June 23. After two inches rain no end of them in chorus.

June 24. Males calling.

June 25. Plenty calling.

June 26. Heard a few.

June 28. Calling commonly.

June 29. Common.

July 1. No end at night.

July 3. Great chorus. Air about 70°.

July 6. Heard one.

July 7. Heard one or two after dark.

July 9. One calling at 8:45 p. m.

July 10. Rain. Great chorus.

July 11. None calling.

July 14. One or two 6:30 a. m. Air 74°.

July 15. Heard them.

July 16. Abundant at Coatbet Pond 8:30–10:00 p. m.

July 17. Calling lustily.

July 23. Some calling at 7:45 a. m.

July 24. *Hyla femoralis* common at night. Several at 8:00 a. m. and 12 noon.

July 27. As night comes on several start up. Black Jack Island.

July 28. Abundantly calling.

July 29. Common.

August 9. Calling along St. Mary's River.

August 10. Several calling.

August 14. Several.

August 15. Two heard.

August 16. Commonly heard.

August 22. *Hyla femoralis* at Billy's Island camp.

1922

June	12.	Chesser Island, few in corn field calling at dark.
June	13.	Few calling in hammock.
June	14.	Several around Coat Bet Pond at night. Few heard around camp during day.
June	18.	Heard one in hammock at 1:00 p. m.
June	22.	Heard several around camp 6:30 p. m.
June	23.	Heard a few pines around open pond near Trader's Hill.
June	25.	Two in hammock at camp.
June	26.	Several calling after sunset.
June	28.	Slight rain. Several heard in hammock.
June	29.	Heard a few in oaks 8:05 a. m.
July	2.	Heard many at Starling Branch 8:30 p. m.–midnight.
July	3.	Rainy 1–3:00 p. m. *Hyla femoralis* calling some.
July	4.	One heard.
July	8.	Several heard in hammock during shower.
July	9.	One heard at Thompson Landing, St. Mary's River.
July	10.	Common in cypress bay.
July	11.	Several heard during the day.
July	12.	Around edge of Coat Bet many calling. A large assembly.
July	13.	One heard at 10:00 a. m. in pine barrens.
July	15.	A few heard.
July	16.	Heard at 7:40 a. m.
July	17.	Several calling 6–7 p. m.
July	18.	Several heard.
July	19.	Common in rain.
July	21.	Many late in evening.
July	23.	A few at Coatbet Pond.
July	25.	Quite a few calling but not as many as we would expect after a hard rain.
July	26.	No end of calling males. Air 86°.
July	28.	One heard on prairie 9:00 a. m.
July	29.	One heard at camp.
July	30.	Several heard at 7:00 a. m.
August	1.	Waycross, Ga. *Hyla femoralis* numerous along Dixie Highway at night.
August	2.	Hopkins, Ga. One heard 11:15 a. m.
August	4.	Several calling in rain p. m.
August	5.	Several calling 7:30 a. m. About 70°F.
August	8.	Big chorus at night. Temperature 79°. After today's rain.
August	9.	Commonly calling after dark.
August	10.	*H. femoralis* quite numerous.
August	11.	Heard a very few at Camp Pinckney—Chesser Island 8:00 p. m. to 12:00 midnight.
August	12.	Several at night.
August	13.	Commonly heard often in chorus 7–10:30 p. m.
August	14.	A very few heard.
August	15.	One heard.
August	16.	Common in Spadefoot ponds.
August	17.	Strong chorus in evening.
August	18.	One heard during evening.
August	19.	Congress at night.
August	20.	Common along road near St. George.
August	26.	One at 9:00 a. m. in hammock.
August	30.	Several heard.

Sept.   9.   Heard at 6:20 p. m.
Sept.   12.   Heard at 6:40 p. m.
Sept.   16.   Several heard at night during heavy rain.

In 1921 in the last of April and first of May we had a good index of *Hyla femoralis* activity. On April 24, April 25 and April 27 under influence of 65–75° temperatures and cloudy weather we heard a few, but on April 30 to May 8 minima range from 40–54°, average 48 or below, maxima from 73–83, average 77 for four stations around the swamp. The cold, brisk, clear weather kept them inactive and none were calling. There was no or little rain before May 11 when several *Hyla femoralis* began to call. The air felt like rain on this date and for two weeks considerable rain fell. *Hyla femoralis* became very active. Minima 60–70, maxima 73–89, average 82. It, therefore, was not the maxima of April 30–May 8 or May 11–25 which played the prominent part but the higher minima 60–70 (not 40–54 of April 30–May 8) and most of all humidity were the important factors. These periods are typical and no need of reviewing the whole period of 1921 and 1922 in necessary.

MATING

Male (From life, June 5, 1921). Cephalic half of pectoral fold pale vinaceous drab to darkish grayish brown, posterior half like the belly. Throat darker than the belly.

Female (From life, June 5, 1921). General color sorghum brown or deep brownish drab or mars brown on back. Black spot between eyes. Another spot with four points two behind and two ahead, the cephalic ends above tympanum. Two on either side of the middle of the back and one over the crupper. Black or deep brown line from snout through nostril to eye narrow. From eye through tympanum to groin where it breaks up into spots. Another of same color on back of fore foot, fore arm, front of fore leg and over vent. Below white line of the vent is a black one. Spots on rear of thighs orange to chrome or light cadmium. One female with grayish white spots instead of orange spots. Under parts white. Pectoral fold pure white to angle of the mouth. Chin white with fine black spots.

Iris ecru drab, drab gray, pale vinaceous drab with reticulation of black in it.

Structural differences. In the Hylidae as Bufonidae we are accustomed to saying that the throat of the female is not dark but more or less like the rest of the venter. In many of the females of *Hyla femoralis* the throat is white but sometimes the prominent white granulations have brown reticulations around their bases. Occasionally only the tip of the granulations is white and the general effect of the throat is very dark.

The measurements of 134 adults, 70 males and 64 females yield the following results: males range 24-37 mm., mode 31 mm., average 30 mm.; females, range 23-40 mm., mode 36 mm., average 32 mm. A study of the modes for these sexes reveals the following: The males and females start about 24 mm. The first mode for the males comes at 28 (9 specimens) mm. while the first female mode is 30 (9 specimens). The second mode for the males is

31 mm. (17 specimens) while the second for females is 33 (8 specimens). The males then taper from 31 mm., down to 37 mm. while the females have another mode at 36 of 10 specimens. The males thus seem to be 2 mm. more or less smaller at each mode and at the largest size than the female. The largest male is 37 while we have two females 40 mm. The bulk of the breeding males and females came from 27 mm. onwards or at the beginning of the second year. The few breeding males and females at 24, 25 and 26 mm. are doubtless also at the beginning of the second year rather than at the end of the first year.

Duration, night or day. On the night of May 18, 1921, at 9:30 p. m. at Long Pond "There was a perfect din in cypress bays and at the north edge of this pond from *Hyla femoralis*. Some were in bushes, other on bay trunks, and others were hopping in moss edges or grassy edges of the pond or amongst the lizard's-tail (*Saururus*). Could find no mated pairs. On the moss edge, not in pond proper found *Hyla cinerea* pair." On the following day, May 19 "the boys at different times brought in females of *Hyla femoralis* found on the ground in different parts of the island. They must be bound for the ponds. We found one in the hammock on the ground near Long Pond (see above May 18)."

On May 21, 1921 after 8:00 p. m. we found a congress of *Hyla femoralis* and these are our rough notes: "We found a *Hyla femoralis* on a log croaking; one or several on the grass; many in trees and bushes 2–4 or 6 feet above ground or water. One male is croaking and crawling up the tree right after another male which is not croaking. The males after a time might dislike the flashlight and walk up the tree for a foot more or less. We found some croaking in amongst some pine bush in the water. Harrison Lee espied a pair mated on a branch of the pine brush. The pair 1–1 1/2 feet above water. We flashed them twice. They did not move. Broke when I captured them. Put them together in a jar. Soon they were mated again. Brought them to camp at 11:30 p. m. At 12:00 midnight put in a porcelain pan for photography. In the morning at 6:00 they had laid and broken." The following night little happened. "One male was calling from bush beside Newt Pond. On the pond no end of *Hyla femoralis* eggs. The males crawl up under grass edges or logs or any cover. Are they more or less subterranean?"

Another congress of June 4, 1921, reveals other points of interest: "No end of *Hyla femoralis*. Where do they come from? On one palmetto within 2 or 3 feet of each other were 5 male *Hyla femoralis* calling. Later Marion Lee found a *Hyla femoralis* pair on saw palmetto leaf 1 1/2 feet above ground. Took another pair on the moss at the edge of pond. Everywhere in the road home were *Hyla femoralis* migrating. In little transient pools no end of *Hyla femoralis*. Took another pair *Hyla femoralis* moving along in the path. Tonight frogs are laying in all sorts of transient places.

In 1922 we made these two pertinent series of journal observations. On "July 3, 8:00 p. m.–1:00 a. m. July 4 in a pond 1/2 mile west of Trader's Hill, Ga., there was a great din of these frogs in a shallow grassy pond. No end of *Bufo quercicus*, a few *Hyla squirella*, 4 *Hyla gratiosa* calling, a few toads, plenty of *Acris*. Never heard such a composite racket, and our ears rang for a long period afterwards. Took no end of *Hyla femoralis* males. Took a pair in the grassy water. At Anna's Pond the *Hyla femoralis* were common in the saw palmettoes around the edge of the open pond. Equally common were *Hyla squirella* which frequent the same place. The call of *Hyla femoralis* is much more rapid than that of *Hyla squirella*. Caught a pair of *Hyla femoralis* at this pond."

On July 11 at night "7:30–11:00 p. m. we hear no end of *Hyla femoralis* in every crossing and cypress pond. At the second 'dreen' we found many of them. They looked very queer as they skipped along the water ahead of the auto lights. They were especially centered about a clump of saw palmettoes. Here Miles Pirnie found a pair and I another. Later on on one blade were two more pairs and one male. In this clump were possibly 20 or 30 males calling. This breeding came after a hard rain."

The females doubtless do not enter the ponds until about ready to lay. On May 19, 1921, "the boys brought in several females on ground hopping along. They must be making for the ponds. Found one on the ground on hammock near Long Pond." In one pond June 5, 1921, after a breeding congress "we found two dead female *Hyla femoralis*." Doubtless they suffer as do females at a *Bufo* congress. All through May, June and July of 1921 the boys on Billy's Island used to find females hiding under grass during the day or hopping around on the island. In 1922 on Chesser Island, June 29, the Chesser girls "caught a female travelling along on the ground. It was gravid yet not swollen like some species." The next day "they found another female on the ground in the chufa field where they were working. It was in the shade." A week later, July 6, "Mr. Chesser hoed out another female in the open field. There has been a chorus of them in the pond nearby. Probably the female was resting here during the day." Five days later, July 11, 1922, we noted "at 10:00 a. m. a female crossing our path in the hammock headed for the pond where in the evening we recorded a great congress." Until a month later, August 6, we saw females hopping along in the hammock from time to time. One on last date was found moving toward a pond at 6:00 p. m. At 7:00 p. m. the chorus at this pond began in real earnest.

Amplexation (*Normal, abnormal, cross*). On May 21, 1921, we found the first pair mated in axillary fashion at about 11–11:30 p. m. They laid before the following morning. Two pairs captured the night of June 4-5 laid the same night and had axillary embrace. We found July 3, 1921, two pairs in overflowed sweet potato fields each normal in amplexation. So also another pair in Newt Pond. "The last pair we wished to observe but a toad butted them and we lost them." On July 2, 1922 between "8:30 p. m.–12:00 midnight caught a pair between 1:00 and 4:00 a. m. Same night they laid their complement. On the night of July 3, 8:00 p. m.–1:00 a. m., July 4, secured two pairs each at a different pond. Like the predecessors they embraced axillary-like and each pair laid eggs the same night between 1:00–7:00 a. m. On July 11, 1922 between 7:30–11:00 p. m. we secured four pairs. Each was normal in amplexation and laid this same night. We recorded no cross embraces in this species. We have this note of males mating for May 21, 1921. "Some of the males caught last night are now mated. These are axillary as was the mated pair." On June 4, 1921, we noted that "One of the *Hyla femoralis* pairs has the male larger than the female. Its left arm comes on to the breast to the middle line and the other hand is in the axilla or a little lower."

OVULATION

Miss M. C. Dickerson (1906, p. 151) writes of it that "Nothing is on record regarding the life history or habits." In 1915 Deckert (p. 3) calls it "one of the shyest of tree toads, rarely caught except during the breeding season, when it frequents certain 'bayous' in thousands."

Habitat. We found breeding congresses in grassy transient pools near the roads in the piney woods, in open ponds in cutover roads, in pools or ditches beside the railroad and roads, in cypress ponds and in cypress bays. We found mated pairs in overflowed grassy fields, shallow transient depressions, in temporary overflows or drenched cultivated fields, swamps or dreens in the cypress bays. Tadpoles were taken in pools beside Indian mounds, railroads, roads, in cypress ponds and sometimes on the prairies, in diverse ponds on the east mainland or in bays outside the swamp.

Period. In 1920 we (1920, p. 29) held that "The . . . tree frogs, like the . . . pine wood's tree frog, lay their eggs from the very last of May to July." Three years later (1923, p. 34) we considered *Hyla femoralis* as one of the five which start breeding from May 15 on to June 1. The next year we (1924, p. 37) made the "Season May 16 to August 21, for *Hyla femoralis.*"

In 1912 we made the following notes: "The breeding season must be about the same period as for *Hyla carolinensis.* The two specimens taken (May 6–23) by Mr. Harper were male and female respectively. The latter was full of ripe eggs. One spent female was captured June 5 and another June 18. From May 30–June 22, numerous gravid females were observed or taken. Far more than half of the adults were females and all of the specimens (11 in all) from 33–37.5 mm., in length were of this sex while the largest male proved 32 mm. In the males the skin of the throat region seems more loose and dark in color as in *Hyla versicolor* males. This large number of females seems indicative of the approach or arrival of the breeding period. The wonder is that none of us ever remembers hearing this form during the day, yet we quite frequently found the species active and the examination of the females showed them at the breeding point. Usually at the height of such periods Hylas call by day as well as by night. No doubt some of the frog chorus of the evening was of this species though we did not identify its call." This implies May 6–June 22.

On the basis of gravid or spent females we have in 1912 records of spent females, on May 29, June 5, June 7, June 15, June 16, June 18–20 (2), June 25–27. Of gravid females we recorded 13 frogs as follows: One before May 28, May 30–June 2 (3), June 1, June 5 (2), June 6–7 (2), June 12 (2), June 18–20, June 21 (2). This means they begin breeding before May 28, and continued after June 21. In 1921 on the same basis we have spent females April 25 (4), May 3, May 17, May 16–23, May 30 (2), June 5, June 23, June 30, July 3.

Gravid females: April 25, April 26, June 3, June 4 (3), June 9 (2), July 3. This gives a period beginning before April–July 3. In 1922 we have spent females from July 3–August 7 and gravid females June 29, July 2, July 3 (3), July 6, July 11, July 12. This gives a restricted period of June 29–July 12.

On the basis of mated pairs we have the first date May 20, 1921, followed by records on May 21, 1921, June 4, 1921, July 3, 1921, July 2, 1922, July 3, 1922 (2), July 11, 1922 (4), or a period from May 20–July 11. On the basis of recorded field eggs we have eggs taken May 21, 1921, May 22, 1921, May 26, 1921, May 27, 1921, June 4, 1921, June 5, 1921, June 6, 1921, July 3, 1921. In 1922 we have field eggs July 3, July 4, July 11, July 13, July 27, August 9, August 17. In 1922, the last chorus was recorded August 20, though some called until mid-September.

Viewed from records of spent or unspent females, choruses, field egg records, mated pairs and transformation dates (June 16–August 9) the ovulation begins as early as April 20 or 25 and extends to late August or September 1.

Temperature and humidity. In 1921 the temperature of ovulation periods were 82–95 maxima and minima 61–74°. Either before, during or after these periods rains of 1.22, 1.60, 2.80, 1.76, 1.00, 2.88, 2.27 and 1.60 inches prevailed in stations around the swamp. In 1922 the maxima were 81–96°, the minima 64–74°, the rains before, during or after breeding were 2.00, .80, .48, 1.80, 1.60 and 3.47 inches in stations about the swamp. With this species, like other southeastern species, humidity is the greatest factor. Temperature is secondary if it be above a certain essential minimum.

Egg-laying process. The films are so like those of *Hyla versicolor* they must lay their eggs in the same fashion. We often found groups of films 3–8 in number. These groups doubtless represented the 500–768 complement of one female. In the first captive pair the one film had 5 centers. The large films of 200, 150, 125 or 100 would not yield more than 3 or 4 films for a complement (500 eggs) if each film of the complement were large.

EGGS

Attachment, egg mass. The first mass identified positively came the night of May 20–21, 1921, for a pair captured that evening. This was laid in captivity. "The mass is 15–16 inches long. All connected, this is partially floating and partially resting on the bottom of the tray. The water is 3/4 of an inch deep. This floating mass suggests the same of *Hyla versicolor*. There are five centers of oviposition apparent." Our first field notes at the same time are: "Found egg band attached to stems of grasses. It is 2–3 inches long and 1/2 inch in width, brown above and yellowish or cream below. Now it is 1/4–1/2 or 1 inch below surface of the water. Was it at surface before today's rain or laid beneath surface? This pond is out in the open. Another complement of three bands; one 3–4 inches long; another 6 inches; the third 4–5 inches, brown and yellowish. This is in water below the surface slightly and amongst grass where two small pine top branches had fallen in the water. Find another complement of four masses one 2 x 2 inches; one 1 x 1/2 inches in diameter; one bandlike. Probably close to surface before today's rain. Place where last two complements are found is directly under the pine brush on which we caught pair last night."

On the following day, May 22 "found an area at the end of pond amongst sticks, trash and chips where eight film packets of *Hyla femoralis* eggs were laid. In the railroad ditches with oil and dirt on the surface the masses stand out as black areas darker than the rest of the surface of the water. In another part of the ditch three films of *Hyla femoralis* with a *Gastrophryne* egg film 4 x 7 inches. In another pond clear 20 x 3 feet found floating amongst grassy edges a packet of 100–125 eggs. They are brown and yellowish. One mass 6 x 3 inches separated from another round mass 2 1/2 x 2 1/2 inches. More eggs in a mass than in *Hyla versicolor*. Insects get into fresh masses and get stuck. Some masses amongst roots. Two masses either side of a floating root, one of them 3 x 3, another 3 x 2 inches.

On May 27, 1921, in a run found numerous spoiled *R. sphenocephala* egg masses beneath the surface. Above these eggs on the surface were *Hyla femoralis* films. The surface temperature is 85–90°. One film floating free on water. One film has 200 eggs, another 150 eggs, another 125 and the rest smaller. Film may be elliptical, circular and otherwise. Films floating some distance. Have seen them go 10 feet in as many minutes. Some films attached to ends of iris leaves. First eggs we recorded were in bands but films are normal. If one touches the surface of a film the part touched adheres to the finger. If loosened the part falls back in a little ball, reveals the yellowish vegetative pole or it will cause the film to take a band shape first recorded for this species. Probably the films were fastened or stuck to grass and rain raised them and gave them the band-like shape as a consequence. One film laid on moss in water's edge."

On June 5, 1921, "in one pond south of our old 1912 camp were no end of *Hyla femoralis* eggs at the water's surface. The litter had all drifted to the masses. Water surface between masses clear. Jelly just covered with trash. Easy to tell where mass was and where not."

In 1922, we have a few additional pertinent notes. Of a mass laid by a captive pair July 4 there is the note: "Eggs are in a loose string. Outer envelopes merge into an outer mass like *Ambystoma* masses. Inner envelopes with vitelli show distinct in the jelly mass. Nevertheless this is a film. *Hyla squirella* does not seem to have this appearance. In another pond were many films which are doubtless *Hyla femoralis* eggs. There are some quite band-like. Are any of these *Hyla squirella* eggs?" On July 27, in a pond covered with spoiled eggs was one fresh mass on the surface 2 x 14 inches in length. The mass was wavy. After a very heavy rain August 17 spadefoots filled a pond with its eggs, every grass blade being bent over with them. All over the surface were little packets of fresh *Hyla femoralis* eggs.

On the night of June 4–5, 1921, a female laid its complement without an attendant male.

Egg description. In 1912 our data were as follows: "The ovarian eggs are brown on the animal poles and creamy or yellowish white on the vegetative poles. In fact they look very much like those of *H. versicolor* and *H. cinerea*.

PLATE XXVIII

Pine wood's tree-frog (*Hyla femoralis*)

1. Pool with egg clusters, Billy Id., Ga. May 22, 1921.
2. Seven egg clusters, showing black on greasy surface of trackside pool, Billy Id., Ga. May 22, 1921.
3. Eggs, Billy Id., Ga. May 22, 1921.
4. Male croaking, Billy Id., Ga. May 16, 1921. Flashlight.
5. Male croaking, Billy Id., Ga. June 29, 1921. Flashlight.
6. 7. 8. Tadpoles, Anna's pond, Folkston, Ga. June 27, 1922. × 1.0.
9. Tadpole with 4 legs, Anna's pond, Folkston, Ga. June 27, 1922. × 1.0.
10. Tadpole with shrinking tail, Chesser Id., Ga. July 13, 1922. × 1.0.
11. Tadpole with stub of tail, Chesser Id., Ga. July 6, 1922. × 1.0.
12. Transformed frog, Chesser Id., Ga. July 2, 1922. Dorsal aspect. × 1.0.

1

4

5

2

6

7

8

9

10

3

11

12

A count of the eggs in the right ovary of the largest ripe female (37.5 mm. long) gives 273 eggs or approximately 500 or 550 for the complete complement. This equals or exceeds the number to be found in the average female Carolina tree frog. The latter may exceed the pine woods tree frog by an inch in length but the extreme slenderness in the loins, even in gravid females does not admit of a large egg complement as in the short stocky *Hyla femoralis* the ripe females of which are discernible at once. The ovarian eggs of these two species are practically the same in diameter and we thus have a relatively larger complement in *Hyla femoralis*. Actually the ovarian eggs of *Hyla cinerea* are slightly larger but this does not vitiate the result. The measurements of ovarian eggs of the two species gives .8–1.2 mm. for those of *Hyla femoralis* and 1.1–1.5 mm. for those of *Hyla cinerea*. In proportions, appearance and habits this species is a miniature *Hyla versicolor* and no doubt its breeding habits are very similar."

In 1921 our field notes on eggs are: "Eggs laid in captivity May 21, 1921 have vitellus .8–.9 mm., inner envelope 1.4–1.6 mm.; outer envelope loose, not distinct from 4–6 mm., sometimes as much as 8 mm. Most of eggs without circular outer envelope distinct because connected with the mass. Small edition of *Hyla versicolor*. Egg cream or yellowish on vegetative pole, brownish on animal pole."

On June 4, 1921, in comparing *Hyla femoralis* and *Hyla cinerea* "*Hyla femoralis* eggs are smaller, vitellus .8–.9 mm., inner envelope 1.4–1.6, outer envelope indeterminate. Vegetative pole quite yellowish or cream, more yellowish than in *Hyla cinerea*."

Laboratory examinations of 58 eggs reveal 18 with vitellus .8 mm., 7 with vitellus .9 mm., 31, 1.0 mm. and 2, 1.2 mm., average .95 mm., mode 1.0 mm. The inner envelopes ranged from 1.4–2.0 mm. The outer envelope was seldom visible, occasionally distinct, 4, 5 or 7 mm. in diameter.

On June 29, 1922, the count of the left ovary of a gravid female showed 384 eggs to be laid, a possible complement of 768 eggs. On the following day another female's left ovary was counted. It gave 382 or a possible 766 in all. The complement reaches from 500–768 eggs.

Dangers. This species lays in any pine barrens pool. Many a shallow grassy pool will have packets of their eggs. Many are caught by hatching; certainly many of the tadpoles never mature. There must be a great loss in this species. On July 3, 1921, they were laying in the flooded furrows of cane, corn and sweet potato fields. These were all lost. On June 4, 1921, we made the notes "Tonight the frogs of several species (*Hyla femoralis* included) are laying in all sorts of transient places."

In 1922 the species bred in great numbers in a crossway on the night of July 11. On July 13 the cross-way was practically dry. "All the *Hyla femoralis* eggs found July 11 were now gone if they ever hatched." On July 27 in one pond we found "all over the pond spoiled eggs of *Hyla femoralis* caught no doubt by a decided change of level."

HATCHING PERIOD

"Eggs laid early morning of May 21, 1921, hatched early morning of May 24, 1921, or three days later." Eggs "collected in the field in the morning of May 22 after the laying of the night of May 20–21 hatched the night of May 23–24" or three days later. Eggs "laid the night of June 4–5, 1921, after midnight were hatched by June 7, 6:00 a. m. or three days after ovulation." The eggs laid by one captive pair July 4, 1921, did not hatch at all. Doubtless captivity, infertility, restricted quarters or laying without male may have caused it.

MATURE TADPOLE

Color description from life (July 8, July 16, 1921). Upper parts of body olivaceous black to dull greenish black. Throat on either side below eye pomegranate purple. Belly on sides and across breast light vinaceous purple; center of belly solid sulphur-yellow. Chin clear with very little or no black dots. In younger tadpoles general color light yellowish olive or grayish olive. All over upper parts are fine light grayish vinaceous or light vinaceous fawn dots and on the muscular part of tail but not on the crests. These dots become larger on dark upper eyelid and give a conspicuous arrangement. In half-grown tadpoles a cream-colored ring under the eye and extending backward on either side of back for a distance. In very young tadpoles the ring is almost complete about the eye but not on the back. This ring faintly present in mature tadpoles and extends backward on to the base of the musculature of the tail. Under the eye it is warm buff, on body buffy brown and cartridge buff or tilleul buff.

Tail. Beginning at body there runs along musculature for one-half or more of its length a white, cartridge buff or pale cinnamon pink stripe marked off by the dark brown or black ground color of the upper half of the musculature and lower crests with prominent large spots black in younger specimens, and clusters of mouse gray on mature tadpoles. The tip of tail (both upper and lower crests) clear of spots. Area of crest next to musculature clear in upper.

General appearance. Tadpole small (36 mm.) full and deep bodied. Tail medium to fairly long, tip acuminate and very pointed. Tail with a prominent flagellum the dorsal and ventral crests of which are usually colorless. Tail deep and dorsal and ventral crests well developed. The dorsal crest may exceed the musculature in depth and extends on to the body to the vertical of of the spiracle or half way between spiracle and eye. Spiracle sinistral, directed more backwards than upwards, far below the lateral axis and visible as an elliptical opening. Eye on the lateral axis, in dorsal aspect on the lateral outline and in consequence visible from the venter. Anus dextral, very near the level of the edge of the lower crest. Muciferous crypts indistinct.

Mouth parts: Teeth 2/3. Upper labium fringed with a continuous row of labial teeth; the papillae extend above and inwards beyond the end of the upper fringe for about 4/11 to 2/5 of the length of the upper fringe. The end of the second row usually is even with the end of the upper fringe. The horny beak is contained about 2.0 times in the upper fringe. The median space between the lateral second upper labial very short, 6–10 times the length of either lateral row. The inner papillae extend under the third row of lower labial teeth making at least two rows of papillae across the lower labial border. In the lower labial corner there is a heavy papillary series of 4 or 5 rows like *H. versicolor* or *H. squirella*. The lower third labial is long and is usually about 1.10–1.2 in the first or second row, longer than in *H. squirella* and is larger than the horny beak. The first and second rows are about equal and 1.4–1.6 greater than the horny beak. This species, like *Hyla versicolor* and *Hyla squirella* has a very angulate upper fringe at its middle.

Measurements. Length of body (8.0–12.0 mm.), in tail (13.5–2.40 mm.) 1.3–2.5, average 1.75. Width (4.5–6.5 mm.) of body in its own length 1.6–2.1, average 1.8. Depth (4.5–7.0 mm.) of body usually slightly greater than body width (4.5–6.5 mm.). Depth of body 1.33–2.2 in body length, average 1.68. Depth (4.5–10 mm.) of tail in length of tail 1.6–2.75, average 2.25. Muscular part (3.5–4.5 mm.) 1.8–2.3 in depth of tail, average 2.1. Spiracle 1.1–1.4 nearer base of hind legs or vent region (5.0–6.0 mm.) than the tip of the snout (5.5–8.0 mm.), 1.24 average. Spiracle 1.5–2.5 nearer eye (2.0–4.0 mm.) than base of hind legs or vent (5.0–6.0 mm.), average 1.87. Eye 1.0–1.75 nearer to spiracle (2.0–4.0 mm.) than to tip of snout (3.2–4.5 mm.), average 1.25. Nostril 1.2–2.3 nearer eye (1.2–2.5 mm.) than snout (2.0–3.0 mm.), average 1.85. Mouth (2.0–3.5 mm.) equal to the internasal space (2.0–3.5 mm.). Mouth contained 1.4–2.0 (average 1.65) in interorbital distance (3.5–6.0 mm.). Internasal space (2.0–3.5 mm.) contained in interorbital space 1.3–2.0, average 1.7.

The dimensions of the largest tadpole are:

	mm.		mm.
Total length	33.0	Spiracle to vent	6.0
Body length	10.5	Spiracle to eye	4.0
Body depth	5.0	Eye to snout	3.2
Body width	6.5	Eye to nostril	1.5
Tail length	22.5	Nostril to snout	3.0
Tail depth	7.5	Mouth	3.0
Musculature of tail	3.5	Interorbital distance	5.0
Spiracle to snout	8.0	Internasal distance	3.5

General remarks. In 1912 we provisionally identified these tadpoles as of *Acris gryllus* because of similar pattern on the tadpole tail and *Acris* rear femur coloration. It was not until June 16,1921, almost a month after first eggs recorded we secured checks to identify these tadpoles. It was not until July 8 ,we dared describe the coloration provisionally. On July 17, 1921, we recorded small tadpoles and only this size. In some ponds July 24, 1921, the tadpoles were almost a pure culture of *Hyla femoralis* and small. On July 26, 1921, we finally decided the identification and described the coloration of mature tadpoles.

In 1922, June 26 "in an open pond were a series of *Hyla femoralis* tadpoles. They have bright red in the tails of many of them, and long light line on the middle of the muscular part of the tail. Associates are *H. squirella, H. gratiosa* and a few *R. sphenocephala.* Their tadpoles are smaller than those of *Hyla versicolor.*"

It might not be amiss to append the description of this tadpole we made in 1912 then believing it to be *Acris gryllus.* The description follows but should not be taken in lieu of the better one which precedes. It is:

"Length of body contained 1.5 to 2.3 times in the tail, average 1.8. Width of the body in its own length 1.4 to 2.05, average 1.8. Nostrils 1.25 to 2 nearer the eye than snout, average 1.6. Eye lateral, usually nearer the snout than the spiracle, occasionally equidistant. Distance between external nares in interorbital distance 1.4 to 2.5, average 1.67; in mouth, .9-1.8, average 1.35. Spiracle sinistral, usually 1.2 to 1.8 nearer the base of the hind legs than the snout, rarely equidistant from the two, average 1.37. Anus dextral. Depth of the tail in its own length 2.0 to 3.7, average 2.9. Depth of the muscular part of the tail in the depth of the tail 1.5 to 2.8, average 2.17. Mouth is contained in interorbital distance 1.0 to 2.0, usual range 1.1 to 1.6, average 1.25. Greatest length 35 mm. Greatest length of body 11.5 mm. Greatest length of tail 23.50 mm. Greatest depth of tail 9 mm.

General color of the back (in spirits) yellowish white thickly covered with fine dark brownish specks or spots or blotches. These spots often appear like intricate star-like clusters connected with each other at their tips. Entire venter is yellowish white, the intestine showing through the skin, the general type of belly coloration reminding one of *Hyla versicolor.* In the tree toad the intestine does not show through or is but slightly visible. The dorsal coloration leaves a yellowish white or cream circle about the eye. The distinctive coloration of this form is that of the tail. The muscular part of the tail has four distinct longitudinal bands. The first band of deep Vandyke brown or umber reaches from the body to the tail tip along the ventral edge of the muscular portion. Above it comes a cream or yellowish white band which reaches two thirds to three quarters of the distance to the tip. This is followed by another brown band to the tail's tip. The two brown bands at the caudal third or fourth of the muscular portion unite and cover this part. Above the upper brown band is a second short cream band which sometimes runs onto the body for a short distance. Then the dorsal edge of the muscular part is more or less brown. The crests are translucent and more or less covered with aggregate brownish or blackish masses of color. These blotches are more prominent or intense around the edges of the crests like the condition in *Hyla versicolor.* These blotches become more numerous as the hind legs develop. The largest tadpoles have a coloration pattern very much like the above tree toad tadpoles but without the scarlet or vermilion while the smaller ones remind one somewhat of the caudal crest coloration of *Hyla crucifer.* Of course the muscular bands separate the cricket frog tadpoles at once.

LARVAL PERIOD

In 1912 we first entered the swamp May 27 or 28 and recorded first activity at once. Collected spent females May 29 and on July 2 found transformed frogs, or 33–35 days afterwards. This, however, is insufficient evidence. In 1921, the first spent females were taken April 25, the first positive ovulation began May 21 and first transformations came June 16, June 21, July 24 and July 26. This would give us roughly 52, 57, 90, 92 days from first spent female to transformation dates (June 16–July 26) or 26, 31, 64, 66 days from first positive eggs to transformation dates. In 1922 the first spent female taken was July 3 and first gravid females June 29, our latest transformations August 4, 9, 13. These ranges give us 36, 41, 45, 32, 35, 41 days. Possibly all these transformations are from eggs before June 29. We doubt if the larval period be shorter than 30 days, and 90 days seems too long. Doubtless 40–70 days are not far from the range.

TRANSFORMATION

Period. In 1921 our first records of transformation came June 16, July 23, July 24 and July 26. In 1922 we have transformations June 16, June 21, June 26, June 27, June 30, July 11, July 12, July 19, July 26, July 27, August 4, August 9 and August 13. We have outlined actual transformations from June 16–August 13. The eggs laid August 17, 1922, must transform as late as October.

Size. On July 2, 1912 we took on Camp Island a specimen which measured 13 mm. On July 24, 1921, on Billy's Island, in Indian Mound Ponds we took nineteen individuals 11.5–15 mm. in size. On July 26 we secured three more 13–14 mm. in size. In 1922 we secured two specimens at Callahan, Fla., June 16, 1922, 14 mm. and 15 mm. In the Okefinokee Swamp in 1922 we secured 31 transformed individuals, 10 mm.–14 mm. in size. In all we measured 57 individuals with a range of size 10–15 mm. The major mode was 13 mm. (15 specimens) and two secondary modes of 12 mm. (12 specimens) and 14 mm. (12 specimens), and the average of the 57 specimens was 13 mm.

In 1928 we discovered several tadpoles labelled *Acris* which are really *Hyla femoralis*. One lot, June 16, 1928 is a transforming series.

Body 11.5 mm.	Tail 14 mm.	4 legs.	Tadpole mouth.
" 11.5 "	" 12 "	" "	Teeth rows gone.
" 11.5 "	" 9.5 "	" "	Tadpole mouth half changed.
" 11.0 "	" 14.5 "	" "	Tadpole mouth no teeth.

On July 23, 1921 we find tadpoles and 4 transformed frogs and beyond, one 11.5 mm., 12 mm., 13 mm., and 14 mm.

General remarks. At transformation many of the tree toad species tend to be green with none of their distinctive markings. In the first identification of these forms the tails of the series not fully transformed often helped materially. Adults of *Hyla femoralis* are not often green (sometimes so) but their transformed life frequently starts with a green livery. They are then hard to separate from *Hyla squirella*, *Hyla cinerea*, etc. On July 18, 1922, "around the edge of a sphagnum bog overgrown with bushes and trees we found transformed *Hyla femoralis*. They were green above." Or on July 27, 1922, "in a pond where we heard *Hyla gratiosa* and took transformed green *Hyla gratiosa* Mr. Pirnie found two transformed *Hyla femoralis*, golden green and resting on stems 1–3 inches above the water. If they were shaken off they swam to another stem and climbed up. They were a prominent green but when transferred to a cocoa can they changed in five minutes to an almost black color."

GROWTH

In 1912 we secured the following material: "On May 28–29, 1912, we took one specimen, 17.75 mm. long, another on June 6–7, 1912, 21.25 mm., a third June 24, 1912, 21 mm., a fourth from the edge of the swamp Sept 11, 1909, 18 mm., and a fifth, 16.5 mm. These measurements 16.5–21.25 mm. from June 1–September 11 represent 10–12 months' old frogs." On February 9, 1911, Professor J. C. Bradley took a 20 mm. at Waynesville, Georgia.

In 1912 on June 6–7 when a 21 mm. was collected two more were taken 31 and 36 mm. respectively. On June 24 besides the 21 mm. specimen we have a 27 mm. and a 31 mm. specimen. On June 5 when a 25 mm. was taken we also recorded 33 and 36 mm. specimens. On June 15 two specimens we have respectively 26 and 31 mm. Possibly on this basis the one year olds extend from 16.5–26 mm.

In 1921 we captured transformation sizes from 11.5–15 mm. On April 25 when we took a 20 mm. specimen we also captured 24, 26, 26, 28, 30 and 33 mm. specimens. On June 3–5 we had a series 20, 24, 25, 27, 27, 27, 30, 30, 31, 31, 32, 33, 33, 34, 34, 37, 37, 37, 40 mm. respectively. Or on May 21 a series of four yielded 25, 28, 31, 33 mm. specimens. With the other material collected in 1921 the line between 1 and 2 years seems to be from 24–26 mm., while in 1912 it is apparently 26–27 mm.; the line between second and third years in 1912 between 32–34 mm., and in 1921 between 32 and 35 mm.

In 1922 we took one specimen of 23 mm., two of 29 mm., and one of 34 mm. On August 13 we secured a 19 mm. specimen on the Sugar House, St. Mary's, Georgia. All the other lots begin with 32 or 33 or 29, 29, 28, or 27 mm. Two series are: July 21–27, 28, 28, 28, 29, 30, 30, 30, 30, 31, 31, 31, 32, 32, 32, 32, 33, 33, 34, 34, mm.; July 11, 28, 28, 29, 30, 30, 31, 38 mm. The 1922 material apparently separate at 25–26 mm. for the line between 1st and 2nd years and at 33–35 mm. for the line between 2nd and 3rd years.

Considering seasonal, yearly or sexual variations the evidence points to 10–15 mm. for transformation size, 17–26 mm. for 1st year olds; 26–32 or 34 for 2 year olds; 32 or 34–40 mm. for 3 year olds.

FOOD

This phase of its natural history we have not examined.

ENEMIES

In 1912 we summarized it thus: "This species was represented in the stomach contents of one black snake (*Coluber constrictor*) of one southern riband snake (*Thamnpohis sauritus sackeni*), of two garter snakes (*T. sirtalis*) and of one pilot snake (*Elaphe o. confinis*). In other words, two distinctly terrestrial species ate it, one aquatic species and one more or less arboreal form. The last, the pilot snake may have captured it in the piney trees, but all the rest doubtless took it on its journey to the breeding pools or while in them, or this species may be more terrestrial in other months and not exclusively arboreal as previously held. This tree frog may be more frequent in the reptilian diet of the swamp because it is more common than its relative, the Carolina tree frog (*Hyla cinerea*)." On July 2, 1922, we saw at night a small garter with an adult *Hyla femoralis* in its mouth. The snake had it head first.

On June 27, 1922, in one pond where we captured the *Hyla gratiosa* tadpole with bifurcated tail and *Hyla squirella* tadpole with one hind leg we found a *Hyla femoralis* tadpole with only one hind leg. Another *Hyla femoralis* tadpole had the forelegs about to burst out and no hind legs at all. Was it abnormal, pathological or were they snapped off by turtles (*Deirochelys reticularia*) or snakes which we captured in this pond?

AUTUMNAL DISAPPEARANCE

The latest records we have are for mid-September, 1922, and August 22, 1921. Some would have transformed in October. Doubtless this month or November are the periods of beginning of inactivity.

AFFINITIES

Holbrook (1842, Vol. IV, p. 128) alludes to Dumeril & Bibron's mistake as follows: "Dumeril and Bibron consider this animal as identical with the *Hyla squirella*, from which it is, however, perfectly distinct.

  1. It is about two-thirds the size (as a matter of fact *H. femoralis* is larger, A. H. W.).

  2. Its general colour and markings are different: there are no white lines along the upper lip, and the yellow spots on the thigh always exist there, and never in the *Hyla femoralis*.

  3. It differs in habits, for it is never found near outhouses or about fences and in old fields."

In 1855 John LeConte (1855, p. 428) refers to the same matter. "It is wrong in Dumeril & Bibron to say that this species is a variety of *Hyla squirella*. In shape and size the difference is not considerable. The latter animal during the warm season is always to be met with about the houses, the *H. femoralis* never. Besides, their notes are entirely different." As late as 1882 Dumeril & Bibron's mistake somewhat influences Boulenger (1882, p. 398) in his statement "Appears to be specifically distinct from *H. squirella*."

This species seems in adult appearance to be a small species of the *Hyla versicolor*, yet is readily distinguishable. The individual eggs look like those of this species and the surface films on the water appear to be of the same sort, though *Hyla femoralis* may lay larger films. Of the tadpoles we have the note (June 27, 1922) that "The tadpoles have the same bright red color in tail as *Hyla versicolor*. Are they related? The color pattern of the tail in alternate light and dark, longitudinal bands is like that of *Hyla andersonii* and *Pseudacris* species. In mouth parts the tadpole falls into the group of *Hylas* with long hind lower labial with rows like *Hyla versicolor*, *H. squirella* and *Hyla arenicolor*.

BIBLIOGRAPHY

1907　Brimley, C. S. Journ. Elisha Mitchell Soc., Dec. 1907, Vol. XXIII, No. 4, pp. 158, 159.
1889　Cope, E. D. U. S. Nat. Mus. Bull. No. 34, 1889, pp. 371, 372.
1914　Deckert, R. F. Copeia, Feb. 14, 1914, No. 3, p. 3.
1915　———. Copeia, May 15, 1915, No. 18, p. 3.
1862　DeKay, J. E. Zoology of New York, Part III, p. 72.
1906　Dickerson, M. C. The Frog Book, pp. 150, 151.
1842　Holbrook, J. E. North American Herpetology, 1842, Vol. IV, pp. 127, 128.
1856　LeConte, John. Proc. Acad. Nat. Sci. Phila., Dec. 1855, pp. 428, 429.
1924　Myers, George S. Copeia, June 30, 1924, No. 131, p. 60.
1924　Schmidt, K. P. Copeia, July 15, 1924, No. 132, p. 68.
1923　Stejneger, L. and T. Barbour. A Check List of North American Amphibians and Reptiles. 2nd Edition, Cambridge, 1923, p. 30.
1923　Viosca, Percy, Jr. Copeia, Feb. 1, 1923, No. 115, p. 36.
1920　Wright, A. H. U. S. Com. Fish. Report 1919, Doc. 888, p. 29.
1923　Wright, A. H. Copeia, Feb. 1, 1923, No. 115, p. 34.
1926　Wright, A. H. Ecology, Jan. 1926, Vol. VII, No. 1, p. 82.
1923　——— and A. A. Wright. The Anatomical Record, Jan. 20, 1923, Vol. 24, No. 6, p. 406.
1924　Wright, A. H. and A. A. Wright. The American Naturalist, July-August, 1924, Vol. LVIII, p. 378.

Hyla gratiosa LeConte

(Pl. II, Fig. 4; V, Fig. 3; VII, Fig. 6; X, Fig. 5; XII, Fig. 2; XV, Figs. 4, 13-16; XVII; XXIX; XXX; Text Fig. 11)

COMMON NAMES

"The Barker." "Barking Frog." "Coat Bet." Florida Tree Frog. Georgia Tree Frog. Florida Hyla. Florida Tree Toad.

RANGE

Check list. "Type locality: 'Lower plantation of Georgia,' evidently one of the LeConte plantations in Lloyd or Liberty County. "Range: South Carolina to Florida and Mississippi."—Stejneger and Barbour Check List, 1923, p. 31.

Supplementary records. In Lousiana Viosca (1923, p. 37) found this species in the "Longleaf Pine Flats. . . . Typically the country is north Floridian rather than Louisianian, and several southeastern species, not found elsewhere in our state, have congenial habits here. *Bufo quercicus, Bufo terrestris* and *Hyla gratiosa* are significant examples." Brimley, C. S. (1907, p. 158) is quite justified in including this species in his Key to the Species of Frogs and Toads Liable to Occur in North Carolina."

The Wilmington type of country very likely will yield it some day. Seven miles north of Millen, Jenkins Co., Ga., Mr. M. D. Pirnie and I started "for an immense chorus of *Hyla gratiosa*. We travelled about 1/2 mile and the chorus seemed 1/2 mile farther on. It was in a dense tangle of a swampy

PLATE XXIX

Florida tree-frog (*Hyla gratiosa*)

1. Cornpatch, Billy Id., Ga. June 6, 1921.
2. Frog on sand, Billy Id., Ga. June 5, 1921.
3. 4. 5. Males croaking in overflowed cornfield, Billy Id., Ga. July 3, 1921.
6. Mature tadpole with forked (abnormal) tail. Petty pond, Trail Ridge, Folkston, Ga. July 31, 1922. Lateral aspect. × 1.3.
7. Mature tadpole, (normal) Chesser Id., Ga. July 3, 1922. Lateral aspect. × 1.3.

stream." Just north of Screven, Wayne Co., Ga., the evening of June 11, 1921, we heard *Hyla gratiosa*. In 1906 Miss Dickerson (pp. 124, 125) writes "unfortunately this tree frog has an unusually limited range. It is very rarely found outside of Florida." The last twenty years has extended its range considerably.

Local Okefinokee records. In 1912 we wrote of this species as follows: "This species was on hypothetical list and escaped us from May 30–July 15, 1912. Between July 15–Nov. 15, 1912, the Lees secured one fine male of the Florida Tree Frog. LeConte (Cope '89, p. 379) had this from Riceborough, Ga., and C. B. Adams (Cope '89, p. 379) took it in Georgia while Brimley's ('10, p. 11) records came from Florida and Mississippi. The present record being intermediate helps to bridge the gap between these two areas."

In 1921 we captured or heard it at Billy's Island, Chesser Island, Fargo, south of Moniac in Florida, near Macclenny, Florida. In 1922 we recorded it on Chesser's Island, near Starling Branch, on road from Chesser Island to Folkston, along road Folkston to Moniac, and in the country generally from swamp to St. Mary's River. It is scarce within the swamp, more common on its outskirts outside the swamp.

GENERAL APPEARANCE

Brimley (1907, pp. 157, 158) characterized it as a large tree frog with no X marks on back, no lateral stripe of yellow, no vermiculations, spottings, variegations of yellow on rear of thighs, but with the feet edged with yellow. Miss Dickerson (1906, p. 125) holds "*Hyla gratiosa* presents a peculiar appearance because of the even granulation of the upper parts. In this characteristic of the skin it differs from all other North American *Hylas*. All others present a surface either smooth and fine in texture, as in the case of the Green Tree Frog (*Hyla cinerea*) or rough with fine warts, as in the Common Tree Toad (*Hyla versicolor*)."

COLORATION OF SPIRIT SPECIMENS (1912)

The coloration of our first specimen of 1912: In spirits purplish brown on the back with prominent darker elliptical or round spots. These may be solid or with lighter centers or with a smaller yellowish spot on them. Tibia imperfectly barred while the bars of the thighs are on the anterior half of the dorsal surface, the posterior half being plain with no bars or spots. Forelimbs with two or three small dark spots on interior edges; fore-arm with two yellowish or whitish bands along its posterior edge; upper labial stripe yellowish or white. The specimen we have is a male and has the prominent vocal sac area of the same color as the back, the breast fold being yellowish as on the rest of the under parts.

STRUCTURAL CHARACTERS

(Based on our lone specimen of 1912, we wrote these notes.)

Upper parts except arms and legs strongly granulate; under surface of hindlimbs only granulate on posterior half of thigh, otherwise smooth; under surface of arm, prominent breast fold and lower throat smoothish or slightly granulate; chin granulate; webbing of hind feet to the discs which are very large, 3 mm., or .5 of the tympanum; discs of fore feet, 4 mm., or .66 of the tympanum; a dorsal fold over the ear to the shoulder and continued often as a loose fold along the side of the body half way to the groin; a tarsal fold; vomerine teeth between inner nares; head ahead of eye short, obtuse; vocal sac well developed.

MEASUREMENTS

(Recent Material)

Head to angle of mouth 1.16 (20 mm. transformation)—1.15 (28 mm.)—1.35 (44 mm.)—1.3 (56 mm. ♂)—1.3 (68 mm. ♂) in width of head; head to rear of tympanum (20 mm. lacking)—1.4–1.05—1.15 (56 mm. ♂)—1.08 (68 mm. ♂) in width of head; head to angle of mouth 3.33–2.8–3.14–3.3–3.4 in length of body; head to rear of tympanum ( )–2.54–2.4–2.9–2.8 in length of body; snout .6–.8–.833–1.0–.91 in first finger; snout .8–1.0–1.27–1.11–.9 in fourth finger; snout .5–.6–.72–.84–1. in first toe; eye 1.25–1.25–1.5–1.5–1.87 in snout; eye ( )–.5–.66–.83–1.07 in tympanum; eye .75–1.0–1.25–1.5–1.0 in first finger; tympanum ( )–2.50–2.25–1.8–1.7 in snout; tympanum ( )–4.75–3.75–2.4–3.0 in intertympanic width; internasal width 1.25–1.2–.8–1.0–.91 in upper eyelid width; interorbital width .71–.85–.51–.77–.66 in upper eyelid width; interorbital width .57–.71–.77–.77–.73 in internasal width; interorbital width ( )–2.7–2.3–1.84–2.6 in intertympanic width.

Forelimb: Forelimb 1.53–1.75–1.82–2.0–2.0 in length of body; forelimb 2.0–2.75–2.66–2.6–2.73 in hind limb; first finger 1.66–1.62–1.66–1.33–1.25 in third finger; second finger 1.25–1.44–1.37–1.2–1.35 in third finger; second finger .75–.88–.83–.9–1.09 in first finger; third finger .8–.92–.84–7.5–.8 in second toe; fourth finger 1.25–1.3–1.08–1.2–1.36 in third finger; fourth finger .625–.6–.56–.75–.72 in first toe; internasal width 1.5–1.6–1.5–1.8–2.18 in first finger; internasal width 2.0–1.8–1.8–2.0–2.0 in second finger; internasal width 2.5–2.6–2.5–2.4–2.72 in third finger; internasal width 2.0–2.0–2.3–2.0–2.0 in fourth finger.

Hindlimb: Length 1.3–1.57–1.45–1.3–1.36 in hindlimb; tibia 1.9–1.64–1.9–2.19–2.12 in length; tibia 2.47–2.6–2.78–2.86–2.9 in hindlimb; tibia 1.23–.94–1.04–1.09–1.06 in forelimb; tibia .81–.73–.87–.98–.93 in hind foot; first toe 1.6–2.0–1.6–1.2–1.5 in second toe; 2.6–3.0–2.3–1.86–2.37 in third toe; first toe 3.2–3.06–3.0–2.0–1.9 in fourth toe; first toe 2.4–3.3–2.1–1.6–2.0 in fifth toe; second toe 1.62–1.5–1.45–1.55–1.58 in third toe; second toe 2.0–1.8–1.86–2.0–1.9 in fourth toe; second toe 1.5–1.66–1.34–1.33–1.25 in fifth toe; third toe 1.23–1.2–1.36–1.3–1.2 in fourth toe; third toe .92–1.1–.93–.85–.84 in fifth toe; fourth toe .75–1.13–1.05–.66–.69 in hind foot; fourth toe 1.31–1.54–1.21–1.41–1.39 in tibia; fourth toe 1.62–1.45–1.26–1.55–1.5 in forelimb; fifth toe 1.33–1.1–1.35–1.5–1.43 in fourth toe; internasal width 1.25–1.2–1.3–1.5–1.45 in first toe; internasal width 2.0–2.4–2.1–1.8–2.18 in second toe; internasal width 3.25–3.6–3.0–2.8–2.34 in third toe; internasal width 4.0–4.4–3.8–3.6–4.1 in fourth toe; internasal width 3.0–4.0–2.8–2.4–2.9 in fifth toe.

HABITAT

In 1856 John LeConte (1856, p. 146) in his description writes of his three specimens as follows: "One of them was taken in the water of a pine barren pond, another was found in a cavity of a sand pit, and the third upon a tree in the forest." In 1922 H. P. Löding (p. 19) makes an interesting note about its great abundance. "Thus, the largest of our tree frogs seemed to be very rare previous to the hurricane of July, 1916, up to which time in all our collecting only two adults and two very young specimens were taken; but suddenly during August of that year the species became very common, in fact could be seen by the thousands in the Satsuma orange orchards throughout Mobile County. Since then it has gradually become scarcer and at present is not seen very often."

We do not know whether its non-ovulation habitat be primarily the pine woods, the hammocks, the fringe of cypress ponds on the edge of cypress bays. In each habitat we have records of "barking frogs."

FIRST APPEARANCE

In 1856, John LeConte, (p. 146) writes: "During the last spring, whilst I was residing in the lower country of Georgia, it was my good fortune to meet with three specimens of the animal described below." Deckert (1915, p. 5) records them in March. T. Van Hyning (1923, p. 68) writes that "On the night of March 18, while some of the boys of the biological class of the University of Florida, Gainesville, Fla., were collecting frogs, among other species taken, were thirty specimens of the Florida Tree Frog *Hyla gratiosa* LeConte..."

GENERAL HABITS

Deckert (1915, p. 4) writes that "*Hyla gratiosa* LeConte, the Florida tree toad, is a handsome species, and the largest of the North American tree toads, reaching a length of $3\frac{1}{4}$ inches from snout to vent. It is heavily built, with large adhesive disks on fingers and toes. It differs from all other species in its evenly granulated skin, and regular pattern of roundish spots. The color is ashen-gray, purplish or green of some shade. The spots are darker than the ground color, evenly distributed over the open surfaces, and may be absent when the frog changes to pale golden green. The arms and legs are banded. The throat of the male is rich chrome yellow or green."

Dickerson (1906, pp. 125, 126) studied this frog carefully in captivity. She observes that: "The Florida Tree Frog has colour changes as marvellous as those possessed by most of the *Hylas*. It may be plain bright green and remain so for months, in fact, one in this phase of colouration was kept for over two years and during this time there was no tendency to become spotted or to turn brown. Also, the brown-spotted phase may likewise endure for months without change. On the other hand, the changes may be very rapid indeed. The tendency for rapid colour change, here as elsewhere among the *Hylidae*, seems to be at its height when the animals are well-fed, and in the season of greatest activity, that is, in the spring and summer months. At this time the greatest variation in colour may be seen in an individual during the twenty-four hours. It may be bright green with vivid spots, dark at their edges and light in their centres. Gradually (within the space of ten minutes) the spots become more and more obscure until the frog is plain green, very light in tone. Again, within the half-hour the spots reappear, become more distinct, darkening in their centres. The ground color becomes ashy in the middle of the back; this colour darkens into a mulberry, which colour spreads, obscuring the green. Meanwhile the spots continue to darken until the whole frog is rich brown prominently marked with darker brown spots."

"The throat-pouch of the male is very large and is bright yellow or vivid green in colour. When the tree frog is taken suddenly into the hand, this sac is likely to be inflated and the frog gives a harsh-sounding squawk. The voice is usually harsh and low-pitched."

"This *Hyla* is a curiously artificial-looking frog. If it did not move, we might well think some one's fancy had moulded it out of wax. When it is angry or startled, it fills the lungs, expanding the body until it is nearly as broad as long. It has the slow tendencies of some of the other large tree frogs. It shows a marked desire to cling to one's finger and will not leave, even when the finger is constantly turned so that the tree frog is head down. It will each time clumsily turn around to bring its head uppermost, tuck its toes well under, and settle for a period of contentment and rest."

We observed that the first male which we captured croaking in a corn field June 5, 1927, would squawk. On June 7, 1927, we noted that "the male would open his mouth once in a while after I captured him. He was in a glass can in my pocket and several times he spoke thus. Later during the next day it would thus do if taken by the legs and pressed ahead of hind legs. Thus held while rubbed on belly or back it will swell up so that it looks perfectly round from above. Often it has a curved appearance; it will bow its head down to ground and back be arched. It can leap 1–1 1/2 feet, possibly 2 feet in awkward, cumbersome fashion. It has a decided secretion from the skin." On July 16, 1921, one of the Chesser boys noticed its odor. He pronounced it bad and "tried three different times to get it off his hands."

VOICE

Deckert (1915, pp. 4, 5) considers "It is not very plentiful anywhere, and rarely met with outside the breeding season. During the latter time it comes down out of the trees and small companies of from four to ten specimens, in widely scattered pools or "bayous" attend to their breeding duties amid the "loud calls of the males. The call can be heard for over a mile, and sounds like a large gong, or church bell, being of unusual depth, and very clear, with a second's interval between each dual note. The male while singing, floats on the water, the large vocal sac throwing the frog into a vertical position with every utterance."

The first time we heard this species to know it as such was on June 5, 1921. After a period of heavy rainfall "We visited in the evening an oak-toad pool near the cultivated fields of Billy's Island, and heard a curious *tonk*, *tonk*, like some one pounding on a hollow, heavy barrel or hogshead. The call was woody, deep. At first it reminded me more of a frog (*Rana*) than a tree frog (*Hyla*). It seemed at first somewhat like the call of *Rana clamitans* only too many times separated and actually the resemblance is only fleeting and slight. Later we found other croakers. One was on the raised ridge of land beside a corn stalk. It was green with the spots usually figured. Another ♂ was lying flat in the water at the edge of a weedy ridge. It was absolutely flat and spread out. It was without the spots and uniform dull, brownish-green like the color of the water. Another was in a furrow between two rows of corn. It was spotted and alert. First one rested on ground more or less horizontally; the second in water horizontally, and the third more or less diagonally upright. The call can be heard at a long distance." Usually the heels are widely separated at croaking and the lower part of the body dips somewhat.

On July 3, 1921, on Billy's island "after a great downpour of rain at 8:00 p.m. heard a ♂ *Hyla gratiosa* calling over in the Hammock. Decided to go out. Found another male near camp in temporary pool. No end of *Hyla femoralis, Hyla cinerea, Gastrophryne, Bufo terrestris* and *Chorophulis ocularis* calling. Found a *Hyla gratiosa* calling but I went past it. When I returned it had moved 10–15 feet away from its first position. It was of a greenish cast of olive in color.

"Found a male *H. gratiosa* beside a grassy bank. He was as big and round as the top of a Mason jar. How his throat would puff out. Was an easy subject to move into good position. Used either a big stick or flashlight or other means."

F. Harper makes these journal notes on this subject. "56 calls in a minute quite regularly spaced. Then 59 to a minute not absolutely regularly spaced. Then 55 to a minute. Even between calls, keeps body puffed out. Inflation of body and throat in calling, alternate as in *Hyla cinerea*. There is a perceptible pause between each note in calling, the throat meanwhile remaining at one quarter its full inflation. The inflation and deflation are accomplished very rapidly, making it quite a trick to catch a good inflation with the flashlight. The throat remains at about this quarter inflation during a considerable pause in calling. Very brownish at night."

On July 15, 1921, on Chesser Island we heard of "Coat Bet" frogs. The first day we thought they must be *Rana virgatipes* but the following evening we found them to be *Hyla gratiosa*. The people on Billy's Island have no common name for them. On Chesser Island they are called Coat Bet because that is the way it sounded to the Chessers. They said the "Coat Bet" call was produced by one frog calling right after another.

On July 3, 1922, in a temporary pool "1/2 mile west of Trader's Hill, Ga., heard 4 or 5 *Hyla gratiosa*. Some would stop calling when we approached and if we came too near they ducked under water and swam away. Finally we captured two. One looked green and one brown."

In conversation with Mr. P. A. Chesser he spoke of "Coat Bets" as follows (July 15, 1921). "Sometimes in rainy weather we hear these around the

house and on the Island. Real season is summer time when there is plenty of
rainy weather. 'Spanish Curlews' once fed on them."

While we were in the swamp we usually recorded this species either as
Barker, the Barking Frog or Coat Bets. The last refers to the normal note in
the breeding pools; the first two to a puzzle that perplexed us for two seasons.

On May 22, 1921, we "heard in a tree a curious note or croak in the hammock near Newt Pond. After a time it croaked more loudly from a moss-
laden black gum and was different. At first I thought it an aberrant *H.
cinerea*. Is it *Hyla gratiosa?*" June 5, 1922, in a cleared field near this
hammock we found 2 or 3 male *Hyla gratiosa* calling in regular fashion. On
July 16, "during the morning we heard a barking frog in the trees south of
camp. We are almost satisfied tonight that it is *Hyla gratiosa*." That night,
in a nearby pond was an immense chorus of "Coat Bets" (*Hyla gratiosa*).

In 1922 the barkers perplexed us even more. Mr. R. A. Chesser told us
"the Barking Frog some folks say is a red-headed scorpion. I believe it is a
frog." On June 24, 1922, at the old railroad pools just south of Trader's Hill
"heard this form. It is in a grove of trees. One of our party wonders if it is
Hyla andersonii?" On June 26, the writer heard one in the high long-leafed
pines north of Starling Branch. On June 27, "at Camp Pinckney heard a
barking like frog. Later, on wild rice in the direction from which the noise
came was a curiously colored *Hyla cinerea*. Is it the barker? Does it call
differently when in high trees and when in breeding waters?" On July 2
"heard a barker near Anna's Pond." On July 11 and July 20 they were
barking on Chesser Island. Not until July 26 did we solve the puzzle. About
three miles along on the road from Chesser Island to Folkston we heard in the
evening "in a cypress pond to the right of the road some *Hyla gratiosa* and
beyond them, a barker or two. Went after the barker. Found one in a small
gum 4–5 feet, possibly 6 feet up. It is *Hyla gratiosa!* I saw him do it. Two
more barkers beside one I caught. Several *Hyla gratiosa* in water calling
normally. Is the barking note the call of the trees before reaching water
level. There is a great chorus of Coat Bets (normal calling frogs) to the northward." On August 16, 1922, at Hilliard, Florida, where we found both
spadefoots and Florida tree frogs breeding, 2–6 p.m., we heard barkers in
the pines near the place. At 7.15 p.m. Coat Bets began to croak in the trees,
but at times they were "Coat Bets" and at other times "Barkers." "Coat
Bets" and "Barkers" are one, *Hyla gratiosa*.

A resumé of the croaking dates for 1921 and 1922 are as follows:

1921

May   22.   Curious croak or note from moss-laden black gum in hammock,
            Billy's Island.
June   5.   3 croaking, Billy's Island.
July   3.   ♂ calling in Hammock. Another in overflow area near camp.
July 15.   During the morning heard barking frogs in trees south of camp.
July 16.   Immense chorus of *H. gratiosa*.

July   17.   Calling loudly.
July   29.   Calling on Billy's Island.
Aug.   3.   Heard at night at Fargo.
Aug.   4.   Heard at night at Fargo.
Aug.   6.   Big chorus near Moniac.
Aug.   7.   More heard south of Moniac in Florida.

1922

June   10.   North of Millen, Ga., large chorus.
June   11.   Near Screven, Ga., heard several.
June   12.   Chesser Island, Ga., no end of *Hyla gratiosa* calling.
June   14.   Several calling but not in chorus.
June   24.   Heard near Trader's Hill in grove of pines.
June   26.   A barker in a high pine.
June   27.   Camp Pinckney 1 or 2 barking frogs.
July   2.   Near Anna's Pond barking frog.   Also near Starling Branch.
July   3.   Near Trader's Hill several in flooded fields.
July   11.   Heard a barker on Chesser Island.
July   12.   Spent an hour searching for a barker in pine tree.
July   13.   Barker calling in hammock.
July   20.   Calling 2:00 p. m.
July   25.   Heard 1 or 2 north end of Island about 9:00.   Temperature 72°.
July   26.   Solved barker.   It is *H. gratiosa*.   Heard barking and normal notes in same pond.
July   27.   9:00 a. m.   Air 84°.   Plenty calling.
Aug.   8.   Along Old Okefinokee Road several heard.
Aug.   10.   One calling near Chesser School.
Aug.   11.   None heard.
Aug.   13.   Very few heard Folkston–Chesser Island, 9–10:30 p. m.
Aug.   16.   Several calling in pines and ponds, 2–6:00 p. m.   Croaking 7:15.
Aug.   20.   Heard a few on Moniac–St. George–Chesser Island Road.

In 1921 on May 21 it rained almost continually; on May 22, we heard our first *H. gratiosa* on Billy's Island.   On June 4 we had a heavy downpour. The following day we found three croaking in an overflowed corn field.   On July 3 after a week of rain it poured; that evening four males began croaking. On July 15, on Chesser Island a thunder storm came in the afternoon.   That evening the Florida tree frogs began a chorus.   The following day, July 16, another storm came and another congress came.   On July 27 and 28 we were flooded and the evening of July 29 the frogs began aga'n.

Weather stations around the swamp.   Rainfalls of 1.22, 1.78, 1.00, 1.47, 2.40, .91 inches respectively usually came before the croaking of this species in 1921.   The air minima are from 66–70°.   The maxima are from 78–96°F. Warm rains are the important factor.   In 1922 when croaking records come the lowest and highest minima are 62 and 83° and the lowest and highest maxima 81 and 98°.   Most minima are from 66–76°, the maxima 87–94°. Most of the large choruses came after rains of 2.05, 2.00, 1.60, 1.35, 1.45 inches.   The average of the minima is 70°, of the maxima 91°.   In 1922 as in 1921 high air temperatures and dampness produced choruses in midsummer. Of the early spring we cannot speak.

MATING

Male (From life, June 5, 1921). Lettuce green on hind legs and forelegs, oil green or cerro green on the back. The encircled spots of the back have a ring of mars brown or bone brown or other browns with green ground color within. There are occasional spots as big as pin heads or twice of bright green yellow or greenish yellow or green yellow. This color is on the groin to just back of arm insertion back of which for one half of an inch is a clear whitish area. The greenish yellow from groin forward demarcates side color from pink white or creamy belly color. From tip of snout along upper jaw under tympanum and along side to within 1 inch to 1/2 inch of leg insertion is a pinkish white stripe. Below it is a line of mars violet or taupe brown (a purplish brown class of color) which expands behind the angle of the mouth into a large area on the side. Same color back of pinkish white or white area back of brachium and antebrachium onto the last finger. Same white line around vent with mars violet below white line. Same combination on the knee. Two or three white patches on foot behind with mars violet between and behind them. Back of femur or thigh dull Indian purple. No spots. Below the expanded mars violet area of the side is a small whitish line 1/2–1 inch long, then comes greenish yellow and finally the belly color. Just back of chin is grayish white speckled with taupe brown. Then comes lettuce green or oil green from angle of mouth around across to angle of mouth, the band 1/2 inch wide when not inflated. Then comes wrinkled part with light orange yellow or deep chrome. This color more or less back to pectoral fold of skin from forearm to forearm.

Iris spotted purplish black and bronzy or some kind of vinaceous.

Male (From life, July 17, 1921). The *Hyla gratiosa* males in botany drum. Upon opening the can one was all green with a few yellowish spots but not the regular circles, the stripe along the jaw and on the side reminding one of the same in *Hyla cinerea*. Hardly any white or purplish shows anywhere. Another was a vinaceous gray with the rings. Another dark green and the others still different.

Female (From life, July 17, 1921). Belly and under side of legs white, a few picric yellow spots on side below band, also rear end of white line on side becomes picric yellow in the groin. Picric yellow in the axilla of forelegs and on either side of light central throat and chin region which is white or sulphur yellow with a few spots. Pectoral region sulphur yellow. Stripe around snout along upper jaw to groin white except for rear and not interrupted as in the male. Spots on back really black encircled. Color of side and chin, spots, rim of jaw, bands on arms hays maroon, chocolate or warm sepia or bone brown. Upper parts calliste green or casse green or apple green.

Structural differences. The color difference of the venter is the most striking difference. One female (68 mm.) long has no hays maroon on the chin as in the color description of the female (July 17, 1921). In the mated pair described the female has the granulations a little less pronounced on the ventral parts, thighs and dorsum than its mate, but the large female above has granulations on venter the least pronounced of the 19 adults we have.

PLATE XXX

Florida tree-frog (*Hyla gratiosa*)

1. Coat-bet pond, Chesser Id., Ga. July 18, 1921.
2. Male, Billy Id., Ga. June 6, 1921. Semi-inflation. Lateral aspect. × 0.4.
3. Male, Billy Id., Ga. June 6, 1921. Before rubbing. × 0.4.
4. Same, after rubbing. × 0.4.
5. Female and male, Chesser Id., Ga. July 23, 1922. × 0.4.
6. Pair on log, Chesser Id., Ga. July 17, 1921.
7. Male, Chesser Id., Ga. July 23, 1922. × 0.8.
8. Egg mass in a pan, Chesser Id., Ga. July 18, 1921.

1

2

3

4

5

6

7

8

On the back they are much reduced in prominence. The upper hind legs and sides have practically none. Our largest female is 68 mm., largest male 68 mm. The smallest male we took is 52 mm. They must show male coloration much smaller than 52 mm. Doubtless the males and females begin breeding three years from transformation. After we had started to measure the two largest frogs each 68 mm. we noted that the male had a tympanal diameter of 7 mm., the female 5 mm. This is the first instance of decided tympanal difference we have noted in Hylas. In the same specimens the male has the two outer fingers of the hand thicker and broader than the similar fingers of the female.

Our first record of mating came the evening of July 16, 1921. "We went out 8:30–10:00 p.m. south of camp to a pond (Coat Bet Pond). Immense deafening choruses of *Hyla gratiosa*, *Pseudacris ocularis*, *Hyla femoralis*, *Bufo quercicus* and *Acris gryllus*. We looked for Coat Bets (*Hyla gratiosa*). One male was on a cypress limb touching the water; another on a tussock of sedges; another on water amongst grass. We caught 9 or 10 males. The pond is generally shallow but water was generally 8 inches–1 1/2 feet deep in places." Found the eggs next morning. In the evening July 17, 1921, "Coat Bets were calling loudly and presently on a log next to the water's surface saw a mated pair of *Hyla gratiosa*. I held my breath but caught them very easily in my can. Thought I never would get the can out of my pocket. When I returned to camp the pair had broken and we put another male with her. One of the Chesser boys presently found a mated pair of Coat Bets on a log. We set up the camera and they leaped away but swam no more than three feet and hid under a fern leaf. I caught them and put them back on the log. Held my hand partially over them while Harper focussed. Then I raised my hand one foot above them ready to seize if need be. Harper trigged the flash a dozen or two times before it went off. The pair remained just as before. When we put them in a can they did not separate."

On August 16, 1922, after a severe rainy period in one of the shallow, temporary spadefoot pools "were several pairs of *Hyla gratiosa*."

All our records of mating came at night.

Amplexation. The amplexation of every pair caught was axillary. So also with the pairs secured from laboratory (camp) mating. Those taken July 16 and 17, 1921, and August 16, 1922, always revealed this type of embrace. Our notes record that in one of the spadefoot pools a male spadefoot had a ripe female *Hyla gratiosa* in the embrace. The male was the larger in size. Unfortunately we have no memory of whether the amplexation was inguinal or abnormal.

OVULATION

Habitat. We have found the eggs or tadpoles in open ponds of cut-over pine lands, in cypress ponds open at one end and shaded on the other or in dense cypress and gum ponds. At times in preference to nearby cypress ponds we have found them in temporary grassy pools (after hard storms of 2–4 or 5 inches) such as spadefoots frequent or open tussocky transient pools beside the road. All in all it is primarily a mainland tree frog with preference for cypress or gum ponds not so dense as the cypress bays or the ponds of some islands. It inclines to more open cypress ponds or cutoff cypress ponds.

Period. In 1915 Deckert (p. 5) writes "I have never heard this species call except during the breeding season which lasts from March to June, beginning with the first warm rains." In 1921 we were in the swamp from last of April to September but in the center the species is scarce. In 1922 we were at Chesser Island from mid-June to mid-September. Based on these two summers' experience in 1923 (p. 34) we wrote "From June 1st to 10th three species begin (to breed), one of which was *Hyla gratiosa*." In 1924 (p. 378) we gave "Season June 10 to August 21." The few ovulations in summer in 1921 and 1922, and its breeding after a severe storm in August 1922 with *Rana aesopus* and *Scaphiopus holbrookii* spring breeders led us to conclude it to be a spring breeder with some tardy ovulation in summer to September 1. The period seems March to August. One might suspect that the late breeders were younger breeders. This is not always the case. Since this was written we have noted the observations of Prof. T. Van Hyning (1923, p. 68) on these very three species. He writes: "On the night of March 18, while some of the boys of the biological class of the University of Florida, Gainesville, Fla., were collecting frogs, among other species taken, were thirty specimens of the Florida Tree Frog, *Hyla gratiosa* LeConte; . . . These and other species were all in a pond breeding near the University. One of the party collected eggs, and brought living specimens which have spawned since, and is keeping records on the incubation and development of each species.

"As there seems to be little really known concerning the breeding, especially of the . . . Florida Tree Frog, I consider the incident worth recording."

Temperature and humidity. (See voice for discussion of rain and temperatures of choruses). On the dates when ovulation or mating occurred the maxima averaged 90° and minima 71°. They were always preceded by heavy rains.

Egg-laying process. We did not see the process in our captive pairs. In nature Deckert (1915, p. 5) says "The eggs are laid singly and sink to the bottom of the pool." Whether they swim from place to place on the bottom ovulating and fertilizing one egg at a time, or whether they ovulate and fertilize several or one at the surface and let them or it sink needs to be observed. The eggs are certainly disposed on the bottom.

EGGS

Attachment, egg mass. On July 17, 1921, about 11:00 a.m. we "went to *Hyla gratiosa* pond. Cypress trees scattering with hurrah bushes (*Leucothae*) around them. In amongst iris, fern (*Woodwardia* broad leaf), tussocks of sedge found eggs. In water 3–6 inches deep with dip net discovered eggs which seemed those of *Pseudacris ocularis*; later single eggs presumably (*Acris*) with citrine upper poles and yellowish vegetative poles; and one or two strings 4–6 eggs of *Bufo quercicus*. The *supposed Acris* eggs are loosely attached to sedge or grass blades or oftener to sphagnum moss on the bottom.

They are easily seen. The *Pseudacris* eggs are harder to see." "None of these eggs are *H. femoralis* eggs. I was careful not to scoop in surface packets which were present. It is possible the yellowish single eggs are not of *Acris* but of *Hyla gratiosa* or some other frog yet unknown."

On the following morning one of the mated pairs had laid a large complement. It filled the pan and was continuous. The pair had no escape and could not strew them singly. Thereafter and the next year whenever there were congresses of this species we never found a continuous film of their eggs on the surface of the water as this check would lead us to expect. It was laid in abnormal surroundings. We compared these positive eggs of our laboratory pair with the supposed single eggs of *Acris* taken in pond the day before. The supposed *Acris* eggs were *Hyla gratiosa* eggs.

Egg description. The measurements of 24–29 eggs give the following results: vitellus 2 of 1.0; 8, 1.2 mm.; 12, 1.4 mm.; 6, 1.6 mm.; 1, 1.8 mm.; range 1.0–1.8 mm.; mode 1.4 mm., average 1.37 mm. The outer envelopes were 1 of 2.3 mm.; 1 of 2.4 mm.; 1, 3.0 mm.; 3, 3.8 mm.; 10, 4.0 mm.; 2, 4.6 mm.; 1, 4.8 mm.; 5, 5.0 mm.; range 2.3–5.0; mode 4.0 mm.; average 4.06 mm. In the field we measured the vitelli as 1.2–1.3 mm., and thought there was an inner envelope. It is, however, the vitelline membrane far from the vitellus and appearing as an inner envelope 1.6–2.0 mm. in diameter. The animal pole is light brown or better olive in preserved eggs and the vegetative pole is pale or yellowish. In nature it is above citrine or greenish brown and yellowish below.

We have not counted the ovarian egg complements of captive females. On July 23, 1922, we counted 1/4 of the area of the photo of the complement of July 18, 1921, and secured 521. This gives a complement of 2084, a fair number for the complement of an average female of this largest tree frog in eastern United States. The female which laid this 2084 complement is 59 mm.; our largest female specimen is 68 mm.

Dangers. In general they choose cypress ponds. In that case the eggs doubtless hatch before any danger from drying up. The males caught June 5, 1921, July 3, 1921 and pairs taken August 16, 1922 were from a corn field, a pool by a wood pile and a shallow grassy temporary hole in the pine woods. Every place would dry up in a few days at the most. The loss of tadpole life would be great. No doubt this species suffers in this regard. It grows to the largest *Hyla* size before transformation and the toll is surely great in this species.

HATCHING PERIOD

The only record we have is from the pair caught the evening of July 17, 1921. This pair laid eggs between 12:00 a.m.–6:00 a.m., July 18. On July 20, we make the following note "No. 553 *Hyla gratiosa* eggs just hatched or better night of July 19–20. Eggs laid in camp." This means two days from laying in camp and in shallow water 1 inch or less. In nature they were in water 3 inches–1 foot in depth.

MATURE TADPOLE

Color description from life (June 23, 27, August 21, 1922). They have considerable greenish, greenish yellow or yellowish in the tail and body and are beautiful tadpoles. Half grown tadpoles have a striking black saddle spot on the back of the muscular part of the tail and two prominent light areas from each eye to the vent.

On the side a patch just ahead of developing hind legs light greenish yellow. Black stripe from between the eye along the base of the upper crest on either side half way to tip of the tail. Light area beneath this black area and around nostril, over eye, along side to base of muscular part of the tail ivory yellow, tilleul buff or pale pinkish buff. Another short line of the same color at the very base of the upper crest and above the black stripe. Muscular part of the tail and crest yellowish citrine, light yellowish olive, mignonette green or courge green. Belly pale vinaceous pink. Either side at gill region congo pink, throat clear. Lower lip like muscular tail, yellowish citrine or courge green.

General appearance. Tadpole medium (50 mm.) largest of Hylid tadpoles of the eastern United States. Tail long. Tip acuminate, with flagellum. Dorsal and ventral crests about equal either equal depth to the tail musculature. Dorsal crest extending on body to a vertical about half way between the spiracle and the eye. Spiracle sinsitral, far below lateral axis, directed upward and backward. Eye on lateral axis, in dorsal aspect in the lateral outline and in consequence visible from the venter. Anus dextral, on a level with the lower edge of the ventral crest. Muciferous crypts indistinct.

Mouth parts: Teeth 2/3. Upper labium fringed with row of teeth; the papillae extend above and inwards beyond the end of this fringe 2/7–1/4 (usually at least 1/4) of the length of the fringe. The end of the second row about even with the end of the fringe. Sometimes the ends unite. The horny beak contained in the length of the upper fringe 1.5–1.75 times. Median space between the two lateral parts of the second rows contained 1.5–3.0 times either lateral row. Inner papillae on either side from end of lateral upper row one or two rows to end of lower third labial row. The lower third labial row with one row of papillae below it, rarely with none, about equal to this single row of papillae, or 2 5/8–3 1/2 times in the length of the first or second rows. The first or second lower labial rows about equal or about 1 1/3 longer than horny beaks. Some of the teeth rows have tendency to be curved on ends or united at other rows or be quite irregular. More so than in any other United States Hylid.

Measurements. Length of body (13.5–20 mm.) in tail (27–32 mm.) 2.3–3.25, average 2.5. Width (9–13 mm.) of body in its own length 1.5–2.0, average 1.7. Depth (9.5–13.5 mm.) of body .82–1.0 in body width, average .9. Depth of body 1.4–1.9 in body length, average 1.62. Depth (10–14 mm.) of tail in length of tail 2.0–2.8, average 2.34. Muscular part (4.5–8.5 mm.) 1.5–2.9 in depth of tail, average 2.0. Spiracle 1.0–1.375 nearer base of hind legs or vent region (8.0–10.0 mm.) than the tip of the snout (10–12 mm.), average 1.2. Spiracle nearer eye than base of hind legs or vent, average 1.9.

Eye 1.07–1.75 nearer to spiracle (4.0–5.6 mm.) than to tip of snout (6.0–7.0 mm.), average 1.3. Nostril 1.0–1.8 nearer eye (2.5–4.0 mm.) than snout (3.5–4.5 mm.). Mouth (3.5–4.5 mm.) usually 1–1.5 larger than internasal space (3.0–4.0 mm.), average 1.075. Mouth contained 1.33–2.4 (average 1.88) in interorbital distance (6.5–8.5 mm.). Internasal space contained in interorbital space 1.62–2.33, average 2.15.

The dimensions of the largest tadpole are:

	mm.		mm.
Total length	50	Spiracle to vent	10.0
Body length	19	Spiracle to eye	5.5
Body depth	12	Eye to snout	7.0
Body width	10.5	Eye to nostril	4.0
Tail length	31	Nostril to snout	4.0
Tail depth	11.0	Mouth	4.5
Musculature of tail	7.0	Interorbital distance	7.0
Spiracle to snout	11.5	Internasal distance	3 5

General remarks. In 1921 we secured nothing on the larvae. In 1922 we "found small tadpoles of this form in the pond 1 mile south of Trader's Hill. They have a striking saddle back spot on the muscular part of the tail and two prominent light areas from each eye to vent." On July 26 "In Anna's Pond found large mature tadpoles of *H. gratiosa*. They are large creatures. They have considerable greenish in the tail and body." On July 28 "in a pond (open) 1 mile east of Chesser School mature tadpoles. The tadpoles were in the drifting masses of vegetation." In 1923 (p. 406) we characterized the tadpoles as follows: "*Hyla gratiosa*—beautiful green tadpoles, deep crests, young with black saddles on base of the tail, light line from eye to tail."

These long-tailed, big-eyed, at times flagellum-tipped tadpoles show the myotomes of the tail musculature particularly along the edges of the musculature. One captured July 31, 1922, has a forked tail-tip. Tadpoles about half-grown, if viewed from dorsum, look to be a perfect wedge from eye to tail tip.

LARVAL PERIOD

In 1922, in April at St. George and Waycross there was only .55 and .69 inches rainfall for the whole month, but in May 8.70 and 7.38 inches respectively. But at St. George and Waycross 6.05 and 4.12 inches of the month rain was from May 24–31. The transforming frogs of July 25–28 were presumably from this May period or 55–65 days as larvae. If, however, they came from eggs laid in the great June 10–14 choruses which we found on arrival, the period is reduced to 41–48 or 50 days.

We incline toward May 24–31 as the period of ovulation because in this pond the tadpoles which transformed July 26–31, 1922, were recorded as half grown in this pond on June 27. June 10 or 12 is too early for these tadpoles, better May 24 onwards or a month for growth to the half way period. This species has to grow to a larger transformation size than any other *Hyla* in the swamp and, therefore, would not be expected to have a short period, but rather a long one. The upper range 41–65 may be a minimum period of development.

TRANSFORMATION

Period. In 1922 on July 10 "found 2 or 3 tadpoles in two-legged condition." On July 17 they were not beyond the two-legged stage. On July 24 "found one two-legged tadpole ready to burst out its forelegs," and on July 25 "the tadpole burst its forelegs this morning." On July 27 we found this tadpole fully transformed. Two days later at same pond found four transformed or transforming. On July 26 in another pond found a transformed frog. A month later, August 21, 1922, in a third pond "Several beautiful mature *Hyla gratiosa* tadpoles. One a beautiful specimen with a very yellowish or greenish yellow (non-Ridgway) colored tail. In one pond we record on August 9 that the *Hyla gratiosa* tadpoles are quite small. All in all we actually took transformed individuals from last of July to the last of August.

On July 26, 1922, when coat bets were having a great breeding congress where we solved the "barker" puzzle we found breeding signs and "found a transformed *Hyla gratiosa* 2 or 3 inches above the water on a spear point leaf of *Equisetum* (horsetail)."

On July 31, 1922, we have these journal observations. "In one pond we found in one haul of the seine 6 *Notophthalmus dorsalis* larvae, *Hyla gratiosa* mature tadpoles, transformed frogs and a tadpole with bifurcated tail. Plenty of *Hyla gratiosa* and *Rana aesopus* tadpoles. Caught two *Kinosternon subrubrum*. In a pond south of this first pond took almost a pure culture of *Hyla gratiosa* tadpoles with a few red-tailed *Hyla femoralis* tadpoles. In pond (corner of Chesser Island and Old Okefinokee roads) secured largest *R. aesopus* tadpole and plenty of *Hyla gratiosa* transformed and tadpoles a plenty." Thus the progeny of our earliest breeders may be transformed or transforming when the later breeders are just beginning. Eggs laid in July or as late as August 16 must transform in September or October. We thus have July–October at least for transformation.

Size. On July 26, 1922, a transformed frog measured 20 mm., on July 27 three were 19, 23, 21 mm. respectively; another of the same date measured 19 mm.; on July 29, two measured 18 mm. and two 20 mm.; on July 31 we have three 19, 20, 21 mm. in length and on August 21, one of 23 mm. We have only 13 specimens with an average and mode of 20 mm., and a range of 18–23 mm. This makes it a larger transforming *Hyla* than *Hyla versicolor* with its 14–20 mm. range.

General remarks. "*Hyla gratiosa* when transformed often shows brownish spots on the back; sometimes has three or four yellow or orange spots like an adult *Hyla cinerea*. Dark vitta from eye backward and three or four disconnected dark spots on sides almost to groin. Another shows the spots of dorsum common and dark green."

As transformation approaches the myotomes of the tail musculature show very clearly. The creature looked like a big-eyed, big-headed creature with very slender waist and hind legs, the head being very broad. The body looks very cuneate from eyes to waist to tip of tail. At transformation the tympanum may not be evident at all. The granulations of the dorsum begin to show before transformation is completed.

GROWTH

At Hilliard, Fla., August 16, 1922, we took males 55, 59, 60 mm. respectively, two groups (?). At Trader's Hill on July 4, 1922, we secured two males 52, 56 mm. On Billy's Island in 1921 we secured males 60, 60, 61. From July 15–17, 1921, Chesser Island, we secured 58, 61, 63, 65, 65, 66, 68 mm. ♂s, 59, 68 mm. ♀s. Our material apparently shows two groups 52–56 mm. and 58–68 mm. with transformation size at 18–23 mm.

A glance over the U. S. National Museum material reveals that Dr. T. H. Bean (U. S. N. M. No. 4742) at Micanopy, Florida, secured two groups 28, 30, 31, 31, 32, 32, 33.5 mm. and 47, 47, 49 mm., and Major J. LeConte (5901) took 51 mm. ♂, 56 mm. ♂, 56.5 mm. ♀ and 60.5 mm. ♂ and ♀. There seems three groups 28–33.5 mm.; and 47–56 mm.; 60.5– . In some ways the evidence seems 18–23 mm. at transformation, 28–34 mm. first year olds; 37–45 mm. second year olds; 47–56 mm. third year olds; 56–68 mm. four year olds.

FOOD

There is little of record regarding the food habits of this species.

ENEMIES

On July 24, 1927, at Anna's Pond 15–20 feet in diameter found "much fewer tadpoles than before. . . . A Green Heron flew up. Twice a chicken turtle (*Deirochelys reticularia*) has been seined out of it and a black snake, watersnake and riband snake taken around or in it. All doubtless take their toll of tadpole or transformed frogs." On July 27, 1927, we found 5 or 6 transformed *Hyla gratiosa*, one with the hind foot gone." A female of a pair captured July 17, 1921, on Chesser Island, had its left forearm and foot gone, and in the front of the right thigh is a sharp cut gauge as if bitten by a turtle or some animal.

AUTUMNAL DISAPPEARANCE

Deckert records it in March–June at Jacksonville, Fla. We at Okefinokee Swamp a short distance away have recorded it from June to September 1. The U. S. National Museum have records of specimens taken Sept. 9, 1912, and Nov. 20, 1912. The known range is March to November 20. It may be more or less active the year through, though seldom seen or heard except at breeding time.

AFFINITIES

This Sabalian frog, like some others has outgrown the "Florida" handle. The singly deposited eggs may place it with *Hyla squirella*, *Acris gryllus*, *Pseudacris ocularis* and *Hyla crucifer*. This I would not emphasize so much as the strewing of eggs on vegetation on bottom.   This suggests more especially *H. andersonii, Hyla squirella, Hyla cinerea.*

On June 26, 1922, when we found numerous mature tadpoles we entered the following note "In relationships, on appearance *H. gratiosa, H. cinerea* and possibly *H. squirella* may be closer much as *Hyla femoralis* seems very close to *Hyla versicolor.*"   In a synopsis of tadpoles on mouth part characters we have associated the tadpole of *Hyla gratiosa* with those of *Hyla andersonii* and *Hyla cinerea.*   In some ways the adult belongs nearer these two than any others.   Yet the size of the tadpole suggests the larger tadpole class size of *Hyla versicolor, Hyla arenicolor* and *Hyla femoralis.*   A perfect adult tadpole has a flagellum-like tip like some of these forms.

BIBLIOGRAPHY

1889   Cope, E. D. The Batrachia of North America, pp. 379.
1915   Deckert, R. F. Copeia, May 15, 1915, No. 18, p. 5.
1906   Dickerson, M. C. The Frog Book, pp. 124-126.
1856   Le Conte, John. Proc. Phila. Acad. Nat. Sci., Aug. 1856, p. 146.
1922   Löding, H. P. Geol. Surv. Ala. Mus. Paper No.5, Sept. 1922, p. 19.
1923   Stejneger, L. and T. Barbour. A Check List of North American Amphibians and Reptiles. 2nd edition Cambridge, 1923, p. 31.
1923   Van Hyning, T. Copeia, May 20, 1923, No. 118, p. 68.
1923   Viosca, Percy, Jr. Copeia, Feb. 1, 1923, No. 115, p. 37.
1923   Wright, A. H. The Anatomical Record, January 20, 1923, Vol. 24, Number 6, p. 9, 406.
1923   ———. Copeia, Feb. 1, 1923, No. 115, p. 34.
1924   ——— and A. A. Wright, American Naturalist, July–August 1924, Vol. LVIII, No. 657, p. 378.

Hyla squirella Latreille

(Pl. II, Fig. 7; V, Fig. 4; VII, Fig. 5; X, Fig. 7; XII, Fig. 9; XV, Fig. 5; XVII; XXXI; XXXII; Text Figs. 1, 10)

COMMON NAMES

Southern Tree Frog. Squirrel Tree Frog. The Squirrel Tree-Toad. Southern Tree Toad. "Scraper Frog." "Rain Frog." Squirrel Hyla. Tree Frog.

RANGE

Check list.   "Type locality: Carolina. Range: Virginia to Florida, west to Texas, and northward up the Mississippi basin to Indiana."—Stejneger & Barbour Check List (1923, p. 31).

Supplementary records.   Deckert in May 1922 (1922, p. 88) in Dade Co., Florida, "saw several in Hammock on shell mound about 5 miles northeast of Cape Sable. Heard their calls at Royal Palm Hammock." Myers (1924, p. 60) reports "several" *Hyla squirella* received from Wilmington, N. C. Schmidt (1924, p. 68) has it from Mt. Pleasant near Charleston, S. C. Holt (1924, p. 95) writes "*Hyla squirella* Latreille. Recorded by Löding from Mobile County only. I have taken the species at Barachias, Montgomery County."

Local Okefinokee records.   In 1912, 1913 and 1914 we did not take this form in the swamp. In 1921 we did not secure it until we went to the eastern

edge of the swamp in the last of July. In August of the same period it was heard several times along the Suwannee and St. Mary's Rivers.

In 1922 from June 10 to September this species was recorded. Our operations were mainly outside the swamp. We have not taken it on any of the islands of the swamp except Chesser Island.

GENERAL APPEARANCE

Brimley (1907, p. 154) gives this frog with "Size small, feet not edged with yellow. Yellow or white band on sides not sharply defined above and below. Back of thigh not marked with yellow spots or variegations. Dickerson (1906, pp. 149) calls it a delicate, smooth-skinned little frog." Some have alluded to the constancy of the transverse bar between eye or a part of it. This sometimes disappears. Even the white on upper lip may be rarely absent. Then the general appearance of the creature is about all one has in identifying it.

MEASUREMENTS

(Recent Material)

Head to angle of mouth 2.85 (20 mm.)–3.1 (28 mm. ♂)–3.3 (28 mm. ♀) –3.27 (36 mm. ♀) in length of body; head to rear of tympanum 2.85 (20 mm.) –2.7–2.8–2.88 in length of body; head to angle of mouth 1.0–1.1–1.23–1.13 in width of head; head to tympanum 1.0–.95–1.05–1.0 in width of head; snout .71–.8–.7–.70 in first finger; snout .71–1.0–.9–.92 in fourth finger; snout .42–.4–.8–.61 in first toe; eye .6–.5–.66–.75 in tympanum; eye 1.0–1.0–1.15– 1.12 in first finger; eye 1.4–1.25–1.66–1.62 in snout; tympanum 4.0–4.25–4.0– 3.3 in intertympanic width; tympanum 2.3–2.5–2.5–2.16 in snout; internasal width 1.0–1.5–1.0–.85 in upper eyelid width; interorbital width .5–1.0–1.0–.75 in upper eyelid width; interorbital width .5–.66–1.0–.87 in internasal width; interorbital 2.0–2.8–2.66–2.5– in intertympanic width.

Forelimb. Forelimb 1.66–2.15–2.07–2.05 in length of body; forelimb 2.75–3.0–2.8–3.1 in hindlimb; first finger 1.6–1.375–1.85–1.55 in third finger; second finger 1.6–1.375–1.55–1.16 in third finger; second finger 1.0–1.0–.75– .87 in first finger; third finger .75–.77–.85 in second toe; fourth finger 1.6– 1.1–1.44–1.16 in third finger; fourth finger .6–.4–.88–.66 in first toe; internasal width 1.6–2.0–1.16–1.28 in first finger; internasal width 1.6–2.0–1.33– 1.7 in second finger; internasal width 2.6–2.75–2.16–2.00 in third finger, internasal width 1.6–2.5–1.5–1.7 in fourth finger.

Hindlimb. length 1.65–1.4–1.35–1.5 in hindlimb; tibia 1.8–1.8–( )– ( ) in length; tibia 3.0–2.5–( )–( ) in hindlimb; tibia 1.1–.8–( )– ( ) in forelimb; tibia .63–.70–( )–( ) in hind foot; first toe 2.0–1.75– 1.25–1.5 in second toe; first toe 3.33–3.5–1.87–2.2 in third toe; first toe 4.0–4.5– 2.37–3.0 in fourth toe; first toe 3.3–3.5–1.75–2.12 in fifth toe; second toe 1.66– 2.0–1.5–2.25 in third toe; second toe 2.0–2.5–1.9–2.0 in fourth toe; second toe 1.66–2.0–1.4–1.41 in fifth toe; third toe 1.2–1.28–1.26–1.33 in fourth toe; third toe 1.0–1.0–.93–.94 in fifth toe; fourth toe 1.16–1.2–1.9–1.75 in hind foot; fourth toe 1.8–1.7–( )–( ) in tibia; fourth toe 2.0–1.44–1.42–1.49 in forelimb; fifth toe 1.2–1.28–1.35–1.4 in fourth toe; internasal width 1.0–1.0–1.15–1.14 in first toe; internasal width 2.0–1.75–1.66–1.7 in second toe; internasal width 3.3–3.5–2.5–2.57 in third toe; internasal width 4.0–4.5–3.16–3.4 in fourth toe; internasal width 3.33–3.5–2.33–2.42 in fifth toe.

HABITAT

LeConte (1825, p. 279) says it "Inhabits under logs, and the bark of decaying trees; I have never seen it in, or near the water." Holbrook (1842, Vol. IV, p. 124) holds "This animal is found on trees, often seeking shelter under the bark of such as are decaying; it frequently chooses old logs for its place of hibernation. Often I have found it about old houses, and under logs and boards." Deckert (1914, No. 3, p. 3) at Jacksonville 1911 and 1912 found them "in gardens and corn fields." The same author (1915, p. 3) in his Further Notes on Salientia of Jacksonville, Fla., writes: "*Hyla squirella* Bosc., the commonest of the southern tree toads, is found everywhere, in corn fields, sugar cane, about wells and under eaves of stable roofs, barns, outhouses, etc. After a heavy thunder shower in September, 1911, hundreds of these little tree toads could be seen hopping along the country roads outside of Jacksonville. That same night the writer took 32 specimens from a velvet bean vine on the backside of his cottage." We found these frogs on porches, in China berry-trees, oaks and other trees, as well as vines around the houses, in fields and gardens around buildings, in open ponds, in pine barrens, in pine and oak groves, along roads, in shallow roadside and pine barren pools. On June 22, 1922, a boy at Camp Pinckney brought me a Scraper taken in his own house.

Viosca (1923, pp. 37, 38, 40) found this species in the alluvial ridges of the lowlands of southeastern Louisiana. "The fauna of these ridges differs least from that of the uplands and there are many species in common. Some forms, such as *Hyla squirella* . . . are typical . . . . Where the beach connects with some alluvial ridge, oaks, bushes, and other ridgeland forms make up the vegetation and the fauna partakes of the nature of alluvial species *Hyla squirella* and *Gastrophyne carolinensis* sometimes reaching to the very edge of the Gulf."

FIRST APPEARANCE

Our earliest record is June 10. In Dade County, Deckert records them in May and June. At Houston, Texas, Pope (1919, p. 90) reports "This species was more abundant than any other Hylas, but was the latest to appear in the spring. The first one was collected April 13." The U. S. National Museum has specimens from L. Tohopikaliga, Osceola Co., Feb. 6, 1906, Biloxi, Miss., Feb. 16, 1914, Dauphin, Ala., Mar. 9, 1892, and from Lake Kissimee, Osceola Co., Fla., Apr. 3, 1901. We have specimens from Bay St. Louis collected in January.

GENERAL HABITS

Metachrosis. This very apparent phase of tree frogs has been discussed more than any other topic. This species is a capital example of the sudden changes of which *Hylas* are capable.

LeConte (1825, p. 39) writes of it at length: "The figure of this species in Daudin is very different from any specimen that I have ever seen, both in colour and in marks; I do not deny but that it may have been fond of a green colour, as he represents it, and marked in the same manner; but the same error occurring in his delineation of the next species, I am inclined to think that it has been coloured from report and description, rather than from the animal itself; indeed, whatever the colour may be, it can scarcely remain unchanged for six months, in a preserved specimen; all that I have ever attempted to preserve, lost their colour in less than two months. There are three principal varieties of this species:

"a. Above cinereous, with a straight, or curved or angular bar between the eyes; *back* with a few spots of dusky, sometimes confluent, and forming different figures of irregular shapes; and sometimes uniting into a line on each side of the body, of greater or lesser length.

"b. Above cinereous, irregularly spotted with darker; the line between the eyes broken into two or more spots.

"y. Above entirely brown, with spots, exterior part of thighs not yellow.

"In all these, the dark band on the head, and the white line on the lips, are the only marks which remain constant; in one variety, even the yellow colour on the thighs vanishes; there are hardly any two individuals alike, and so different are they from one another, that a person who had not observed them accurately for a length of time, would be led to think, that there were almost as many species as individuals."

Holbrook (1842, p. 124) remarks that "The colours of this animal are even more changeable than in any species with which I am acquainted. I have seen it pass in a few moments from a light green, unspotted and as intense almost as that of *Hyla lateralis*, to ash-colour, and to a dull brown with darker spots; the spots also at times taking on different tints from the general surface. The markings, too, vary exceedingly in different individuals, the white line on the upper lip and the band between the orbits alone are constant."

LeConte (1855, p. 429) again writes of it as follows: "Color varying at the will of the animal from green to brown of different degrees of intensity, spotted and speckled irregularly with darker and dusky and sometimes with paler, often however of a uniform color. A darker line extends from the nostrils to the eyes and through them to the insertion of the arm (this is sometimes evanescent); beneath this darker line extends a white one which reaches nearly to the groin; sometimes interrupted or broken into three or four parts. The dark line on the vertex between the eyes never fails entirely, although it is sometimes reduced to a rather large spot on each eyelid."

Dickerson (1906, pp. 149, 150) remarks this wonderful change of colour the "scrapper" shows. "Of all the tree frogs of North America, this one has perhaps the greatest power for rapid colour changes, and during these changes presents the greatest variety of colours and shades of colour. At any given moment, *Hyla squirella* may wear any one of the following costumes: Unspotted dark chocolate brown or dark brownish olive; light purplish brown with dark brown spots; light yellowish or greyish brown without spots; any medium shade of brown with green spots; olive green unspotted; light yellow green spotted with brown; unspotted light pea-green; light greenish gray; light fawn colour, or still lighter shades ranging down to flesh colour."

"Most curious is the fact that although these changes take place under the influence of various stimuli, such as light, moisture and heat, they may go on without these stimuli. Frogs shut in a dark pail with no change of conditions will not appear twice alike when the pail is opened at intervals during the space of several hours. Some may be green and others brown; some spotted, others not; some light while others are dark. And at any given time of observation those that were dull and spotted before may be a light, unspotted green, the ones that were light may be dark, and so on. The light line along the jaw undergoes great changes also. This tree frog furnishes a most interesting case for the study of metachrosis."

VOICE

Deckert (1915, p. 3) at Jacksonville, Fla., describes its cry as follows: "The cry is rather coarse, sounding like 'cra, cra, cra', etc., with a second's interval between each note." The same author (1921, pp. 22) in Dade County, Florida, "Their rasping calls were heard in May and June at 19th Street, Miami, at Donn's nursery and at 22nd Street in company with the toads mentioned previously. After heavy rains in July, August and September they were heard also at Cocoanut Grove, Lemon City, Little River, Arch Creek and Fulford."

Pope (1919, pp. 96, 97) at Houston, Texas, gives considerable details of its calls. "The call is a harsh, rasping trill not so loud nor so musical as that *H. versicolor*. From a distance the chorus resembles that of *H. crucifer*, but the call is much harsher when heard close at hand. The throat pouch of the male is large and expands to nearly the size of the body. . . . July 31. Have heard a few frogs almost every night lately, calling from trees near sleeping quarters. They do not begin to call until ten or eleven o'clock at night, and may continue intermittently till daylight. Usually a single one begins to call and is joined by half a dozen or so more until there is quite a chorus."

The first squirrel tree frog the writer ever heard came June 10, 1917 beyond Tuskagee, Ala., and 30 miles from Montgomery. We went through a fine series of lowland woods and over several wooden bridges. "Here first saw *Sabal serenoa*. Heard Whiteeyed Vireo, Acadian Flycatcher, Carolina Wren, Hooded Warbler, Southern Parula Warbler, Tufted Titmouse, Carolina Chickadee, etc. . . . In a moist field heard no end of *Acris gryllus*. After dark heard another note which proved a male *Hyla squirella*. Took one on top of a bush 8 feet high. Another we supposed high in a tree although we found it on a bamboo-like cane 5 feet from the ground."

In 1921 we first heard them on July 21. "Probably the tree frog we heard in Chinaberry tree at Mr. Rider's house during the storm was *H. squirella*,

the Scrapper Frog. Mr. Rider avowed that they were all around and that
they can change color to suit their environment. Some of them he maintains
have no conspicuous marks."

Harper made the following notes on this species on his trip in August on
the Suwannee and St. Mary's Rivers: "At Fargo a number were heard during
a hard rain on the afternoon of August 5, and one was found on a potted
prickly pear (*Opuntia*) on the porch of a house. Here it was occasionally
giving its rather weak and leisurely diurnal note: *Waaaake, waaaake,* etc. It
has a sort of grating or scraping quality and might well be compared to the
scraping of a hollow reed with a fine-toothed comb. It is probably not to be
heard at a distance of more than 50 or 75 yards. In the evening of the same
day a big chorus was heard at Moniac.

"On August 14 and 15, in late afternoon and early morning, several were
heard in a pine grove on the St. Mary's River (Georgia side) about five miles
south of Traders's Hill. On August 15 and 16 several were heard in damp
woods on the south side of this river near Boulogne, Fla.

"During a thunder shower on the afternoon of August 16 a number began
calling at Camp Pinckney, and one was captured among the leaves of a live
oak about 15 feet from the ground. After dark numbers were on the ground,
especially in or about a temporary pool, in a road through level oak woods,
where their chorus was deafening. The nocturnal note is similar to the diurnal one, but stronger, louder, and more regular; in fact, it is almost a continuous call. I found it being given at the rate of 90–95 times per minute.
In the alternate inflation of throat and body, the throat sac attains about
half the size of the body. When sitting on the ground, croaking, this frog has
more or less the appearance of a large, fat *Acris*. Some individuals were
green, and others, I think, brown.

"On the morning of August 18 several others were heard farther down the
river at Kings Ferry and vicinity."

In 1922 our first introduction to this species came seven miles north of
Millen, Ga. "Here at 7 p. m. we heard several and took two in the small
trees at the edge of a swampy tangle. Also heard them in higher trees. An
imminent storm made them noisy. The following morning we heard a few."

On June 19 "At Camp Pinckney hear a *Hyla squirella* across the St.
Mary's River on the Florida side. On the ground saw one hopping along.
We mistook it for a frog (*Rana*). It was brownish with spots. Leaped on to
some dead branches. It can leap. When the thunderstorm came several
Hyla squirella were to be heard and some *H. versicolor*. We captured one in
a tree near the sawmill." On June 23, near the old railroad pools near
Trader's Hill heard one or two scrapers in the afternoon. On June 26 at
Anna's Pond heard one calling. On June 27 at Camp Pinckney heard several
in mid-afternoon. "On a fence heard a *Hyla squirella*. A little later heard
another frog note from a fence where the *H. squirella* was. Were they the
same? Is it versatile in its calling? Later a thunderstorm threatened; heard
several *Hyla squirella*."

On July 2 at 11:00 p. m. heard only one or two near the house. On July 3 we heard them along the Folkston Road. "At 7:15 p. m. we started for the hill. We began to hear *H. squirella* on our way back from the Trader's Hill ponds (1 mile south) and came to a pond 1/2 mile west of Trader's Hill. It was a grassy overflow pool. In a clump of bushes and saw palmetto were several *Hyla squirella*. In grassy shoals in shallow water were several, one of which we photographed. In same grassy overflow were three or four *Hyla gratiosa* calling, *Hyla femoralis* common, *Bufo quercicus* abundant, *Acris gryllus* more or less present. This was at 9:50 p. m. There were *Bufo terrestris* present. Along on Folkston Road in road in temporary pools and ditches with *Bufo terrestris* were plenty of *Hyla squirella*. At 9:30 I heard a *Hyla squirella* give 67 pumps in 45 seconds. There is more vibration in the call of *Hyla femoralis*. Could not hear the *Hyla squirella* a few rods away. The calls of *Hyla femoralis* and *Bufo quercicus* drown it out. *Hyla squirella* does sometimes croak from water surface when sprawled on the water."

On July 9 we heard only one at Thompson's Landing. On July 20, 3 miles from Jacksonville, Florida, we heard another about 4:00 p. m. On July 24 heard a few in mid afternoon at Camp Pinckney. On August 1 several were heard in late afternoon and evening at Waycross and Hebardsville, Ga. On August 8 in mid forenoon we heard many near Starling Branch. The following day in Spanish Creek woods heard them during rain at noon. "As we approached Trader's Hill heard many *Hyla squirella* at 1:00 p. m."

On August 11 "at Camp Pinckney 2–3:00 p. m. heard several. At 8:30 returned to Camp Pinckney. No end of *Hyla squirella*. They were on the ground in a road filled with temporary pools, water 1–3 inches deep. Countless males. Sac hyaline, more or less inflated for some time. Not so fast in calling as *Hyla femoralis* but swift nevertheless. Those in water greenish. Those on edges of pools or in road brownish. . . . Could find no females. Some males, though quite small, are croaking."

On August 13, on a trip from Chesser Island to St. Mary's, Ga., we heard them in several places but especially from 7–10:30 along the Folkston Road." From August 15–17 we heard several at Callahan and Hilliard, Florida, and 1 or 2 at Moniac, August 20. Our last record of calling came September 15, 1922.

Temperature and humidity. In 1921 the great chorus of "scrapers" came August 5. They were calling during the rain or because of rainy weather. The combined rainfall of three places around the swamp was 7.02 inches, maxima 90–95°, minima 70–73°. Thereafter until August 18 a few were heard, maxima 87–97°, minima 68–76°. On August 16, F. Harper and Marion Lee found them calling vigorously from their tree homes in daytime at Camp Pinckney when the thunder storm came on. After dark, numbers were on the ground, especially in or about a wet place in the road thru oak woods, where their calling was deafening. Act like *Hyla cinerea*, throat large inflated, about half the size of the body. Scraper frog called 'Rain Frog' by natives here about. One I timed gave about 15 calls in 10 seconds, three times when I timed it and about 16 times in 10 seconds the fourth time. A very regular and mostly continuous call.

In 1922 on June 19 at Camp Pinckney a severe storm came from 1:00 to 3:00 p. m. *Hyla squirella* were calling vigorously.

On June 23, two inches of rain fell at St. George and scrapers were calling. On June 26 a half inch to an inch of rain fell, and the *Hyla squirella* were calling strongly at Anna's Pond on that day and on June 29 at Camp Pinckney. On the afternoon of July 2 and through some of July 3 considerable rain fell and the species were common in roadside ditches west of Trader's Hill, in Anna's Pond, Starling Branch, Cornhouse Creek and several other places. Another great chorus came August 16 and 17 after a half day's rain when about two inches of rain fell, maxima 82–91°, minima 65–74°. Spadefoots and *Rana aesopus, subterranean species* came out to breed and *Hyla squirella* as well.

In general this species calls even by day in rain or before an imminent rain (July 9). After a downpour of warm rain 1–5 inches they became very active. As every observer has remarked heavy warm rains bring them out in midsummer. During our 1922 study June 10–August 20, maxima were 81–90°, minima 62–74°, averages 90°, maxima minima 70°.

MATING

Male (From life, June 22, 1922). Back citrine or buffy citrine in one; on another ecru-olive or light yellowish olive; rear back and top of hind legs chrysolite green to lime green. Under parts of hand also hind foot orange rugous, xanthine orange to orange chrome; hind limb posterior and anterior faces and throat raw sienna or mars yellow; throat of another aniline yellow or other hind leg parts raw sienna. Stripe on upper jaw on to body greenish or lemon yellow. Belly cream color or ivory yellow. Tympanum hazel or russet. Iris spotted black and army brown, a fawn in one deep chrome and antique brown in another. A light area of greenish on either side of throat but not clearly defined or definite as in *Hyla andersonii* and *Hyla cinerea* males.

One male held in hand in good light became courge green and another oil green. A small last year's *H. squirella* was light dull-green-yellow above and upper jaw stripe light chalcedony yellow. Sometimes those in water may be greenish while those on edges or on land may be brownish.

Female (From life, July 3, 1922). Four females of four different pairs had under parts white with no discolored throats. Throat slightly primrose yellow, reed yellow or white. Forelimbs, groin, hindlimbs before and aft, tibia and hind feet reed yellow, olive yellow. In one yellow ocher on fore and rear part of femur, under side of tibia and foot and fore foot. The females unless very large have none of the bright orange rufous, xanthine orange or orange chrome of the males.

Structural differences. In the four mated pairs the pairs were in size as follows: ♂ 31 mm., ♀ 30 mm; ♂ 29.5 mm., ♀ 28.5 mm.; ♂ 27 mm., ♀ 27 mm.; ♂ 28.5 mm., ♀ 35 mm. In other words in two cases the males were larger, in one case male and female equal and one where female was much larger. We have females 27 and 35 mm., and twelve males from one place ranged from 27.5–35 mm., average 32.4 mm., mode 32 mm.

These are about the maximum size. Of 92 specimens measured in the U. S. National Museum there were only three of 30 mm., one of 31 mm., two of 32 mm., one 33 mm., and one 35 mm.

Of a group of 35 specimens collected at South Jacksonville, Florida by Thomas Hallinan in 1922 for the American Museum of Natural History there are of females (26) two 23 mm., two 24 mm., five 25 mm., one 26 mm., three 27 mm., three 28 mm., one 29 mm., one 30 mm., three 31 mm., three 32 mm., one 33 mm., and one 36 mm.; of males (7), one 23 mm., two 24 mm., one 25 mm., one 28 mm., one 30 mm., and one 34 mm.; and of doubtful but apparently females one 19 mm., one 20 mm., three 21 mm., four 22mm., one 23 mm., and one 25 mm. One lot of three specimens (Am. Mus. Nat. Hist. Nos. 14968, 14969, and 14970) collected by Jay A. Weber, 1921, at Ocalawacochee Slough, Lee Co., Florida, are respectively 20, 23, 24 mm., but we record that "they look like females but are they or are they immature?" This American Museum material shows males from 23–34 mm., females from 23–35 mm., but, however, doubtful females from 19–25 mm. Sizes from 21–24 mm. do not always reveal the sex externally. The extreme size of females found is 37 mm., and of males 36 mm. Han Geyer (1902 pp. 98, 99) reports that he had one 45 mm. in length.

The female has the light throat and the males the more intense throat. In twelve males taken at same time in spirits none had a dark pigment on throat except one which was heavily spotted with dark.

Duration. On July 3, 1922 "About 11:55 or midnight we were at Anna's Pond. Heard the *Hyla squirella* at a distance between two distant houses. In the saw palmettos and grass stools around the pond were many scrapers. One pair found in grass near the edge. Other pairs: three were found in saw palmettos near edge of pool as were the *Hyla femoralis* in pairs. The pair of *Hyla squirella* we photographed hopped upon the road some 8 or 10 or more feet from the pond. By 7:00 a. m. the next morning all four males were not mating. All four females had laid during the evening."

Night or day. Most large choruses come at night though severe rain storms might bring breeding in day time. The frogs prefer the security of night to come down to the ground.

Amplexation.—(Normal, abnormal). All the males of our mated pairs had the axillary embrace. On August 11, 1922, at Camp Pinckney we make the note "Once in a while a male chases another away or at times tries to mate with it."

OVULATION

Habitat. We found them breeding in a roadside ditch, in an open saw-palmetto-surrounded pond (once pine woods), in grassy pools in open land and near a road. The tadpoles we found in some of the above places, and in pools beside an old railroad embankment.

Period. Pope (1919, p. 96) at Houston, Texas, on "April 24, 1918, found them breeding abundantly in a shallow pool after a warm rain." "May 4. A heavy warm rain this evening brought out *Hyla squirella* in force. This seems to have been the regular breeding season and for some time after I

1

2

3

4

5

6

7

8

heard very few of these frogs except for a little after every rain." We have breeding in June, July and August but transforming frogs recorded from June 26–July 10 implies early spring or spring breeding is common. In 1923 (p. 34) we held that "From June 1st to 10th, three species begin (laying). *Bufo quercicus*. . . . *Hyla squirella* chooses the bottom for its singly laid eggs as does *Hyla gratiosa*." In 1924 (p. 378) we give the season June 10–August 21. Doubtless the bulk of laying in the Okefinokee country comes from April to June because of the transforming tadpoles in June and July.

Temperature and humidity. Actual ovulation or mating in 1922 came once after a 2 inch rain, maxima 87–96°, average 92°, minima 68–72°, average 70°; after 1.42 rain; after 1.60 inch rain, maxima 81–93°, average 89°, minima 65–83°, average 72°; after 1.80 inch rain (August 16) maxima 82–91°, average 88°, minima 65–74°, average 71°. In combination we have rains 1.42–1.80 inches, maxima 81–96°, averages 78–92°, minima 65–83°, averages 70–72°.

Egg-laying process. We did not see the egg laying of any of the four pairs we had in captivity. Apparently they lay single eggs. Whether they are of the *Hyla crucifer* type or *Hyla andersonii* type or like *Hyla gratiosa* we cannot say. Whether they remain at the top and strew eggs singly (*Hyla andersonii*) or several at a time, or whether they progress on the bottom like *Hyla crucifer* and lay single eggs remains to be observed.

EGGS

Egg mass. Pope (1919, p. 96) is one of the only workers to record their eggs. On April 24, 1918, at Houston, Texas, he "Caught one mated pair and they laid eggs in a jar the next day. The eggs are laid singly, but tend to cling loosely to the bottom of the jar and to each other."

We have in every instance thus far held that they were singly laid. But on June 22 at Camp Pinckney we found in one of the water pits a surface film. At first we naturally concluded they were *Hyla femoralis* eggs. Closer examination made of the individual eggs made us question "Are they *H. squirella* or *Hyla versicolor* eggs? Later we found *Hyla versicolor* tadpoles in the pond." Still they may be *Hyla squirella*. Our observations on ovulation in this species are too few.

Egg description. Pope (1919, p. 96) describes the eggs laid in captivity for him as follows: "In color they are light brown above and nearly white underneath. Diameter of egg not quite one mm., vitelline sac about .12 mm. in thickness, jelly outside that .25 mm. thick."

On the night of July 3–4, 1922, "at Anna's Pond 11:55–12:00 or later we heard the *Hyla squirellas*. . . . Four pairs we brought home. All laid between 1–7:00 a. m., July 4. Eggs smaller than those of *Hyla femoralis*. Do they lay singly or below the surface? The outer envelope is very close to the inner envelope." We finally concluded (1923, p. 406) they laid single eggs deposited on the bottom. More observations are needed.

The actual count of the egg complement of one of the four females (above mentioned) which laid its eggs in captivity was 942. Another egg complement count is 972.

In 1922 field examinations of the eggs gave the following summation: "vitellus .8–1.0 mm.; inner envelope 1.2–1.6 mm., outer envelope 1.4–1.8 mm. Eggs brown above, cream below."

Laboratory examinations gave .9 mm. as average vitellus, range .8–1.0 mm. inner envelope, average 1.4, range 1.4–1.6 mm.; outer envelope average 1.6 mm., range 1.4–2.0 mm.

Dangers. On August 11, 1922, at Camp Pinckney "we found countless males in temporary pools 1–3 inches deep. Must be that they lay single eggs. Must lay in shallow pools. No end of the tadpoles must be lost from drying of breeding places."

HATCHING PERIOD

The eggs laid July 3–4 hatched in laboratory in about two days. In fact some of the eggs (No. 998) laid July 4, 1:00–7:00 a. m. hatched July 5 at 12:00 noon or 36–43 hours after ovulation or 1 1/2 or 1 3/4 days required for hatching. This was in a period when maxima averaged near 88–90° and minima close to 70°F.

TADPOLE

Color description from life (June 23, 1922). General color of body citrine drab. In general it has a greenish cast like tadpoles of *Hyla cinerea* and *H. gratiosa.* Developing ventral flap between hind legs ecru-olive; throat from line of eye to eye to mouth same color. Area behind gill area ocher red. Belly pigmented testaceous and chalcedony yellow. These make a solid iridescence which on the sides and across the middle venter becomes replaced with black.

Tail. Muscular part of tail dark olive buff. Muscular part without prominent clusters of blackish spots. The dots are uniformly scattered over the muscular part but slightly thicker near the tip. The tail reminds one more of a Ranid tadpole tail in coloration.

Iris more or less black with a rim of testaceous or light coral red and chalcedony yellow spots amongst the black.

General appearance. Tadpole small (32 mm.) full and fairly deep bodied. Tail long, tail tip acuminate a flagellum present. Dorsal and ventral crests well developed and tail in general deep. Dorsal crest not so deep as the tail musculature. Dorsal crest extends on to the body about to the vertical of the spiracle. Spiracle sinistral directed upwards and backwards, well below the lateral axis, the spiracular opening prominent elliptical lateral axis, is in dorsal aspect on the lateral outline and in consequence is visible from the venter. Anus dextral, opening at the level of the edge of the ventral crest. Muciferous crypts indistinct.

Mouth parts: Teeth 2/3. Upper labium fringed with a continuous row of labial teeth; the papillae extend above and inwards beyond the end of the upper fringe for about 1/2–3/10 of upper fringe. The end of the second upper labial row is usually even with the end of the upper fringe. The horny beak is contained about 1.8–2.0 times in the upper fringe. The median space between the lateral second upper labial rows of teeth short, 3.25–5 in the length of either lateral row sometimes very narrow (6 in lateral row). The inner papillae extend under the third row of lower labial teeth making at least two rows across the lower labial border. In the lower labial corner there is a heavy papillary series sometimes 3 or 4 rows wide like *H. versicolor* or *H. femoralis*. The lower third labial row is long and is usually about the length of the first or second lower labial rows and longer than the horny beak. The first and second rows are about equal and 1 1/2–1 3/4 greater than the horny beak. This species, like *H. versicolor* and *H. femoralis* has the upper fringe very angulate at the middle.

Measurements. Length of body (10–12 mm.) in tail (16–20 mm.) 1.55–2.05, average 1.75. Width (5.0–6.6 mm.) of body in its own length 1.7–2.2, average 1.875. Depth (5.0–7.0 mm.) of body equals body width, or slightly greater. Depth of body 1.5–2.2 in body length, average 1.81. Depth (6.0–8.0 mm.) of tail in length of tail 2.3–3.3, average 2.8. Muscular part (3.0–4.2 mm.) 1.5–2.33 in depth of tail, average 1.87. Spiracle 1.15–1.75 nearer base of hind legs or vent region (4.0–6.5 mm.) than the tip of the snout (6.5–8.0 mm.), average 1.47. Spiracle 1.4–2.2 nearer eye (2.8–3.5 mm.) than base of hind legs or vent, average 1.7. Eye 1.1–1.6 nearer to spiracle (2.8–3.5 mm.) than to snout (4.0–5.0 mm.), average 1.38. Nostril 1.5–2.4 nearer eye (1.2–2.0 mm.) than snout (2.8–3.5 mm.), average 1.8. Mouth (2.0–3.5 mm.) usually equal to internasal space (2.5–3.5 mm.). Mouth contained 1.1–1.8 (average 1.50) in interorbital distance (4.0–5.5 mm.). Internasal space contained in interorbital space 1.33–2.0, average 1.58.

The dimensions of the largest tadpole are:

	mm.		mm.
Total length	32	Spiracle to vent	6.5
Body length	12	Spiracle to eye	3.0
Body depth	6.5	Eye to snout	4.0
Body width	6.0	Eye to nostril	1.2
Tail length	20.0	Nostril to snout	3.0
Tail depth	6.0	Mouth	3.2
Musculature of tail	4.0	Interorbital distance	5.0
Spiracle to snout	7.5	Internasal distance	3.5

General remarks. In 1923 (p. 406) we characterized these outstanding characters as "bodies greenish, tail uniformly sprinkled with black dots."

LARVAL PERIOD

On July 3, 1922, at Trader's Hill, we found the species very active in congress. On August 9, 33 days later there were "small tadpoles at Trader's Hill ponds. If the tadpoles transforming July 10 ,were laid in the very rainy last week of May, 1922, they were 40–45 days in the larval life.

The eggs laid in camp July 3–4 hatched July 5 developed by July 30 to tadpoles 11 mm. long but proper food conditions were not at hand. Some of them fixed August 21 measured 16 mm. or one-half normal tadpole size 48 days after ovulation. Even with these 25 or 30 days more or 50–55 days probably would have sent them to transformation if put into natural pond. 40–50 days or even two months may elapse for the larval period.

TRANSFORMATION

Period. On June 26, 1922 we "found our first series from tadpole to transformation in Anna's Pond 3/4 mile northeast of Starling Branch crossing. It is an open pond or sink hole with no trees nearby." On the following day we made more records of tadpoles. On July 10 the *Hyla squirella* tadpoles at above pond were much fewer. "Some of them transformed and some of them have left the pond." Our transformation notes of actual transformation are from June 26–July 11 but eggs laid in July and August 1922 must transform much later.

Size. One lot taken June 26, 1922, measured 11, 11, 12, 12, 12, 12, 12, 12, 12.5 and 13 mm. respectively. Seven taken June 27 measured 11.5, 12, 12, 12, 12, 12 and 12.5 mm. respectively. Another lot of twenty specimens had one at 11 mm., two at 11.5, eleven at 12 mm., four at 12.5 mm., and two at 13 mm. One group of six collected July 11, 1922 have the following points of interest: 1 mature tadpole; one 12 mm. long, tail 12 mm., forelimbs almost ready to burst through; complete tadpole mouth; a third 12 mm. long, tail 15 mm., tail filament, forelegs through, tadpole mouth but without teeth; a fourth 12.5 mm., tail 13.5 mm., tadpole mouth just past; a fifth 11 mm., tail 10 mm., forelimbs not quite out, tadpole mouth complete except for third lower row of teeth; and a sixth, 11.5 mm., tail 11 mm., no tadpole mouth, mouth half frog-like, fore legs out. The range of the forty-one specimens is from 11–13 mm., the mode 12 mm., the average 12.3 mm.

General remarks. These little frogs are best identified by their tails as long as they have the crests. Thereafter no key could identify them. They have not the whole line on upper lip, no spots on back, nor vitta back of eye. Like many *Hyla* transformed frogs they are hard to distinguish unless followed through the stages or unless tadpoles be known.

GROWTH

On June 26 and 27 we had 36 specimens 11–13 mm. at transformation. On August 16, 1910, Professor J. C. Bradley took one at Lakeland, Fla., 14 mm. in length. Seven miles north of Millen, Georgia, we took June 10, 1922, two *Hyla squirella* of two growth groups one 20 mm., and a male 28 mm. All the twelve croaking males of July 3, 1922, and all the four pairs of July 3, 1922 (another pond) are from 27–35 mm. in length. Have we three forms 11–14 mm. at transformation; 20 mm. one year old and 27–35 two year old?

In 1922 (March 9) Hurter took (U. S. National Museum Nos. 58117–58124) specimens of two groups, two 22 and 23 mm., and six 27.5, 28, 29.5, 32, 33, 33 mm. LeConte in Liberty County took two (U. S. National Museum No. 3645) 21 and 27 mm. respectively. Dr. Schwartz and Mr. Barber (U. S. N. M. 61690–1) at Paradise Key, Fla., took two 21 and 26 mm. On July 18,

1901, P. R. Paine at Charleston, S. C., took 16 specimens (U. S. National Museum No. 29229–29243) 17.5, 17.5, 19, 19.5, 20, 20, 20, 20.5, 21, 22, 22, 23, 23, 23, 24.5, 25 mm., respectively 17.5–25 mm. William Wittfield took (U. S. National Museum No. 12008) twelve specimens 15, 16, 19, 21, 24, 24, 25, 25, 26.5, 27.5, 28, 28.5 mm. respectively. Material taken by Professor A. M. Reese, Lake Kissimee ranges from 20–27 mm. (one 31 mm.) for 23 specimens, (U. S. N. M. Nos. 36202–10, 29065–66, 36249–36260), an average of 23.5 mm. All combined it seems as if 11–14 mm. is transformation size, 17.5–25.5 mm. is one year old size, 25–35 mm. is two year old size.

Very recently we discovered considerable material in the U. S. National Museum from one locality, Charleston, S. C. in the fall of 1923 and the summer and fall of 1924. They were taken by J. T. Rogers as follows. On June 19, 1924, he secured (U. S. N. M. Nos. 67425–42) all adults 23–33 mm. (Males 24, 25, 25, 27, 27, 28, 28, 33; females 23, 24, 24, 25, 25, 25, 26, 26, 30) —all possible two year olds 23–33 mm. but the 30 and 33 mm. individuals are possibly apart. On Sept. 17, 1924, J. T. Rogers took (U. S. N. M. Nos. 67714–67730) the following: 14.5, and 17, 18, 18, 18, 19, and 21, 22, and 26.5, 27, 27, 27, 28, 28, 28, 29, and 32 mm. Have we three groups, 14.5 mm., 17–22 mm., 26.5–32 mm.? On November 16, 1923, Rogers took 4 specimens (U. S. N. M. 66804–7) 17.5, 20, 20, 22 mm. Does all this material shape as follows: 14.5 mm.; 17–22 mm.; 23–30 mm.; 32, 33 mm.?

After measuring the American Museum material their data seems to fall thus: 13 mm. transformation; 19–23 mm. or 25 mm. for the first year olds; 25 or 26–36 mm. for 2 year olds. Several specimens from 19 to 23 mm. or in one instance 25 mm. we recorded as doubtful in sex. Doubtless they were all one year olds. But the males and females clearly so externally 23–25 mm. are doubtless individuals older than one year.

FOOD

Deckert (1921, p. 22) in Miami, Dade Co., Florida, finds that "A few have established themselves in the velvet bean vines covering the writer's back porch, and at night will sit flattened out against the window panes, catching the insects that are attracted by the light within."

ENEMIES

On June 27, 1922, in one pond "we found a *Hyla squirella* tadpole with one hind leg. Yesterday found one tadpole with forelegs about to burst out but it had no hind legs. Either lost or never developed." In this pond we took southern riband snakes and chicken turtles (*Deirochelys*).

AUTUMNAL DISAPPEARANCE

Deckert (1921, p. 22) records them after heavy rains in September in Dade County, Florida. Pope (1919, p. 97) at Houston, Texas, heard it as late as September 20. "Have heard very little of *Hyla squirella* lately, but rain fell all last night and tonight they were singing loudly again, although it turned cool after the rain." Our latest record is September 17, 1922, (F. Harper). In the U. S. National Museum are the following captures: J. T. Rogers, Sept. 17, 1924, Charleston, S. C. (U. S. N. M. 67714–67730); same collector, Nov. 16, 1923 (U. S. N. M. 66804–7); J. T. Rogers, Sept. 15, 1924 (U. S. N. M. 67731).

AFFINITIES

In 1855 (p. 429) LeConte holds "It is wrong in Dumeril and Bibron to say that this species (*Hyla femoralis*) is a variety of *Hyla squirella*. In shape and size the difference is most considerable. The latter animal during the warm season is always to be met with about houses, the *H. femoralis* never. Besides, their notes are entirely different."

Cope (1889, p. 364) maintains that "This species approaches nearly some forms of *H. regilla*, of which it may be considered the southeastern representative, though the regions inhabited by both approach in Texas. It may be always distinguished by the more depressed head and weaker canthus rostralis; it is rarely so robust and usually of more delicate and less striped coloration. *H. miotympanum* Cope replaces it in Mexico; the resemblance between them is offset by greater palmation and smaller tympanum of the latter."

Hyla squirella on the basis of eggs, if judged on manner of deposition, would fall in the group of singly deposited eggs: *Hyla gratiosa, Hyla andersonii Acris gryllus, Hyla crucifer,* but this may mean little. But if we analyse the egg characters it may fall closer to *Hyla femoralis, Hyla cinerea,* etc. In our synopsis of tadpoles, *Hyla squirella* apparently falls with *Hyla versicolor, Hyla arenicolor, Hyla femoralis,* the group with long lower hind labial row. On June 17, 1922, we note that "the tail of the tadpole reminds us of the tail of some Ranids in color."

BIBLIOGRAPHY

1907 Brimley, C. S. Jour. Elisha Mitchell Soc. Dec. 1907. Vol. XXIII, No. 4, p. 154.
1889 Cope, E. D. U. S. National Museum Bull. 34, 1889, p. 364.
1914 Deckert, Richard F. Copeia, Feb. 14, 1914, No. 3, p. 3.
1915 ———. Copeia, May 15, 1915, No. 18, p. 3.
1921 ———. Copeia, March 15, 1921, No. 92, p. 22.
1922 ———. Copeia, Nov. 20, 1922, No. 122, p. 88.
1842 De Kay, James E. Zool. of N. Y. Part III, p. 72.
1903 Geyer, Hans. Natur und Haus Jahrgang XI, Heft 7, Jan. 1, 1903, pp. 97-99.
1842 Holbrook, John Edwards. North American Herpetology. Vol. IV, Phila., pp. 123-125.
1924 Holt, E. G. Copeia, Nov. 18, 1924, p. 95.
1825 LeConte, John. Ann. Lyc. Nat. Hist. N. Y., Vol. I, Part II, N. Y., 1825, pp. 38, 39.
1855 ———. Phila. Acad. Nat. Sci. Proc. 1855, p. 429.
1924 Myers, George S. Copeia, June 30, 1924, No. 131, p. 60.
1919 Pope, Philip H. Copeia, Dec. 31, 1919, No. 76, pp. 96, 97.
1924 Schmidt, Karl P. Copeia, July 15, 1924, No. 132, p. 68.
1923 Viosca, Percy J. Copeia, Feb. 1, 1923, No. 115, pp. 38-40.
1923 Wright, A. H. The Anatomical Record, Jan. 20, 1923, Vol. 24, No. 6, p. 406.
1923 ———. Copeia, Feb. 1, 1923, No. 115, p. 34.
1924 ——— and A. A. Wright. The American Naturalist, July, August, 1924, Vol. LVIII, p. 378.

Hyla versicolor (Le Conte)

(Pl. II, Fig. 9; IV, Figs, 3, 8; VII, Fig. 2; X, Figs. 9, 10; XII, Fig. 12; XV, Fig. 6; XVII; XXXIII; Text Figs. 1, 18)

(See Life History in Carnegie Publication No. 197, 1914, pp. 44-51).

COMMON NAMES

Common Tree Toad. Common Tree Frog. Tree Toad. The Northern Tree-toad. Chameleon Hyla.

RANGE

Check list. Maine, southern Canada, west to Minnesota, south to the Gulf States (Texas and Arkansas in part only).—Stejneger & Barbour, 1923, p. 32.

Supplementary records. Edith R. Force (1925, p. 25) records *Hyla versicolor* in Okmulgee County, Oklahoma, in 1924.

In Alabama Holt (1924, p. 95) records this species from Sand Mountain, Jackson County.

In 1917 we found it on May 31 at Petersburg, Va.; on June 2 at Dinwiddie, Va.; on June 11 several near Flatwood, Ala. From 1913 to 1925, we have taken this species from Dorset, Ontario, to near Jacksonville, Fla., and thence west to Beeville, Texas.

Local Okefinokee records. In 1921, F. Harper recorded this species about ten miles south of Moniac on the Georgia side. Again "during the evening of August 16, after a thunderstorm several individuals were found in voice at Camp Pinckney." In 1922 we heard them from June 16 onward at Camp Pinckney, Trader's Hill, Spanish Creek Woods, Thompson's Landing, St. Mary's River, also along road from Folkston to Chesser Island.

MEASUREMENTS

(Recent Material)

Head to angle of mouth 1.0 (18 mm. transformation)–1.33 (28 mm.)–1.41 (44 mm. ♂)–1.5 (56 mm. ♀) in length; head to rear of tympanum (absent)–1.2 (28 mm.)–1.17 (44 mm.)–1.17 (56 mm.) in length; head to angle of mouth 3.6–3.1–3.66–4.1 in length of body; head to rear of tympanum ( )–2.8–3.0–3.3 in length of body; snout .66–.63.1.07–.94 in first finger; snout 1.0–1.1–1.15–1.3 in fourth finger; snout .5–.54–.7–.60 in first toe; eye 1.2–1.37–1.08–1.4 in snout; eye ( )–.75–.50–.66 in tympanum; eye .8–.87–1.16–1.33 in first finger; tympanum ( )–1.83–2.16–2.12 in snout; tympanum ( )–3.0–4.5–4.0 in intertympanic width; internasal width .75–.83–1.12–1.0 in upper eyelid space; interorbital width .8–1.2–.9–.83 in internasal width; interorbital width .60–1.0–1.0–.82 in upper eyelid width; interorbital width ( )–3.6–3.1–2.66 in intertympanic width.

Forelimb: Forelimb 1.8–1.4–1.9–1.6 in length of body; forelimb 2.2–2.2–2.5–2.12 in hind limb; first finger 2.0–2.3–1.3–1.6 in hind finger; second finger 1.6–1.6–1.2–1.3 in third finger; second finger .8–.7–.94–.8 in first finger; third finger .62–.62–.83–.77 in second finger; fourth finger 1.33–1.25–1.2–1.18 in third finger; fourth finger .5–.5–.6–.45 in first toe; internasal width 1.0–1.16–1.75–1.6 in first finger; internasal width 1.25–1.6–1.87–2.0 in second finger; internasal width 2.0–2.3–2.25–2.6 in third finger; internasal width 1.5–2.0–1.87–2.2 in fourth finger.

Hindlimb: length 1.22–1.5–1.36–1.25 in hindlimb; tibia 2.5–1.7–2.2–2.15 in length of body; tibia 3.1–2.75–2.95–2.7 in hindlimb; tibia 1.4–1.25–1.15–1.26 in forelimb; tibia .71–.875–.90–.92 in hind foot; first toe 1.66–1.5–1.33–1.8 in second toe; first toe 2.33–2.66–2.2–3.33 in third toe; first toe 3.00–3.66–2.9–3.9 in fourth toe; first toe 2.33–2.66–2.1–2.4 in fifth toe; second toe 1.8–1.8–1.66–1.77 in third toe; second toe 1.8–2.44–2.16–2.16 in fourth toe; second toe 1.8–1.8–1.6–1.33 in fifth toe; third toe 1.3–1.375–1.3–1.2 in fourth toe; third toe 1.0–1.0–.93–.75 in fifth toe; fourth toe 1.1–1.27–1.4–1.23 in hind foot; fourth toe 1.55–1.45–1.54–1.3 in tibia; fourth toe 2.2–1.8–1.77–1.7 in forelimb; fifth toe 1.3–1.375–1.35–1.6 in fourth toe; internasal width .75–1.0–1.22–1.0 in first toe; internasal width 1.25–1.5–1.5–1.8 in second toe; internasal width 1.75–2.66–2.5–3.33 in third toe; internasal width 2.25–3.66–3.25–3.9 in fourth toe; internasal width 1.75–2.66–2.4–2.4 in fifth toe.

HABITAT

This form we found only from ten miles south of Moniac on the St. Mary's River to Folkston really Camp Pinckney on the St. Mary's River but not within the swamp.

Holbrook (1842, Vol. 4, p. 117) writes "This animal is commonly found on trees and about old stone fences, overgrown with mosses and lichens, the color of which it so closely resembles that it frequently escapes observation even when sought for. It very commonly chooses old and decaying plum trees for its abode, probably because insects on which it feeds are most abundant in such situations."

FIRST APPEARANCE

In Ithaca our first appearance records for this species come in mid April or earlier. Surely in Southern Georgia they must be abroad even earlier in the spring. In 1921 we spent April and May within the swamp where the species is not but in 1922 we encamped in June and on June 19 we heard them in Camp Pinckney.

In Houston, Texas, Pope (1924, p. 95) made "the following notes on it: Feb. 13, 1918. Have heard several in the past few days calling from trees in camp, but have not seen any yet. April 15 collected one specimen, a male that was calling from the branch of a pine tree. April 24 found one calling in rain pool where *H. squirella* was breeding. I heard them frequently on warm evenings, answering each other from trees in the woods near camp. After the first of May they became silent and I heard and saw no more of them for the season. If they laid eggs in any of the pools near camp they made no such noise about it as they do in the North." We heard and collected them in Beeville, Texas, March 24, 1925.

PLATE XXXIII

Tree-toad (*Hyla versicolor*)

1. Old turpentine pit at Camp Pinckney, Ga. June 22, 1922.

2. Male croaking, Camp Pinckney, Ga. August 11, 1922. Flashlight.

3. Male, Beeville, Texas. March 26, 1925. Dorsal aspect. × 0.8.

4. Male croaking on pine tree about $1\frac{1}{2}$ feet above ground, Camp Pinckney, Ga.
   August 16, 1921. Flashlight.

5. Transformed frog, Chesser Id., Ga. June 29, 1922. × 1.0.

6. Egg packet attached to *Potamogeton* leaf, Ithaca, N. Y.

7. Female and male, Chesser Id., Ga. August 12, 1922. Ventral aspect. × 0.60.

GENERAL HABITS

Metachrosis. LeConte (1825, p. 281) called it *Hyla versicolor* in allusion to its metachrosis. Harlan (1927, p. 343) in his description alluded to its "colour varying with the will of the animal from pale-brown to cinerous and green." Holbrook (1842, Vol. IV, p. 115) spoke of it thus: "This is a beautiful species of *Hyla;* its colours seeming almost to vary at the will of the animal." DeKay (1842, Part III, p. 71) says "its facility of assimilating the color with that of the tree on which it rests, renders its capture very difficult." Since that date writers have alluded to this phase of the tree toad's life more than any other one topic. It is too well known to require further discussion.

VOICE

This is a familiar phase of its life history. Holbrook (1842, Vol. IV, p. 117) writes:

"It is very noisy towards evening in cloudy weather or before rain, its voice consisting of a liquid note, terminating abruptly, like l-l-l-l-l-l-luk. At the close of spring, and during a great part of the summer, when the toad has become silent, this note may be heard especially in the evening from various shallow pools, to which the animal resorts for the purpose of depositing its spawn."

DeKay (1842, Part III, p. 71) asserts "I have been assured by many credible persons that it possesses ventriloquial powers in no considerable degree, and often deceives the most attentive observers."

Cope (1889, p. 375) characterizes it as follows: "Its voice is a loud, coarse, resonant trill, uttered with a uniform pitch, and continued for two or three seconds. It is heard about bodies of water in the spring, when the sexes are depositing and fertilizing the eggs. Later in the season it proceeds from fences, hedgerows, and orchards, as well as from the forest, often at no great elevation from the ground. They are especially noisy towards evening after a rain."

In 1906 Fowler says that "The vocal sac when inflated is very marked, though apparently it does not distend to the extent of that of *pickeringii*. It collapses by a series of jerks as the cry is emitted. They usually do not begin to call much before late April."

The same year Dickerson (1906, p. 119) writes: "At dusk or on rainy days a loud resonant trill comes from the trees and vines. The sound has the charm of contentment in it; in fact it is much like the purring of a cat, only louder. At a distance it sound something like the bleating of a lamb. The pitch is uniform, but may vary with the individual, from G above middle C to E above. It continues for two or three seconds at a time, then ends abruptly. It may be given several times in rather close succession. If we see the tree frog trilling, we are surprised that the whole body is so greatly agitated and that the throat extends into so large a sac. The size of the sac decreases between each two trills and at the end collapses, leaving a very wrinkled throat."

Overton, a pioneer in amphibian flashlight photography, has studied the calls of our northeastern frogs very assiduously. He discusses this form thus.

"The voice of the tree frog is a loud musical trill, like a low-pitched whistle. It may be recognized by its extremely pronounced trill. Each individual call lasts about two seconds and may be repeated at intervals of ten to twenty seconds.

"When a tree frog sings, it distends a throat pouch to about the size of its head. The vocal pouch vibrates with the trilling and so its photograph will often be blurred. The frog usually sings while sitting upright in a dry place, such as a lily pad or a branch over the water. It is not especially shy, and is usually easy to photograph.

"Besides the trill, the tree frog has another note that is not generally known and recognized. This note is exactly like the sound made by a hen turkey that is calling to her mates. It is a low, mournful "chow, chow, chow, chow, chow," whistled with a descending pitch, repeated about three times a second for two or three seconds. When I first heard the sounds, their source was a mystery, for they were infrequent. But at last I discovered the musicians. Sitting on a small limb just above the water were two tree frogs about six inches apart. Turning about and facing each other, one gave its turkey call by chirping, while nodding its head and body with every chirp-like and puppy barking. It was at once answered by the other in the same way. The two then quickly turned about and resumed their ordinary songs. This performance was repeated several times while I watched them with aching feet, for they waited a long time between their turkey calls. The Long Island negroes name the call a 'turkey root' from a superstitious belief on the virtues of roots in conjuring and magic. A negro calls any mysterious sound or sight a conjure or "root,' and he will run a mile to avoid hearing a 'turkey root.' "

We (1914, pp. 45, 46) have discussed their voice and calling at length and will not attempt its characterization here.

In 1921 on my way to the Okefinokee Swamp I stopped at Raleigh, N. C. where I heard males calling April 15 and many calling April 16.

In 1921, August 16, at Camp Pinckney, F. Harper and Marion Lee of our party heard this species. The former notes that: "Their habitat here was about some temporary and permanent pools in level woods of live oaks and other oaks, with a few pines. Some were trilling on the ground, while others in voice were clinging in a vertical position on the trunks of pine or oak within a couple feet from the ground. The note is a rather vigorous high-pitched trill: r-r-r-r-r-r-r-r-r-r-r-r-t, etc. Ten or eleven calls were given in the space of half a minute and each one lasted about 2/3 of a second. At its maximum inflation the throat sac attains a size a little larger than the head, and in the intervals between trills it is deflated to about half that size."

In 1922 we heard it from June 19–August 12. On August 11 "at Camp Pinckney from 1–3 p.m. were heard several males in the trees. At 8:30–10 p.m. we found several in the oaks. One in black gum (small tree 4 feet high) beside pond No. 4 where we found *Hyla versicolor* tadpoles the last time we came. Several males low in bushes on south side of Pond No. 3. Several were in trees 10–15 feet up or more. Took a female on the bole of a tree near

Pond No. 5. She was perched sidewise on the trunk and 3 feet or more farther up was a male. In Pond No. 5 took an adult *Hyla versicolor*. These males seem more marked and barred on hind legs than our northern tree toad and more orange appears on the groin and hind legs."

On August 13 tardy breeders in Spanish Creek woods were calling loudly and almost in chorus.

On our way from Ithaca to Okefinokee we heard it from Pennsylvania to Georgia June 2–June 12, 1922.

A resumé of our few records of calling in 1921 and 1922 follows:

1921

August   8.   10 miles south of Moniac.   Heard this species.
August 16.   Several calling at Camp Pinckney.

1922

June   19.   Several calling during the rain.
June   27.   Several calling when rain threatened.
July   9.   Thompson's Landing.   Heard in the woods.
July   24.   Heard in Spanish Creek Woods.
August   9.   Heard near Trader's Hill two *H. versicolor*.
August 11.   Several calling 1–3, more 8:30–10 p. m.
August 13.   Several calling along Folkston-Chesser Road-Spanish Creek Woods.

At the nearby U. S. Weather Bureau Stations the temperatures were maxima 81°–96°, average 91°, minima 62°–76°, average 70°. None of our temperatures from 6:00 a.m. to 9:00 p.m. or sometimes midnight were below 71° for these periods of calling. As every one knows it calls most frequently before, during and after rains.

MATING

Female. "Under parts entirely white, whiter than in the males. Otherwise the same."

Structural differences. The males average slightly smaller. In several pairs taken we have these measurements: Tallulah Falls, Ga., June 22, 1909, ♂ 44 mm., ♀ 45 mm.; Camp Pinckney, Ga., Aug. 12, 1922, ♂ 45 mm., ♀ 53 mm.; Ithaca, N. Y., June 1, 1906, ♂ 46 mm., ♀ 50 mm.; Ithaca, N. Y., June 14, 1907, ♂ 46 mm., ♀ 50 mm.; Ithaca, N. Y., June 10, 1907, ♂ 48 mm., ♀ 59 mm.

The males have the dark vocal sacs. The underparts of the female are pure white, rarely so in the male. There is little of difference in fingers or tympana in the two sexes. Probably two-year-olds begin breeding. A male 30 mm. has a dark throat.

Duration. Mating takes place largely at night and a pair mated at night usually lays the same evening as mated.

Amplexation. In this species the embrace is axillary. On August 11, 1922, 8:30–10:00 p.m. "at Camp Pinckney we took several males. Two males were put together, embraced and continued thus for several hours. It was an axillary amplexation. In this pair the upper male was much lighter, the lower one much darker."

OVULATION

Habitat. We made little effort for the life history of this species in Okefinokee Swamp country. We found their tadpoles in water pits at Camp Pinckney; and in suitable ponds and places near Spanish Creek Woods they must have laid. On June 1, 1917, when we did not know *Acris* eggs, at Dinwiddie, Va., we found in a shallow pool (10 x 8 ft. in diameter and 4 inches deep) no end of eggs packets on the surface. Normally we would have instantly called them *Hyla versicolor* but we had heard *Acris* in this direction. When nightfall came, in the bushes around this pool were several *Hyla versicolor* males. They were *Hyla versicolor* eggs not those of *Acris*.

Period. At Ithaca we have records of breeding from May 10–June 17. They were active in 1922 from June 3–June 12 onward on our trip from Ithaca to Georgia. We heard them several times in Pennsylvania, at New Alexandria, Va., Roanoke River, Cary, and Everett's Pond, N. C. We heard them in the Okefinokee country from June 10–August 13, 1922. We might not be inclined to think of them breeding, were it not that a female taken August 11 had ripe ova. Mature tadpoles (some with two legs) June 22, must have been laid in early days of May, as early as May 1, or the last of April. On July 5, 1922, we found eggs at Camp Pinckney, Ga., eggs which we suspected were those of *Hyla versicolor*.

Temperature and humidity. The eggs we found July 5, 1922, were laid in the period of rain (every day from July 1–5) when 2.97–3.20 inches fell, when minima reached from 68°–72°, and maxima from 83°–96°. The greatest period of activity came August 8–13 when minima were 68°–74°, maxima 81°–93° and rainfall for this period was 2.35 inches, 1.48 inches, 1.49 inches, 2.35 inches and 4.06 inches for stations around the swamp.

Egg-laying process. In 1914 (pp. 48, 49) we described the process.

EGGS

In Dinwiddie, Va., June 1, 1917, the tree toad eggs were as recorded for Ithaca, N. Y. Some of the packets were larger than ever recorded before. Occasionally it looked as if several packets were merged. In 1924 (p. 378) we characterized the eggs as follows: "Eggs deposited in a mass. Egg mass a surface film. Egg envelope outline indistinct, more or less merged in the jelly mass; jelly gelatinous; egg brown above, cream or yellow below. Egg packets small, masses seldom if ever over 20 sq. in. (125 square centimeters), or 4 by 5 inches in diameter (10 by 12.5 cm.). Inner envelope small 1.4 to 2.0 mm.; outer envelope 4 to 8 mm. Packets small, seldom over 30 to 40 eggs; vitelline 1.1 to 1.2 mm. Egg complement, 1802. Season May 10 to August 12." The above complement is compiled from a female captured August 12, 1922. The count of the left ovary was 901.

TADPOLE

Color description from life (*Non Ridgway*). General color of back olive green. Background of back yellowish, several with many fine hair-like black markings and golden and black spots, becoming orange in the head region and sometimes almost vermillion about the eye; the golden and black spots are more pronounced toward the tail; on the sides is a decided iridescence. The eye is slightly bronzy. The venter in general is conspicuously white or light cream and slightly iridescent. The belly is covered with fine golden spots. From the gill-region forward the venter is greenish, a coloration produced by black and golden spots. The background of all the tail except the base is scarlet or orange-vermillion. The base of the tail is like the body. The tail is covered with black blotches, more prominent around the edges of the crests. These blotches become much more numerous as the hind legs develop.

General appearance. Tadpole medium (46.6 mm.) full and deep bodied. Tail very long, deep, tip very acuminate with a prominent flagellum. The dorsal crest is as deep as the musculature, and extends on to the body to the vertical between the spiracle and the eye or to the spiracle. Spiracle sinistral, directed more backwards than upwards, far below the lateral axis and visible as an elliptical opening. Eye on lateral axis, in dorsal aspect on the lateral outline and in consequence visible from the venter. Anus dextral, very near or at the level of the edge of the lower tail crest. Muciferous crypts indistinct.

Mouth parts: Teeth 2/3. Upper labium fringed with a continuous row of labial teeth; the papillae extend above and inwards beyond the end of the upper fringe for about 1/3 of the length of the upper fringe. The end of the second row usually is even with the end of the upper fringe. The horny beak is contained about 2 times in the upper fringe. The median space between the lateral second upper labial rows quite short, 3.25–5 times the length of either lateral row. The inner papillae extends under the third row of lower labial teeth making at least two rows of papillae across the lower labial border. In the lower labial corner there is a heavy papillary series of 2 or 3 rows not so pronounced as in *Hyla squirella* or *Hyla femoralis*. The lower third labial teeth is long and is contained usually about 1.10–1.25 times in the first or second row. The first or second rows about equal and 1.8–2.0 greater than the horny beak. This species like *Hyla femoralis* and *H. squirella* has an angulate upper fringe at its middle.

Measurements (Okefinokee specimens). Length of body (14.5–16.5 mm.) in tail (27.4–21.2 mm.) 1.75–2.1 average 1.22. Width (9.6–11.4 mm.) of body in its own length 1.38–1.6 average 1.5. Depth (8.2–10.0 mm.) of body 1.0–1.2 in body width, average 1.08. Depth of body 1.5–1.8 in body length, average 1.64. Depth (6.6–9.0 mm.) of tail in length of tail 3.1–4.0, average 3.6. Muscular part (4.6–5.0 mm.) 1.72–1.9 in depth of tail, average 1.6. Spiracle 1.3–1.6 nearer base of hind legs or vent region (6.6–9.0 mm.) than the tip of the snout (9.8–11.4 mm.). Spiracle 1.12–1.5 nearer eye than base of hind legs or vent, average 1.33. Eye to spiracle (5.0–6.0) about equal to eye (5.0–6.0 mm.). Nostril 1.36–1.6 nearer eye than snout. Mouth (3.4–4.0 mm.) 1.1–1.36 in internasal space (4.2–4.8 mm.), average 1.25. Mouth contained 1.65–2.05 (average 1.8) in interorbital space 1.35–1.6, average 1.45.

The dimensions of the largest tadpole are:

	mm.		mm.
Total length	46.6	Spiracle to vent	7.6
Body length	15.8	Spiracle to eye	6.0
Body depth	10.0	Eye to snout	5.0
Body width	11.4	Eye to nostril	2.2
Tail length	30.8	Nostril to snout	3.0
Tail depth	6.8	Mouth	3.6
Musculature of tail	5.0	Interorbital distance	4.2
Spiracle to snout	10.0	Internasal distance	6.0

These tadpoles have long tails, 1.75–3.5 in the length of the body and scarlet or vermillion in color, with black blotches more prominent near the margins of the crests. The intenstine does not show through the skin.

LARVAL PERIOD

In the North it takes 50 or 60 days for development from the egg to transformation. Sometimes the period may be only 45 days or in other cases as great as 65 days. In the Okefinokee country the period may be shorter.

TRANSFORMATION

Period. The only transformation we found came June 27, 1922 at Camp Pinckney. "In the *Hyla versicolor* pond some are almost transformed." This is almost a month earlier than any we have recorded at Ithaca, N. Y. (July 18–August). Were they (June 27, 1922) tadpoles from eggs laid in the first (May 1–5), middle (May 15–22), or last of May (May 28–31) when rain prevailed, either 57 or 52 days or 42–36 days or 33–28 days?

Size. In 1914 the size of 87 specimens at Ithaca measured 13.6–20 mm. at transformation, the average 1.6 mm., the mode 16 mm. The material transforming June 27, 1922, at Camp Pinkney measures as low as 13 mm. in body size.

GROWTH

In 1920, we concluded that tree toads were 14–20 mm. at transformation, average 16 mm.; at 1 year old 20 mm.–30 mm., average 25 mm.; at 2 year old 30–41 mm., average 35 mm.; at 2 year old 41–51 mm., average 45 mm. If they transform at 14–20 mm. the specimen we found at Ithaca, May 16, 1915, must have been transformed at the smaller size of 14 mm. It measured 18.5 mm. and was doubtless of the previous fall's transformation. The smallest breeding frog (outward signs) was a male taken at Petersburg, Va., June 1, 1917. The males taken the same day at Dinwiddie were 34, 35, 37, 38, 39, 40, 41, 42 mm. The frogs taken at Camp Pinckney August 16, 1921, June 16, 1922, and August 11, 12, 1922 measure 39, 40, 41, 42, 42, 43, 43, 44, 44, 45 all males and one female 53 mm. Transformation came at 14–20 mm. Possibly 20–30 mm. represents one year olds; 30–42 mm. represents two year olds; 42–53 mm. three year olds; 53–59 mm. four year olds. The largest we have is a female 59 mm. in length.

AUTUMNAL DISAPPEARANCE

Our latest record at Ithaca, N. Y., is October 24, 1905. The latest record we have for the Okefinokee country is Aug. 12, 1922. It must continue to be abroad until November at least. Harlan (1835, p. 109) relates how "A specimen was dug up from the root of an apple tree in Bartram's Botanic Garden, in the winter of 1828, several feet beneath the surface."

AFFINITIES

In 1825 (1825, p. 282), LeConte writes: "It is surprising that this species, so common in the part of America that has been most visited by foreign naturalists, has as yet been noticed by no one. It may have been confounded with the *H. viridis* of Europe, which, however, it but little resembles."

In 1842 Holbrook (1842, Vol. IV, p. 117) alludes to the same oversight. "It is remarkable that an animal so common and so very noisy should so long have escaped the attention of naturalists. The first mention made of it is in Kalm's 'Travels in North America'; he, however, only describes its habits, and refers to *Rana arborea* of Linnaeus, to which it bears but a slight resemblance. . . . ."

LeConte (1855, p. 428) writes that "This animal is the analogue of the *Hyla arborea* of Europe."

On method of egg deposition it lays packets on the surface like *Hyla femoralis*. On egg characters it seems to fall with *Hyla femoralis* and *Hyla arenicolor*, but the latter lays single eggs. On coloration of tadpole tail *Hyla versicolor* is more like *Hyla arenicolor* than *Hyla femoralis*, yet all three may have scarlet or vermilion in the tail. On tadpole mouth characters it falls into the group with long lower third row of labial teeth. The adult reminds one more of *Hyla femoralis* or *Hyla arenicolor* than other Hylas of the United States.

BIBLIOGRAPHY

1889   Cope, E. D. U. S. Nat. Mus. Bull. No. 34, p. 375.
1842   DeKay, James E. Zool. of N. Y., Part III, p. 71.
1925   Force, Edith R. Copeia, April 30, 1925, No. 141, p. 25.
1906   Fowler, H. W. N. J. S. Report 1906, p. 114.
1827   Harlan, R. Journ. Acad. Nat. Sciences Phila., Vol. V, Part III, 1827, p. 343.
1835   ———. Medical and Physical Researches Phila., 1835, p. 109.
1842   Holbrook, E. N. A. Herpetology Vol. IV, p. 117.
1924   Holt, E. G. Copeia, Nov. 18, 1924, No. 135, p. 95.
1825   LeConte, John. Ann. Lyc. Nat. Hist. N. Y., Vol. I, Part II, 1825, p. 282.
1855   ———. Phila. Acad. Nat. Sci. Proc., 1855, p. 428.
1914   Overton, F. Mus. Brooklyn Inst. Arts and Sciences, Science Bull. Vol. II, No. 3, pp. 32, 33. Nov. 3, 1914.
1919   Pope, P. H. Copeia, Dec. 31, 1919, No. 76, p. 95.
1914   Wright, A. H. Carnegie Publication No. 197, Sept. 8, 1914, pp. 48, 49.

Rana aesopus (Cope)

(Pl. III, Fig. 5; IX, Fig. 4; XI, Figs. 1, 2; XIII, Fig. 4; XVI, Fig. 2; XVII; XXXIV; XXXV;
Text Figs. 1, 22)

COMMON NAMES

Gopher Frog. Florida Gopher Frog. Southern Gopher Frog. Florida Frog.

RANGE

Check list. Range, Florida. Type locality Micanopy, Fla.—Stejneger
Barbour (1917, p. 36).

Rana capito LeConte. Range "Florida District." Cope. Type locality
Riceborough, Ga.

Supplementary records. Mr. Richard T. Deckert (1920, p. 26) reports
"an adult male, collected in May, 1919, by Chas. E. Snyder, near Pinelands,
Hampton Co., South Carolina, and it is quite likely that the species extends a
good deal further north and east than even this locality."

This record north of the type locality of *Rana capito* LeConte prompts the
query whether *Rana capito* is an isolated colony of the *R. areolata* group
separating *R. aesopus* into northern and southern colonies or whether the
more reasonable conclusion might not be that *Rana capito* and *R. aesopus* are
one species extending from Pinelands, S. C. far down into Florida. See discussion under Affinities.

Local Okefinokee records. In 1921 we secured it at Chesser Island July
17, and on August 9 Mr. Francis Harper photographed one along the St.
Mary's River, Florida, six miles north of Macclenny (1 mile east of Smith
Bridge). In 1922 we secured adults or tadpoles from Trader's Hill, Ga., for
several miles along the Trail Ridge to the big bend of St. Mary's River and
across St. Mary's at Hilliard, Fla., August 17, 1922.

Our records are along the Trail Ridge which extends north and south from
Georgia into Florida, the southernmost record of our trip being Hilliard,
Fla., and northernmost between Chesser Island and Folkston, Ga. Residents,
however, report them from farther north at Braganza and Hickox, Ga.

GENERAL APPEARANCE

This species has had several apt characterizations. Cope remarks (1889,
p. 412) "This singular form may be known at once by the short and squat
form of the body as compared with the size of the head, resembling in this some
of the Australian Cystignathidae." Miss Dickerson (p. 194) writes "The
Gopher Frog of Florida is very different from other frogs in general appearance.
It is squat and toad-like, having an unusually large head, with a prolonged
muzzle, and eyes prominent and bulging even for a frog. Because of the
unusual length and breadth of head, this frog has a mouth relatively larger
than those of other North American frogs. These structural characteristics
give the frog so peculiar an appearance that although it may agree with *Rana
palustris* and with *Rana pipiens* in colour and in being prominently spotted,
there would never be any difficulty in distinguishing it as a different species."

Plate XXXIV

Gopher frog (*Rana aesopus*)

1. Cypress pond, Hilliard, Fla. August 17, 1922.
2. Male croaking at base of bush, Coat-bet pond, Chesser Id., Ga. July 17, 1921. Flashlight.
3. Male, Chesser Id., Ga. July 23, 1921. Ventral aspect. × c.4.
4. Female, Chesser Id., Ga. July 1, 1922. Ventral aspect. × 0.46.
5. Gopher frog at entrance of gopher turtle hole, Oak ridge, St. Mary's river, Fla. August 9, 1921. Flashlight.
6. Eggs, stained, Hilliard, Fla. August 18, 1921. × 1.5.

MEASUREMENTS

(Recent Material)

Head to angle of mouth (28 mm.)—1.32 (66 mm.)—1.34 (68 mm. ♂) —1.31 (82 mm.♂)—1.58 (95 mm.♂)— 1.33 (95 mm. ♀)—1.2 (108 mm. ♀) in width of head; head to rear of tympanum, .92 (28 mm.)—1.07 (66 mm.)— 1.13 (68 mm.♂)— 1.2 (82 mm.♂)—1.32 (95 mm.♂)— 1.18(95 mm. ♀)— 1.11 (108 mm. ♀) in width of head; head to angle of mouth (   )–3.0–2.61– 2.5–3.06–3.06–3.0 in length of body; head to rear of tympanum 2.15–2.44– 2.2–2.34–2.55–2.36–2. in length of body; snout .5–.92–.93–.88–.88–1.03–.83 in first finger; snout .35–.84–.80–.63–.78–.61–.80 in fourth finger; snout .43– .70–.57–.53–.60–.7–.50 in first toe; eye 1.74–1.73–1.4–1.68–1.54–1.5–1.7 in snout; eye (   )–.93–.65–.83–.82–.7–.8 in tympanum; eye .875–1.6–1.3–1.67– 1.36–1.5–1.4 in first finger; tympanym (   )–2.7–3.5–3.3–2.9–3.37–3.2 in intertympanic width; tympanum (   )–1.85–2.1–2.2–1.9–2.12 in snout; internasal width .66–1.0–1.0–.94–.8–.94 in upper eyelid width; interorbital width .64–1.5–1.16–1.0–1.36–1.0–1.25 in upper eyelid width; interorbital width 1.0–1.62–1.16–1.0–1.45–1.23–1.33 in internasal width; interorbital width (   )–4.75–3.8–3.5–4.5–4.1–4.5 in intertympanic width.

Forelimb: Forelimb 2.33–2.0–1.8–2.05–2.06–2.1–2.5 in length of body; forelimb 2.75–2.75–2.9–2.8–2.82–3.0–3.4 in hindlimb; first finger 1.28–1.08– 1.15–1.06–1.13–.94–1.21 in third finger; second finger 1.8–1.3–1.5–1.6–1.7– 1.37–1.5 in third finger; second finger 1.4–1.2–1.3–1.5–1.5–1.4–1.25 in first finger; third finger 1.1–1.2–.90–1.06–1.06–1.15–.95 in second toe; fourth finger 1.8–1.09–1.36–1.45–1.3–1.58–1.3 in third finger; fourth finger 1.2–.82–.72– .82–.77–1.1–.64 in first toe; internasal width 1.16–1.84–1.85–2.14–1.87–2.19– 1.9 in first finger; internasal width .9–1.5–1.4–1.4–1.25–1.56–1.5 in second finger; internasal width 1.5–2.0–2.14–2.28–2.12–2.06–2.25 in third finger; internasal width .93–1.7–1.57–1.57–1.62–1.3–1.75 in fourth finger;

Hindlimb: length .84–.72–.63–.72–.73–.71–.75 in hind limb; tibia 2.54– 1.9–1.7–1.9–2.0–1.9–2.1 in length; tibia 3.0–2.6–2.67–2.6–2.7–2.7–2.8 in hind limb; tibia 1.09–.94–.925–.93–.96–.9–.81 in forelimb; tibia 1.4–.9–.925– .95–.91–.90–.90 in hind foot (without tarsus); first toe 1.66–1.7–1.75–1.77– 1.8–1.65–1.88 in second toe; first toe 2.–2.5–2.56–2.55–2.35–2.52–3.1 in third toe; first toe 3.13–3.33–4.18–4.3–4.0–3.4–4.5 in fourth toe; first toe 2.0–2.55– 2.25–2.44–2.4–2.17–2.87 in fifth toe; second toe 1.4–1.45–1.46–1.3–1.3–1.5– 1.64 in third toe; second toe 1.2–1.45–1.3–1.3–1.33–1.31–1.53 in fifth toe; third toe 1.42–1.33–1.65–1.5–1.7–1.4–1.43 in fourth toe; third toe .82–1.02– .87–.94–1.02–.86–.93 in fifth toe; fourth toe 1.55–1.05–1.1–1.05–1.1–1.15–1.14 in hind foot; fourth toe 1.1–1.16–1.19–1.1–1.2–1.25–1.25 in tibia; fourth toe 1.2–1.1–1.1–1.02–1.15–1.12–1.0 in forelimb; fifth toe 1.06–1.3–1.86–1.7–1.66– 1.6–1.5 in fourth toe; internasal width 1.0–1.4–1.14–1.28–1.25–1.4–1.15 in first toe; internasal width 1.66–2.3–2.0–2.4–2.25–2.37–2.12 in second toe; inter-nasal width 2.33–3.4–2.9–3.3–2.7–3.6–3.5 in third toe; internasal width 3.33– 4.6–4.8–5.5–5.0–5.0–5.0 in fourth toe; internasal width 2.0–3.5–2.55–3.14– 3.0–3.12–3.25 in fifth toe.

HABITAT

This species seems to be restricted almost solely to the burrows of the Gopher Turtle (*Gopherus polyphemus*) which is common in the higher pine barrens and sand hills along the swamp's eastern border. All the turtle burrows might have frogs but these seem to be localized in colonies. Possibly, the breeding habitats (cypress and other ponds) indicate the grouping of these colonies or the animal associates of the gopher turtle may limit or terminate whole or incipient groupings.

Occasionally the frogs live in other covers than turtle burrows. In one colony near Chesser schoolhouse as we started to walk into the turtle area at 6:00 p.m., June 30, 1922, we heard something go into a small opening which looked like a rat hole. The hole extended 18 inches into the ground and the end was only 9–12 inches below the ground. Therein we found a female gopher frog. Near another turtle's burrow we saw a similar hole with a smooth worn spot about 8–12 inches away, the resting place of the frog. This observation the residents have often made and two of them remarked about this worn spot a foot or less from the hole.

On our previous trips 1912–1921, we have never found this species in the Pocket nor on Billy's Island nor on any of the other islands within the swamp. Like subterranean mammals (gophers, moles and shrews) subterranean turtles (gopher turtles) and other subterranean amphibia (spadefoots) it tends to avoid these situations which may be unduly flooded at times, or where a shallow burrow may reach water level. On Chesser Island, where a small narrow tongue of wooded swamp separates it from the mainland we occasionally secure shrews, moles quite frequently, and spadefoots rarely. Are gopher turtles and frogs also there? The gopher turtles occasionally appear but are immediately sought by the inhabitants. "Though the few Gopher Turtles which reach Chesser's Island are soon killed off by the residents (not only because of damage to the peanut crop but also because their burrows form too safe a retreat for hunted rabbits), the frogs remain, . . . ," (Harper). Whether the frogs come coincident with the gopher turtles, we have not determined, but on July 17, 1921, we made our only record of the frogs on Chesser Island. About a dozen males were recorded croaking. Thereafter neither in the summer of 1921 nor 1922 were they found on this Island where no gopher turtles are allowed, yet they are present as our one record proves. The residents assure us that the frogs betake themselves to rat-like holes, hollow stumps, holes beneath stumps, trees and logs. And I can well believe that this species, were gopher turtles absent, might also resort to crayfish burrows (Gaige 1914, p. 4), a retreat for *R. areolata*, a closely related species.

Doubtless no other frog proves quite so typical of the higher pine barrens unless it be the oak toad (*Bufo quercicus*). Occasionally the toad (*Bufo terrestris*) the spadefoot (*Scaphiopus holbrooki*) and the swamp cricket frog *Pseudacris nigrita* may be found in the same plant association. The other animal associates are discussed under the enemies of the gopher frog.

"Gopher Frog (*Rana aesopus*). One male specimen was taken from burrow No. 7 in the Cedar Creek locality on February 19, 1922. A Gopher Tortoise (7 x 5 1/4 inches) was also taken from this burrow at the same time. Two specimens were taken from burrow No. 10 in the Dinsmore locality on March 26, 1922. They were observed on two days just before sunset, resting in the entrance about two feet down the burrow and they were not seen at other times during the day. A Gopher Tortoise (11 x 8 inches) was taken from this burrow at the same time. One specimen was observed about sunset at the entrance of a burrow in the Brentwood locality on March 19, 1922. Two specimens were taken from burrow No. 11 in the Dinsmore locality on April 12, 1922. They were observed several times resting in the burrow about two feet down in the entrance just before sunset. A Gopher Tortoise (10 x 7 1/4 inches) was taken from this burrow, at the same time. In the Dinsmore locality during the week of April 15, 1922, a pair of Gopher Frogs was observed on several days about sunset resting just inside of the entrance of a burrow. In the Cedar Creek locality on June 25, 1922, one specimen was seen at 1:30 p.m. resting in the grass about 15 feet outside of the entrance of a burrow and when disturbed made three hops and entered. The frog rested motionless for a short interval of time between the jumps but the actions were quick.

Gopher Frogs are not always found associated with Gopher Tortoises as a Gopher Frog was taken in the Dinsmore locality on March 28, 1922 in about 6 inches of loose sand; another in about 8 inches of sand; and two specimens were taken in a hole about two inches in diameter under a dead stump." (Hallinan).

FIRST APPEARANCE

The earliest records we can find for the spring out coming are: March 18, made by Prof. T. Van Hyning at Gainesville, Florida; and April 1918 made by N. R. Wood at Auburndale, Florida. Thomas Hallinan's records above are: Feb. 19, Mar. 19, Mar. 26, Apr. 12, Apr. 15 and June 25, 1922.

GENERAL HABITS

This species is more common than usually held. In collections it is rare. Most specimens have been taken at the critical period in the animal's life, its breeding season when more frogs pay the toll than at any other time. In its normal all-the-year-around habitat, the sand hills and turtle burrows they are seldom seen unless one deliberately seeks them. They usually rest at the mouth of the burrow, sometimes a foot or so down the decline or just within the mouth. More rarely they may be one foot or more from the incline, or be on little clear, smooth places 6 inches in diameter a short distance away from a rat-like hole. One area we visited quite frequently. Usually from mid-forenoon to mid-afternoon or later they were seldom out. For example, on July 2, 1922, we visited this area at 3:20 p.m. and found only one out but at midnight we readily found eight. My journal reads: "Called again at 12 midnight. Francis's special friend not to be seen. Anna's friend was under a log. The entrance a foot or more away because we had dug it back from under the log. Suddenly something tumbled from under the log into the hole before I realized what had happened. Francis found another at a hole nearby. I found one and Miles saw three. One from 1 foot to 1 1/2 feet from the hole entrance proper. This one I caught. It is a female. Tried for one or two more but did not succeed. They are not so strongly held by light as are most Anura.''

Nine days later, July 11, 1922, we have: "At 7:15 p.m. we started for gopher frog area near Chesser School. Found 7 or 8 at entrance to holes or a foot or two out. At one hole Miles saw a *Peromyscus gossypinus*. At another I saw a *Sigmodon*. We captured three frogs. I caught one by hand. Could have taken 3 or 4 more. Miles took the net without the handle. Interposes it between frog and pole. Frog like a woodchuck makes for the hole and jumps into the net. Sometimes this works, sometimes it does not. At first I espied a frog at the entrance and tried to steal upon it from opposite the incline. It heard me. Wonder if I could catch them with baited hook and line. One was obliging and allowed us to photograph it. First one this year. It turned around twice during the process then hopped in.'' With effort we could have photographed others. In 1921, August 9, Mr. Harper stalked another just north of Macclenny near the St. Mary's River on an oak ridge. In both instances a log rests over the entrance. This is a favorite cover for both frogs and turtles. The turtles seem at times to prefer to dig their hole under fallen logs and the frogs often apparently prefer such gopher turtle burrows or burrows with saw palmettos near by.

The gopher frog though often in colonies seldom in our experience lives with another frog in the same burrow. This may be possible but not usual. We never saw two in one burrow. R. F. Deckert (1914, p. 3), however, writes that "Two or three frogs will inhabit the same turtle burrow," and more recently (Feb. 1, 1923) Thomas Hallinan (1923, pp. 19, 20) records several instances of two in one burrow. His notes are definite, excellent and might be given *in toto*.

Several authors from captive specimens have noted the color changes of this form. Shufeldt (p. 154) holds "Gopher frogs are very clever at hiding, and when doing so they change color at will, assuming a whitish tinge or brown or deep purple, to intense black," while Miss Dickerson writes (p. 195) "The general color of these frogs varies considerably. It may be grey or brown, somewhat yellow or purple in tone. The spots may vary in size and in number. In any individual frog, the color changes are striking and rapid. The frog may change from nearly black to white, through shades of brown or purplish grey." Possibly educated frogs may thus operate with speed and some of our captives showed different color phases and adaptation to different environments, but I question whether a gopher frog might in its normal relations vary suddenly from white to black. The general average of frogs is of the grayish hue. I never saw as sudden changes in this species as in Hylidae. A captured frog away from its burrow and placed on the neighboring sand, may squat for protection and match its background beautifully. If disturbed it will start off with unexpected dash, travel a short distance and stop as abruptly as its start was sudden. Several times I tried laying a female on her back. Motionless she would lie. Then I would tickle the belly and she would draw up her head and hind feet with the hind toes extended. Then I would draw the head to within 1 to 1 1/4 inches of the under side of the femur, place the creature on its haunches. A ludicrous sight it was from the side or front. After a minute or so of such posture, when we were in the midst of our laughter, this inert idol would rapidly right itself and quickly scurry off with short rapid hops. Indeed in the sandy saw palmetto oak ridges and pine barrens coloration is its best asset if away from its burrow, its poisonous secretions doubtless helpful and its quick dashes deceiving to the startled eye.

VOICE

This was heard positively on the evening of July 17, 1921 and August 17, 1922. In the former instance about a dozen began croaking in a cypress pond on Chesser Island before darkness came on. The fact that they did not begin on the former day after a hard rain makes me believe these to be stragglers in breeding, possibly tardy on this island. Later in the afternoon when they began one of the residents called it "the monster." At first while wading in the deeper water of the pond in the early evening we would hear this mysterious note in amongst the cypress trees usually at their base or on logs. The frog would espy us first and all we could determine was a big splash doubtless made by a large frog. Finally we heard one in shallow water in a tussock of sedge 2 feet across and 1 foot high and another near the base of a cypress in deep water. By waiting for some time two of the residents located them. They were truly *R. aesopus*. After two hours work on *Hyla gratiosa* we sought out a group of gopher frogs we were hearing in the shallower western portion of the pond. One was beside a cypress tree in a depression of fibrous roots. After we had focussed on it it literally crawled around to a different position near by. I put the light on its nose and tried to push it back with my fingers. Then it leaped. At the base of a pine on a pile of chips 1 1/2 feet above the surface was another croaker. After a time (i.e., after it had had light on its face a short period) it would "bat" its eyes toward the bullseye. We secured two flashlight photographs of it. Another male was in fibrous roots at the base of a black gum tree. A fourth was at the base of a "Cassenya" (also "spice bush" pond spice (*Mala-poena geniculata*). Another was under a log where a tussock of sedge was over-hanging. These frogs were not hard to catch when discovered but they were shy. Often when first put under the light they would sink back in the fibrous roots, depressions and covers. One (the croaker, Pl. XXXIV, 2) was spread out in the water among the spice bushes. The influence of nearby croakers seemed to stimulate this one as it does others. We caught several, put them in a bag, induced these to croak, and in this way our sprawled-out specimen responded beautifully with his croaks. To induce the captives to croak we would swing the bag round and round or rub them through the cloth or occasionally press and hold in hand a male just ahead of the hind legs. We were sure we ought to find pairs and eggs in the pond the following day and evening. We discovered neither but I am now sure the eggs found the following day were some of the *Rana aesopus* eggs and not solely *R. sphenocephala* as I then pronounced them. This fact alone showed how closely this species resembles the southern meadow frog in this regard.

The preceding record (July 17, 1921) was of frogs from an island in the edge of the swamp where they do not normally live in gopher turtle burrows. The second experience came August 17, 1922, on the Trail Ridge (oak ridge) near Hilliard, Fla. After an excessive rainy period we were detouring on the Dixie Highway when Mr. Harper heard spadefoots in some shallow pine barren ponds. Later in the afternoon before and after 5:00 p.m. I thought I heard frogs on the higher open places in the pine forests. We suspected they were gopher frogs and queried "Are they on the ground or at the gopher turtle burrows or moving to their breeding places?" We never found one and one of the party thought it a ventriloquial effect from a distant cypress pond. When darkness came on this pond was suddenly resonant with gopher frog calls in chorus. These chose similar perches to those described for 1921. One was at the base of a stump and above the water. Another was in the notch of a floating log. A third at the base of a cypress. A fourth was beside a stump and mostly sunk in the water. A fifth was at the edge of a small subsiding pine. With all four of us searching we saw only one croak and all the rest never responded when we were near. Several times Mr. Harper focussed on males but we never secured the desired reaction. They were very shy. This evening they frequented the edges of the pond where stumps, logs, and debris were but were thickest in grassy and sedgy areas. These frogs called all night. The chorus stopped at daybreak. Occasionally until 9:00 or 10:00 a.m. of June 18 they would break out in a choral call, then subsided for a long period.

The vocal vesicles Shufeldt pronounces most unusual (1917, p. 154), but we doubt whether he or any writer who had captive specimens has ever seen them at their maximum. This is possible at night in the field. In this regard it is an exaggerated *R. pipiens* or *R. sphenocephala* with the vocal sac extending almost to the groin. It constitutes the most striking development in vocal sacs I have seen in North American Salientia.

"The croaking is a very remarkable performance. A lateral pouch is inflated on each side of the neck and keeps swelling posteriorly until it extends halfway down the side of the body, attaining a size nearly equal to that of the frog's head. The creature's form is then strongly suggestive of a bat-fish (*Ogcocephalus vespertilio*). The note—and likewise the inflation—lasts for a second or so." It is a deep, hollow roll, somewhat intermediate between a snore and a groan: yawhhhhh, yawhhhhh. At the start the intervals between notes may range from ten seconds to nearly half a minute, but as the frog warms to the performance, a croak may be given every two or three seconds. The sound will probably carry a quarter of a mile." (F. Harper.) In 1922 both Mr. Harper and three more of us noticed the call might extend considerably over a second's time.

When we first heard the note (July 17, 1921) one of the residents thought it a woodpecker but I recorded that it "seemed more like *R. sphenocephala* in tone" before I knew its close relationship to this form. At 7:30 a.m., August 18, 1922, several gopher frogs and southern meadow frogs were calling. The call of the latter was 3 or 4 rasping croaks, then 3 or 4 clucks, i.e., dissimilar notes. The call of *R. sphenocephala* is like a rattle compared to the uniform continuous roar of *R. aesopus*. To Mr. M. D. Pirnie it sounds like a snore, Deckert also (1914, No. 5, p. 3) states that "Its call is a loud deep snore, . . ." In chorus it sounded to Mrs. Wright and myself like the surf or a deep gutteral roar (possibly a trill at times) like rolling r's down deep in the throat. We also likened it to a snore. The chorus seemed to go in waves and have decided crests.

Deckert (1920, p. 26) records of a captive specimen that "When the interior of the large glass jar in which it lives is sprinkled, and after this certain noises are made, like rustling paper, or water running from the tap, this frog "sings. . . ." During the calls, which are repeated about every two seconds and are of from three to five seconds' duration, the vocal vesicles over the arms are distended into hemispheres about the size of large hazelnuts." We doubt whether these gentlemen or any writer who had captive specimens have ever seen them at their maximum.

MATING

Male (From life July 20, 1921). Sides of head, dorsum of limbs and sides below costal fold French gray or lilac gray. Fore and hind legs with numerous black bars. These bars broken at times or more or less speckled with French gray. Costal fold from honey yellow to mustard yellow or buff (yellow to greenish yellow depending on the degree of dark specking on it.) Another similar stripe along upper jaw and over the arm insertion. All the tubercles on the back with same color. Iris upper part black then buff yellow or honey yellow over the pupil. Black in front and behind the pupil. Two lilac gray areas beneath pupil separated by black. Between the costal folds about four rows of black spots. Under parts white with hair brown or fuscous or purplish black spots on throat and chin. Posterior faces of hind limbs purplish vinaceous.

Female (From life, July 2, 1922). General color on the sides is French gray, cinereous or pale purplish gray and some pallid purplish gray. These colors become on the lateral fold, canthus rostralis, upper eyelid, beneath eye and fold back of angle of mouth, cream buff or tilleul buff. Ground color of back between lateral folds a combination of lateral fold color and side color. Between the lateral folds are four more or less irregular rows of black roundish spots. Below the lateral fold are 3 such rows to the rictal fold. Ground color of body on dorsum of hind and fore limb with black cross bars. Undersides of feet and hand and femur vinaceous lavender. Spots on the throat bister to snuff brown. Those on sides of belly, army brown. Iris black with prominent bar of colonial buff or tilleul buff above the pupil. Below the pupil may be two small bars of body color, namely French gray, cinereous, pale purplish gray or pallid purplish gray. In another specimen two lower bars united. Rest of eye black with a little dotting (irregular) of the two combinations (upper and lower bars) of colors.

Structural differences. Some of the differences in males and females appear summarized below:

1. In describing the coloration we noted that "the males have yellows on the folds, tubercles, iris, axilla and groin somewhat wherein the females have little or no yellow. Possibly LeConte's description of *R. capito* is from a male. This may need more rechecking.

2. The male has the thumb enlarged and the female not, but the thumb is not as enlarged as in some species.

3. The males average smaller. The adult males externally are first revealed at 68 mm. and reach to 101 mm., while the females range from 77–181 mm.

4. The antebrachium is very much wider in the male than the female and this widening may even reach up to the brachium.

5. Under Voice attention is called to the sacs which in *Rana aesopus* as well as *R. areolata* may be immense and in alcohol may appear as extending far beyond shoulders. In life sometimes they look to reach even farther backward.

6. Some notes on alcoholic specimens are:
   (a) 68 mm. ♂. Thumb enlarged.
   (b) 68 mm. ♂. Thumb enlarged. Sac partially developed. Very spotted on throat and pectoral region.
   (c) 81 mm. ♂. Thumb somewhat enlarged and slightly colored. Sacs fairly developed.
   (d) 85 mm. ♂. Thumb enlarged. Sacs show.
   (e) 87 mm. ♂. Thumb somewhat enlarged and darkened. Beautiful sacs half way to groin.
   (f) 90 mm. ♂. Thumb well enlarged, dark sacs well developed.

Amplexation. It is presumably axillary but we have recorded no pairs of this species.

OVULATION

Habitat. We found it breeding in a cypress pond with no open center. We found tadpoles in an open centered cypress pond, in an open centered pond with bay tree circle, in an open pond with St. John's wort (*Hypericum*) circle, in an open pond in pine woods or an old field, no special circle of vegetation, in an open pine forest pond at the edge of a wet savanna.

Period. We have long suspected that this form bred in the first half of the year. In 1921 we were within the swamp and missed this form until July. In 1922 we arrived June 11. Deckert (1914, No. 5, p. 3) writes: "Its call can be heard from late February to the end of May. These frogs croak only at night, and are then easily caught by the light of a lantern. The writer has also collected this species during the breeding season in February near Jacksonville, Fla., in 1912 (Deckert, 1920, p. 26). It would seem then that it bred from late February to August 17, the bulk of the ovulation comes before summer or possibly it starts early and continues intermittently until September like its relative *R. sphenocephala*. The period of ovulation, as we ourselves know it for eggs is from July 17–August 17. Mature tadpoles discovered July 18–August 25 indicate that the eggs must have been laid in the late spring at least, late April or in early May. We, therefore, derive a period from late April to mid August.

Since the above evidence was considered, we found Prof. T. Van Hyning's (1923, p. 68) pertinent note "On the night of March 18, while some of the boys of the biological class of the University of Florida, Gainesville, Fla., were collecting frogs, among other species taken, were . . . eight specimens of the Gopher Frog, *Rana aesopus* (Cope). . . .

"These and other species were all in a pond breeding near the University. One of the party collected eggs, and brought living specimens which have spawned since. . . ."

Temperature and humidity. The data for August 17, 1922, is as follows: The maximum air temperature for the day before for nearby localities was from 18–91°, average 87°, or for the day of the record 82–91°, average 86°, the minima 69–72°, average 70°, and 69–74°, average 72° respectively. At Hilliard on August 16, 1922, .56 inches of rain fell, on August 17, 3.47 inches or 4.03 inches in two days or 7.03 inches from August 16–21. For July 17, 1921, we derive 85–87°, average 86° air maxima for the day before and 83–88° for the day of the record, average 85°, minima for the day preceding 69–72°, average 70° and 68–74°, average 71°, the precipitation for day before was heavy as much as an inch or more. At camp on July 17, 1921, it was 75° at 7:30 a.m.

The tadpoles of the summer must have been from eggs laid the last of May or the first of June, 1922. From May 25 to June 4 at Hilliard there were 6 days of .90 inches of rain or more, at Glen St. Mary's seven days, the total at Hilliard was 13.33 inches, at Glen St. Mary's 11.93 inches. It would seem these eggs must have been laid May 26–28 or May 30–June 1 when there was as much as 4–6 inches of precipitation in three days. If these July and August records be late breeders apparently an inch or more of rain is needed to start the stragglers for breeding and air temperatures of 68–74°, average 71° or 81–91° maxima, average 86° seem to obtain.

Egg-laying process. This species we did not observe in the egg-laying process. In its breeding habits it is so like the meadow frog we could readily believe it lays its mass as does this species. Doubtless the oviposition when once begun is completed in 5–15 or 20 minutes. Very evidently one position is maintained throughout the process.

EGGS

Attachment, egg mass. On August 17, 1922, we found several masses of gopher frogs eggs laid in a cypress pond. On the north edge in water 6–8 inches deep and 30 feet from the edge of the pond I found at the base of a small cypress (10 feet high) and amongst some brush a mass attached to an upright twig. It was one inch below the surface, was a plinth of eggs black above and cream below. The eggs looked larger and farther apart than are those of *Rana sphenocephala*. Near by a large cypress stump in an open grassy area where pine cones were on the bottom a large mass was attached to a sedge stem. Its top was level with the surface of the water. The water was 9 inches deep. The mass was 4 x 5 inches square and 1 1/2 inches thick. At first the mass impressed all of us as bluish and two of us independently likened it to *R. sylvatica* in this respect. The lower pole may be cream at first but it soon becomes white. The whole mass when turned over reveals the same white mass impression *R. sphenocephala* and *R. pipiens* egg masses give.

On the southeastern side of the pond where Mr. Pirnie was watching the frogs the previous night he also found two masses among young cypress and attached to sedges was one mass 6 x 8 inches square and 1 1/2–2 inches thick. It seemed to be emarginate but when the lobes were drawn out the mass became 12 x 4 inches square. The second mass was amongst "all spice bushes," (*Malapoena geniculata*) was also attached to sedges and was 4 x 5 inches across. It was only 1 1/2 inches below the surface.

On one occasion, August 21, in a pool filled with *R. aesopus* tadpoles we found a suspicious mass of jelly 6 x 6 x 3 inches, an intact mass of jelly evelope of a frog complement which I believed to be that of *R. aesopus*. On another occasion July 28, 1922, in the grassy center of a very large open pond I found an immense mass of eggs, then assumed to be *R. sphenocephala* eggs but they were those of *R. aesopus*. The jelly envelope as in *R. pipiens* and *R. sphenocephala* tend to stay together some time after the egg has hatched.

The egg masses vary from 4 x 5 x 1 inches through 4 x 5 x 1 1/2, 6 x 6 x 2, 6 x 8 x 1 1/2 to 12 x 4 x 2 inches in dimensions. They may be attached to grass, sedges, pickerel weed, or other aquatic plant stems, twigs and brush or be free at times on the bottom as in *R. pipiens* or *R. sphenocephala*.

LeConte's comment on *R. capito* may have led workers astray from the gopher frog because they did not know its breeding habits. Obviously (p. 425) his word that it "inhabits Georgia in the ditches of the rice fields" pertains to its short breeding habitat.

Egg description. In *Rana aesopus* the outer envelope ranges from 4.4 to 6.0 mm. in diameter, the usual range 4.8–5.4 mm., the average 5.3 mm., the mode 5.2 mm.; the middle envelope is from 3.1–4.4 mm., the average is 3.9, the mode 3.8; the vitellus is 1.8–2.4 mm., the average is 2.0 mm., the mode is 2.0 mm.; the vegetative pole is cream at first later white, the animal pole is black. The rough measurements of some ovarian eggs of July 25 were 1.6–1.8 mm. Possibly they were not fully developed. The vitellus and inner envelope of *R. aesopus* is somewhat larger than in the meadow frogs (*R. pipiens* and *R. sphenocephala*). On August 10, 1922, I divided the eggs of the left side of a female in eight equal parts. One of these parts had 313 or for the whole side 2504 or 5008 for the whole complement. The eggs look larger than those of *R. sphenocephala* and farther apart in the mass.

Dangers. The dangers from drying up little affect the gopher frog in contrast to some of the other Salientia of pine barrnes, e.g., the oak toad, southern toad and pine woods tree frog. It chooses in general permanent open ponds and cypress ponds.

HATCHING PERIOD

We have only one observation on the period of hatching. Eggs laid in the night time between 8:oo p.m., August 16, and 9:oo a.m., August 17, 1922, in a cypress pond hatched on August 21, 1922, or in about 4 to 4 1/2 days. On the same date near by in an open shallow pond spadefoots began laying in the day time where water was at least 80° F. or higher. These eggs hatched in 1–1 1/2 days. In mid-day the water was warm. We had no thermometers but the water doubtless reached 90–95° or 100° F. The shade of the cypress pond, however, lengthened the period for the gopher frog and the temperature did not go above 70 or 80° F.

MATURE TADPOLE

Color description from life (August 1, 1922). At times the tadpole has a very greenish cast. Color on top of the head oil yellow, olive green, olive lake or old gold ahead of level of eyes. Back of eye level yellowish citrine or olive citrine where there are no black spots.

About four irregular series of black spots between lateral line series of spots of either side. Lateral line pores closely set and lateral line canal distinct to the tip of the tail. A dark spot on each upper eyelid. A dark spot or spots in interorbital space. Top of head ahead of eye with several fairly large spots. Spots most distinct and numerous from nostril to base of muscular part of the tail, being on the sides interspersed with light pinkish cinnamon or pinkish buff. This color is present on muscular tail and slightly on upper and lower crests as small clusters. This light pinkish cinnamon or pinkish buff merges into the block color of the belly which is cream-buff, colonial buff, or naples yellow. This block color breaks up in gill or bronchial region becoming clusters of fine dots or spots. Below eye to either side of bronchial region is some light vinaceous cinnamon or vinaceous fawn. Middle of bronchial region without these colors but with a slight fine speckling of black lines.

Background color of the tail mignonette green. Upper crest and muscular part with large spots of black. Lower crest without large distinct spots except at the tip.

Iris rim around pupil orange or dandelion orange to light cadmium. Rest of iris black with mignonette green or apple green fine dots.

General appearance. Tadpole large (84 mm.) full and deep-bodied. Venter strongly pigmented so that viscera do not show through in life or in preserved condition. Tail long, tip obtuse or acute. Dorsal crest in depth sometimes equal to or greater than the depth of the musculature and extending on to body somewhat ahead of the vertical of the buds of the hind limbs. Spiracle sinistral, directed upward and backwards. Spiracle distinctly below the lateral axis. Eye above or slightly on lateral axis, and near lateral outline in dorsal aspect than mid dorsal line. Muciferous crypts distinct. The dorsal row from either side of the insertion of the dorsal crest extends obliquely forward and outward to join the principal lateral row which extends from above the middle of the tail musculature to back of the eye. Here it forks, sending a supraorbital branch far past the nostril to snout and an infraorbital branch also to the snout and quite far below the nostril in its course. Below the principal lateral series is a lower one on side around the spiracle but forward it is not very distinct.

Mouth parts. Teeth 2/3. Edge of upper labium slightly larger than beak and fringed with teeth. In either corner a row of teeth about 1/3–1/4 of the upper fringe. The outer end of this lateral row usually (abnormal in figure in this regard) does not extend beyond the end of the upper fringe. The median space between lateral rows is one to two times either row, nearer the condition in *R. pipiens.* The third lower row about equal to or slightly larger than single row of lower labial papillae, 1/3–2/7 shorter than first or second rows which are equal and larger than the beak. The tadpole is clearly of the *R. pipiens* or *R. sphenocephala* type.

Measurements. Length of body (28–33.5 mm.) in tail (74–81 mm.) 2.15–2.85, average 2.62. Width 13.5–19 mm. of body in its own length 1.6–2.07, average 1.8. Depth (12–15 mm.) of body .88–1.7 in body width, average 1.14. Depth of body 1.5–2.4 in body length, average 2.01. Depth (10–18.5 mm.) of tail in length of tail 2.6–3.5, average 3.05. Muscular part (6–9 mm.) 1.45–1.9 in depth of tail, average 1.75. Spiracle 1.1–1.7 nearer base of hind legs or vent region (14–16.5 mm.) than the tip of the snout, average 1.36. Spiracle 1.4–2.0 nearer eye than base of hind legs or vent, average 1.55. Eye 1.0–1.3 nearer to spiracle (5.0–7.0 mm.) than tip of snout (6–9 mm.), average 1.12. Nostril 1–1.5 nearer eye (2.5–5.0 mm.) than snout (3.0–6.0 mm.), average 1.25. Mouth (3.0–5.0 mm.) usually .84–1.26 larger than internasal space (2.8–5.0 mm.), average 1.06. Mouth contained 1.25–1.66 (average 1.5) in interorbital distance (4.5–8.0 mm.). Internasal space contained in interorbital space 1.3–1.9, average 1.57.

The dimensions of the largest tadpole are:

	mm.		mm.
Total length	81	Spiracle to vent	14
Body length	29	Spiracle to eye	7
Body depth	14.0	Eye to snout	9
Body width	15.0	Eye to nostril	4
Tail length	53.0	Nostril to snout	6
Tail depth	15.0	Mouth	5
Musculature of tail	8.0	Interorbital distance	8
Spiracle to snout	17.0	Internasal distance	4.2

General remarks. For a long time there were two forms *R. aesopus* and *R. virgatipes* whose tadpoles we did not know positively. At that time there were two tadpoles we were collecting we had not placed; one was not placed until late in the season and proved to be the larva of *R. heckscheri.* The other by elimination had to be *R. aesopus* or *R. virgatipes.* When these larvae began to show four rows of spots on the back of the tadpole before hind legs were well developed we were quite certain. But with the coming of the hind legs and outpushing of the fore legs, the coloration of the dorsum of the adult gopher frog was clearly foreshadowed. Although the mature *R. aesopus* tadpoles are very much like those of *R. sphenocephala* they are too big for the latter species. No doubt in their earlier stages they may cause workers difficulties for some time to come.

LARVAL PERIOD

When we arrived on June 11, 1922, residents held that frogs of many species were calling and active about two weeks before in very heavy rains of that period. Inasmuch as this form is so strongly of the *R. pipiens* group in breeding habits I believe it has about the same larval period, i.e., about 75 to 90 days. The transforming gopher frogs of August 25 to September 15 were doubtless from eggs laid between May 25 to June 5. For example, at Hilliard, Fla., straight east of Chesser Island and across St. Mary's River the precipitation from May 25 to June 5 was 13.37 inches or 3.30 inches May 28, 3.20 on May 31 and 2.80 inches on June 1. In this same period Glen St. Mary south about 10 miles had 10.66 inches. This would mean a larval period of 85–106 days.

TRANSFORMATION

Period. After the discovery of the suspected *R. aesopus* tadpoles, it was a whole month before we were positive that these tadpoles of several open ponds on Trail Ridge were actually *R. aesopus* larvae. For example our notes would run somewhat as follows: "Aug. 9. Holt's pond, east of Starling Branch Crossing. Found several of the tadpoles like those of Nigger Pond, *Hypericum fasciculatum* pond and other Old Okefinokee Road ponds. They are very large with no leg buds apparent or leg buds are very small. Tadpoles too big for *Rana sphenocephala*." On August 21, 1922, in one pond we secured them at an advanced two-legged stage. Two days later, three-legged stages were recorded. The illustration represents an individual with the right arm appearing before the one of the spiracular side. On the same day one or two had reached the four legged, long tail stage. On August 25 the short tailed four-legged stage was reached. These were carried in a tin can on the running board of the Ford on our northward journey and on August 27 and 28, 1922, completed transformation. These are the only observations on actual transformations. Many of the tadpoles of these open ponds probably would not have transformed before September 15 or October 1. It is very doubtful that the tadpoles from the eggs of August 17, 1922, transformed before October 20 or November 1. On October 26, 1922, Thomas Hallinan found a specimen just past transformation. Transformation may then be from August 15–November 1. But if this species begins breeding in late February or March Deckert's transformation must come by May 1 or before. What puzzled us was our absence of any records of transformed individuals from June 11–August 25. We left August 25 and, therefore, had no opportunity to watch the dispersal of the newly transformed frogs, their choice of habitat, etc.

Size. The transforming frogs of August 22–27, 1922, from a pond near Chesser School (see U. S. Geo. Survey quadrangle), Ga., measured 28, 32.5 and 33 mm. respectively. On the basis of tadpoles approaching transformation we have one note on transformation as follows: "28–35–(?) mm. In the American Museum material (Nos. 5930–32, 5896, 5897) are five specimens from N. P. Fry of Eureka, Florida. These are 32, 27, 28, 33, 36 mm. respectively and from near Arlington, Florida, Thomas Hallinan takes a specimen 31 mm. These all must be at or near transformation. Possibly transformation extends from 27–35 or 36 mm. It makes its transformation size comparable to the upper part of the transformation range of *Rana pipiens* (19–28 mm.) or of *Rana sphenocephala* (19–33 mm.). It is evident if we had enough material that the mode and average of *Rana aesopus* would be higher than that of *Rana pipiens* (22 mm. and 24 mm.) or of *Rana sphenocephala* (25 mm. and 23 mm.).

GROWTH

We have only transformation and adult sizes. The intermediate stages we missed. From analogy one would believe that at least 3 years were required for their maturity and possibly 6 years for the maximum sizes. Deckert (1914, p. 3) writes "The one-year-old frogs of this species I have repeatedly caught, wandering from the high ground and its burrows into the swampy meadows below, where the insect life is more abundant. On being discovered, they will not dash away with long leaps, like other frogs, but squat close to the ground, motionless, like some toads, and are then easily picked up."

This species apparently transforms at 28–33.5 mm. Our adult material begins with sizes of 66, 68 mm., 73, 82, 85, 95, 95, 108 mm., and it seems to sort into groups of 68–73 mm., 82, 95 mm. and 108 mm.

In Levy Co., 1892, J. Hurter (U. S. N. Mus. Nos. 57533–35576–78) collected 62, 69 mm., 71 and 74 mm. specimens—apparently one group 62–74 mm. In July, 1893 (U. S. N. Mus. No. 20513) H. G. Hubbard collected a 65 mm. specimen and on June 20, 1894, two specimens (U. S. N. Mus. Nos. 21702, 21703) 71, 73 mm. respectively or one group 65–73 mm. At Auburndale, Fla., N. R. Wood secured in 1917 (No. 59413) a 74 mm. specimen and another in April, 1918, 49 mm. in length, apparently two groups. The type is 52 mm. and they have a specimen 83 mm. Boulenger's material was as follows: 68, 73, 77, 80, 82, 84, 85, 88, 91, 93, 95 mm. respectively. One lot taken at same place is 68, 84, 85 and 93 mm., two groups 68 and 84–93 mm.; another lot is 73 and 95 mm., two groups; and another lot 80 mm., apparently one group.

The American Museum material seems to sort: 27–36 mm.; 49–55 mm.; 62–76 mm.; 78–85 mm.; 90–102 mm.

In the Museum of Comparative Zoology series were 12 specimens taken in 1919 at Orlando by Dr. Thomas Barbour. These are 58, 61, 63, 64, 67, 67, 68, 70, 70, 71, 76, 93 mm. The same year Dr. Barbour secured several 10 miles north of West Palm Beach, Florida. They are 82, 86, 89, 89.5, 90, 94. Other records they have are:

No. 3574	Fruitland Park,	A. G. Reynolds,		1914,	40 mm.
5137	Gulfport, Fla.	" "	"	1919,	52 mm.
7081	" "	" "	"	1920,	41 mm.
5938	Sebastian, Fla.,	George Nelson,		1919,	74 mm.
4907–10	New Smyrna, Fla., March 1919,			79, 86, 89, 91 mm.

This material might be interpreted as 40–52 1st-year-olds; 58–64 2nd-year-olds; 67–76 3rd-year-olds; 79–86 mm. 4th-year-olds; 89–94 5th-year-olds.

Our material apparently fell into groups as follows: 28–33 mm. at transformation and adult modal groups of 68, 85, 95 and 108 mm. Does it mean four or five different years? The whole material of the U. S. National Museum, American Museum, Boulenger's eleven specimens and our own might be interpreted as falling in groups 28–38–(?) mm. at transformation; 38(?)–52 mm. first-year-olds; 52–65 mm. for 2-year-olds; 66–77 mm. 3-year-olds; 78–88 4-year-olds; 89–102 mm. 5-year-olds; 102–108 mm., 6-year-olds.

FOOD

The writer has made few direct observations on the feeding habits. Much which has been written has been on captive specimens. Shufeldt ('17, p. 155) asserts that "Gopher frogs feed upon small birds and insects, but most commonly upon toads, the last giving them no end of discomfort on account of the acrid secretions from their parotid glands. Indeed after a meal upon a big toad, this frog has been observed to go through a series of somewhat extraordinary spasmodic movements, frantically trying to clear its mouth with its fore feet of the semi-poisonous juice the batrachian he had endeavored to swallow had squirted into it. So big is the mouth of this gopher frog that it can manage to swallow a full-grown specimen of our common toad—a feat, however, that it in no way appears to enjoy."

Miss Dickerson holds (p. 196) this frog seems especially fond of toads as an article of diet. It ejects the poison from the mouth as soon as it has swallowed the toad. A toad of surprisingly large size can be managed, owing to the unusual development of the jaws and throat of this species. If the toad is too large to be swallowed at once, so that the poison can be sent out through the mouth almost immediately, the frog gives up the attempt and disgorges the toad after about fifteen minutes. This time, however, is sufficient to allow some action of the poison to take place, and the frog shows many signs of discomfort. It has convulsive movements of the muscles, it leaps blindly upward, and finally, lowering the head and opening the cavernous mouth, uses the hands in frantic efforts to remove the irritation from there. During several weeks of captivity, *Rana aesopus* fed almost wholly upon toads, of the species *lentiginosus, woodhousei* and *fowleri.*"

Deckert (1920, p. 26) records that his "specimen is in fine condition and not at all shy, taking meal worms, roaches, and spiders and occasional earthworms from one's fingers, if not approached too suddenly."

In 1920, Dr. Thomas Barbour (1920, p. 55) presented before the American Society of Ichthyologists and Herpetologists notes on this species. His observations on the "dispersal and the habits of feeding on the small oak toad, *Bufo quercicus,*" I did not hear and they are not expanded in the abstract of the proceedings of this meeting.

ENEMIES

The gopher turtle's burrow seems to be the permanent or temporary resort of most of the animals of the drier pine barrens. Many smaller forms like the oak toad (*Bufo quercicus*), the six-lined lizard (*Cnemidophorus sexlineatus*) glass snake (*Ophisaurus ventralis*), smaller snakes, peculiar insects, cotton mice (*Peromyscus gossypinus gossypinus*) enter in and out of the burrows, but it is not especially conceivable that they would seriously injure large adult gopher frogs. If the young frogs live also in the burrows they might succumb to some of the forms above. Those who like to think of the pine snake, the gopher snake, the diamondback rattler, the cottontail rabbit, the gray fox, the skunk, the burrowing owl all living in amity together will no doubt point out that the snakes and possibly some of the others feed on warm-blooded prey. Experience proves, however, that the gopher snake may eat glass snakes as well as rats, that the pine snake and diamondback may take cold-bloods occasionally and that the carnivorous mammals would not wholly avoid frogs. The shell of the turtle makes it almost immune from attack. The gopher frog has two defences, one its poisonous secretion and the second its ability to crowd down in the sand of the burrow. The first defence we can hardly believe wholly effective with all snakes and possibly some carnivorous mammals. the second defence is not as strong proportionally in the frog as in the turtle. One wonders if the turtle be in any way a protection or shelter to the frog? One male, 95 mm. in length has no left hind leg except for the thigh. What enemy took the rest?

In its breeding habitat if it be in an open pond the water snakes prove serious foes at night and in cypress ponds both water snakes and moccasins are searching for all frogs.

This species has as distinctive an odor as *Rana palustris* or *Rana septentrionalis* or *R. virgatipes*. The containers in which we have kept gopher frogs may be frothy as we have experienced with *R. palustris*. We have never tried putting other species of frogs with them to see how the other species would withstand these secretions.

AUTUMNAL DISAPPEARANCE

Our own personal acquaintance with it is from July 17–August 9, 1921, June 14–September 1, 1922, when our party encountered it in the Okefinokee region. The type of Cope's *Rana areolata aesopus* U. S. National Museum (No. 4743) was taken by Dr. Bean Dec. 23, 1886. In the American Museum material is one small specimen (31 mm.) taken "in the grass about 40 yards from a cypress swamp near Arlington, Florida" by Thomas Hallinan on October 28, 1922. This is in the very year of our experience with the same species.

AFFINITIES

I believe first that *Rana capito* LeConte is *Rana aesopus* Cope and secondly that *Rana aesopus* thus understood (*R. capito* and *R. aesopus*) is closely related to *R. sphenocephala* and *R. pipiens*.

First, I have long suspected that *R. aesopus* was *R. capito*. Two summers' acquaintance with the so-called *R. aesopus* in a region intermediate between Riceborough, the type locality of *R. capito* and Florida (range of *R. aesopus*) confirms this belief. "A few days ago I tried an experiment on my three as-

PLATE XXXV

Gopher frog (*Rana aesopus*)

1. Gopher turtle hole, Trail Ridge, Folkston, Ga. July 5, 1921.
2. Male at base of pine, Coat-bet pond, Chesser Id., Ga. July 17, 1921. Flashlight.
3. Male on the sand, Chesser Id., Ga. July 23, 1921.
4-6. Series of tadpoles, Chesser Id., Ga. Aug. 22, 23, 1922. × 1.2.

1

2

3

4   5   6

sociates of the summer of 1922 (Mrs. A. H. Wright, Messrs. F. Harper and Miles D. Pirnie). I showed them LeConte's figure of *Rana capito* with the label hidden and gave no intimation of locality at all. One instantly proclaimed it the gopher frog (*Rana aesopus*) on general appearance. Another called it the gopher frog because of its waist and general appearance. The third thought the figure a gopher frog but felt it too slim in the waist until when shown a photograph of a gopher frog (Ventral view July 1, 1922, Pl. XXXIV, Fig. 4) in a similar position she pronounces the two as one without reservation." All four of us who have called upon gopher frog adults at all times of day and night feel the two too close to be considered separate forms.

To be sure some may yet prefer to make *R. areolata capito* the northern subspecies from Riceborough, Ga., northward and may restrict *R. areolata aesopus* to the southern form. I see no real difference in the forms nor use for this interpretation. *Rana capito* was described in 1855 by LeConte (1855, p. 425) from the material secured in the ditches of the rice fields of Riceborough, His description reads like the Gopher frog (*R. aesopus*). In 1886 (1886, pp. 517, 518) Cope gave the four forms of *R. areolata* as *R. a. areolata* Baird & Girard (Austroriparian region *R. a. circulosa* Rice & Davis (North Central Eastern region, Illinois), *R. a. capito* LeConte (Floridan district) and a new form *R. a. aesopus* Cope (Florida). Observe that Cope speaks of *R. a. capito* as of the Floridan district. The combined ranges of *R. capito* and *R. aesopus*, therefore, extend from Florida to South Carolina in the lower coastal region, and we thus see *R. capito* more in agreement in range with other Floridan forms.

Cope (1889, p. 409–416) uses the same groupings of four subspecies and and writes "This well-marked species (*R. areolata*) is related to the *R. palustris*, but is easily distinguished."

We strongly incline toward the group which hold *Rana aesopus* separate from *Rana areolata* and equally believe *Rana capito* and *Rana aesopus* the same, but until more material is collected in Georgia and Carolinas, we little wish hurriedly to make any changes from *Rana aesopus* to *Rana capito*, though some may hold more or less rightly that consistency dictates such action on our part.

Our second consideration that *R. aesopus* is closely related to *R. pipiens* and *R. sphenocephala* does not militate against some relationship with *R. palustris* but *R. palustris* is not the nearest relative. We have silhouettes and other photographs of the gopher frog that remind one very much of *R. pipiens*, and *R. sphenocephala* or even *R. palustris*. Like *Rana pipiens* and *R. sphenocephala* and unlike *Rana palustris*, the gopher frog has a plinthlike egg mass, black and white eggs, similar breeding place (with *R. sphenocephala*), tadpoles very similar and lateral vocal sacs. *R. aesopus* has vocal sacs extending to the groin of either side, *R. sphenocephala* has them as spheres and *R. palustris* is without them. *R. aesopus* and *R. sphenocephala* egg masses and tadpoles are quite similar and perplexed us for a long period.

In breeding habits it did not need to be strongly differentiated from *R. pipiens* and *R. sphenocephala* as these resort to the same type of place for ovulation.

In its non-breeding behavior, (protection, food, etc.) it appears most peculiar. It had to adapt itself to the arid pine barrens and sandy oak ridges wherein the only common moist retreat for a non-burrower is the gopher turtle hole.

BIBLIOGRAPHY

1920 Barbour, T. Herpetological Notes from Florida. Copeia July 31, 1920, No. 84, pp. 55-57.
1886 Cope, Edward Drinker. Synonymic List of the North American Species of Bufo and Rana, with descriptions of some new species of Batrachia, from specimens in the National Museum. Am. Phil. Soc. Proc., Vol. 23, Dec. 1886, No. 124, pp. 514-526.
1889 ———. The Batrachia of North America. Bulletin U. S. Nat. Mus. No. 34, 1889, pp. 1-525.
1914 Deckert, Richard F. Further Notes on the Salientia of Jacksonville, Fla. Copeia April 15, 1914, No. 5, p. 3.
1920 ———. Note on the Florida Gopher Frog. Copeia March 25, 1920, No. 80, p. 26.
1906 Dickerson, M. C. The Frog Book, pp. 193-196.
1914 Gaige, Helen Thompson. A List of the Amphibians and Reptiles Observed in Richland County, Illinois, in May 1913. Copeia October 15, 1914, No. 11, p. 4.
1923 Hallinan, Thomas. Observations Made in Duval County, Northern Florida, On the Gopher Tortoise (*Gopherus polyphemus*). Copeia February 1, 1923, No. 115, p. 11-20.
1855 LeConte, John. Descriptive Catalogue of the Ranina of the United States. Dec. 18, 1855. Proc. Acad. Nat. Sci. Phila., Vol. VII, 1854, 1855, Phila. (1856), pp. 423-431.
1917 Shufeldt, R. W. The Florida Gopher Frog. Aquatic Life. August 1917, Vol. 11, No. 12, pp. 153-155.
1917 Stejneger, Leonhard and Barbour, Thomas. A Check List of North American Amphibia and Reptiles. Cambridge 1917, pp. 1-125.
1923 Van Hyning, T. A Collecting Note on Florida Batrachians. Copeia May 20, 1923, No. 118, p. 68.

Rana clamitans Latreille

(Pl. III, Fig. 2; V, Fig. 11; VIII, Fig. 1; XI, Figs. 3, 4; XIV, Fig. 7; XVI, Figs. 4, 5; XVII; XXXVI; Text Figs. 1, 16)

COMMON NAMES

Green Frog. Pond Frog. Spring Frog. Bullfrog. Bawling Frog. Yellow-throated Green Frog. Belly Bumper. Bully. Screaming Frog. Black Frog.

RANGE

Check list. Range: Eastern North America. Canada to Florida and Louisiana, west to Michigan, Illinois and Arkansas (Stejneger & Barbour 1923, p. 35).

Supplementary records. (Not sought).

Local Okefinokee records. We have taken this species on Billy's Island, Chesser Island, Mixon Hammock, and in ponds along St. Mary's River and in ponds beside the Folkston-Moniac road and in edge of cypress bay along the eastern edge of the swamp.

GENERAL APPEARANCE

To the general lay it is a "yellowthroated bullfrog" and is usually confused with its bigger congener, the bullfrog. In Copeia (1916, pp. 53, 54) R. F. Deckert and Fowler 1918 (Copeia, p. 84) reported a green frog which saw an albino. The first writer noted the scarcity of albino frogs. I have only seen in the field one albino green frog, one albino meadow frog and *Bufo americanus*. I have received two specimens of albinistic tadpoles of *Rana heckscheri*.

COLORATION OF SPIRIT SPECIMENS (1912)

(Spirit specimens of 1912). On the back the color may be from deep grayish olive through chaetura drab or mummy brown to olivaceous black or almost black; in the young the colors incline the lighter side of the above range and in these there are two, at times three prominent cross bars on the femur and tibia, also cross barring on the tarsus and outer surface of the foot and indistinctly on the forelimbs. In many of the adults these bars or spots do not show at all or are faintly indicated; in a few they appear but may be broken up. In the adults the small dark circular spots of the young are absent or seldom present and the upper parts are almost a monochrome. In most of the adults a black oblique bar extends from the angle of the mouth on to the brachium and the back border of the forelimb has a prominent black bar on the brachium and antebrachium; in all the adults the upper jaw ahead of the eye is like the general dorsal color except for the snout which at times is spotted with white spots; the whole edge of the lower jaw is a series of conspicuous alternate blotches of yellowish white or white and brown or black. Except in very black individuals there is a yellowish white or white line from beneath the tympanum (rarely from beneath the eye) over the arm insertion. Tympanum brownish with a central disc of body color; the posterior faces of the thigh are mottled with black and the anterior faces of the thigh less so; the inner edge of the tibia has three or four short cross bars; also along the outer face of the tarsus is a broad black band with a yellowish white line at its lower border. This black band usually runs on to the two outer metatarsals. In all the specimens are the more or less characteristic dark blotchings of the sides, these spots being partly on the dorsal color and partly on the light ventral color. The ventral color is white or yellowish white but is not immaculate as in our northern specimens. In many the under parts are heavily marbled or reticulated with black, being the strongest on the throat and upper breast regions and on the under sides of the thighs and legs. In some where quite light beneath the reticulations or markings are faintly outlined over the whole venter. In one specimen, a female, the throat and upper breast region is almost solid black. In our northern forms when transforming or just transformed, the frogs are very spotted or dotted on the throat and under parts of the legs, but in the adults these marks are more or less lost. In these southern forms the young are even more spotted on the venter and the process consists in an intensification of spotting the reverse of the northern tendency.

STRUCTURAL CHARACTERS (WRITTEN IN 1912)

In none of these forms is the skin rough to the touch. On the dorsal surface there are fine round mamillations, most coarse on the sides; the head is without these and is merely pitted, the most rugose part being the outer half of the upper eyelid. On the ventral parts the skin is smooth except on the buttocks which are decidedly pustulate and on the throat which is sometimes lightly mamillate. Top of the head smooth, plane or rounded. A broad short fold of skin on which is a yellowish white stripe extends from the angle of the mouth over the arm's insertion. It is usually broken just ahead of the arm by the fold which comes down the caudal border of the tympanum and circles in front of the arm's insertion on to the breast. Sometimes the ends of these last folds are connected across the breast by a faint fold or indentation. The main fold with which this post-tympanic ridge is connected usually runs from the eye backwards two-thirds of the distance to the hind limbs. At its end it may break up or sometimes reach only halfway to the hind limbs. In two small males these costal folds run little back of the tympanum and soon cease. First and fourth fingers about equal. Third finger longest, subarticular tubercles moderate or small; metatarsal tubercle small, third and fifth toes about equal; last two phalanges of the fourth toe free, not webbed; tongue in some broad and in others quite narrow, forked behind in all the specimens, free for its posterior half and along edges of the anterior half; vomerine teeth between inner nares or slightly behind line of nares, small, usually obliquely set and closer together.

MEASUREMENTS
(Recent Material)

Head to angle of mouth 1.1 (28 mm.)–1.24 (56 mm. ♂)–1.2 (82 mm. ♂)–1.2 (95 mm. ♂) in width of head; head to rear of tympanum .83–.92–.967–1.01 in width of head; head to angle of mouth 3.1–2.82–3.28–3.05 in length (snout to vent); head to rear of tympanum 2.33–2.15–2.64–2.53 in length; snout .7–.9–.916–1.0 in fourth finger; snout .7–.8–.83–.73 in first toe; eye 1.1–1.25–1.5–1.36 in snout; eye .625–1.12–1.62–1.27 in tympanum; eye .77–1.12–1.5–1.36 in first finger; tympanum 2.4–1.33–1.3–1.25 in inter-tympanic width, tympanum 1.4–1.11–.92–1.07 in snout; internasal width 1.0–.91–1.0–1.14 in upper eyelid width; interorbital width .875–1.67–1.40–1.6 in upper eyelid width; .875–1.71–1.4–1.4 in internasal width; 2.1–3.4–3.4–3.5 in inter-tympanic width.

Forelimb 1.86–1.8–2.0–1.75 in length; 2.72–2.77–2.7–2.71 in hind limb; first finger 1.2–1.33–1.33–1.26 in third finger; second finger 1.57–1.5–1.45–1.35 in third finger; 1.28–1.0–1.09–1.07 in first finger; third finger 1.0–1.0–1.12–1.0 in second toe; fourth finger 1.0–1.14–.91–1.0 in first toe; 1.56–1.7–1.45–1.26 in third finger; internasal width 1.28–1.5–1.71–2.14 in first finger; 1.0–1.25–1.57–2.0 in second finger; 1.58–2.0–2.3–2.7 in third finger; 1.0–1.16–1.57–2.14 in fourth finger.

Hindlimb: length 1.46–1.53–1.33–1.53 in hind limb; tibia 2.0–1.86–2.0–1.9 in length; 2.92–2.77–2.7–2.92 in hind limb; 1.07–1.0–1.0–1.08 in forelimb; 1.07–1.64–.902–.96 in hind foot; first toe 1.56–1.5–1.8–1.72 in second toe; 2.28–2.25–2.2–2.54 in third toe; 3.14–3.75–3.5–3.91 in fourth toe; 2.0–2.56–2.7–2.72 in fifth toe; second toe 1.45–1.5–1.22–1.42 in third toe; 2.0–2.5–1.94–2.26 in fourth toe; 1.27–1.70–1.22–1.52 in fifth toe; third toe 1.375–1.66–1.59–1.59 in fourth toe; .875–1.14–1.22–1.07 in fifth toe; fourth toe 1.36–1.1–1.05–

1.11 in hind foot; 1.27–1.03–1.17–1.16 in tibia; 1.36–1.03–1.17–1.25 in forelimb; fifth toe 1.57–1.46–1.3–1.48 in fourth toe; internasal width 1.0–1.33–1.42–1.57 in first toe; 1.57–2.0–2.57–2.7 in second toe; 2.28–3.0–3.14–3.85 in third toe; 3.14–5.0–5.0–6.14 in fourth toe; 2.0–3.4–3.85–4.14 in fifth toe.

HABITAT

Suitable ponds whether on the higher banks of St. Mary's River under oaks or in overflow and cutoff pools with river swamp flora (Thompson's Landing), or whether they be the fringe of cypress and gums of a cypress pond (Long Pond) or roadside ponds, sphagneous (Spanish Creek Woods) or not or ponds in hammocks (Billy's Island)—all are used. The factors of pond and shade both seem to enter. They were most abundant in chorus in the island edges of the cypress bays or their counterparts, the fringe of trees around a cypress pond. We also found them in the "dreens" (Cypress Bay) between Chesser Island and the mainland.

In our experience with this species it is neither common within the swamp nor outside the swamp. Probably it is easier of observation in ponds outside the swamp or on the swamp's border but we are not prepared therefore to say it is more common outside the swamp.

FIRST APPEARANCE

The earliest record we have is April 28, 1921, but it must appear earlier.

GENERAL HABITS

In 1912 we made the following observations regarding their general habits: "Its habits in the swamp quite generally agreed with its known habits elsewhere. It was found both outside and inside the swamp. All our captures were from ponds and its tadpoles were found in the more permanent ponds or swamp's cypress thickets on the islands. We seldom saw it on the prairies or along the cypress runs where the common form was *Rana grylio*."

VOICE

The voice of the green frog is quite generally known to naturalists. Miss Dickerson (1906, p. 199) says "it is explosive, prolonged, and low-pitched and is likely to be repeated five or six times in succession. When we hear it given with less than its usual force, we may be deceived into thinking that we hear the drumming of a woodpecker. It may be imitated very well by cutting on a table, with heavy shears, some kind of coarse resisting cloth. Or it may be imitated less well by tearing heavy cloth in a jerky fashion. It resembles the croaking of the Pickerel Frog, but has more strongly accentuated notes in it."

"The explosive character of the sound will be better understood from watching the frog when he is croaking. He works hard; there is no appearance of external vocal pouches (as in the Leopard Frog, Fig. 9), but the yellow throat and the sides expand with such force as to jerk the whole body forward.

Slowly the distended parts sink in as the vigorous sounds proceed. Then the throat and sides swell out again, and there follows another explosion of sound. And so on over and over. . . ."

Overton (1914, p. 37) writes of the green frog call as follows: "Its song is an explosive note resembling that made by plucking the string of a bass violin. It swells out its throat and cheeks during its song."

A resume of the croaking for 1921 and 1922 follows:

1921

April 23. Entered swamp.
" 28. One male croaking.
May 14. Heard one or two lone males.
" 16. An occasional male calling.
" 18. One or two calling at 9:30 p. m.
" 19. Tried to photograph a few calling males.
" 21. One or two calling tonight. Air 70°
" 22. Green frogs croaking.
" 24. Quite a few calling 10:00 p. m. Air 77°.
" 26. Several calling.
June 3. An occasional *R. clamitans*.
" 8. Hear green frogs.
" 25. Hear no end of green frogs. Hear some in the forenoon.
July 2. Green frogs croaking their greatest.
" 3. Mainly green frogs calling in some ponds.
" 4. Several green frogs calling.
" 5. Many calling and several egg masses.
" 11. Great chorus last night.
" 12. Green frogs are now croaking in real earnest.
" 13. In east side of swamp no end of *Rana clamitans* in early forenoon.
" 15. Hear green frogs. Eggs found.
Aug. 19. Last record we made for calling.

1922

June 12. We encamped.
" 22. First green frog heard.
" 25. Hear a few in cypress pond.
" 27. Hear several.
July 1. One heard in cypress bay.
" 4. At 6:00 p. m. several calling.
" 7. One or two heard 7:00–9:00 a. m.
" 10. In early forenoon commonly heard in cypress bay.
" 27. One heard near camp. One heard about 2:00 p. m.
", 28. A few in bay.
Aug. 3 &4. Heard a few in center of swamp.
" 11. Heard a few on St. Mary's River at Camp Pinckney.
" 15. Hear several.
" 31. Still calling on prairie.
Sept. 5. One calling in mid afternoon.

When temperatures range in maxima 80°–88° and minima 59°–67° they begin sparingly but when maxima reach 90° or more and minima 68°–75° they begin to reach chorus stage, e.g., in 1921 the choruses were greatest from July 2–11 when the temperatures were: maxima 88°–94°, average over 90° and minima 69°–74°, average 70°.

In 1922 the day we most commonly heard them was July 10 when some of the maxima was 88°–93° and minima 68°–71° for nearby stations. On August 31 they were calling on the prairies, temperatures maxima 88°–91°, minima 63°–64°. The last date we have is September 5 but they doubtless call much later in the season.

The late June or early July choruses came mainly at night, but often extended far into or throughout the day as well. Occasionally one will hear them at mid afternoon, mid day and mid afternoon before chorus stage is reached. Our record for September 5, 1922, is a mid afternoon call. F. Harper characterizes the call as follows: ". . . its twanging bass note is heard at considerable and probably irregular intervals, of, say half a minute or more. Ordinarily a single *clung* or *c'tung* is given; but sometimes there is a rather rapid series of several notes: *clung–clung–clung–clung* or *c'tung*." The note is not loud nor has it far reaching carrying effect. The male rests on a mat of vegetation at the surface or amongst grass, or aquatic plants or freely sprawled out on the water. Usually the hind quarters are slightly submerged. It is extremely difficult to secure a good flashlight of its throat when slightly inflated. In the first place it does not swell out its throat as far as in *Rana grylio,* and its call is usually one note of very short duration. Furthermore when under observation long intervals often elapse between croaks. All in all it is one of the more difficult frogs to catch at the full inflation of the throat. Three different evenings we tried for flashlights and none show the fully swelled out throat.

MATING

Male (From life, June 21, 1921). Top of head from snout to between nostrils, over upper lids along back to the vent sudan brown to brussels brown or cinnamon brown to Prouts brown or snuff brown to bister. Top of fore limbs and hind limbs and sides same but less intense. Side of snout under eye cosse green to light bice green. Same color on back end of upper eyelid. Spot under tympanum to shoulder insertion, spot over shoulder insertion, ring in middle of tympanum with dark center, throat and spots on lower jaw bright chalcedony yellow. The throat reticulated or spotted black and bright chalcedony yellow. Rim of lower and upper jaw black, the former with three or four spots on each side. Tympanum same color as back with some black, then bright chalcedony yellow ring, finally dark center. Under parts white with black reticulation or deep brownish drab on under parts of hind legs. Some bright chalcedony yellow on front and inner side of fore limb. Fore limb with a black stripe continuous from lower jaw to arm insertion on to the fore arm. Fore arm with rear edge and palm of hand black. Back of thighs deep brownish drab, black and color of the back.

Iris ring around pupil lemon yellow or part of it light cadmium or orange. Iris background black but so covered with orange or cadmium yellow spots as to obscure most of the black.

Female (From life, July 5, 1921). Top of head slightly lighter than back, near Prouts brown; rest of back and back of tympanum mummy brown or darker. Or it may be head olive brown and the rest of dorsum clove brown.

Tympanum like back. No different rings like the male. Spot from arm insertion under eye and forward obscure in part, pale ochraceous buff or light buff. Under parts with deep brown drab reticulations and cloudings. Spots on lower jaw pale chalcedony yellow. For remainder of description see the male.

Two specimens (From life August 18, 1922). A female dark olive buff uniform above. The smaller specimen wood brown to avellaneous and uniform above. In both back of eye and side of head and over angle of mouth apple green. Bars on hind legs absent in this female; scanty in smaller specimen.

Structural differences. Enlarged thumbs and tympana in male; rings of color in male tympana; throat with bright chalcedony yellow.

"In 1912 we had 14 adults of which twelve were males. Male specimens of 59–65 mm. show ear drums well developed and this sexual difference may possibly appear in even smaller specimens. All the males have the forefingers more or less swollen; in the two taken after July 15 it is least developed and the three with it most highly developed were taken June 1 and 12, 1912. A female taken June 5, 1912 was spent and another female taken May 28–July 15, 1912, is with ripe eggs. These ovarian eggs are 1.2–1.5 mm. in diameter and this female has no more than 1,000 eggs to lay. In size she is only 67.5 mm. in length, much more slender and smaller than the average of our northern green frog females which have from 3,500–4,500 or more eggs to lay."

Duration. In general mating with an individual male is of short duration. But the species in the northern states breeds for a long period, last of May to August. In the south it is one of the last to begin breeding and doubtless is not one of the forms which breeds most of the year. There are one or two species in the south which might breed almost every month in the year (except one or two months), but in the south the green frog is not in this class.

Night or day. In general this shy species in the Okefinokee Swamp mates or begins mating mainly at night. Sometimes in the dark shades of cypress ponds or "bays" it mates by day.

Amplexation—(Normal, abnormal). Normally it is pectoral in this species. The first amplexation for this species I ever recorded at Ithaca was more *Hyla*-like than *Rana*-like. The first record for Okefinokee Swamp is of the same sort. A pair mated in laboratory on Billy's Island, July 4, 1921, were more axillary in embrace than pectoral. With only these two examples one might go astray. The males, however, almost invariably seize the females in pectoral fashion.

OVULATION

Habitat. They seek small, permanent ponds in the hammocks, the island edges of cypress ponds and cypress bays in the shade. Under *Rana grylio* we noted in one cypress pond how *Rana grylio* males were calling in the center of the open pond amongst *Pontederia cordata*, the *Hyla cinerea* males were in the bushes where open pond and wooded fringe of pond meet and the *Rana clamitans* males were in the shade of the large trees near the land's edge. They are greater shade lovers than any other frog of the swamp region unless it be *Rana heckscheri*.

PLATE XXXVI

Green frog (*Rana clamitans*)

1. Egg mass, Billy Id., Ga. July 5, 1921.
2. Eggs, stained, Chesser Id., Ga. July 16, 1922. × 1.2.
3. Tadpole with four legs, Chesser Id., Ga. August 1, 1922. × 1.2.
4. Tadpole with short tail, Chesser Id., Ga. August 11, 1922. × 1.2.
5. Transformed frog, south of Spanish Creek, Folkston, Ga. July 29, 1922. × 1.2.
6. Adult female and transformed *Rana clamitans*, Billy Id., Ga. May 18, 1921. × 0.3.
7. Transformed *R. clamitans* and *R. grylio* compared, Billy Id., Ga. April 28, 1921. Lateral aspect. × 0.4.
8. Transformed *R. clamitans* and *R. grylio* compared, Billy Id., Ga. April 28, 1921. Ventral aspect. × 0.4.
9. Male croaking, Billy Id., Ga. May 24, 1921. Flashlight.
10. Male, Billy Id., Ga. April 29, 1921. Ventral aspect. × 0.4.

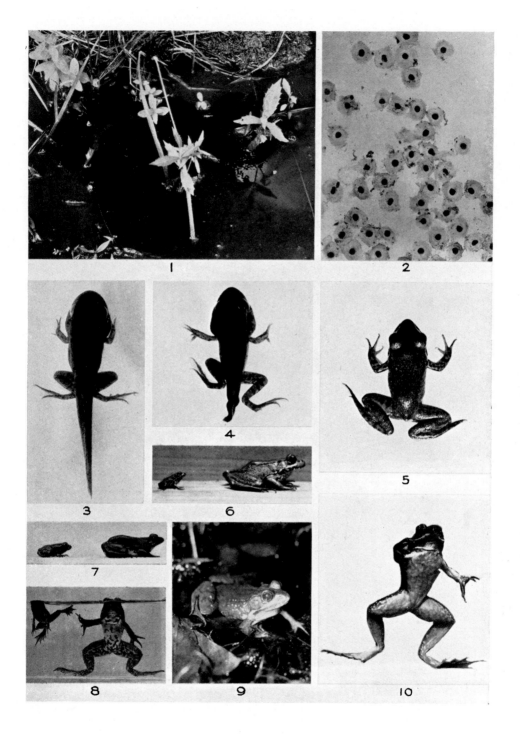

In 1922 we found different types of habitats in addition to the above records. In Civil War times at Camp Pinckney the Confederate Army dug five or six large pits. They were going to hide turpentine in barrels in them if need be. These ponds are now filled with water. In these ponds, some of which are very much shaded, were several green frogs. The surface of the water was one continuous mat of fine green vegetation. On July 24 in one of these ponds we found three fresh masses attached to the base of large grass (4 feet high) in the middle of the pond. On the road south of Folkston and south of Spanish Creek is a moist woods, on the side a high sandy ridge. Here in very small sphagnaceous spring ponds beside the road we found eggs on the moss in the water.

On July 9, 1922, at Thompson's Landing in a cut off pool left by high water of St. Mary's River we "found a male *R. clamitans* at the edge of this pool under some overhanging rootlets to which a film of eggs was attached. They are almost hatched. These are not all at the surface. Rains have raised the level of the pond. These wooded banks of the St. Mary's River have considerable shade."

Period. In the north the extreme dates for ovulation have been May 23 and August 10. The period of greatest ovulation has been in June and first of July.

In 1912 our data for Okefinokee Swamp is: "On June 2, 1912, on Billy's Island near Billy's Lake we found in ponds at the edge of the island some green frog eggs. On the following day in a shallow pond where the water was 1 foot deep more were recorded. On June 9, we found another mass and by June 12 these eggs were hatching. Finally on June 12, 1912, on the north edge of Lee's clearing we found a pond 15 x 10 feet and 3 x 4 feet deep in places. Here we took three male *R. clamitans*. In the pond were *Gambusia*, narrow-mouthed toad, meadow frog and toad tadpoles. Two masses of eggs were found, one fresh and the other hatching. The masses were films on the surface of the water as with our northern forms."

In 1921 the first eggs found came July 5 and the last record July 15. In 1922 we found eggs at Thompson's Landing, St. Mary's River July 9, south of Spanish Creek July 15 and at Camp Pinckney (near Folkston), St. Mary's River July 24. In both years July seems the climax month. We thus have a recorded period from June 2–July 24 for the three years of observation.

Temperature and humidity. In 1921 on July 3 we had very hard rains in the swamp; on the 4th, Waycross had an inch. Humid weather preceded the high period of ovulation July 4–5. No minima went below 69° or 70° and maxima hovered from 88°–92°. On July 15 minima ran from 69°–72° and rain occurred throughout the Okefinokee area.

In 1922 the day before July 9 the minima were 66°–72° the maxima 82°–93° and precipitation .25 at St. George, July 9. Our records for July 8 at Chesser Island were temperatures 92° at 2 p.m., shower at 5:30 p.m. and 73° about midnight July 8–9, and eggs found July 9. On July 15 and the day preceding ovulation at St. George, Ga., minima are 66°–68°, maxima 94°–96°, our lowest at Chesser Island 68° and highest 88° but no rain in either place. On

July 24 the eggs were found at Camp Pinckney. There were no rains at Chesser Island, Hilliard, St. George that day or before. Temperatures were minima 69°–71°, maxima 90°–95°. More often I believe precipitation or considerable humidity precede laying, but the above data shows laying without previous precipitation. The minima range from 66°–73°. Our conclusions for Ithaca were that the species begins breeding normaliy at 65°–74°.

Egg-laying process. Every egg mass recorded in 1912, 1921 and 1922 was a continuous film implying that the pair do not move about during oviposition. In some cases little packets are found scattered on the water amongst floating vegetation. We have assumed that currents, floods, etc., have broken the original mass in these cases, yet it is possible an occasional pair may move about during ovulation (e.g., as in *Hyla versicolor*).

EGGS

Attachment. In 1912 the film taken June 9 was amongst some pine needles at the edge of the pond in a hammock and the other masses were about the edges and attached to growing vegetation. On July 5, 1921, we found at least 5 masses in all, four in one pond and another in a large pond. "The first was surrounded by vegetation and grass. A *Myrica* was overhanging. Another mass was at the base of a gum tree in small weeds. The third mass was in shallow overflow water amongst some growing weeds. The fourth mass was also amongst weeds and more or less broken up into packets. The fine mass was attached to the base of a gum tree. There were several male *Rana clamitans* around. The masses at a little distance can be easily seen because of a vegetative scum or oily scum or air bubbles amongst the eggs. The mass often looks blackish and is sharply outlined on the surface as with films of *Hyla femoralis* eggs."

Egg mass. In 1912 we recorded only the film form for this species in Okefinokee Swamp. On July 5, 1921, we found one mass 6 x 12 inches in diameter. Seldom does either diameter reach a foot. "It is on the surface of the water, one continuous film, each egg not appearing to be separate in the film as in *Gastrophryne* eggs." We found another mass 9 x 10 inches in diameter and another mass 10 x 10 inches. In all there were four masses in one small pond. In general the green frogs of Okefinokee seem smaller than some of the north and the egg complements are smaller. One complement of July 15, 1922, we counted. "The total count of the eggs was 1451. This was a small complement. I hold the complements here (Okefinokee) get twice as large."

Egg description. In 1914 we described the eggs of *Rana clamitans* at Ithaca as follows: "The eggs have white vegetative and black animal poles. The outer envelopes range from 5.6 to 6.0 mm. in diameter, 5.7 mm. being the average, 6.0 mm. the mode. The middle envelope may be other than spherical and often has an elliptical form; it varies from 2.8–4.0 mm. in diameter, the average is 3.3 mm., the mode 3.0 mm. The vitellus ranges from 1.2 to 1.7 mm., the average 1.4 mm., the mode 1.2 mm."

In 1912 amongst some of the Okefinokee green frogs we noted some eggs with elliptical inner envelopes.

In 1921 some of the first eggs of July 5 were as follows: Vitellus of one 1.4 mm., two more each 1.6 mm.; vitelline membrane of one vitellus 1.6 mm. is 2.2 mm. in diameter, the vitelline membrane may be quite remote from the vitellus, sometimes as development proceeds the membrane shows more distinct than the inner envelope; inner envelope usually pyriform, elliptic or sometimes circular, inner envelopes of 2.6, 2.8, 3.0, 3.2, 3.4 mm., most of them at least 3.0 mm. or more. The outer envelope is seldom distinct if present but probably becomes a part of the film or jelly matrix of the mass. Later the same day we make this notation in regard to some other *R. clamitans* eggs: "These eggs are fresh. Others described are not so fresh. The inner envelope is round, 3.2–3.6 mm.; the vitelli 1.2, 1.2, 1.3, 1.4 mm.; vitellus black and white."

Dangers. None of the *Ranas* of the swamp lay in such precarious places as the green frog. It chooses the edges where water levels change most quickly. I believe in my experience I have found proportionately more spoiled *R. clamitans* masses than with any other species. On July 5, 1922, in one pool the water reached two inches in depth and the eggs were about at the hatching stage. Many a time we found the green frog tadpoles in cut off shallow pools of cypress ponds. In our own pond (at Ithaca) we find that the frogs, particularly males and sometimes females, are easier of capture at breeding time. The toll of frogs from water snakes (*Natrix s. sipedon*) is considerable. We have seen water snakes seize more green frogs than any other species of frog and have often made these snakes release their quarry.

HATCHING PERIOD

In 1912 one mass of June 9 hatched in three days.

MATURE TADPOLE

Color description from life (Non Ridgway). Background of back very dark and covered with very fine yellow spots, the whole consequently having an olive green color with numerous distinct dark spots. Belly deep cream color without decided iridescence. The throat and sides are mottled with dark green. A slight coppery iridescence on the venter is more decided on the sides and on the tail. The tail appears green, mottled with brown; it is covered with fine yellow spots like the back.

General appearance. Tadpole large, not deep bodied. Tail fairly elongate, tip acute. Dorsal crest not so wide as musculature, extending forward on body slightly ahead of the vertical of the ends of the hind legs. Spiracle sinistral, just visible from dorsal aspect, directed obliquely upwards and backwards. Spiracle below lateral axis. Spiracular opening elliptical and plainly visible as such. Muciferous crypts very distinct in life, indistinct in most preserved specimens. Eye on or above lateral axis and near lateral outline in dorsal aspect than mid dorsal line. Anus dextral, opening on level with edge of ventral crest.

Mouth parts. Edge of upper labium fringed with teeth and about equal to upper horny beak in length as in *R. grylio.* In either corner, beneath this fringe is a very short row (sometimes absent) which is from 2/15–1/16 the upper fringe. The ends of the lateral row not extending beyond end of upper fringe. Median space between lateral rows six to eleven times the length of either row. The first lower labial row slightly longer or equal to horny beaks in length, and sometimes divided in the middle. The second row almost equal to first. The third row quite short not nearly as long as in *R. catesbeiana* usually almost 1/2 of the first row not 3/4 or 4/5 as in *R. catesbeiana*, or 2/3 as in *R. grylio*. It is contained one and one-half times in the horny beak and as much shorter than the single row of lower papillae. On the side of the labium the inner papillae (inside outer row) extend mesially beyond and beneath the second lower labial row of teeth, but not to third row (more like *R. grylio*).

Measurements. Length of body (12.2–27.8 mm.) 1.5–2.1 in tail (18.4–57 mm.), average 1.75. Width (9.8–21 mm.) of body 1.25–1.7 in its own length (12.2–27.8 mm.) average 1.47. Depth of body 1.13–1.32 in body width, average 1.22. Depth of body 1.9–2.3 in length of body, average 2.14. Depth of tail (7.4–16.6 mm.) 2.5–3.7 in length of tail (18.4–57 mm.) average 3.1. Muscular part (3.8–10.4 mm.) 1.35–1.95 in depth of tail (7.4–16.6 mm.). Spiracle 1.35–1.8 nearer base of hind legs or vent region. (5.4–12.4 mm.) than the tip of the snout (8.2–19 mm.). Spiracle 1.06–1.38 nearer eye (4.4–9.4 mm.) than base of hind legs or vent (5.4–12.4 mm.) average 1.24. Eye distinctly nearer to tip of snout (3.6–7.8 mm.) than to spiracle (4.4–9.6 mm.). Nostril decidedly nearer eye (1.4–36 mm.) than snout (2.2–4.8 mm.). Mouth (2.6–4.8 mm.) .8–1.35 larger than internasal space (2.8–4.8 mm.) average 1.06. Mouth contained 1.3–1.8, average 1.5 in interorbital distance (3.8–8.2 mm.) Internasal space contained in interorbital space 1.25–2.05, average 1.6.

The dimensions of the largest tadpole are:

Total length	64.8	Spiracle to vent	12.2
Body length	27.8	Spiracle to eye	9.6
Body depth	17.2	Eye to snout	7.4
Body width	20.6	Eye to nostril	3.6
Tail length	37.0	Nostril to snout	4.0
Tail depth	15.6	Mouth	4.6
Musculature of tail	10.0	Interorbital distance	8.0
Spiracle to snout	19.0	Internasal distance	4.8

General remarks. On July 9, 1922, at Thompson's Landing, St. Mary's River we found in a pond some tadpoles almost white in appearance yet they were not albinos. They were in a little pool with chalky white water and were colored accordingly.

LARVAL PERIOD

Normally I believe this species spends one winter as a tadpole. In 1921 it was difficult to find tadpoles inside the swamp after May 15. In 1922 we found more in shaded ponds on the outside east of the swamp. On July 15 in one sphagneous pool where the species was laying we found a few tadpoles nearing transformation. On August 11 at Camp Pinckney we found quite a number of large tadpoles in five deeply shaded pools. But even on the outside mature tadpoles after June 1 are scarce. I am aware of Swingle's striking experiments with hastening transformation in this species, and am also fully conscious this species has a longer growing period each year in the south than in the north, but I nevertheless believe one year its normal tadpole life in the Okefinokee region.

TRANSFORMATION

Period. In 1912 the writer was in the swamp from May 28–July 4 and the species was almost finished transforming by the later date. In 1921 we have definite records for April 27 and May 14. Our collections show 14 transformed or recently transformed from April–August, 1921.

In 1922 we found on July 15 and July 17 some tadpoles with large hind legs but they would not have transformed before August 1 or 10. One transformed July 28. Most of the transformation comes in the spring and early summer. Transformation stages were hard for us to find in the Okefinokee Swamp after June 15 or July 1.

Size. At Ithaca the range of transformation size is generally 28–38 mm. but many of those of the Okefinokee are smaller. In 1912 on June 9 we found some tadpoles one of which would have transformed in a week or ten days. It was 23 mm. long without the tail. From May 28 to September a series of frogs just transformed measured 25.5–33.5 mm.

In 1921 on April 27 we visited a large cypress pond west of camp. In little cut-off pools where there was little vegetation and mainly pine needles we found two transformed green frogs, 23 and 25 mm. in length. Fourteen more specimens collected from April–August, 1921, measure 20, 21, 22, 22, 22, 22, 23, 24, 24, 24, 24, 25, 25, 28 mm. respectively. On May 14, 1921, we took two transformed frogs 21 mm. and 24 mm. in length.

In 1922 on July 17 in one pond we found a few tadpoles nearing transformation. One transformed July 29, 1922, at the small size of 20.5 mm. We have a range of 20.5–33.5 mm., or probably with an average near 25 mm. or at least 7 mm. smaller than the average transformed green frog of the Northeastern States.

General remarks. Possibly inasmuch as the adult of this species in the Okefinokee region never attains the size of the northern representatives, we have a smaller size at transformation as well. In any event both adult and transformation sizes are smaller. The transformed frogs are easy to tell because of their prominent heavily spotted breasts. These numerous small spots are grayish white.

GROWTH

Of 27 adults, 4 were from 52–58 mm., 16 were from 60–69 mm., and 7 from 70–79 mm. It must be rarely that Okefinokee representatives of this species exceed 80 mm. in body length, yet northern forms may reach 100 mm. The mean range of adults is between 60–70 mm. On June 12, 1912, we took male frogs 52, 66, 67, 70, 72 mm. in length or on June 5, 1912, one 29 mm. and a female 58 mm. Between May 28–June 25, 1912, we found small frogs from 25–33 mm. in length. In the same period we took adults 52–75 mm. but none in the gap of 34–51 mm. In 1921 we secured only two in this intermediate category, one 43 mm. June 24, 1921, and one 40 mm. July 5, 1921. On this later date we secured one 40, 65, 69, 71 mm. respectively. We took two young of 22 and 32 mm. from April 22–May 23, 1921, 14 young from 20–28 April–August, 1921, two young 28, 32 mm. June 20, 1921, and one 33 mm. July 26, 1921—in other words 20–33 mm. in range. This gives a clue in April and May of 1921 of transformed frogs 20–33; others 40–43 mm.; others 56–62 mm.; others 65–72 mm., or in June and July, 1922, we took frogs 20.5 mm. at transformation, others 59 and 60 mm., and others 61–77 mm. The growth stages then seem 20–33 mm. at transformation; 33–43 mm. the first year's growth; 43–52 mm.; 52–63 mm.; 64–77 mm. Possibly these four presumptive years based on measurements of frogs taken at the same period should be shortened to three years.

FOOD

We have made no study of the food of the specimens we captured.

ENEMIES

In 1912, the only enemy of which we had positive evidence is the moccasin. One moccasin taken June 22, 1912, had a two-thirds grown *R. clamitans* in its stomach and another secured in June, 1912, had a full grown frog.

In 1922 an amusing episode reveals another unusual enemy. On June 27, at Camp Pinckney (near Folkston), Ga., on the St. Mary's River were some big ponds (formerly dug by Confederate Army to hide turpentine in barrels). Here we found several green frogs. "I captured one and started for another pond. Halfway I lost the frog and began to chase it but an old hen ran in and seized it ahead of me. It ran off with the prey and ate it. The frog was two-thirds grown." See ovulation (dangers) for discussion of water snake as an enemy.

AUTUMNAL DISAPPEARANCE

Our latest record is for September 5, 1922.

BIBLIOGRAPHY

See General Bibliography under synonymy Boulenger, G. A. (Proc. Am. Acad. Arts & Science, LV, 1920, p. 425).
1914   See previous notes, A. H. Wright, 1914, Carnegie Inst. Publ. No. 197, pp. 70-76; 1920, Rept. U. S. Bur. Fisheries, Doc. 888.
1914.   Overton, Frank. Brooklyn Mus. Quarterly, March, 1914, p. 37.

Rana grylio Stejneger

(Pl. III, Fig. 8; VIII, Fig. 4; XI, Figs. 5, 6; XIV, Fig. 5; XVI, Figs. 3, 6; XVII; XXXVI, Fig. 8; XXXVII; Text Figs. 1, 15)

COMMON NAMES

Southern Bull-frog. Joe Brown Frog. Pig-frog. Lake Frog. Bull Frog.

RANGE

Check list. Rana grylio Stejneger. "Range: Southern Mississippi to to peninsular Florida. Type Locality: Bay St. Louis, Mississippi."—Stejneger & Barbour (Check List, 1917, p. 38).

Supplementary records. Dr. Stejneger (1901) had it from Kissimee, Pensacola, Florida and Bay St. Louis, Mississippi, and gave its range as "Florida and Gulf Coast west to Mississippi." In 1906 Miss Dickerson reported it from Ozona, Florida. In 1912 the author captured several specimens and saw many more in Okefinokee Swamp, Georgia. From 1914–1922 Deckert reported it from Jacksonville, Royal Palm Hammock, Musa Isle, Miami River, Florida. In 1916 T. Barbour reported it in some of the Florida lakes and in 1920 he notes it near Palm Beach, Florida. In 1922 Löding included this form with the comment "Alabama records: none." However, the distinctive note of this frog has been heard by the writer and others in Mobile County. In 1917 our transcontinental party of 13 individuals (Am. Naturalist, April, May, June 1919) camped near Theodore, Alabama. Prof. J. C. Bradley remarked "Across the road from our camp, some peculiar alligator-like grunts proved to be emanating from the southern bull-frog, *Rana grylio.* This species was described only about fifteen years ago." We captured and photographed two or three of these adults. In 1921 and 1922 we found them through the Okefinokee Swamp. In two different articles Viosca in Louisiana (1923), noted their presence throughout "the entire southern portion of this state," a westward extension of its range. Earlier in 1918 Viosca writes "During the last year I have made positive identification of this species in many localities in the southern part of Louisiana." Boulenger (1920) secured specimens from New Orleans and Plaquemine, Louisiana. It is now known from Georgia, Florida, Alabama, Mississippi and Louisiana.

Inasmuch as we called this species a Sabalian species in 1924 (Ecology, January 1926, Vol. VII, p. 82) we would expect it to extend to South Carolina or Wilmington, N. C., and records from eastern coastal Texas are to be expected.

Local Okefinokee records. This is one of the characteristic notes of all the water lily prairies of the swamp and the open cypress ponds. We also recorded it in the grassy or weedy cypress bays, along the river swamps of the Suwannee and St. Mary's Rivers, along the floating vegetation of the edges of water courses or lakes in the wooded swamp. It is decidedly aquatic and breeds in its accustomed habitat of the rest of the year.

GENERAL APPEARANCE

This is a southern bull-frog of the Sabalian or Humid division of the Lower Austral Zone with shorter snout, narrower head and shorter fourth toe. In coloration it is an overgrown *Rana virgatipes* without two dorsal stripes, and is a beautiful frog.

COLORATION OF SPIRIT SPECIMENS (1912)

General back color is olive citrine or brownish olive, bone brown or blackish brown all over. In small specimens there is hardly a dark spot, but in the olive forms the dorsum from the tympanum backwards is covered with prominent black blotches with those on each side from tympanum to groin, more or less merged. On the forelimbs of all the specimens there are no spots or bars. On the hind limbs of the younger forms and in the olive colored group there may be three cross bars on the front half of the femur, three or four bands across the tibia, and three or four on the tarsus and foot. In the rich or deep brown specimens the dark spots obscurely show. Occasionally in these specimens the black body color or sometimes a black color almost wholly covers the upper two-thirds of the posterior faces of the thighs. In all the specimens the body color covers one-half to two-thirds of the posterior faces of the thighs. Occasionally the body color is replaced by black. Beneath this area of body color comes a longitudinal yellowish white or yellowish stripe followed by a prominent dark, black or brown band. Sometimes this is succeeded by another yellowish line followed by a wonderfully brilliant mottling of brown and yellow. In almost all of the largest forms where mottling on under surface of the legs is prominent these yellowish lines are yet indicated by two broken up longitudinal rows of yellow spots. In some the second yellow line is absent. The smaller specimens of females have the underparts except the thighs immaculate. One large male has the whole under parts the most striking black or brown and yellow we have seen in a North American frog. On the posterior face of the tarsus and foot is a prominent dark band with a yellowish line below it on the tarsus. This coloration shows best in young forms. These specimens have the forearms unicolor above. The sides of some of the specimens are unspotted while others have some mottling of black chocolate brown and yellow like the venter. Three large males have the under surface of the leg speckled, mottled or reticulated. On either side of the breast and in front of the arm insertion, the dark body color, gray or brown extends as a special area almost or actually to the middle line. Most of the specimens have the whole upper head unstriped or unspotted. The tip of the snout is more or less white. The web is dusky, in adults very clouded; in young, clear with numerous spots or mottlings.

STRUCTURAL CHARACTERS (WRITTEN IN 1912)

Head smooth, other parts minutely mammillate and pitted, sometimes round on the sides, throat, and lower belly; snout more pointed than in *Rana catesbeiana*; eyes elevated, large; eyelid rough; nostrils equidistant from eye to tip of snout or slightly nearer the snout; a prominent fold of skin from the eye over the tympanum to above the shoulders; no lateral fold; groove down middle of back halfway to the vent or sometimes absent; first, second and fourth fingers about equal, long; inner metatarsal tubercle small; no outer tubercle; subarticular tubercles very small; Stejneger ('02) found the percentages of toes measurements in *Rana grylio* and *Rana catesbeiana* to be as follows: in *Rana grylio* the third toe in the length of the fourth toe is .81–.84; second toe in the fourth toe, .55–.61; first toe, .34–.39; in *Rana catesbeiana*, third toe, .70–.76; second toe, .47–.51; first toe, .27–.33. In some of our specimens of *Rana grylio* the proportional length of the third toe in the fourth is even greater than Stejneger found, being sometimes .85 or .86 while the second toe may be as much as .65 and the first toe .43. The head measured at the tympanum is perceptibly narrower than *R. catesbeiana*; vomerine teeth

Plate XXXVII

Southern bullfrog (*Rana grylio*)

1. Male, Billy Id., Ga. April 29, 1921. Ventral aspect. × 0.4.
2. Female, Billy Id., Ga. June 22, 1921. Ventral aspect. × 0.4.
3. Transforming frog, Billy Id., Ga. April 26, 1921. Lateroventral aspect. × 0.4.
4. Male croaking, Long pond, Billy Id., Ga. May 19, 1921. Flashlight.
5. Mature tadpole, Billy Id., Ga. August 4, 1922. × 1.0.
6. Tadpole with four legs, Billy Id., Ga. June 5, 1921. × 0.4.
7. Transformed frog, Billy Id., Ga. April 26, 1921. × 0.4.
8. Site of egg mass in cypress glade west of Minne Lake, Ga. June 10, 1921.
9. Bullfrog pond looking S. S. W. Billy Id., Ga. June 16, 1921.

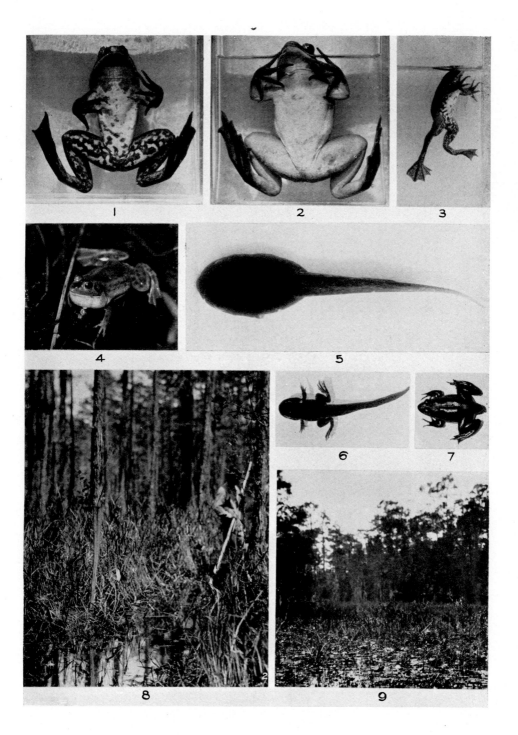

close together often obliquely placed; tongue with moderate forks like *Rana catesbeiana* or with extreme elongate thin attenuate horns; no dorso-lateral glandular fold; webbing of hind feet less emarginate than in *Rana catesbeiana*.

MEASUREMENTS

(1912-1914)

The measurements of 7 specimens follow. The total length reaches from 53–101 mm.; average 82.3 mm.; the head is 21–39 mm., average 31.6 mm., usually in males larger than the width of the head, in females equal to or less than the width of the head; the length of the head is contained in the length of the body 2.3–2.8 times, average 2.5; width of the head, 21.5–40.5 mm., average 30.6 mm.; snout 8–15 mm., average 11.5 mm., greater than eye in all, in males usually less than (rarely equal to) the tympanum, in females greater than the tympanum; eye 7–11 mm., average 9.6 mm. less than snout, less than the tympanum in males, equal to or greater than tympanum in females; tympanum 5.5–17 mm., average 10.9 mm., large in males, moderate in females; interorbital distance 3.5–6 mm., average 5 mm., from 1–2 times in upper eyelid; femur 25–51 mm., average 38 mm., equal to tibia; tibia 25.5–50 mm., average 39 mm., slightly less than rest of the foot without tarsus; tarsus 15.5–29 mm., average 22.5 mm.; rest of foot 28–34 mm., average 22.5 mm.; rest of foot 28–54 mm., average 41.8 mm., anterior limb from axilla 30–52.5 mm., average 41.6 mm., more than femur or tibia, less than equal to or more than rest of hind foot; posterior limb from groin 77.5–141 mm., average 114.2 mm., 1.3–1.5 times the total length; posterior limb to heel reaches the front of the eye or even to the nostril.

(Recent Material)

Head to angle of mouth 1.02 (50 mm.)–1.02 (51 mm.)–1.13 (82 mm. ♂) –1.08 (95 mm. ♂) in width of head; head to rear of tympanum .95–.975–.94– .95 in width of head; head to angle of mouth 3.37–2.68–2.82–2.71 in length; head to rear of tympanum 2.8–2.55–2.34–2.375 in length; snout 1.0–1.12–.92– 1.0 in fourth finger; 1.06–1.12–1.15–1.06 in first toe; eye 1.14–1.14–1.44–1.6 in snout; eye .70–.85–1.44–1.6 in tympanum; eye 1.14–1.29–1.55–1.5 in first finger; tympanum 2.4–1.66–1.2–.93 in intertympanic width; 1.6–1.33–1.0–1.0 in snout; internasal width .88–.875–.857–.85 in upper eyelid width; inter-orbital width 1.33–1.16–1.2–.86 in upper eyelid width; 1.5–1.33–1.4–1.0 in internasal width; 4.0–3.33–3.1–2.14 in intertympanic width.

Forelimb: 1.68–1.7–1.64–1.86 in length; 2.6–2.56–2.56–2.8 in hindlimb; first finger 1.44–1.33–1.28–1.33 in third finger; second finger 1.27–1.2–1.12– 1.25 in third finger; .94–.9–.87–.93 in first finger; third finger 1.21–1.08–1.33– 1.25 in second toe; fourth finger 1.21–1.0–1.25–.937 in first toe; 1.64–1.33– 1.51–1.25 in third finger; internasal width 1.77–2.25–2.0–2.14 in first finger; 2.0–2.5–2.3–2.3 in second finger; 2.55–3.0–2.57–2.85 in third finger; 1.55–2.25– 1.71–2.3 in fourth finger.

Hindlimb: length 1.5–1.51–1.56–1.51 in hindlimb; tibia 2.0–2.0–1.95–2.04 in length (snout to vent) 3.0–3.08–3.04–3.13 in hindlimb; 1.15–1.2–1.19–1.18

in forelimb; 1.04–1.08–1.14–1.06 in hind foot; first toe 1.64–1.44–1.6–1.49 in second toe; 2.10–2.11–1.93–2.0 in third toe; 2.09–2.55–2.93–2.64 in fourth toe; 2.23–2.11–2.33–2.17 in fifth toe; second toe 1.64–1.46–1.2–1.36 in third toe; 1.8–1.76–1.83–1.8 in fourth toe; 1.35–1.46–1.45–1.48 in fifth toe; third toe 1.39–1.2–1.5–1.32 in fourth toe; 1.05–1.0–1.2–1.08 in fifth toe; fourth toe 1.04–1.17–1.09–1.09 in hind foot; 1.0–1.08–.95–1.02 in tibia; 1.16–1.3–1.13– 1.13 in forelimb; fifth toe 1.31–1.2–1.25–1.21 in fourth toe; internasal width 1.88–2.25–2.14–2.43 in first toe; 3.1–3.25–3.43–3.57 in second toe; 4.0–4.75– 4.14–4.85 in third toe; 5.55–5.75–6.3–6.43 in fourth toe; 4.02–4.75–5.0–5.3 in fifth toe.

HABITAT

This is ideally a frog of the prairie or open centers of cypress ponds which are an extension or separation from the prairie types themselves. Waterlilies, hardheads (*Xyris*) neverwets (*Orontium*), wampee (*Peltandra*), watershield (*Brasenia*), bladderworts (*Utricularia*), floating heart (*Nymphoides*) prevails. Where this habitat approaches islands, bays, or a circle of trees, maiden cane (*Panicum*), fern (*Woodwardia*) and duck grass (*Rhynchophora*) occur. Where this latter assemblage of plants occur in bays, etc., *Rana grylio* may be or where some of it may be along water courses.

FIRST APPEARANCE

The earliest definite date of their reappearance is Dr. Barbour's note. At Palm Beach, Florida, "*Rana grylio* reappeared in 1920 on March 17 after not being seen all winter." We have not been afield in its range except in April to September in which period it was active in 1912, 1917, 1921 and 1922. Deckert in observations from February 23–December 8, 1920, first heard this species grunting April 4, at Musa Isle, Dade Co., Florida.

GENERAL HABITS

Mr. Robert Ridgway found them "so excessively shy and wary that he had failed to secure any specimens" for Dr. Stejneger. "Requests were sent to various correspondents to catch and forward specimens, but they were equally unsuccessful." Stejneger 1901 (p. 211), also Dr. E. A. Mearns reported them very difficult of capture. In 1914 Miss Dickerson says "It seldom leaps; its strong instincts when frightened are to dive and hide." Deckert found it in 1911–1912 (1914, Copeia, No. 3) at Jacksonville, Florida "not rare, but very shy." Later he pronounces that "It is one of the shyest of all frogs, usually floating in water two or three feet deep, under branches of a floating dead tree, or among other debris, so that it is almost impossible to get within capturing distance without alarming it. Its size is 4 to 5 inches from snout to vent." In 1921 he writes "No effort was made to take specimens, as it is impossible to secure living material during the daytime, and without a boat, the species being so thoroughly aquatic and exceedingly shy." In (1920) Dr. Barbour calls it "very shy and wholly aquatic." Viosca in 1918 (p. 161) writes "It appears to be confined to the alluvial section of Louisiana, where it frequents the freshwater marshes, and is especially abundant in the many lakes and lagoons of these regions. The individuals are very shy, and are seldom seen by daylight, as they hide among the aquatic vegetation of the lakes, and when closely approached quietly take to the water and hide in the mud—not diving with the splashing retreat of the common bullfrog. They are entirely aquatic and are rarely caught on the land."

In 1912 the following notes on their habits and habitat were made: "One will never forget his first capture of the 'Swamp bullfrog'. The prominent black or brown and yellow reticulations of the under parts are very conspicuous. Sometimes we succeeded in killing them with an oar or pole while pushing through the bonnets and occasionally the members of the party captured them when visiting set trap lanterns for insects."

On April 25, 1921, "we went with flashlight after *Rana grylio*. On the vegetative carpet and lily pads were untold numbers of *Acris*, on the lily pads and on the bushes *Hyla cinerea*, and amongst the pickerel weeds different sizes of *Rana grylio*. In all, three of us secured only 6 adults and one transformed specimen. Later I found that they could be picked up rather easily with a flashlight. On May 6, Dave Lee went out on Billy's Lake at night with a torch to catch small fish for bait. With a small dip net he would scoop in front of a *Rana grylio* and usually catch them."

On May 10, 1921, we found one cypress pond with plenty of all stages of *Rana grylio*. Our comment is that they are "easy of capture at night except for adults and these even can be taken." On May 11 we found plenty of *R. grylios* at night along the edges of Billy's Lake. "They usually were at the edge near the bushes or under them or amongst brush or in maiden cane. Usually when one tried to photo them they were too much surrounded with vegetation or sticks. We could approach closely but in clearing away brush for the flashlight photo we would scare them. Often we would hear them go skipping along across the lake or along the edges like a *Rana catesbeiana*." As with most shy frogs they can be captured if females are around. In some cases the females led the way to where a male might be. Where we succeeded in flashlighting a croaking male we were quite certain females were near because of eggs found there soon afterwards. On June 20 we found another method of capture. We never dreamed it would work for *Rana grylio*. We would pull in hurriedly, masses of floating maiden cane and in the corner at the bottom of the boat all kinds of life would drop. On this night we caught 2 *Rana grylios*, one a fine ripe female. All in all our main reliance was to wade about at night on the prairies or in open cypress and to catch them by hand. One must, however, keep his bearings.

Anent this species it might be interesting to include some comments of Percy Viosca, Jr., in a letter to Dr. H. F. Moore, U. S. Bureau of Fisheries. On July 11, 1923, he writes: "It might also interest you to know that *Rana grylio* is abundant in this State, but we have found it is a thoroughly aquatic species and not very hardy in captivity, and would not be suitable for frog culture even though it is a fine flavored species and we believe much superior to flesh of the *catesbeiana*. It would be only suitable for planting in shallow lakes of the lagoon type, but once established it would be difficult to collect, except by experienced night hunters. It would be a species very difficult to ship. Although we have shipped them successfully, the frogs need individual care."

VOICE

In 1901, Dr. Stejneger remarked that "A few years ago Mr. Robert Ridgway, returning from a collecting trip in Southern Florida assured me that the bullfrog there had such a peculiar voice that he could scarcely believe it to be the same species as the one found elsewhere in the United States." This was the genesis of Dr. Stejneger's interest in this new form. Later Dr. E. A. Mearns sent some from Kissimee, Florida "with the statement that their voice was entirely different from that of northern bullfrogs, resembling the grunt of a herd of pigs."

In 1906 Miss Dickerson held that "The frog might be unknown now, if it had not been for the persistent reports of its voice. The sounds produced are said to resemble the grunting of a herd of pigs, thus differing entirely from the familiar bass notes of the common bullfrog."

"*Rana grylis* Stjr.," Deckert, 1914, writes "is called the 'Pig-frog' owing to its loud grunting call, repeated three of four times. . . . The call is heard at any time, day or night, from deeply wooded bayous, oftenest in March, April and May." "In May 1922 we heard it at Royal Palm Hammock, Dade Co., Florida."

To Dr. Barbour in 1920 "Its call, which is heard at night, or on damp days, resembles the grunting of a pig, and consists of but one sound oft repeated. Dr. J. C. Bradley in 1919 (June 12) called its note 'some peculiar alligatorlike grunts'. . . . Its note is altogether different from that of our northern species."

In 1918 Viosca held "The voice is entirely different and is much less musical than that of the common bullfrog. The individual call is a series of grunts, usually eight uttered in quick succession. When several are calling, the noise is not unlike that of as many hogs, and 'pig' frog might prove an appropriate popular name."

In 1912 we made the following notes on the swamp bullfrog in Okefinokee Swamp. "From June 13–June 19 we heard several of these within the swamp. On June 18, 1912 at the Still Heronry amongst the swampy tangle of buttonbush (*Cephalanthus occidentalis*) 'hurrah bush' (*Leucothoë racemosa*) and *leather* leaf (*Clethra alnifolia*) we heard plenty of southern bullfrogs from 8–11 a. m. The water was waist deep and the bushes 8–12 feet above the water. One of their notes was very much like that of *Rana catesbeiana* of the north. Another note frequently given in chorus was mournful, reverberating, prolonged and deep, not at all like the regular bullfrog chorus note. There were a number in the chorus and it sounds like one continuous long deep roar. The following day, June 19, from 7:10–11 a. m. when the sun was very hot we heard several in the tree-covered overflowed banks of the Suwannee River. On June 13 while travelling through Minne Lake Run we heard the deep, guttural notes of the 'Swamp Bullfrog' all along the bonnet borders and through the cypress woods on either side."

In 1917 on June 12 two miles from Theodore, Ala., we "heard the croak or grunt (4 or 5 notes) of the southern bullfrog. Hard to find. Lost the first one. They are amongst cat briars. Found a young one and later took a large male. To one member of the party there seems something of the human in its voice. To another it had an alligator quality. Certainly it differed from the northern bullfrog."

In 1921 we began hearing *R. grylio* from the very first of our entrance into the swamp. On April 23 we heard the first one and it continued a puzzle for about two days. From April 25 we heard them most commonly from 7 to 8:00 p. m. onward. Several also called during the day. From April 30–May 1 I have the note "No *Rana grylios* heard." "Too cold for *R. grylio* calls." From April 23–April 29 our lowest temperatures in early morning (6–7 a. m.) were 62° and our highest 68°. On April 30–May 1 it was very cold and the early morning temperatures were 45°–52°. From May 1–7, 45°–57° obtained and very few were heard. From May 8–14 a few were heard, low minima 60°–65° obtaining at night. From May 16 onward there were plenty of *R. grylio* calling in early evening or wonderful choruses at midnight or in early morning hours before dawn. Minima were from 67°–70° or higher. There after in June and July we heard them commonly at night and occasionally they were abundantly heard in the daytime. In general 45°–65° minima are not conducive to calling. From 65°–70° starts calling in numbers and large choruses are from 70°–85° or higher. Humidity and rainfall are, however, even more important than temperature in determining their activities.

The records of 1921 and 1922 combined give the croaking period as April 23–September 5. Doubtless had we been in the Okefinokee before and after these dates we would have heard them.

In 1921 we have the following notes on the call of the southern bullfrog. On June 25 in mid forenoon "I heard the croak of one frog in the middle of Long Pond. It sounded like the roar of our northern *Rana catesbeiana*. Heard several normal *Rana grylio* at 10:30 a. m." On April 25 we record the call as "two or three grunts of less than a second each. Sometimes there are more." The *R. catesbeiana*-like call given June 25 was not in abnormal conditions but on April 25 we carried several in a bag to our camp. Several times on the way one male uttered a "distress" or "mercy" note not unlike the familiar "jug-o-rum" of *Rana catesbeiana*. On May 11 we went to Billy's Lake at night. Along the lake either side were numerous *R. grylio* croaking —just two or three croaks to a male."

In 1920 (p. 21) the author wrote of the call as follows: "In Southern Alabama he recorded croaking males as not uncommon in overflowed areas and swamps (Plate IX No. 2) of clear streams, especially if overgrown with a thick mat of cat briars (*Smilax*) and arrow arums. In the main their croakings consist of four or five notes and are wholly unlike the call of the Northern bullfrog. To some people there is something of the human voice in their call; to others it sounds like an alligator. If the ventriloquial males be in tangles they are hard to discover. These croaking males may also occur along the deep wooded overflowed banks of southern rivers."

Some of the residents call this species the "Joe Brown" frog because of a fancied resemblance of the grunt to this name. The croak can be heard at a considerable distance and a midnight chorus might be pronounced "loud."

Mr. Francis Harper describes the note as follows: "Its deep bass note is a rough, guttural, grunting *grro, grro,* . . . It is usually double (as just represented), but sometimes single, and occasionally it runs into a series of from three to ten notes."

The male frog has "internal vocal sacs" says Boulenger. In this regard it is like *Rana clamitans* and *Rana catesbeiana.* The green frog inflates its vocal sac more on the sides below the angle of the mouth and less beneath the tips of the lower jaw. On the bullfrog it is one swelling below lower jaw. In the southern bullfrog the inflation is greater than in the other two species. There is one inflation but on either side of the middle is a subsidiary inflation giving the internal sac a tripartite appearance (Pl. XXXVII, Fig. 4). These creatures are hard to flashlight at the moment of inflation. The frog is spread out on the surface of the water amongst the water plants. The call is very short.

Probably Bartram's description is of *Rana grylio* when he says that "The largest frog known in Florida and on the sea coast of Carolina, is about eight or nine inches in length from the nose to the extremity of the toes; they are a dusky brown or black colour on the upper side, and their belly or under side white, spotted and clouded with dusky spots of various size and figure; their legs and thighs also are variegated with transverse ringlets of dark brown or black, and are yellow and green about their mouth and lips; they live in wet swamps and marshes, on the shores of large rivers and lakes; their voice is loud and hideous, greatly resembling the *grunting of swine* (our emphasis), but not near as loud as the voice of the bullfrog of Virginia and Pennsylvania; neither do they arrive to half their size, the bullfrog being frequently eighteen inches in length, and their roaring as loud as that of a bull."

MATING

Male (From life, April 25, 1921). Upper parts rich brown with black spots obscured. Tympanum outer circle deep brown, center green or dark green. Top of head dark green. Belly creamy. Throat lemon yellow with dusky fine blotches on underside of fore limbs and hind limbs. Lower belly blotched or reticulated with cream and brown. On sides of body and legs cream replaced by yellow. First finger of male much enlarged. In another male head deep bottle green. Tympanum center black, middle ring light brown, outer ring brownish black. Throat almost orange yellow on either side of the breast. On either side of breast between arm insertions a deep green area. On rear of femur the yellow extends as a yellow line with brown black on either side of it. This line golden or orange yellow. More intense than yellowish or cream of undersides of legs. In some the black spots of the back are farther apart. Black spots of back surrounded by green and the centers with bronzy brown. Top of toes brown and yellow. Under side of toes brown. In half grown male under color cream slight wash of yellow. Femoral stripe cream not yellow. Ear drum small all brown. Two pectoral patches dusky not green. (Non Ridgway.)

Female (From life, June 21, 1921). Upper lip from tympanum to snout medal bronze also on top of head; upper parts olive citrine with a few dark spots on the posterior back and groin. Upper part of legs saccardo olive with cross blotches. Throat baryta yellow or better straw yellow. Where dorsal color reaches light venter, so also on fore and hind legs there is one clear dull green yellow or light dull green yellow. Venter marguerite yellow, also same color on top of toes and fingers. Two patches on either side of throat and near pectoral region, so prominent in the male, is light yellowish olive, not pronounced as in male. No reticulations on venter except for faint reticulations on under side of hind legs and the slightest indications on the groin region. Rear of femur with one long band of sea foam yellow with line of quaker drab below and dark quaker drab or black above. Iris with bright green yellow ring around pupil. Iris black with lots of bright green yellow spots. Green yellow outer circle around the black.

Structural differences. The smallest male to show enlarging of tympanum is 67 mm. or about one year after transformation. All the other of this series are as follows: None of the other year-olds show secondary male characters except one at 67 mm. where the tympana are enlarging; in some of the two-year-olds (73–86 mm.) the tympana are enlarged and half of them have the thumb discolored. Not until the three old stage (91–102) is reached do they have the tympana very large and the intertympanic space much reduced. The thumb is very well developed but never so swollen and stubby as in *R. virgatipes, R. clamitans* or *R. catesbeiana.* The males have more pointed narrower heads than the females, are slimmer, have the intertympanic space much reduced in males, thumbs discolored and somewhat swollen. The females become larger than the males.

Duration. It doubtless is shorter in this species than in *R. sphenocephala* or species which begin ovulation earlier in the season. It is conceivable that this member of the *R. catesbeiana* group like the *R. catesbeiana* might continue amplexation for a long time. One *R. catesbeiana* male was recorded mated with a dead female which doubtless died from a long amplexation. This is the exception. Normally we would expect *R. grylio* to be of a short amplexing group.

Night or day. The immense choruses come at night and the vast majority of mating must come at night. Some rainy or showery days or humid overcast diurnal weather may make them active in mating. We have no positive records of mating being initiated by day though when crests come no doubt some mating carries over into the day or begins about dusk or late afternoon.

Amplexation. (Normal, abnormal). I have seen only two embraces of this species, the first one pectoral, the second abnormal. No doubt the first is normal. In the evening of April 29, 1921, I have this entry: "In Long Pond I heard *R. grylio.* The males were out in the middle of the pond among the *Pontederia.* The *R. grylios* can easily be picked up with a flashlight. Sometimes a frog will move a foot or two or three. They rest on the surface. If one keep quiet and put out the flashlight you can hear them jump once in a while on the surface. Took a female *R. grylio* where there were several males.

Concluded I might mate them. Brought them back and put them in a fish can (absolutely dark within)." The following morning we noted "This morning at 6 the *Rana grylios* were mated." We tried later to photograph them but they broke the embrace.

One journal entry is our only evidence. On May 21, 1921, we have "After supper I went down to Billy Lake Landing. *R. grylio* going strong. Air 70°F. at 7 p.m. Tonight at 8 we went to *Chorophilus* pond and *Engystoma* ditches. Air 70°. In the bays around Billy Lake at 12 midnight a wonderful *R. grylio* chorus. In the *Engystoma* ditches caught a female *R. grylio* which was in the middle on trash. She jumped towards the vicinity of a male. Caught her. Later caught a male. Put them together. He mated axillary. Later with one arm behind and one ahead of forearm. Once his finger seemed to extend down as in a normal *Rana* male but this is normally axillary in this male."

OVULATION

Habitat. (See non-breeding habitat.)

Period. In 1912 report we note of our 7 specimens only two are adult females. One was taken on the Suwannee River, June 17, and the other on Floyd's Island Prairie June 26, 1912. Both were spent and this would indicate earlier breeding. It appears that the breeding may come in May and through June because of the chorus June 18 and the fact that males taken from June 15–July 15 or even later had the first finger strongly swollen. At the herony we took tadpoles 18 mm. long which we took to be this species." In 1923 the author reported (Copeia, 1923, p. 34) *R. grylio* as one of five species to begin breeding from May 15 on to June 1. In July–August 1924 (p. 379) Mrs. Wright and I pronounced the "Season, May 24 to August 21."

Inasmuch as we not uncommonly hear them in chorus or abundance until September 1 just before darkness comes on, all through the night and at daybreak we suspect this species to breed until September 1. Our latest record of numbers comes September 5. We actually found eggs on May 24, 1921, May 28, 1921, June 8, 1921, June 10, 1921, July 28, 1922.

Temperature and humidity. On May 24, we found our first masses. My records for that day are somewhat as follows: "In Long Pond this morning I found where we formerly photographed the male *R. grylio*, two masses of *R. grylio* eggs. They were about ready to hatch. Must have been laid the night of May 21–22 or that of May 20–21. In another place in middle of pond found two more masses probably laid night of May 22–23. At 10:30 a.m. temperature in air 1 foot above water 94°, water's surface 85°. The Cox boys report having found May 21 in afternoon a fresh mass of *R. grylio* eggs along the edge of Billy's Lake." This coincides with our belief for the ovulation of the record for May 24. On May 21 it rained continually in the swamp; our temperatures were not below 70°; those outside ranged from 67–80° and rain was general at St. George, Hilliard, Waycross, etc. The temperatures for localities outside the swamp for four days preceding May 24 were minima 62–69°, maxima 78–94°, our temperatures 64–94°.

The film of May 28 probably was laid May 25 when rains were general at St. George, Hilliard and Waycross. For four days before May 28 minima ranged from 60–70°; maxima, 87–97°. Our temperatures were 64–94°.

On June 8 the fresh eggs were not laid in rainy weather. The temperatures for 4 preceding days on the outside of the swamp were minima 56–70°, maxima 84–87°. Our temperatures were 63–82°.

The next record June 10, 1921, was preceded for four days by maxima 75–90°, by minima 55–70° for outside stations and by our temperatures 63–84°, and no percipitation for 4 or 5 preceding days.

In 1922 on July 28 found them breeding. For several days before July 28 it had rained. For four days before the nearby Georgia and Florida stations had minima 72–76°, maxima 91–96°. These general conditions of 72–76° precipitated general choruses.

In general we expect this species to breed when the air is humid, and nights and general temperature conditions are 63–70°, but the optimum period is when minima are from 68–78° or higher and maxima mount to 85–96°.

Egg-laying process. No actual observations on the egg-laying process have been made by us or is in print to my knowledge. The film being similar to that of the greenfrog or bullfrog is doubtless laid in the same fashion.

EGGS

Attachment. The eggs are usually attached to pickerel weed (*Pontederia*) stems in midpond, in the cypress pond on the islands or to "bonnets" on the prairies or amongst the maiden cane along the water courses.

On May 28, 1921, we found them amongst pickerel weed and lizard's tail or in the outer edge of the *Saururus* Zone or attached to flag (*Iris*). On June 10, 1921, we had to make a detour to the west of Minne Lake (then filled from lumbering) in a cypress bay. Beside the temporary boat trail in a rather open place among the cypress we found a mass amongst saw grass, maiden cane and wampee.

On July 28, 1922, in a cypress pond outside of the swamp near Station Branch, found a mass hatching near the outer edge of a mass of arrow-leaved species of plant.

Egg mass. On June 12, 1917, at Theodore, Alabama, we were informed that the large southern bullfrogs which we had captured "laid small beadlike eggs in large masses on the surface of the water."

The masses found May 24, 1921 were films at the surface of the water. These films are generally one or two eggs thick. One mass was 15 x 18 inches in diameter; another 12 x 12. All four masses were at least a foot in diameter. The mass the Cox boys found May 21 was also a film. On May 28, 1921, the first mass was 10 to 12 inches x 18 to 20 inches; the second 15 x 10 inches. On June 10 'Bud Carter brought me in some fresh bullfrog (*R. grylio*) eggs. They found them in maiden cane in Billy's Lake. He said the mass was "15 inches across it." On July 28, 1922, found a film about 16 x 16 inches in diameter.

In 1920 we wrote (p. 26) "The eggs of the southern bullfrog are not known, and we are not very familiar with its breeding habits. In Georgia, Florida and Alabama the writer has chanced upon this species in full croaking season in June and July. This species is reputed to lay small eggs in large masses on or at the surface of the water in the early summer, and if this be true the habits of this form are closely similar to those of the northern bullfrog."

In 1923 (p. 34) the author asserts "And *Rana grylio* has large films, one by two and a half feet across much as does *Rana catesbeiana*."

In 1924 (p. 379) A. A. Wright and I state the "egg mass (to be) over 1 sq. ft. in area (144 to 288 sq. in. or 900 to 1800 sq. cm.) or 12 by 12 inches to 12 inches by 25 inches in diameter; usually in midpond; . . ." Some *Rana grylios* reach a size (almost as large as *Rana catesbeiana* and no doubt lay films of about the same size as occur in the common bullfrog.

Egg description (Field). The first fresh eggs secured June 8 were measured roughly at night with a lantern light lest we lose the record. These records were "vitellus 1.6 mm; inner envelope 3.6.; outer envelope 4.5–6 mm. These will be revised tomorrow." On the morrow, the measurements were made as follows: "vitellus 1.55–1.85 mainly 1.6 mm.; a vitellus of 1.6 has vitelline membrane 1.8 across it; outer envelope 6 mm., sometimes 7 mm., some 4 mm.; inner envelope 3.6–4.0 mm.; vegetative pole white, animal pole black."

No eggs were laid in camp by captives and our identification is presumptive but strongly supported. No *R. catesbeiana* are present. The only form which might prove confusing are individual *R. clamitans* eggs. Whenever we visited the places where the two were present *R. grylio* was in the middle of the pond while *R. clamitans* was always in the wooded tangles at the edge of the pond—*Rana grylio* in open pond, *Rana clamitans* in the most shaded parts near the land's edge—distinctive habitats.

In other field notes we have: outer envelope 3.8–4.0 mm.; 4.5–6 mm.; 4–6 or 7 mm.; inner envelope 2.8–3.2 mm.; 3.6 mm.; 3.6–4.0 mm.; vitellus, 1.8 mm.; 1.6 mm.; 1.55–1.85 mm. After careful laboratory checks the measurements when summarized are:

Outer envelope 3.8–7 mm., merging more or less into the general glutinous mass; inner envelope 2.8–4.0 mm.; mode 3.0 mm.; average 3.45 mm.; vitellus, 1.4–2.0 mm., mode, 1.8 mm., average 1.7 mm. Egg complement, 8,000 to 15,000.

In the possession of inner envelope the egg of *Rana grylio* appears more like that of *Rana clamitans* than that of *Rana catesbeiana*.

Dangers. Sometimes one can see a spoiled mass very readily. On May 28, 1921 "in a pond southwest of the boys' swimming hole found at the surface of the water amongst pickerel weed (*Pontederia*) and lizard's tail (*Saururus*) a mass of *R. grylio* eggs. I saw it some distance away because of the bluish appearance of spoiled eggs. Sometimes a mass is revealed by a few eggs dried or drying above the water on an iris or pickerel weed stem. Occasionally the cypress ponds raise considerably after eggs are laid and some of the films may be 3–8 inches below the surface. The most serious condition is where sudden sinkings of level leave eggs attached far out of the water. Where most of the eggs are laid, namely, on the prairies the loss probably is not so serious as in isolated habitats. I know of no animal enemies which feed on the eggs.

HATCHING PERIOD

The eggs of the morning of May 24 were about hatching on that date. If they were laid on the night of May 21–22 or on that of May 20–21 we would have 56 to 78 hours elapsing previous to hatching. On May 21 on Billy's Lake one of the boys found fresh eggs in the afternoon. Those eggs found May 24 were probably laid at the same time or about 78–80 hours after deposition. With temperatures of 65–95° obtaining it is easy to expect that 2–3 days would be a normal period for these surface eggs. Often in shallow water or surface water at this time the temperatures were 85–90°.

MATURE TADPOLE

Color description from life. Belly is between citron yellow and pale lemon yellow or lemon yellow with a prominent reticulation of brownish black. On the sides the lemon yellow spots are surrounded sometimes by pinkish vinaceous or orange vinaceous, or coral pink. All the throat region back to the pectoral region is a clear black. Across the pectoral region is apple green or light bice green. On either side of the throat and below the eye and over the snout and in front of nostril are spots of belly color. Over the back overlaying black spots and between them is forest green or dark green or elm green. When a tadpole is young it has a pinkish vinaceous line of spots or stripe on the upper jaw to be.

Tail. The lemon yellow spots on the sides are also on the base of the muscular part of the tail as more or less rounded spot with more prominent pinkish vinaceous. About an inch from the base of the muscular part the spotting goes along on to the middle of the muscular part for an inch or less as a long band of pinkish vinaceous or as a row of spots. Below this band are some rounded pinkish vinaceous spots like the band. Those extend on to the lower crest. More or less of a long black line of spots above this pinkish vinaceous band. This black line starts in the middle of the muscular part but as it approaches the tip of the tail it bends down toward the muscular black line. Upper crest with no yellow or whitish spots. Lower crest with many spots for first two inches.

Pupil yellow or bronzy-rimmed. Iris flecked all over with bronzy. Background of iris purplish. One looked greenish like the body color.

General appearance. Tadpole quite large (100 mm.) with black gular area and speckled belly which is so heavily pigmented the intestine does not show through in preserved specimens. Ventral contour narrower than in *R. catesbeiana* and more of the *R. clamitans* type. Tail elongate, tip sharply acuminate. Dorsal crest at widest part about equal or slightly less than width of musculature, and extending on to dorsum slightly ahead of the vertical through the buds of the hind legs. Spiracle sinistral, just visible from the dorsal aspect, obliquely directed upwards and backwards, opening elliptical but little revealed from side. Spiracle opening just touches lateral axis (muscular axis). Eye on or just above lateral axis.

Anus, dextral, opening at edge of ventral aspect.

Muciferous crypts present but rather indistinct, this species easily separated from *R. clamitans* in this regard.

Mouth parts: Teeth 2/3. Edge of upper labium about equal or slightly longer than the length of the upper horny beak, and fringed by a continuous row of teeth. In either corner, beneath this fringe is only one very short row about one-sixth to one-eighth of the length of the upper fringe. Median space between these two short rows is two and one-half to four and one-half times the length of either of these rows. The outer end of the second upper row does not extend beyond the end of the upper fringe of teeth. The third lower labial row of teeth much shorter than the single separate row of papillae, much more than length of horny beak (contained 1½ times in it) and 1/3 shorter than the second or first lower rows of teeth. These two rows about equal to horny beak in length and equal to each other. The first row may be continuous or interrupted in the middle. In mouth parts it is distinctly of the *R. clamitans* type and nearer this species than *R. catesbeiana*.

Measurements. Length of body (31.0–35.6 mm.) in tail (55.0–70.5 mm.) 1.7–2.4, average 1.84; width (17–22 mm.) of body in its own length 1.5–2.15, average 1.8. Depth (14–20 mm.) of body equal to (1.0) or slightly less (.8–.9) than body width. Depth of body 1.5–2.55 in body length, average 1.98. Depth (17–23 mm.) of tail in length of tail, 1.45–1.8, average 1.7. Depth of tail 1.05–1.5 deeper than depth of body, average 1.2. Muscular part (9.5–14.5 mm.) contained in depth of tail 1.3–1.7, average 1.5; in smaller specimens 1.75–2.1. Spiracle 1.1–1.6 nearer base of hind legs or vent region (13–19 mm.) than the tip of the snout. Spiracle 1.25–1.9 nearer eye than base of hind legs or vent, average 1.56. Eye 1–1.35 nearer to tip of snout (7–10 mm.) than to spiracle (8–12.5 mm.); in some younger tadpoles occasionally near (.88–.95) spiracle. Nostril 1.0–1.4 nearer snout than eye, rarely equidistant. Mouth (4–6 mm.) usually 1.–1.6 larger than internasal space (3.6–5.5 mm.), average 1.15. Mouth contained 1.5–2.37 (average 1.94) in interorbital distance (7–12.0 mm.). Internasal space contained in interorbital space 1.8–2.6, average 2.16.

The dimensions of the largest tadpole are:

	mm.		mm.
Total length	100.0	Spiracle to vent	19.0
Body length	36.6	Spiracle to eye	10.0
Body depth	20.	Eye to snout	9.8
Body width	22.0	Eye to nostril	5.0
Tail length	64.4	Nostril to snout	3.5
Tail depth	23.0	Mouth	5.5
Musculature of tail	13.5	Interorbital distance	11.0
Spiracle to snout	21.5	Internasal distance	5.5

General remarks. The large tadpoles are difficult of capture. Usually it is impossible to haul a minnow seine where they occur. Occasionally when a cypress pond dries up, they can be caught in the centrally cleared space, the normal alligator hole of the pond. Rarely one catches them in the scoops of a dip net and smaller stages frequently come in the floating maiden cane masses we often pull over the gunwale into the boat. Rarely one chances on shallow water areas cut off from cypress ponds, and in these localities we had our best luck. We found few mature tadpoles.

LARVAL PERIOD

On August 3 and 4, we found in two different ponds "plenty of *R. grylio* tadpoles of two different sizes. Does it stay two years as a tadpole or only one year as in *R. clamitans*? Some of them seem still to retain a black rim on the lower crest ridge." Our largest *R. grylio* tadpole reaches 100 mm. and transformation ranges from 43–51 mm. *Rana catesbeiana* tadpoles may reach 140 mm. and transform at 43–59 mm. *Rana clamitans* tadpoles may reach 84 mm. and transform at 28–38 mm. *R. septentrionalis* tadpoles may reach 99 mm. and transform at 29–40 mm. In the north *R. catesbeiana* takes two years for transformation but some *Rana catesbeiana* sent by Viosca to Japan developed in one year of tadpole life. Do those of Louisiana do the same? If so possibly *Rana grylio* may transform after one year of tadpole life. It may take two years in some instances even in Gulf Coast environment. Some of the *Rana clamitans* 70–84 mm. tadpoles winter over to transform at 28–38 mm. Then possibly to attain greater growth *R. grylio* may take a slightly longer period. In the South generally development progresses faster and breeding periods are longer. For example, in the Northern States we would be surprised to have *R. catesbeiana* breed in February as it did in San Antonio parks February 1925.

TRANSFORMATION

Period. In 1912 we had "only one transformed specimen which measures 44 mm. It was taken May 30, 1912, from the stomach of a snake."

In 1921 we found a transformed frog April 24.

On April 25, 1921, we caught a young recently transformed *R. grylio* amongst the *Pontederia*. Later caught a second with a stub of a tail present.

In a cypress pond which had almost dried up we found transformed southern bullfrogs. In the center was a small circular water area. "Around this small pool was a large moist mud flat where a pig was rooting up frogs, etc. Underneath the mats or carpets of grass which originally was in the water found little transformed *R. grylio* in small moist pockets dug in the mud. With them were *Manculus quadridigitatus*, a salamander, a ring-neck snake (*Diadophis punctatus*) and a skink. In the pool were pygmy sunfishes (*Elassoma*) tadpoles of *Rana sphenocephala* and water beetles. Florida Blue Herons and Florida Grackles as well as the pigs were having a feast at this pond." No doubt the young southern bullfrogs suffered.

On May 6, 1921, Dave Lee "caught three *R. grylios* of three sizes from Billy's Lake: 1 transformed; one intermediate; and one adult male." On May 9 two more were taken; on May 10 we saw plenty of small southern bullfrogs in one pond. On June 1 we saw several just transformed southern bullfrogs in a pond outside the swamp. On June 15 we had some tadpoles transform. On June 19 we have a record of one transformation. Beside the above notes from our Journal we have the following dates for transformation: May 1, June 20, July 11, July 19.

In 1921 our dates extend from April 24–July 19.

In 1922 on June 14 when we arrived at Chesser Island, there were several transformed frogs found. In the same place two weeks later we still found transformation in process.

Size. In 1920 we held "Some of the southern bullfrog tadpoles may transform in the very last of May and the minimum size recorded is 1 3/4 inches." The transformation size of our lone specimen of 1912 measured 44 mm. At the same time May 30 we secured another specimen 53 mm. in length of body. In 1921 we have the following measurements: On April 24, we have two transformed at 43 mm. (C. U. 266) and 51 mm. (C. U. 265). On April 25, two were captured and measured 48 and 47 mm. respectively. Another of April 25 measured 53 mm. but it is, however, past transformation. On April 26 one (C. U. 213) measures 43 mm. One was captured May 6 but is not at hand. Another (C. U. 291) found June 19 is 45 mm.

Besides the above notes from our Journal we have the following specimens: May 1, two at 37 and 39 mm. respectively; June 15, one at 32 mm. transforming but progress not completed; July 11, two at 38 and 47 mm. respectively; and July 19 two at 41 and 43 mm. respectively.

In 1922 we secured transformed individuals as follows: June 14, one at 49 mm., July 17 one at 42 mm.

In general in 1912 we have a 44 mm. specimen; in 1921 specimens from 32–48 mm.; in 1922 specimens from 42–49 mm. The measurements of 32–49 mm. about represents the size at transformation, although we believe the 32 mm. rather small for a normal *R. grylio* transformation. This places this species intermediate between the transformation size (28–38 mm., average (Ithaca) 3.2 mm.) size of *Rana clamitans* and the size (43–59 mm., average 53 mm. (Ithaca) of *Rana catesbeiana*.

General remarks. When the hind legs are well formed the upper fringe is generally gone and the upper lateral ridge of teeth also, but some of the lower labial teeth may yet be retained.

These young frogs after transformation stay in the same habitat as the adults. We captured them by hand at night with flashlight amongst the bonnets of cypress ponds. Occasionally they could be caught along the maiden cane edges with a dip net and torch light. On July 7, 1922, we found many of the young ones in the shade of the small wooded islets (houses) of the prairies. They would start off with a startled cry as one approached and in this respect reminded one of young *Rana catesbeiana*.

On May 14, 1921, at 8 p.m. we found plenty of the young transformed frogs and somewhat larger young frogs resting on the sphagnum mat or vegetation of a cypress pond and caught several of them by hand.

On July 17, 1921, on Chesser Island we took a 40 mm. *Rana grylio*. Two days later in the same place we caught a mature male *R. virgatipes* (vocal sacs and thumb developed) of 43 mm. They looked very much alike but the fourth toe character separates them. The male *R. virgatipes* has a more pointed head, much thicker legs, broader body and heavier darker ventral spots with larger white interspaces. The dark speckled or spotted venters are typical of transformation size in *R. grylio, R. catesbeiana, R. clamitans* and *R. virgatipes* and as growth begins all come to have venters with larger dark spots with larger light interspaces. In *R. virgatipes* the 2nd finger is equal to or less than the first finger, in *R. grylio* the second finger is usually larger than the first finger.

GROWTH

Of the 1912 collection we wrote as follows: We have only one transformed specimen which measures 44 mm. It was taken May 30, 1912, from the stomach of a snake. A specimen taken May 30, 1912, on Honey Island measures 53 mm. and doubtless represents a year old, while another taken at the same time and measuring 72 mm. looks to be a two year old. Another taken June 15, 1912 on Billy's Island measures 88 mm. or one from Floyd's Island June 26, 1912, measures 88 mm. These doubtless are three year olds. Three others taken in the same summer measure 96.5–101 and easily are four years old. These measurements 44, 53, 72, 88, 96.5–101 fairly well represent the growth for 4 years after transformation.

Some of our records for 1921 follow: On April 24 and 25 we secured seven specimens 100, 92, 95, 82, 50, 44, 44 mm. respectively, the last two at 44 mm., being transformed individuals. They seem to fall into 4 groups 100, 92–95, 82, 44–50. From April 22–May, 6 sizes: one female 112 mm.; two males of 99 and 100 mm. respectively; two males 94–97 mm. respectively; one female 83 mm.; another 77 mm.; and two transforming at 37 and 39 mm. Those taken May 10–23 fall into three groups: one at 91 mm., the next group with 86, 77, 76 mm. respectively; the last group with 58, 62 mm. respectively. June 15–20, 1921, we have transformed example 46 mm. and one 73 mm. Specimens taken July 11–19 are 38, 41, 43, 47, 61, 67, 67 mm. respectively or of two groups.

In 1922 from June 14–August 9 we took specimens 42, 49, 56, 60, 61, 69, 80, 84, 84 mm. in length.

The 1921–1922 material seems to fall into the following groups:

(1)   32–49 mm., average 41 mm. tranformation.
(2)   56–69 mm.,   ”   62.5 mm. one-year-olds.
(3)   73–86 mm.,   ”   80 mm. two-year-olds.
(4)   91–102 mm.,   ”   96 mm. three-year-olds.
(5)   107–115 mm.,   ”   112 mm. four-year-olds.

This species may reach 150 mm. Dr. Stejneger's type (U. S. N. M. No. 27443 is 125 mm. and U. S. N. M. No. 30951 is 148 mm.).

Since this paragraph was written we have examined some specimens Dr. Barbour has. Some of these are as follows 120 mm. ♂, 125 mm. ♀, 136 mm. ♂, 143 mm. ♀, 161 mm. ♀ and 161 mm. ♀. These are bigger than any others in collections. The author, however, has also seen equally large individuals in the Okefinokee Swamp.

FOOD

We have not examined the sixty of more individuals we have for food.   I know of no records in print.

ENEMIES

On the basis of our 1912 specimens we wrote: Out on the open prairies the southern water snake (*Natrix fasciatus fasciatus*) is a bitter foe of the southern bullfrog.   One water snake had taken nearly two transformed frogs of this species.   Along the bonnet "runs" the moccasin and pied water snake make life miserable for these frogs.   Among the birds, the herons, and ibises relish them.   We have not examined our snakes, turtles or fish of the 1921 and 1922 collections and are unable to determine which fed on southern bullfrogs.

AUTUMNAL DISAPPEARANCE

If it be like a bullfrog in the South, it will spend four or five months in hibernation.   The months from November 1–March 1 or later are doubtless usually inactive for the species.   In some cases they go into hibernation before November 1 or come out before or after March 1 as does *Rana catesbeiana*. For example, I have heard *Rana catesbeiana* croaking in the first or second week of February in Texas.

AFFINITIES

Indirectly Dr. Stejneger indicates the affinities of *Rana grylio* with *Rana catesbeiana* by the title of his paper "A New Species of Bullfrog from Florida and the Gulf Coast."   In diagnosis he pronounces it "Similar to *Rana catesbeiana*, but with the fourth toe much shorter in proportion; the third toe, measured from the inner metatarsal tubercle, being more than three and one-half times the difference between the third and fourth toes."   Further in his description he says:

"These differences in the relative length of the toes, being capable of the most concise definition, have been utilized primarily for the characterization of the new species, but there are numerous other features which prove it to be very distinct from *R. catesbeiana*.   Thus, for instance, the snout is much shorter and less high, so that the nostrils appear to be nearer the tip of the mouth; the head is also narrower behind; the vomerine teeth are very close together, with hardly any space between two patches; the tongue is much less broader and thinner, with remarkably long and thin 'horns,' which are very far apart; the color is apparently much darker brown, though there may be *R. catesbeiana* nearly as dark.   Add to this the difference in voice and we have clearly one of the most distinct species of frog in the United States."

"The general habitus of *R. grylio* is that of *Rana catesbeiana*, including the large tympanum and the absence of a dorso-lateral glandular fold.   It is also a large frog, though whether it reaches the extreme size of *R. catesbeiana* may be doubted."

In 1914 R. F. Deckert holds it to be "a beautiful frog closely related to the common bullfrog," while Miss Dickerson calls it a frog "really very different in appearance from the common bullfrog, not resembling it in shape, propor-

Plate XXXVIII

River-swamp frog (*Rana heckscheri*)

1. Thompson's Landing, St. Mary's River, Ga. July 9, 1922.
2. 3. Mature tadpoles, Alligator swamp, Callahan, Fla. August 18, 1922. × 1.0.
4. Mature frog, small size, 56 mm. Alligator swamp, Callahan, Fla. August 17, 1922. Lateral aspect. × 0.75.
5. Mature frog, large size, 95 mm. Alligator swamp, Callahan, Fla. August 17, 1922. Lateral aspect. × 0.66.
6. Mature frog, large size, 95 mm. Alligator swamp, Callahan, Fla. August 17, 1922. Ventral aspect. × 0.5.

1

2   3

4

5   6

tions of body or coloring. The long narrow, pointed head, with its large eyes set close together, tell the story at once. But other evidences lie in the ratio of the lengths of head and body (. . .), in the greater length of toes (except the fourth) (. . .), and in the finely pitted texture of the skin. In addition to all these points, there is that of coloration. . . . *Rana grylio* shows close relationship to *Rana virgatipes* of New Jersey in shape and proportion, metallic coloring, texture of skin, large size of eyes and ears, in lacking the lateral folds, and in aquatic habits."

In 1914 the author in the light of his 1912 experiences with *Rana grylio* made the following unfinished memoranda: "In many ways *Rana grylio* approaches *Rana virgatipes*. Like the latter it has on the posterior faces of the hind limbs alternating horizontal bands of dark and light colors. The general mottlings of the venters and the coloration of the hind limbs to toe tips are almost duplicate. The webbing of the hind toes is more or less similarly mottled. The fore limbs of *Rana grylio* are more or less unicolor without the characteristic dark anterior faces of *R. virgatipes*. Both have no dorsolateral glandular folds. The four dorsal stripes of *R. virgatipes* are missing in *R. grylio* and *R. virgatipes* has two phalanges of the fourth toe free." In 1924 (p. 141) in discussing *Rana heckscheri* we held "These southern bullfrogs or 'Joe Browns' are very distinct in adult, tadpole and egg characters from the bullfrog, *Rana catesbeiana*."

In 1916 Dr. T. Barbour writes: "I think our familiarity with *Rana grylio*, the big frog found swimming among the 'bonnets' in some of the Florida lakes, has made this frog's relationship to the New Jersey sphagnum frog seem doubly striking, for their coloration in life is astonishingly similar, and in fact one seems to be but a miniature representative of the other."

In 1920 Dr. Boulenger (p. 425) thought *Rana catesbeiana* and *Rana grylio* near the intermediate form from which the other *Ranas* of North American come rather than from *Rana septentrionalis* (Cope's belief).

Rana grylio adults surely, as Dr. Barbour states, seem big editions of *Rana virgatipes* in general coloration and general habitus. A young transformed *Rana grylio* might more quickly be confused with an adult or half-grown *Rana virgatipes* than with any other species of *Rana*. Their ranges overlap in the Okefinokee. Both are very aquatic species and *Rana virgatipes* might be held the northern offshoot. Usually we say *R. grylio* has not the two or four lateral yellow brown or golden streaks on the body as has *Rana virgatipes*. But I have seen several recently transformed *R. grylios* with light streaks from eye backward where a dorsolateral fold would be if present. And Viosca (1918, p. 161) writes "Four lighter longitudinal bands of orange brown are sometimes discernible on the back, especially in young specimens."

In egg mass it has a film like *Rana catesbeiana* and *R. clamitans*, but in egg characters it has an inner envelope of jelly like *Rana clamitans*. In tadpole the body seems more like *Rana clamitans* but in size it is midway between *R. clamitans* and *R. catesbeiana*. In mouth parts it is more of the *R. clamitans* type. In transformation it occupies a median position between the two species. It belongs in the *Rana clamitans-catesbeiana* group with close affinities also for *R. virgatipes*.

BIBLIOGRAPHY

1916 Barbour, T. Copeia, Jan. 24, 1916, No. 26, p. 6.
1920 Barbour, T. Copeia, July 31, 1920, No. 84, p. 55.
1791 Bartram, William. Travels through North and South Carolina, Georgia, East and West Florida, etc. Phila., pp. 276, 277.
1920 Boulenger, G. A. Am. Acad. Arts Sci., Vol. 55, No. 9, August, 1920, pp. 415, 421, 422.
1914 Deckert, R. F. Copeia, Feb. 14, 1914, No. 3.
1914 ———. Copeia, April 15, 1914, No. 5.
1921 ———. Copeia, Mar. 15, 1921, No. 92, p. 20.
1922 ———. Copeia, Nov. 20, 1922, No. 112, p. 88.
1906 Dickerson, M. C. The Frog Book, N. Y., pp. 226-227. Plates LXXXV, LXXXVI.
1922 Löding, H. P. Geo. Survey Ala Mus. Paper No. 5, p. 20.
1923 Pratt, H. S. 1923, p. 183.
1901 Stejneger, L. Proc. U. S. Nat. Mus. XXIV, 1901, pp. 211-215.
1918 Viosca, Percy, Jr. 3rd Biennial Rept. La. Dept. Conserv. pp. 161, 162.
1923 ———. Copeia, Feb. 1, 1923, No. 115, pp. 39, 43.
1920 Wright, A. H. U. S. Bur. of Fisheries Rept., 1919, Doc. No. 888, pp. 10, 19, 21, 26, 34.
1923 Wright, A. H. Copeia, Feb. 1, No. 115, p. 34.
1924 ———. Proc. Biol. Soc. Wash. Vol. 37, pp. 141-152.
1923 Wright, A. H. and A. A. Wright. The Anatomical Record Vol. 24, No. 6, Jan. 20, 1923, p. 406.
1924 ———. Am. Naturalist, Vol. LVIII, July-August, 1924, pp. 376, 377, 379.

Rana heckscheri Wright

(Pl. III, Fig. 4; XI, Figs. 7, 8; XIV, Figs. 1, 2; XVII; XXXVIII)

COMMON NAMES

Greenback. Heckscher's Frog. River Swamp Frog

RANGE

Check list. Described since Stejneger & Barbour's 2nd edition.

Supplementary records. The type locality where first recognized (1922) is Alligator Swamp, Callahan, Florida. The known range is from Savannah, Georgia to Fargo (on Suwannee River) and Folkston (near St. Mary's River) in Georgia, all along the St. Mary's River on both Georgia and Florida sides and in Florida to Callahan. In 1928, June 9 and 10, we visited the type locality and also found them in Mr. Davis's clay pit. It ought to be farther north along the coastal strip to Wilmington and westward to Louisiana.

In American Museum of Natural History we found three specimens taken by T. Hallinan. One, a male (No. 16096), 95 mm. long, was taken at East-port, Florida and two more, males (Nos. 16666-67) 97 and 91 mm. long were secured near Jacksonville, Florida.

In a recent letter (Nov., 1929) Mr. O. C. Van Hyning writes me that he has found 12 miles from Gainesville, Florida, at Waldo, some tadpoles of *Rana heckscheri*. His captures he compared with some freshly caught tadpoles of *Rana heckscheri* which I left with him at Gainesville, Florida in June 1928. In June 1928 we captured many intermediate sizes of this species but these like some of the 1922 specimens are now missing.

Since the three preceding paragraphs have been written two more records have come in recent letters. On August 19, 1931, Mr. O. C. Hyning who had formerly found this species in Georgia west of Okefinokee Swamp in 1930, writes that "he has a *Rana heckscheri* adult from 2 miles east of Gaines-

ville, Florida." On August 15, 1931, Morrow J. Allen, of the Caribbean
Biological Laboratories, Biloxi, Mississippi, sends me "under separate cover
two specimens of a tadpole that were taken last month in the overflow of a
stream along with about 25 others. I have never seen this tadpole before
and ask if you will give me the identification. I notice that the plate of the
tadpole of *Rana heckscheri* in your synopsis of North American tadpoles somewhat resembles it." They are *Rana heckscheri* tadpoles.

Local Okefinokee records. No adult specimens have been taken within the
swamp.

GENERAL APPEARANCE

It looks like a big *Rana clamitans* with melanistic and sulphur venter. It
has more rough dorsum than *Rana clamitans*, *Rana catesbeiana* or *Rana grylio*.

COLORATION OF SPIRIT SPECIMENS (1922)

In spirits, four 95 mm. males of four species are as follows: bister or mummy
brown on dorsum of *R. catesbeiana*, brownish olive in *R. grylio*, deep grayish
olive in *R. clamitans*, and deep mouse gray in *R. heckscheri*; upper parts without very distinct dark spots in *R. clamitans* and *R. catebeiana*, with prominent
large black spots in *R. grylio*, and with many small dark spots *R. heckscheri*;
venter of *R. clamitans* clear white except for the yellow throat, venter of *R.
catesbeiana* heavily blotched with black, so also in *R. grylio*—all three, however, with a white background color but in *R. heckscheri* the deep mouse gray
or dark color so prominent it becomes the background color and the white,
scattering spots; light spots on upper and lower jaws more prominent than in
R. clamitans. Throat in males prominently deep mouse gray, deep neutral
gray or violet slate while female's throat is whitish.

MEASUREMENTS
(Recent Material)

Head to angle of mouth 1.2 (36 mm.)—1.25 (44 mm.)—1.2 (56 mm.)—
1.31 (82 mm. ♂)—1.17 (95 mm. ♂)—1.2 (113 mm. ♂—1.16 (125 mm. ♀)
in width of head; head to rear of tympanum 1.0–.93–1.04–1.11–1.08–1.09–1.09
in width of head; head to angle of mouth 3.0–3.–3.66–2.8–2.82–2.71–2.82–3.0
in length of body; head to rear of tympanum 2.5–2.75–2.43–2.41–2.5–2.56–2.9
in length of body; snout .84–1.0–.9–.71–.69–1.0–1.05 in fourth finger; snout
1.0–1.35–.8–.78–.81–1.06–1.05 in first toe; eye 1.4–1.07–1.43–1.55–1.6–1.36–
1.4 in snout; eye .60–.54–.70–1.3–1.3–1.36–.85 in tympanum; eye 1.2–1.08–
1.3–1.33–1.3–1.36–1.4 in first finger; tympanum 3.66–3.86–3.1–1.5–1.61–.53–
2.2 in intertympanic width; tympanum 2.33–2.0–2.0–1.16–1.23–1.0–1.65 in
snout; internasal width 1.0–.9–1.08–1.43–1.07–1.0–1.0 in upper eyelid width;
interorbital width 1.0–1.0–2.0–1.14–.83–1.36–1.2 in upper eyelid width;
interorbital width 1.0–1.11–1.83–1.0–.77–1.36–1.2 in internasal width; interorbital width 2.75–3.0–5.16–2.57–2.33–1.3–3.25 in intertympanic width.

Forelimb: 2.0–2.0–1.93–2.34–2.0–2.5–2.2 in length (snout to vent); forelimb
2.72–2.9–2.9–3.4–2.83–3.5–2.8 in hind limb; first finger 1.33–1.43–1.11–1.08–

1.23–1.23–1.3 in third finger; second finger 1.0–1.0–1.375–1.18–1.09–1.06–1.05 in first finger; third finger 1.125–1.3–1.2–1.36–1.3–1.3–1.16 in second toe; fourth finger 1.16–1.35–1.14–1.1–1.18–1.06–1.0 in first toe; fourth finger 1.33–1.43–1.42–1.1–1.45–1.23–1.2 in third finger; internasal width 1.5–1.4–1.63–1.71–1.85–1.8–2.0 in first finger; 1.5–1.4–1.36–1.57–1.71–1.7–1.9 in second finger; 2.0–2.0–1.8–1.85–2.3–2.2–2.5 in third finger; 1.5–1.4–1.27–1.43–1.57–1.8–2.1 in fourth finger.

Hindlimb: length 1.36–1.46–1.5–1.45–1.4–1.4–1.28 in hind limb; tibia 2.5–1.9–1.93–2.0–2.11–2.0–2.17 in length; tibia 2.8–2.7–2.89–2.9–2.95–2.86–2.7 in hind limb; tibia 1.03–.95–1.0–.853–1.04–.80–.96 in forelimb; tibia 1.03–1.0–1.03–1.04–1.06–.93–.95 in hind foot; first toe 1.26–1.45–1.5–1.63–1.61–1.5–1.4 in second toe; 1.85–1.84–1.87–2.72–1.84–2.1–2.1 in third toe; 2.57–2.2–3.37–3.45–3.23–2.9–2.7 in fourth toe; 1.8–1.7–2.25–2.63–2.3–2.1–2.0 in fifth toe; second toe 1.44–1.27–1.41–1.61–1.14–1.4–1.5 in third toe; 2.0–1.6–2.25–2.11–2.0–1.9–1.9 in fourth toe; 1.4–1.23–1.5–1.55–1.42–1.4–1.4 in fifth toe; third toe 1.38–1.2–1.59–1.31–1.75–1.4–1.2 in fourth toe; .96–.91–1.06–.96–1.25–1.0–.95 in fifth toe; fourth toe 1.0–1.1–1.11–1.13–1.14–1.0–1.02 in hind foot; .97–1.1–1.07–1.07–1.07–1.07–1.07 in tibia; 1.0–1.05–1.07–.92–1.12–.86–1.04 in forelimb; fifth toe 1.44–1.31–1.5–1.35–1.4–1.37–1.35 in fourth toe; internasal width 1.75–1.9–1.45–1.57–1.85–1.9–2.1 in first toe; 2.25–2.6–2.18–2.57–3.0–2.85–3.0 in second toe; 3.25–3.5–3.08–4.14–3.43–4.0–4.4 in third toe; 4.5–4.2–4.9–5.43–6.0–5.47–5.7 in fourth toe; 3.12–3.2–3.2–4.0–4.3–4.0–4.2 on fifth toe.

HABITAT

It seems to be a frog of the swampy edges of rivers and streams, a truly fluviatile species.

On August 18, 1922, with a light we captured eight or ten frogs of various sizes from probably one year frogs to full sized adults. We found them in shrubbery and on the banks about the bases of trees. More were captured than lost. They were rather awkward in their escape and would tumble off from their perches. Later in the evening we lost all but three of our capture.

If this were truly a wooded river swamp species, it is hard to explain its presence in the brickyard clay hole in Callahan. It is only a short block from Alligator Swamp, the type locality. Either they were introduced or they invaded the place from the nearby Alligator Swamp. The clay hole is immense in breadth, artificial, yet it is becoming already very swampy in character. These pools have waterlilies, arrowhead (*Sagittaria*), water hyacinth, water pennywort (*Hydrocotyle*) and countless other water plants. Some of the residents told us that when ditches for the clay hole were dug they were absolutely crowded with seething masses of black tadpoles which must be the larvae of this species. No other tadpole is so distinctive in the eastern U.S.A.

Outside and inside the swamp. On the western edge of the swamp the day we entered the swamp in 1912 (last of May) "We secured a frog which puzzled us. We saw it only for a few moments. We soon lost it in the rigors of the trip." It was a fine male of *Rana heckscheri*. We have no positive specimen from within the swamp.

GENERAL HABITS

Two journal notes of 1928 (June 8) reveal some of its habits and its habitat.

"June 8 . . . This afternoon went to type locality of *Rana heckscheri*. . . . Went along in pickerel weed (*Pontederia*) on the east side of the bridge (Dixie Highway) where it is shady. 5 p.m. Finally saw a large frog. Slowly approached from water side with net in right hand and came close enough to catch the frog with the left hand. Started skirting several edges. Soon saw another on the bank amongst pickerel weeds. Crawled towards it on my hands and knees and caught it. It squealed as do some greenfrogs, bullfrogs or southern bullfrogs when caught. The children went along and startled another which gave a startled note of the *Rana catesbeiana* type. Another big frog amongst pickerel weed on land and not at water's edge. It leaped along and into the water before I could capture it. Some three or four lost, partially because six children trailed along in their anxiety to help. . . . Mrs. Wright thinks it a different frog. These two frogs we captured are larger than the three we secured in 1922. They are bigger than any greenfrog. They have no costal folds. Saw no intermediate sizes."

"June 8. . . Went out tonight to the type locality of *Rana heckscheri*. Saw a female near the edge of *Pontederia* bank. Later heard a big frog jump in. When I approached that area, found a male, a arge one on the bank, amongst vegetation and not at water's edge. Saw and took another female. Later in going down a little run where we frightened a *Rana heckscheri*, heard a male *Rana clamitans*. Then the boys called me for a large frog they saw. It proved a female *Rana grylio*. Went back after the male *R. clamitans*. Just before I reached it, in the water resting on a submerged log was a fine male *Rana heckscheri*. In the shade of trees on the bank was the croaking male green frog. Small for *Rana clamitans* but it croaks. It is different from *Rana heckscheri*, so also is the *Rana grylio* female I caught here. This *Rana heckscheri* is not *Rana catesbeiana* though we have not caught the latter here."

This species is not so dextrous as some of its related species. Some of the boys reported "lots of them. We catch them by hook and with sticks."

VOICE

The discovery of the adults came in this fashion. On August 18, 1922, we visited Alligator Swamp at Callahan, Florida, because of some curious large tadpoles we saw there one month earlier. "Mrs. Wright discovered a queer looking green frog as she supposed and as she was calling to us we were startled by a call unlike any other *Rana* we ever had heard. To one it was a snore, to another a snort, and to others neither. The queer green frog and the author of the call proved of the same species and not green frogs of which we captured some for comparison."

Mr. F. Harper, while traveling down the St. Mary's River in August, 1921, "heard a number of times, in addition to the regular snoring call, a peculiar explosive snarling grunt." Then he associated the call with *Rana aesopus* but now he believes it this species. He heard it from August 10 or 11–17 early

in morning, in mid forenoon, at noon, and in late afternoon, or from about
Moniac to Camp Pinckney.

In 1928 on the afternoon of June 8, we did not hear the regular call of this
species in the type locality. Only the squeal of a captured frog and the
startled note of an escaping frog did we record. In the evening of June 9 "in
the brick yard pools heard no end of *Rana grylio*, two deep notes. Once in a
while we would hear the snoring notes (3 or 4 of them) of *Rana heckscheri*."
Certainly the calls were sporadic and this exact period was not a breeding
season for the species.

MATING

Male (From life, August 18, 1922). General dorsal color citrine drab to
grayish olive becoming on top and sides of head and center of tympanum
dark olive buff, isabella color or cinnamon brown. Ear drum except middle
mummy brown. On back of body and on head and on some of the sides is
some serpentine green. Under parts spotted white with glaucous gray or
light Payne's gray or pale drab on throat and breast. Throat with a little
citron green or deep chrysolite green. Spots on lower jaw rim four or five, seafoam yellow, to deep colonial buff in the spot just back of the angle of the
mouth. This spot except above surrounded by black.

Black spot just below angle of mouth to and across the insertion of the
brachium. Three black spots on the front edge of the antebrachium. Rear
of fore legs black to tips of fingers and webs. Tops of the fingers with seafoam
yellow or deep colonial buff spots.

Narrow black bars across the dorsum of the femur, tibia and hind foot.
Rear of femur with white unconnected spots on the bone brown ground color.
Rear edge of hind foot to tip of fourth and fifth toes black.

Iris outside rim bright green-yellow, inner rim capucine orange; and interval black with orange rufous spots.

A younger specimen 65 mm. long is dark olive or deep olive on entire upper
parts and very warty. Throat is deep grayish olive.

Two green frogs from the same place were: one, a female, dark olive buff
uniform; and a smaller one wood brown to avellaneous uniform; back of eye
and side of head and over angle of mouth apple green. Bars on hind legs
absent in female, scanty in smaller specimens. Both with costal folds.

Male (From life, June 10, 1928). Back, top of head, top of fore legs and
hind legs citrine or buffy citrine. Under parts white spotted with olivaceous
black (3) or in lights becoming pale olive gray. So also on under sides of fore
arms and hind legs. Rear of femur with spotting of white or pale vinaceous
fawn. Not in lines of white as in *Rana grylio*.

Throat with wash of oil yellow or sulphine yellow on a light mineral gray
background. Edge of lower jaw with light spots of white, pale chalcedony
yellow or cartridge buff. Back of angle of mouth and below tympanum is a
spot of light greenish yellow or pale chalcedony yellow. Another one back of
the first. Beginning at angle of mouth an oblique area of black or light
vinaceous drab extends to arm insertion, around it into axilla. A branch goes
up back of tympanum. Rear of forearm has area of same on dorsum. Webs

cloudy with black or olivaceous black (3) or light vinaceous drab. Lower sides mottled with black and light vinaceous fawn. Sides of face buffy brown. Tympanum olive brown or natal brown. Center circle buffy brown. A dark area in inguinal area.

Iris black dotted with orange rufous. Pupil rim cadmium yellow. Iris encircled by pale green-yellow or bright green-yellow.

When first caught very black and white beneath.

Another male is olive or dark greenish olive above.

Female (From life, June 10, 1928). Much the same as male but upper parts much more spotted with black. Head spotted. Tympanum with blotches of black or olivaceous black (3). Half bars on femur. Bar across arm insertion. Throat with no or little oil yellow or sulphine yellow. White spots or pale vinaceous fawn spots on rim of lower jaws prominent. Underparts not quite so spotted. Iris same as in male.

Young transformed frogs. (June 10, 1928). A young transformed frog has a prominent eye. Sometimes brick reddish. Often mars orange predominates over black and iris rim is orange rufous or brighter. Entire under parts finely speckled white and deep olive gray or deep grayish olive.

Structural differences. The male has very enlarged tympana, enlarged thumb and doubtless is much more intense in ventral coloration if the younger underdeveloped males be a criterion or index of the species type. Females and young undeveloped males more often agree in coloration. Most of these we lost and can remember them only as lighter in appearance. Probably the species is of the *R. clamitans* or *R. catesbeiana* type in amplexation. (1922).

The characters given in 1923 hold but in addition we discover that the males average somewhat smaller and rougher on the back and sides. Our eight adults (two of 1922 and six of 1928) are five males and three females. The males are 82, 95, 102, 110 and 113 mm. in body length and the females are 122, 123, and 125 mm. respectively.

Amplexation. We have no observation. The enlarged thumbs and all general assumptions or presumptions in the case point to a normal *Rana* embrace.

OVULATION

Habitat. See General Habits and particularly General remarks under Mature Tadpole.

Period. In 1922 we had no positive record of ovulation. Recalling the small tadpoles of June 16, 1912, the tadpoles of Aug. 7–16, 1921, and the small tadpoles of St. Mary's River July 17, 1922 we then thought the period might be from June 1 to July 1 or 5.

The previous paragraph of 1923 is now supplemented by the impressions of 1928 (June 8–10). There were transforming tadpoles, 80 or 85 mm.–100 mm., and some with leg buds slight or none from 80–70 mm. at the type locality. In the brickyard were transforming tadpoles and the small gold-banded tadpoles of three groups (10–15 mm., 20–25 mm., 30–35 mm.). These last three sizes indicate three breedings in the spring previous to June 1. Possibly they may be coincident with previous rainy periods in 1928 if there

were such and the period of ovulation extends from the last of April or May 1
to July 5 or 8. The voice records of June 8–10, 1928, Aug. 10–17, 1921, and
Aug. 18, 1922 might indicate breeding from June 8–Aug. 18. At none of these
periods were choruses heard. Of the three females taken June 8–10 one was
unspent and two spent. June 10 therefore is not past the ovulation period.
No doubt as in *Rana clamitans*, *R. catesbeiana* and *Rana grylio* this species
occasionally breeds in August.

EGGS

In 1922 we found on July 17 at Thompson landing, St. Mary's River
many small *R. heckscheri* tadpoles. Then we thought them *H. cinerea*. It
was not until a month later in another place we found large tadpoles and
adult frogs which evidence revealed that it was a new form, *R. heckscheri*.
Not until recently did we recall that in a nearby pool (20–30 ft.) away from
the place of the little *Rana heckscheri* tadpoles did we find (July 9) a large
film of eggs which we then interpreted as *Rana clamitans*. Besides a *Rana
clamitans* male was in this pool. This happened eight days before the discovery of the small tadpoles. We now label the photo. *Rana clamitans—
R. heckscheri* (?). They may have been the latter. One would expect it to
lay a film of many eggs. In 1923 (p. 406) we placed the tadpole under those
frogs which laid their eggs in films. It was a mistake to place them so positively. They should have been placed in a category of "eggs unknown". An
estimate of the eggs of the two ovaries of the unspent female (123 mm. long)
is 8000–6000. This complement is greater than that of *R. clamitans* but no
more than that of *Rana grylio* or *Rana catesbeiana*. The an mal pole is black;
the vegetative pole is white. The vitellus in diameter approximately ranges
from 1.5–2.0 mm. Not enough material is at hand to compare eggs carefully
with the above species. Mr. O. C. Van Hyning reports their eggs and adults
from Georgia in 1930.

MATURE TADPOLE

In 1923 (p. 406) we characterized the tadpole thus: "*Rana sp.*— black-
rimmed and black-banded tail, bluish venter, dorsum with greenish yellow
flecks."

Color description from life (July 21, 1922). Body dark greenish-olive or
olive, finely covered with pale green-yellow or pale greenish-yellow flecks or
spots on the dorsum. On venter they are vinaceous fawn, vinaceous cinnamon
or orange vinaceous. Just back of angle of mouth in a mature tadpole and on
the venter is a clump of 4 to 6 much larger spots. Lower belly pale forget-me-
not blue to upper belly and breast jay-blue, Chapman's blue or grayish
violaceous blue. Spots of black become thicker on lower belly and at times
almost touch or make patches of color. Lateral line pores very prominent on
the head and body.

Ventral half of muscular part of the tail light salmon orange or apricot
buff or vinaceous cinnamon or ochraceous salmon. Upper half of the muscular
part with a black band on caudal two-thirds and more or less merged into
body color at its basal third. The black bandlike effect is produced by oblique

bars of black where the myocommas are. These overshadow the intervening body color. Whole rim of tail or edge of crests black, least just in front of the vent.

Iris rim above and below orange cinnamon, tawny vinaceous, tawny or orange rufous or better vinaceous rufous. Iris rim in front and behind pupil black.

General appearance. Tadpole quite large (97 mm.), usually black of body, and the most striking of all our (U. S.) *Rana* tadpoles. Belly pigmented so intestine does not show through in preserved specimens. Tail elongate, tip acuminate; dorsal crest not as wide as musculature width; not much different from lower crest and not extending on body beyond the vertical through the buds of the hind limbs. Spiracle sinistral, just visible from dorsal aspect, divided backward and somewhat obliquely upwards. Spiracle usually with a distinct semicircular impression on body and opening. Opening, leaving exposed an elliptical or hemispherical patch on body. Spiracle clearly below lateral axis (musculature axis). Eye on or just above lateral axis but in dorsal aspect nearer lateral outline than mid-dorsal axis. Anus dextral opening at edge of ventral crest.

Muciferous crypts distinct, white: a short dorsal row of a few pores on either side of middle line of the back from the dorsal crest forward; from above the middle line of insertion of tail musculature on body to a short distance behind eye a prominent dorsolateral row; apparently resumed behind eye after an interval and continued as supraorbital and infraorbital lines to above and below the nostril; another lateral row from above insertion of hind legs to gill region where a ventral commissure goes across to the row of the other side. A third of the distance across the ventral branchial region a branch from the commissure goes outwards and forwards along the jaw region almost to the mouth.

Mouth parts. Teeth 2/3 or 3/3. Edge of upper labium greater than length of upper horny beak and fringed by a continuous row of teeth. Sometimes this fringe is broken up as in figure. In either corner, beneath this fringe is a short row of teeth about one-fourth to one-third of the length of the upper fringe. The outer end of this second row never reaches outward beyond the first fringe. Median space between these second rows of teeth, one to one and one-half times the length of either lateral series of the second row. In some median-sized tadpoles the space may be greater and the second row much shorter or rarely absent. The third upper row very short, frequently absent in young and medium-aged tadpoles. From above the end of the first upper labial row of teeth to beneath the end of the third lower labial row are two or three irregular rows of papillae which are continued across lower labium's edge as one serrate row. The third labial row longer than this single row of papillae equal to length of horny beak but 1/4–1/5 shorter than first and second rows which extend beyond the ends of the horny beaks. The first row is continuous or broken in the middle.

Measurements. Length of body (32.0–41.5 mm.) in tail (50–57.5 mm.) 1.4–1.85, average 1.625. Width of body (15.0–22.5 mm.) in its own length

1.4–2.4, average 1.8. Depth (13–20 mm.) of body .9–1.6 in its own width, average 1.14, rarely greater than body. Depth of body 1.8–2.46 in body width, average 2.08. Depth of tail (14–18 mm.) in length of tail 2.6–4.6, average 3.2. Depth of tail .8–1.3 in body depth, average 1.02. Muscular part (9–11 mm.) of tail in its own tail depth 1.45–2.0, average 1.72. Spiracle .86–1.2 nearer vent than snout, average 1.0, i.e., about equidistant in general; spiracle to snout (17–22 mm.) and spiracle to vent or base of hind legs (17–23 mm.). Spiracle to eye (8–12 mm.) in eye to snout (8–11 mm.) .85–1.2, average .99, i.e. eye to snout and spiracle to eye usually equidistant. Nostril to eye (4.0–6.0 mm.) equals the distance from nostril to snout (3.5–6.0) mm. Mouth (3.0–7.0 mm.) usually 1.0–1.5 greater than the internasal space (3.0–6.5 mm.), average 1.2. Mouth contained 1.1–2.0 (average 1.46) in interorbital distance (5.0–10 mm.). Internasal space contained in interorbital space 1.4–2.0, average 1.75.

The dimensions of the largest tadpole of the 1922 collection are:

	mm.		mm.
Total length	95.0	Spiracle to vent	23.0
Body length	41.5	Spiracle to eye	11.5
Body depth	17.0	Eye to snout	10.0
Body width	17.0	Eye to nostril	6.0
Tail length	53.5	Nostril to snout	6.0
Tail depth	16.0	Mouth	6.5
Musculature of tail	11.0	Interorbital distance	10.0
Spiracle to snout	21.0	Internasal distance	5.0

In 1928 we took one 95 mm., one 96 mm. and one 97 mm. in total length.

General remarks. On June 16, 1912, at the Fargo, Ga., heronry amongst a swampy tangle of buttonbush *Cephalanthus occidentalis*, "hurrah bushes" (*Leucothoë racemosa*) and "lather leaf" (*Clethra alnifolia*) the author found some black tadpoles with yellowish white crossbands and surmised that they were the tadpoles of *R. grylio*. That was a mistake.

In 1921 when I returned from the swamp three tadpoles were referred to me from the U. S. Bureau of Fisheries. They were unlike anything we had seen before. Our reply was solely as to the identity of the material. The correspondent, a doctor from Savannah, Georgia, was concerned to know if albinism was common in tadpoles. Some of them were albinos and some normal. A week or so later, August 7, 1921, Mr. Francis Harper and Marion Lee found a small tadpole in the St. Mary's River, Baker County, Florida, about 10 miles south of Moniac, Georgia. On August 16, 1921, at Camp Pinckney (3 miles southeast of Folkston, Ga.) St. Mary's River, they secured three (Nos. 32–34) more larger tadpoles. These and the Savannah tadpoles were at hand when we surmised they might be Gopher Frog (*R. aesopus*) or Sphagnum Frog (*R. virgatipes*) tadpoles. They are of neither species.

In 1922 on July 17 at Thompson landing (south of Folkston) St. Mary's River in a cut off overflow pool we found in the water almost a pure culture of a small black tadpole with a gold and white transverse band like those of June 16, 1912.

My journal reads thus: "In one cut off pool in a water course (which now is a succession of separated pools) we hauled the seine. It was covered with a wriggly mass which at first looked like water beetles to Miles (Dr. M. D. Pirnie). I must confess I would have seen them the same way if I had not seen them before. The tails are transparent and were hardly in evidence. They have a band across the back. In another cut-off from the river proper (St. Mary's River) in shallow water they were in immense numbers and presented a very beautiful sight in sunlit situations with their dark bodies and transverse bands. Were it not for the transverse bands, they would look like toad tadpoles. Then I provisionally placed them with the green tree frog, *Hyla cinerea*, which sometimes has somewhat the same appearance."

Three days later, July 20, we started for Jacksonville, Florida. "At Callahan, Florida, (just north) near a large concrete bridge for the Dixie Highway, a car was stuck on the smaller bridge to the west in the detour and we had to wait. In the areas beside the new Dixie Highway were shallow ponds or overflowed areas. These were tributary to Alligator Swamp which in turn is a part of Mills Swamp (U. S. Geol Survey Sheet, Hilliard). At first I saw a few cross-banded forms of the Thompson's landing sort which I took to be *Hyla cinerea*. Now I suspect they are probably *R. aesopus* or *R. virgatipes*, probably the former. We collected a few and went on. They are very conspicuous with black rimmed crests and black bands on upper half of tail musculature and a light color on lower musculature. In one-third grown ones the cross bands show through faintly. When full grown it disappears."

On July 21, on our return from Jacksonville "we stopped at Callahan (Alligator Swamp). The tadpoles of July 20 were abundant. They travel in big schools as no other big tadpoles do. They remind me of a school of mature *Bufo* tadpoles. Once in a while amongst the fair sized ones were monsters almost as big as a bullfrog tadpole. And these monsters have no suggestion of hind leg buds. Does this species winter over one or two years as a tadpole?"

We checked up our Thompson Landing (Georgia) and Alligator Swamp (Florida) material and found them all of the same species. We later found they could not be tadpoles of *Rana aesopus* or *Rana virgatipes*.

On June 8, 1928, we went "to the type locality for *Rana heckscheri*. Saw plenty of tadpoles amongst vegetation under the Dixie Highway bridge. Captured about 12 transformed individuals. Can approach them when head is out of water and can catch them by hand. Or they may rest on mudflats where we also secured some. Many are with 4 legs and a long tail. . . . The transformed frogs are somewhat like greenfrogs but with more intensified spottings on the belly. These as transformed frogs and as adults have no lateral folds."

One June 9 "at Mr. Davis's brick yard in the large clay pool in the shade of the trees amongst *Polygonum hydropiper* were plenty of these tadpoles and transformed frogs near or at the edge of the water. Here in the shade they hopped about in amongst the weeds. They hid amongst vegetation, under boards and sticks or finally hopped into the water. There were a few bigger ones with them but they were more wary. Countless tadpoles are in this immense clay hole. Sometimes the tadpoles are so thick that one can reach in with his hands and catch them."

"On the east side saw prodigious schools of little black tadpoles with yellowish cross bands on the body. Amongst them are some bigger ones, about one-half inch in body length. This means two lots or breeding periods this year."

Oftentimes these schools would mass like a school of young catfish. At times one tadpole would lead out and the whole school would go in single file or the head and tail of the line might meet and all merge into mass formation again. Frequently smaller schools of the bigger size would be segregated from the smaller ones. All kinds of formations were made and the tadpoles are striking, either young or old. These pools have waterlilies, *Sagittaria*, water hyacinth, *Hydrocotyle*, etc.

LARVAL PERIOD

If I did not know that in the South there are some *Rana catesbeiana* which transform in one year or in the North *Rana septentrionalis* which sometimes spend two winters in the tadpole stage, I would feel inclined to believe this species always spent two winters in the tadpole stage. The largest tadpoles reach about 100 mm. When we caught them in July (21st) or in August (18th), there were at least two or three distinctive sizes of tadpoles. The largest ones were scarce. Doubtless the vast bulk of tadpoles at this time July 21–August 18 were one year olds or newly hatched tadpoles.

Our tentative conclusions above of 1922 in general express the situation as we see it in 1928. In 1928 we took tadpoles which drop into two groups namely, small and very large. The first of the clay pit of Callahan, Florida, are manifestly of the first year and appear to fall into three sizes: 10–15 mm. (body 7 mm.), 20–25 mm. (body 10 mm.), 30–35 mm. (body 12–15 mm.). Apparently this means three different breedings in the spring. The other group are the large transforming or near transforming tadpoles. Certainly it seems as if two years might be needed to arrive at the maximum size yet we found in 1922 and 1928 no intermediate tadpoles between the very large ones (75–100 mm.) and the 30–35 mm. sizes which might imply a shorter larval period.

In 1921 the three secured from the U. S. Bureau of Fisheries from Savannah, Ga., measured 44, 60 mm. albinos and 70 mm. normal. The three taken by Mr. Harper and Marion Lee measured 83, 88 and 90 mm. respectively. Except for one of these last the hind legs were pigmy in size. This material does not seriously militate against two years for larval life though one year may be all.

TRANSFORMATION

Period. On July 20, 21, 1922, and August 18, 1922, there were few of the large tadpoles. Doubtless transformation comes mainly before July. The few mature tadpoles of these dates were quite clearly stragglers. They might not have transformed before September 10th or 15th.

The paragraph before was more in the nature of negative evidence and conjecture but on June 8–10, 1928, countless mature tadpoles were approaching transformation. Our series of 89 frogs transformed and transforming could have been materially increased had we wished. Probably as in *Rana catesbeiana*, *R. clamitans* and some of the other large bodied tadpoles transformation is largely accomplished by the end of June. A few of the transformed ones (40–49 mm.) might indicate transformations in May, and some of the mature, about-to-transform tadpoles might not transform before July 1 or possibly July 15. In other words before the period in which we observed them in 1922.

Size. In 1922 we held that "some of the largest tadpoles with large bodies and well developed hind legs had body lengths of 32–41.5 mm. and the transformation size probably falls within this range." On June 8 and 9, 1928, we took 89 transformed or transforming frogs:—transformed (41) or nearly so with short tails (3–29 mm.) (48 specimens). Almost invariably if there was an appreciable stub the mouth was not the full-developed frog mouth. We can properly say that the range of size reaches from 31–49 mm. The 89 start with three at 30 mm., reaches the mode at 33 mm. with 22 specimens, and almost ceases with three at 38 mm. The record onwards is 1 at 39 mm., 1 at 41 mm., one at 43 mm., 44 mm. and 45 mm., 3 at 46 mm., 1 at 48 mm. and 1 at 49 mm. We thus see there are only nine of the 89 which are 40 mm. or more. The normal range is from 30–39 mm. yet there is clearly another smaller group with a mode about 46 mm. The average of the 30–39 mm. is 34 mm. or of the whole 89 specimens from 30–49 mm. is 35.5 mm.

GROWTH

On August 18 we captured at least four different sizes of frogs some (8–10 frogs). The same evening we later lost all but three of them. These are 56, 82 and 95 mm. respectively. The range of body length of seven large tadpoles with hind legs well started is 36–40, average 38, mode 39 mm. It is true we have given 32–40 or 41 for transformation size but the bulk of it probably comes within the narrower range of 36–40. This would give us 32–41 for transformation. The 56 mm. specimen may be two years old, the 82 mm. specimen a four year old and the 95 mm. specimen a five year old. They were all taken at the same time and there was another group of sizes between 56–82 mm. amongst the 8–10 specimens originally captured. (1922).

The conclusions above of 1922 are hardly correct for the 56 mm. specimen —the smallest frog we then had. If transformation sizes of June 8 and 9, 1928, vary from 30–49 mm. the 56 mm. can not be two year olds. It seems quite likely that some of the frogs which are almost transformed may retain their tails some time thereafter or that transformation may at times be delayed beyond the normal 30–39 mm. The premise of 1922 that 32–41 mm. was the probable transformation size is not far from the normal 30–39 of 1928. An unusual 49 mm. transformed frog would have to grow only 7 mm. to attain 56 mm. which can hardly be a two year old.

In 1928 we collected many intermediate sizes between transformation and 82 mm., but they were mislaid. These with the last 5 live intermediates of 1922, might have outlived the possible growth groups. With our meager material we might compare it with the possibly comparable *Rana grylio*. We might postulate: 30–49 mm., average 35.5 mm., transformation; 56 mm., 1 year old; 82 mm., 2 year old; 91, 95, 95, 97 mm. ♂s, 102 mm. ♀, 3 year olds; 113 mm. ♂, 4 year old; 125 mm. ♀, 5 year old.

ENEMIES

On June 8, 1928 we found a large southern water snake (*Natrix sipedon fasciata*) on the mud flats where transformed frogs were or at times it was coursing in water where countless tadpoles were. The pied water snake is also an enemy of these tadpoles and young frogs. On June 9, 1928, in the clay hole where the youngest tadpoles were numerous large mouthed black bass lived. These doubtless feed on the tadpoles. At the same time Florida grackles were apparently feeding on the transformed frogs along the edges of the pond.

At the type locality we took one transformed frog with all of left leg gone below femur. Another had the left leg completely severed and the toes clean cut from the right foot. In this hole we took *Sternotherus minor*. The above work is quite clearly the work of turtles or possibly fish.

AFFINITIES

The original diagnosis is pertinent in this instance.

Diagnosis. Like *Rana grylio* and *Rana catesbeiana*, it has no dorso-lateral fold and no phalanx of the fourth toe is totally free of web; third toe in 56 mm. specimen is 1 to 3 mm. shorter in *Rana heckscheri* than in the other two species of bullfrog or 3 to 6 mm. shorter in 82 mm. specimen or 6 to 9 mm. shorter in 95 mm. specimen; third toe 3.8 (95 mm.)–3.56 (82 mm.)–3.3 (56 mm.) in length (snout to vent) in *R. heckscheri* while 2.7 to 3.1 (95–56 mm.) in *R. grylio* and *R. catesbeiana*; third toe 1.6–1.7 in fourth toe in *R. heckscheri* while 1.2–1.5 in fourth toe in the other two species; first finger decidedly longer than second, while in the other two species it is usually shorter or sometimes equal; first, second, third and fifth toes shorter than corresponding toes of *R. grylio* and *R. catesbeiana*; fourth finger 8.6 (95 mm.)–8.2 (82 mm.)–8.0 (56 mm.) in length (snout to vent) while 6.0 to 6.3 (95 mm.)–6.8 to 7.4 (82 mm.)–5.6 to 7.1 (56 mm.) in the other two specimens; internasal space less than upper eyelid width, 1.07–1.43 in it while .85–1.0 in *R. grylio* and *R. catesbeiana*; tympanum in males is proportionately greatest in *R. grylio*, somewhat smaller in *R. catesbeiana* and *R. clamitans* and smallest in *R. heckscheri*; intertympanic width of 95 mm. male in length (snout to vent) 4.52 in *R. heckscheri*, 5.43 in *R. clamitans* and 6.3 in *R. grylio* (*R. catesbeiana* males of 95 mm. have tympanum poorly developed, but a 136 mm. has it 4.85); in general, intertympanic width broadest in *R. heckscheri* and *R. catesbeiana* and narrowest in *R. grylio*; distance from the rear corner of the eye to the same corner of the other eye much greater than the intertympanic width in *R. grylio*, somewhat greater in *R. clamitans*, about equal in *R. catesbeiana* and equal in *R. heckscheri*, i.e., in the males.

In the field at night we mistook the first one for a green frog until another specimen called, but in our original description we called it a new bullfrog. More material and more life history clues are needed to establish its place in the *Rana catesbeiana–Rana clamitans* series.

BIBLIOGRAPHY

1923   Wright, A.H. The Anat. Record, Vol. 24, No. 6, p. 406 (as *Rana sp.*).
1924   ———. Proc. Biol. Soc. Washington, Vol. 37, pp. 141-152.

Rana septentrionalis Baird

(Pl. III, Fig. 1; IX, Fig. 1; XI, Fig. 11; XIV, Fig. 3; XVI, Figs. 9, 10; XXXIX)

COMMON NAMES

Mink Frog.   Northern Frog.   Hoosier Frog.   Rocky Mountain Frog.

RANGE

Check list.   Type locality: Northern Minnesota.   Range: Northern New England and Northern New York, west through Michigan to Minnesota, Canada, northward to Hudson Bay.   Stejneger & Barbour Check List 1923, p. 37.

Supplementary records.   Miss Dickerson relying on Cope says "It is reported from the Adirondack Mountains, from Lucknow, Ontario, and Fort Ripley, Minnesota, and from Moose River and the Hudson Bay region. Strictly speaking, Madrid and Garrison's Creek, N. Y., are not Adirondacks proper but Paulmier found one on Black Lake in the Fulton Chain.   On June 13 and 14 A. H. and A. A. Wright found the species from White Lake to Old Forge, N. Y.   On June 28, Messrs. S. C. Bishop, C. K. Sibley, C. R. Crosby, M. D. Leonard, P. W. Claassen and L. West found it at Hart or Clear Lake (Mt. Marcy region).   On July 7, Mr. C. W. Leister also recorded it there as did Mr. and Mrs G. B. Upton from July 7–12.   On July 13–15 Dr. S. C. Bishop studied it in this place.   Mr. C. W. Leister has also seen it in Connery Pond, about four miles northeast of Lake Placid.   G. A. Boulenger (1920, p. 424) in his range Southern Canada and New York to Montana and Utah omits Pope's records 1914–1918 from Maine, yet No. 8 in his measurements from Eustis, Maine, must be a Pope specimen.   With Pope's discoveries of this species in Franklin County, Me., with the general distribution of this species in the Adirondacks, search at the right time ought to reveal the species in New Hampshire, Vermont and possibly in the Catskill Mts., N. Y. and doubtless in some of the swamp area around Oswego, N. Y., or north of Auburn, N. Y.   Nash, (p. 10) holds that it extends in Ontario from "Bruce County and northward and westward, not common."   He doubtless is considering the Lucknow record. The parallel of Lucknow 44° about represents the more common southern limit of its range in Ontario and New York but records are already at hand as low as 43°, 30′ in New York State.

In Ontario, it is knows from Haliburton to Bruce Counties and doubtless it is in the country east of Haliburton Co., Ontario to Madrid, N. Y.

Two years after the above paragraphs were written, we examined the U. S. National Museum series. We find a Vermont record: Newport, Clyde River, Evermann & Bean, July 23, 1894 (U. S. N. M. 39813-4). A New Hampshire accession of 4 specimens (U. S. N. M. Nos. 36463-6) from First Connecticut Lake, N. H., July 21, 1904, is made by the Bureau of Fisheries. This gives a continuous stretch of states or provinces from Maine to Manitoba. To me the most interesting recent record is the three series of accessions (U. S. N. M. Nos. 28450; 28336-46; 28354-58) of Mrs. E. P. Miller and Mr. Gerrit S. Miller Jr., from Peterboro, Madison County, N. Y. These are the farthest south in New York State unless it be E. A. Mearn's record for the Catskills (Am. Mus. Bull. Vol. 10, 1898, p. 325). These Peterboro records strengthen the probability of *Rana septentrionalis* being in the Catskills.

GENERAL APPEARANCE

This frog is a small representative of the bullfrog-green frog group. The sides are heavily mottled, the rear of the femur heavily reticulated, the back may be almost uniform, may be mottled with large dark areas set off by a tracery of light lines around or amongst them, or the back may be spotted with widely separated spots. Sometimes the forward part of the back is uniform and the rear part spotted. The legs are spotted or with a few bars. The mottling on the femur is suggestive of the *R. virgatipes-R. grylio* group. In young specimens the sides may be speckled and throats mottled.

MEASUREMENTS
(Recent Material)

Head to angle of mouth 1.2 (36 mm.)—1.07 (44 mm.)—1.24 (56 mm. ♂)—1.1 (56 mm. ♀)—1.25 (66 mm. ♂)—1.13 (66 mm. ♀) in width of head; head to rear of tympanum .92–.94–.9–.95–1.04–.93 in width of head; head to angle of mouth 3.6–3.13–3.4–3.3–3.3–3.47 in length of body; head to rear of tympanum 2.66–2.75–2.54–2.9–2.75–2.87 in length of body; snout 1.16–1.14–1.11–1.18–1.1–1.15 in first finger; snout 1.16–1.14–1.4–1.31–1.4–1.16 in fourth finger; snout 1.25–1.28–1.0–1.125–1.4–1.05 in first toe; eye 1.5–1.27–1.13–1.45–1.1 in snout; eye .75–.81–1.13–1.0–1.06–.92 in tympanum; eye 1.75–1.45–1.26–1.74–1.3–1.7 in first finger; tympanum 3.3–2.44–1.3–2.01–1.4–2.33 in intertympanic width; tympanum 2.0–1.6–1.0–1.45–1.11–1.6 in snout; internasal width 1.0–.75–.8–.9–.91–1.0 in upper eyelid width; interorbital width 1.4–.86–1.8–2.25–1.83–1.66 in upper eyelid width; interorbital width 1.4–1.14–2.2–2.5–2.0–1.66 in internasal width; interorbital width 4.0–3.14–4.4–6.0–4.0–4.56 in intertympanic width.

Forelimb: Forelimb 1.9–1.9–1.8–2.1–2.3–2.3 in length of body; forelimb 3.1–2.7–2.66–2.9–3.3–3.2 in hind limb; first finger 1.3–1.4–1.47–1.3–1.66–1.3

Mink frog (*Rana septentrionalis*)

1. Male, collected by S. C. Bishop at Hart (Clear) Lake, Adirondack Mts., N. Y. July 5, 1923. Lateral aspect. × 1.0.

2. Female, collected by S. C. Bishop at Hart (Clear) Lake, Adirondack Mts., N. Y. July 5, 1923. Ventral aspect. × 1.0.

3. Beaver dam, Hellgate pond, Onekio, N. Y. June 12, 1923.

4. Egg mass, photographed by S. C. Bishop, Hart (Clear) Lake, Adirondack Mts., N. Y. × 0.5.

5. Transforming frog with short tail, Onekio, N. Y. July 4, 1923. Dorsal aspect. × 1.0.

6. Adult, photographed by C. W. Leister, Hart Lake, Essex Co., N. Y. July 7, 1923. × 0.6.

1

3

4

5

2

6

in third finger; second finger 1.3–1.4–1.33–1.4–1.6–1.3 in third finger; second finger 1.0–1.0–1.0–.95–1.0–.91 in first finger; third finger 1.66–1.3–.93–1.2– 1.05–1.0 in second toe; fourth finger 1.3–1.45–1.16–1.2–1.3–1.3 in third finger; fourth finger 1.07–1.15–.70–.85–.8–.9 in first toe; internasal width 2.0–2.0– 1.74–1.9–1.75–2.2 in first finger; internasal width 2.0–2.0–1.9–1.8–1.83–2.2 in second finger; internasal width 2.6–2.87–2.5–2.5–2.9–2.9 in third finger; internasal width 2.0–2.0–2.05–2.1–2.25–2.2 in fourth finger.

Hindlimb: length 1.64–1.46–1.45–1.37–1.45–1.3 in hind limb; tibia 2.0– 2.0–2.0–2.2–2.2–2.2 in length; tibia 3.2–2.93–3.0–3.0–3.2–3.03 in hind limb; tibia 1.05–1.07–1.08–1.03–1.0–.93 in forelimb; tibia 1.08–1.13–1.08–1.1–1.03–1.03 in hind foot (without tarsus); first toe 1.3–1.55–1.53–1.55–1.63–1.45 in second toe; first toe 2.0–1.9–2.6–2.1–2.04–2.3 in third toe; first toe 2.66–2.66–3.5– 3.1–2.7–3.1 in fourth toe; first toe 1.9–2.0–2.3–2.16–2.2–2.1 in fifth toe; second toe 1.5–1.2–1.7–1.4–1.25–1.6 in third toe; second toe 2.0–1.8–2.3–2.0– 1.7–2.1 in fourth toe; second toe 1.4–1.3–1.5–1.3–1.4–1.5 in fifth toe; third toe 1.3–1.47–1.36–1.46–1.4–1.35 in fourth toe; third toe 0.93–1.05–.9–1.03 1.13–.93 in fifth toe; fourth toe 1.3–1.3–1.3–1.4–1.53–1.34 in hind foot (with tarsus); fourth toe .925–.9–.91–.91–.96–.96 in tibia; fourth toe .95–.94– 1.01–.94–.96–.9 in forelimb; fifth toe 1.38–1.4–1.5–1.43–1.2–1.4 in fourth toe; internasal width 2.14–2.25–1.54–1.80–1.83–2.0 in first toe; internasal width 3.0–3.5–2.3–2.8–3.0–2.9 in second toe; internasal width 4.4–4.25–4.0–3.8– 3.75–4.6 in third toe; internasal width 5.7–6.25–5.4–5.6–5.1–6.2 in fourth toe; internasal width 4.1–4.5–3.4–3.9–4.25–4.3 in fifth toe.

HABITAT

Garnier (p. 945) pronounces this species a river frog. "It inhabits spring creeks and rivers, but in lakes and ponds of the purest water I have never seen it nor captured a single specimen." "It is . . . emphatically a river frog. It is never seen in fields nor woods lurking. . . ." Pope (1915, Copeia No 16) records "one from a wood road, which passed through a sphagnum bog," "*Rana septentrionalis* common along the banks of Ciss Stream, which flows from Round Pond into Caucmogomoc Lake, Piscataquis Co. (Me.) . . . . They were found on the marshy banks of the stream where bull frogs (*Rana cates-beiana*) were abundant." Mr. Arthur H. Norton (Pope, Copeia 1915, No. 16) observed it "in VanBuren and Caswell, (Me.), August 15-16, 1914. It was found to be numerous in two dead water ponds in Caswell, locally called Mud and Guard Ponds. They were more conspicuous than *Rana clamata*, inhabiting similar places, i.e., tussocks of sedges on the edges and the beds of lily pads near the shore. At Van Buren they were found in ditches by the railroad track and were common." Pope concludes the mink frog is found in the same localities as *R. catesbeiana* and *R. clamitans*, not tending to replace either species. Later Pope (Copeia Dec. 31, 1918, p. 96) "found it abundant at Tim Pond, Eustis, Franklin Co., Me. It occurred all around the pond; along rocky, wave-beaten shores, in marshes, and in the outlet close to the lake, but never far from water."

In 1913 (Copeia October 15, 1915, pp. 46-48). "On July 7 in peaty lake with a clear sphagnum border we found several *R. septentrionalis*." On July 16th and 17th we examined the place closely. "All along the north edge of the lake were white water lilies, yellow spatterdocks and water shields. These three made a perfect carpet on the water's surface. On these plants during the day the frogs rested." "In the outlet to Otter Lake (Ten Mile Creek between Lake of Bays and Otter Lake) we found them common, July 24, on muddy bottoms where water lilies were abundant. In the same kind of situation they occurred on Porridge Lake, July 28. Another habitat we discovered August 31 was a beaver lake where *Cassandra* and all the associated heath-like plants grew. Finally, in Fletcher Lake, September 1 we found them in the shallow, sandy shores amongst pipeworts (*Eriocaulon articulatum*)." "This species cannot be called solely a river species; . . ."

To the last conclusion I still adhere. In general we have found it most commonly in lakes or ponds or if streams these are usually inlets or outlets of ponds or lakes. On June 13-14, 1923, we found it more or less along the whole Fulton chain of lakes, Adirondack Mts. from White Lake to Seventh Lake. Sometimes a few might be in temporary pools beside the state road where they must have travelled over land to reach these places. All in all, it is distinctly an aquatic species. On June 14, 1923, we found most of our frogs at Hellgate Ponds, Onekio, N Y. Here in driftwood pools below a beaver dam we took several *R. clamitans*, *R. catesbeiana* and *R. septentrionalis*. Later took several more mink frogs in muddy pools among granite boulders.

On July 9, and July 26, 1900, Mrs. E. P. Miller and Gerrit S. Miller Jr., recorded these frogs in Peterboro Lake and Peterboro Mill pond on floating *Nymphaea* leaves, the same habitat in which Bishop in the Adirondacks and we in Algonquin Park found them.

FIRST APPEARANCE

None of our records are in the spring and the earliest record of the year is Garnier's statement "It makes its appearance in April" at Lucknow, Ontario.

GENERAL HABITS

Variations in color. This topic is not fully treated or considered. Some scattering notes on some U. S. National Museum specimens are:

No. 39813. Male 58 mm. Dark spotted on upper head. Green from tympanum to snout in sharp contrast to top of head. Green involves edge of eye except upper eyelid.

No. 39814. Just transformed 31.5 mm. Sometimes dark spots have light centers.

No. 39792. 55 mm. ♀. Almost no spots on upper parts but mottling on sides, rear of femur and legs barred.

Nos. 28354–58. 51 mm. ♂, 66 mm. ripe ♀, 57 mm. ♂, 56 mm. ♂, 66 mm. ♀. These have large spots on back, some light encircled, some not.

Nos. 36096–99. 62 mm. ♂, 62 mm. ♀, 57 mm. ♂, 56 mm. ♂. These are all with distinct and separate spots on back.

No. 3632. 41 mm. Speckly on sides.

Nos. 28450–56. 41 mm.–48 mm. ♀, backs almost uniform.

No. 3437. 53 mm. ♂. Spots few on rear of back only. Legs much spotted.

72 mm. ♀. Forward part of body less spotted.

No. 5245. 58 mm. ♀, 67 mm. ♀. In general mottled with large dark areas and a tracery of light around them.

This species is quite common in more northern parts. Except at its short croaking period it is generally passed by as a small bullfrog or green frog, and as a consequence is pronounced "not common," "rare." It is called northern frog from its specific name and from its northern distribution,—a not inappropriate name except it is not individualistic. Garnier like others subsequently noted its secretions. He writes (1883, p. 945) "If taken in the hand it emits a strong odor of musk and garlic, or more properly the disagreeable scent of the mink; this is sufficiently powerful to adhere to the hand for a time, but soon passes away." (p. 948) "The tadpole has the odor of the frog, though not so strong; . . ." In 1913 I thought the term "mink frog very apropos for this species, at least for Ontario specimens. . . ." I have since noticed some have it more than others and possibly the males have it strongest at the breeding season. At times some *Rana septentrionalis* have the scent very faint and do not always respond with the secretion flow when rubbed. All in all, this is the best name suggested. One day I put several in a glass jar with several meadow frogs, some *R. virgatipes* and two green frogs. Almost all were dead on the following morning including the two mink frogs. Did the secretions cause it as some times happens with *R. palustris*? The terms "hoosier frog," "Rocky Mountain frog" seem inappropriate.

Of its general habits Garnier writes (pp. 940, 948) "In summer they may often be seen with the head and a bit of the back out of water, resting among plants on the borders of streams, and where the Potamogeton is in bunches, or the Ranunculus is in beds, the herpetologist may likely secure his specimens." "But if the frog once disappears, he generally keeps from view till all probable danger is past. It is useless to expect it to reappear at the spot it left, as it dives several yards, it may be, rods, before it stops. I have occasionally waited half an hour or more, watching one that has so dived beside a stone, in the current or otherwise. Perhaps they may have been so really frightened and the feeling of fear may have remained, or they may have followed some law of nature implanted with them in keeping concealed for such a protracted period. Occasionally I have heard their notes after they were secured and in my collecting case; but then it seemed truly a note of distress, and was in a different tone and key from that rarely heard in the open stream."

The experience of several subsequent collectors prove them not hard to capture at all at the breeding period and Mr. Simpson's capture of 30–40 at one time in August from lily pads with an insect net hardly accords with Garnier's results. Possibly stream or river specimens may be harder to secure.

VOICE

Garnier (1883, pp. 949, 950) writes "that (croaking) of the mink frogs is a rapid squeaking croak almost like the notes uttered by a toad when seized, with the finger and thumb, by its arm pits. I have since heard the same love cry late in the evening, on the banks of the stream and have well recognized its peculiarly sharp ringing croak." "Occasionally I have heard their notes after they were secured and in my collecting case; but then it seemed truly a note of distress, and was in a different tone and key from that rarely heard on the open stream. . . . There are no 'chant amour' or love notes, in spring" (pp. 947, 948). In 1913 near Dorset, Ontario, "from July 7–14, we heard at night along the shore of Otter Lake the peculiar note which later proved the croak of the mink frog. On the 15th of July at 10:00 p.m. we heard several frogs and started with flashlight for Peat Lake where the species was in chorus. The air temperature ranged from 52° to 55° F., but the water of Otter Lake at its surface registered 69° F. . . . After July 15th and 16th we heard no more choruses. . . . (This species) has a 'chant amour' which at chorus season can be heard one-third to one-half of a mile away; . . ." (Wright 1915, Copeia No 23, pp. 46, 47). In Maine, P. H. Pope writes of it as follows: "Through the kindness of Mr. Arthur H. Norton I am permitted to publish the following data collected by him:

'At Mud Pond, Caswell, they were heard calling, and the same is true of *R. clamata.*

'The call of *R. septentrionalis* was found to be similar in nature to that of *R. clamata,* but differed strikingly in tone, being higher and slightly metallic, resembling closely the sound produced by striking a long nail on the head with a hammer in driving it into heavy timber.' " Pope (1915, No. 16, p. 2). Later Pope in a subsequent note (Copeia, 1918, p. 96) remarks "I also heard the call of these frogs and find that Mr. A. H. Norton's description, quoted in the paper mentioned above, fits it admirably. While keeping some of these frogs in camp in a tin can I heard them give a slightly different call suggesting the bubbling note of *Rana pipiens* but shriller and not quite so loud." F. Harper (1926, p. 11) writes as follows of these frogs at Clear Lake, Adirondacks: "The notes were heard occasionally by day during cloudy weather, but perhaps more frequently by night. There are guttural, vigorous, and rather rapid: *Cuck-cuck-cuck-cuck.*"

From the previous published data, croaking has been recorded from July 7–August 16. In 1923 some captives we took June 14 later croaked, but we did not hear them in the field. On June 28 at Clear or Hart Lake, Adirondack Lodge, N. Y., Messrs. S. C. Bishop, P. A. Claassen, C. R. Crosby, M. D. Leonard, C. K. Sibley and L. West heard them. On July 7, 1923, Mr. C. W. Leister heard them in the same place and also near Saranac Lake. About the same time Mr. and Mrs. G. B. Upton also heard them at Hart Lake. On July 14 Mr. S. C. Bishop found them in chorus at Hart Lake. At Onekio, N. Y., Hellgate Pond on July 14 I heard many individual croaks in the daytime.

On July 2 at Adirondack Lodge, Hart or Clear Lake (2155 ft.) Messrs. S. C. Bishop and C. K. Sibley found mink frogs croaking at 8:30 a.m. in broad sunlight, at mid-day and in the evening. "On July 13 in the same place S. C. Bishop heard males croaking just at daybreak in the middle of the morning and rarely in the afternoon." On July 14 he records "Frogs croaked all night. The male croaking expands the throat and sides of head below ears. The common note is a cut-cut—with sometimes a 'burred' gh-r-r-r." On July 15 "dark and rainy. Only a few frogs croaking during the night and very infrequently in the daylight. P.M. No croaking this period."

This species seem to have about the same sac development as *R. palustris*. In some from Onekio, N. Y. it seemed that the head if viewed from dorsum appears at croaking to have no perceptible lateral sacs. Viewed from below the central throat swells out with a sac on either side of this central part. This sac however appears to be just below corner of the mouth or directly below the vertical of the tympanum but not directly below the ear or between ear and shoulder .

From these we concluded it did not swell out as in a Cope's frog male. A male Mr. Bishop brought me from Clear Lake has the lateral sacs extending between tympanum and shoulder. The caudal margin of the lateral sac beyond the rear vertical of the tympanum or even to the vertical of the rear arm insertion. In this frog it is very apparent from the dorsum but not so striking as in Cope's frog. This frog, as with other species of frog, can be made to croak by seizing it just in front of its hind legs or better by laying it on its back and by rubbing its belly. Then it will croak continuously. Each individual croak in nature occupies about one second or less. If not in chorus their croaks are not heard long distances when their associates, green frogs or bull-frogs are calling. At Onekio, N. Y. we heard them. On July 14 we could hear the males croaking 60–100 yards away. In croaking one or two frogs seemed to move forward in the water with every croak and the body return to position immediately after each croak. The vocal sacs were not very well revealed in the field. A frog usually gave two croaks, occasionally one, occasionally 5 or 6. Its croak is different from that of the Cope's or Carpenter frog though Norton makes a carpenter comparison in describing the croak.

MATING

Male (From life June 18, 1923). On back buffy olive, light brownish olive or olive; this same color becomes isabella color on upper side of hind legs, amongst this buffy olive, etc. are wavy lines or spots of oil yellow, yellowish citrine; on the middle of the back are two irregular rows of black spots often round, widely separated, at times elongate. Region of dorsum forward of rear of tympana is without black spots but buffy olive with plenty of cosse green or lettuce green interspersed. This color solid on the upper jaw to level of nostril to tympanum. Above and below tympanum a line of courge green. Just back of tympanum courge green or yellow green spots and lines with black. On sides mixture of yellow-green, black and hazel (or tawny olive or fawn). Tympanum tawny olive, buffy brown or isabella color. Upper parts of fore legs citrine drab or buffy brown with black spots of fore edge and rear edge distinct and small. Hind legs with vermiculation of buffy olive, etc., and black on dorsum. On posterior thighs fine black and old gold or olive lake. Rear thigh parts if viewed from venter suggest *R. virgatipes* somewhat and *R. grylio.* Throat of male sulphur yellow or pale green yellow, rest of under parts seafoam yellow. Pupil rim green yellow; iris finely spotted black and vinaceous tawny or xanthine orange. Thumb somewhat enlarged.

(From life July 14, 1923). Upper jaw solid courge green, cosse green or lettuce green; also this color more or less predominant on head back to tympanum. This color less prominent in back because of large black spots which are outlined by these greens. Amongst these black spots are smaller snuff brown spots. On hind legs are sulphur yellow or in places aniline yellow vermiculating the black of the thighs and bounding the black cross bars of the lower legs. More or less longitudinal bar on thigh bister or brownish olive. On sides mixture of black, green yellow or even yellow-green and hazel (very slightly). Upper parts of fore legs yellowish oil green with black. Throat maize yellow or sometimes baryta yellow while the rest of underparts are light chalcedony yellow. Some of the largest males may have maize yellow on entire under parts. Iris as in description of male of June 18.

Female (From life July 14, 1923). Several seem more spotted on under part of hind legs than in males. Sometimes spots on either side of the throat. Hazel of back more prominent and more hazel on sides and usually more spotted on the head. Underneath they are white or whitish except for the throat which may be pale chalcedony yellow or seafoam yellow.

Structural differences. Some of the differences are:

1. Males have tympana larger than rarely equal to the eye while those of the females are clearly smaller than or equal to the eye. For example, extreme tympana may be as follows: ♂ 56 mm., tympana 8 1/2 mm., eye 5.5 mm., or ♂ 56 mm., tympana 7.5 mm., eye 6.5 mm., or ♂ 54 mm., tympana 8.5 mm., eye 7.5 mm. Occasionally the tympanum may reach 10 mm.

2. A pair taken at Hart Lake, Adirondack Lodge, July 14, 1923, show the following differences in ventral coloration. The male's throat has some maize yellow or baryta yellow while the rest of the under parts are light chalcedony yellow; the female has a seaform yellow throat with some chartreuse yellow while the rest of the under parts are white or whitish.

3. Vocal sacs (see Voice). In a 57 mm. ♂ from Peterboro, N. Y., a little inclination toward a sac back of tympanum.

4. General coloration (see Mating coloration).

5. Tympanic borders prominent in male. Old males are often with the tympanic border standing out prominently from the surrounding body.

6. The males have the characteristic swollen thumb of our North American Ranas.

7. Males probably do not breed until two years from transformation. In our series we have no positive male (externally) before 50 mm. In the U. S. National Museum series is one 48.5 mm. Of one specimen in our series, 46.5 mm., we record that it "begins slightly to show maleness in tympana and thumbs."

8. In like fashion the females do not breed until two years from transformation. In our series the first positive female is at 50 mm. In the U. S. National Museum series we recorded in Miller's specimens from Peterboro, N. Y. a ♀ 47 and a ♀ 48 mm. In our own material we have one questionable female at 48 mm.

9. The range of size for positive breeding males is from 48.5–66 mm., for females from 50–72 mm.

Duration, night or day. The mating habits of this species still rest on few observations. The period of mating begins in the latter part of June and extends well into August. Garnier (1883) found eggs June 24 and July 30. Norton records frogs then calling August 15–16, 1914. Possibly June 24–August 16 represents the range of the mating period. In general the bulk of mating must come from June 28–July 30. In 1913 the choruses at Otter Lake, Ontario, were from July 7–15. This year (1923) at Onekio, N. Y. they were not mating June 14. On June 28 at Adirondack Lodge, Hart Lake, Messrs. S. C. Bishop and C. K. Sibley found them in chorus and the males very impulsive but no eggs present. About July 7 Mr. C. W. Leister also heard them at Hart Lake as did Mr. and Mrs. G. B. Upton independently. On July 14 I found the species mating and breeding at Hellgate ponds, Onekio, N. Y. My friend Dr. S. C. Bishop at Hart Lake also found them breeding there July 14. About the same time July 8, 1923, Dr. S. E. Simpson at Otter Lake, Dorset, Ontario, reports by letter that he had recently found them breeding. It would, therefore, appear that July 7–15 is an almost certain mating date for this species if three of us independently find the eggs July 8–14.

This species usually is most active at night. On July 14 I saw about 9:30 a.m. six or eight males spread out on the surface around a mass of sedges. They were vigorously croaking and from time to time rushing at each other, the rushee thinking the other to be a female. They lie spread out with hind legs on the surface. On July 2, Messrs. Bishop and Sibley took on Clear Lake "24 specimens of which 23 were males and one juvenal female. These males were swimming and floating in open water 3 or 4 rods from shore or resting on pads of the yellow cow lilies." On July 13 and 14 we have the following notes from Dr. S. C. Bishop. On July 13 he "took two mature females; one specimen with eggs extruding was resting at the surface of the water with no male in her vicinity; the other female was at the surface and near the shore. On July 14 placed at 9:00 a.m. a male with first female (extruding eggs) in a pan and kept dark. By 9:30 they were mated and so remained until 2:00 p.m. when the female was found to be dead. The male grasped the female with the first two fingers above and in front of the brachium and the other two fingers behind the brachium. Later the male had one arm wholly ahead of the female."

The ripe females seem to be very rare and the males in the lake greatly predominate. Immature females are more common near shore. Dr. Bishop, as do I, believes that the females stay near shore in hiding until ripe, then swim out toward males which rush for them or to meet them. Doubtless then the pair sink to the bottom or soon the female seizes a stem for ovulation. I believe the embrace is normally pectoral because of the cross embrace with *R. clamitans* and the swollen thumb.

Mr. Garnier's notes on mating are "On the 24th of June I collected a number of *R. septentrionalis* and placed them in a large white earthen vase. They remained quiet for a time and I put in some chips and a quantity of *Ranunculus*. Next morning three couples were paired and lying at the bottom of the vase, and secreted among the *Ranunculus*. One pair were on the surface, but the female had been injured. It thus seems they accouple in the night, and immediately sink and hide. Occasionally there was a trivial chant amour from the last pair, evidently so given, but the others were mute. . . . The male seizes the female by the lower portion of the axilla, near the upper third of the dorsal vertebrae, but not by the lumbar regions. At this time the tinting on the chin and throat was a fine gamboge-yellow, and was deeper toned in some specimens than others, but not particularly more in the males than in the females. In both sexes it was equally beautiful. I could not help being struck by the extreme stillness of the pairs in coitu among the *Ranunculus*. Nothing seemed to induce them to move in any manner. They were at rest. I carefully examined since on all opportunities, and searched the streams and pools to find some in coitu, if possible, to observe them in their natural embrace but as yet without success. . . .'

"Thus it may be justly inferred that after the female is grasped the pair sink to the bottom and conceal themselves from view, and that they bury themselves in the mud or seek the covering of water plants, after the manner of those in the earthen vase. It is likely some prompting of nature that thus makes them bury themselves from sight to protect themselves from enemies that could, at that time, make them an easy prey, and in security perform their process of fecundation. I kept my specimens referred to for over a fortnight, but no spawn was deposited."

Amplexation, (*Normal, abnormal*). We have no data on the actual mating. The very secretive nature of this animal's life, at the non-breeding period, its attachment to cover in the day unless it be overcast would lead one to expect it to mate at night. Most surely its amplexation must be pectoral as its enlarged thumb would indicate. The duration of mating must be very brief and the concourses of this specialized species shorter than with most species.

Cross embraces with other species were not provided for. On July 14 we placed several males with two green frogs in a dark fish can. When we reached home 12 hours later we found one male *R. septentrionalis* embracing a female *R. clamitans* with arms dug into the axils. Its arms could not span farther i.e., reach around on to the breast.

OVULATION

Habitat. The normal habitat for the non-ovulation period is retained for ovulation. We clearly believed the eggs would be found in connection with water lilies, hence our choice of habitat for the mink frog in "Frogs: Their Natural History and Utilization" U. S. Bureau of Fisheries Report 1920, App. Plate VIII, p. 17. Our experience at Onekio, N. Y., Hellgate Pond, July 13 and 14 tended at first to lead us to believe Garnier's observed habitat the preferred one but the records of S. C. Bishop and S. E. R. Simpson to be related later prove the water lily habitat as best. Garnier (pp. 950) writes: "Today is the 30th of July. . . . There is plenty of spawn in the streams." On July 14, 1923, Mrs. Wright and I found plenty of frogs below a beaver dam where the outlet of a pond flowed. Just below the dam was a large area in which were the tadpoles of *Rana clamitans* and *Rana septentrionalis*, redbellied dace (*Chrosomus erythrogaster*), common shiner (*Luxilus cornutus*), horned dace (*Semotilus atromaculatus*), fall fish (*Leucosomus corporalis*), cutlips (*Exoglossum maxillingua*) and blacknosed dace (*Rhinichthys atronasus*). Below this pool came an area with cobblestones with water between and under, evidently usually covered with water and normally swift. The cobblestone area was succeeded by a broad deep area of water 2 1/2 feet, brown in color, more or less clear and with sediment in the bottom which might be easily stirred up. About this area are granite boulders amongst which are regal's fern, deciduous holly, Mt. holly, red maple, meadow sweet, toothed haw, tall meadow rue, Mt. maple, clematis and polypody. Here we had the bullfrog, greenfrog and mink frogs in areas. The bullfrogs were calling above the dam in the pond proper. In this broad area below the dam on the west side was an open sunlight edge of grasses, sedges, Joe Pye weed, and monkey flowers. Here beneath the shades of *Myrica Gale* bushes were fresh masses of greenfrog eggs. On the east side near a boulder and fringe of overhanging alders (*Alnus incanus*) was a group of six or eight male mink frogs floating among some scattered, broad-leaved sedges in deep water. Farther under the alders and all along the stream under the alders at their bases were *R. septentrionalis* males. Sometimes where a mass of driftwood might be we would find five or six gathered or they would be floating on royal fern leaves which were on the surface. Just beneath the five or six males first discovered we found in the sedges a mass 2 1/2 inches below the surface. It was so covered with sediment we thought it farther along in development than it proved to be. The tips of the sedges were floating in the water. We photographed the mass in place, picked the sedge on which it was attached and returned fifteen minutes later and searched the whole spot over again. Here directly beneath the first mass some 3 or 4 inches was a second mass. How we missed it is hard to understand except that the sediment so obscured it. When we at last saw it, it looked like a brown stone encircling a sedge, an impossibility. The mass reminded me very much of *R. virgatipes* eggs of the Okefinokee Swamp or *R. palustris* eggs not so brown and yellow. The first mass was a plinth 2 or 2 1/2 x 1 1/2 inches. The second one was no

more than 2 x 2 x 1 inches.   This species doubtless like others lays many
complements in special areas.

   Mr. S. C. Bishop on July 13, 1923, at Adirondack Lodge "found one small
lot of eggs (12) on the sandy bottom of the lake in about 8 inches of water.
They were being eaten by a newt when found.   Either the newt may have
carried them there or they may have been a few laid by a female which laid
a few before the main ovulation.   On July 13 p. m., day mostly bright
and windy.   Found three egg masses of the mink frog (*Rana septentrionalis*
Baird) fastened to the stems of the yellow cow lillies.   They were attached 8,
12 and 18 inches below the surface in plinth masses from 4 to 5 1/2 inches in
largest diameter.   The lilies are 4–6 rods from the shore in 6–8 feet of water.
Lost one egg mass.   The egg mass is slightly heavier than the water and sinks
slowly when detached.   July 14.   Found 2 egg masses.   This date 1st—about
16 to 18 inches below the surface.   The embryos already hatching.   2nd lot.
2 feet below surface, freshly laid, collected and photographed.   Newts very
common in the lake are the enemies of the eggs and embryos.   In mass of
hatching young one newt was found in middle of the mass.   In attempting
to photograph eggs in lake newts came and attempted to crawl into the mass.
During the day many males left the open lake to hide along the shore.   Eggs
are apparently laid at night—at least we could find no females in act of laying
during the day or early night when using the flashlight nor in the early
morn at 5:30 a.m.

   "July 15, a.m.   Dark and rainy.   Three egg masses found.   One lot 4 1/2–
5 feet below the surface; the 2nd with embryos ready to leave egg mass 3
feet below the surface was 6 inches in greatest diameter, and the jelly ready
to disintegrate; the third mass 18–20 inches below the surface.   July 15 p.m.
Two egg masses one about 4 feet below surface in 7 feet of water was 6 inches
in long diameter and fastened to two stems of yellow lily (*Nymphaea varie-
gata*).   The mass (well developed embryos) was longer than wide with the
supporting stems running through one side; 2nd egg mass smaller about
2 x 4 inches and 3 feet below the surface."

   I have long felt they laid far below the surface on water lilies and Mr.
Bishop told me how he proceeded.   At first he found eggs by casual observation from the boat.   Then later he had some one row him about and he
laid on his stomach in the prow and in this water discovered masses 4–5 feet
below the surface.   On July 16 I received the following in a letter dated
July 8 and written by S. E. R. Simpson at Dorset, Ontario:

   "I believe I have found the mink frog eggs.   They are in a long brown
ribbon-like mass rounded.   The eggs are very small and oval shaped, not
round.   They were attached to the stems of weeds either floating at the
surface or else half way between the bottom and the top.   I found them at
Peat Lake all along the shore among the lily pads.   If I have any luck I should
be able to get some tadpoles.   There are lots of them and we got about 18
bunches."   In this same place, I collected adult frogs in 1912 and in 1919
in the middle and last of August Mr. Simpson took sixty or more with a net
from the lily pads.

Period. Previous to 1923 we knew nothing positive of the eggs except Garnier's records. Several of my friends volunteered to help in the search that summer, and at least three of us independently found the species breeding in different places. Mr. S. C. Bishop had kindly invited me to join him at Hart Lake July 13 and 14. I could not make the proper plans and he went to Hart Lake and Mrs. Wright and I to the Fulton Chain of lakes, Adirondacks. We found only two masses at Onekio, N. Y., the species just beginning while Mr. Bishop reported the species well launched in Hart Lake, Adirondack Lodge, near North Elba and Mt. Marcy. On July 16 I saw a letter from Mr. S. E. R. Simpson who at Dorset (Otter Lake), Ontario, reported on July 8 that he believed he had found the mink frog eggs. These three independent discoveries July 8–14 would seem to indicate the first of July as a part of the crestal period of ovulation. Mr. Garnier's records June 24 and July 30, 1883, are yet the extreme dates of ovulation. We, therefore, have from June 24 to July 30, possibly August 16 as the egg period with the bulk of eggs laid in July. Most of the U. S. National Museum accessions are for the month of July when this inconspicuous species is croaking and most in evidence. U. S. National Museum No. 36097 is a female 67 mm. and ripe. It was taken July 9, 1903, at Cross Lake, Aristook Co., Me., by Mr. W. C. Kendall. On the same day of the month, July 9, 1900, G. S. Miller Jr., secured a ripe female 61 mm. (U.S.N.M. No. 28355) at Peterboro, N. Y. These help to reinforce the impression that July is its principal breeding month.

Egg-laying process. Doubtless the bulk of egg laying is at night. The males await the coming of the females. When they approach the males rush for them and soon they amplexate. It would seem they soon sink to the bottom. As with other Ranas which lay plinths the laying after it has begun probably lasts from a few to 15 or 20 minutes. As yet no one has seen the actual process.

EGGS

We have already seen that the mass is a plinth with its greatest diameter rarely as large as 6 inches, although 3–5 inches are the more usual dimensions. In breeding habits the species reminds me of *Rana virgatipes*, each with plinths except that *R. septentrionalis* has an inner envelope around each egg, or of *R. palustris* which has a globular mass of eggs more brown and yellow. *R. palustris* has the more brownish and more yellowish eggs; *R. virgatipes* is next and *R. septentrionalis* eggs have a slight brownish and yellowish cast at times. In the two masses we found at Onekio the fresher bunch had almost black above and cartridge buff below. Later the lower color was almost white. The older bunch had the eggs seafoam yellow or light chalcedony yellow below and a dark brown above. Mr. Bishop held that "the upper half in freshly laid eggs is black; the lower half creamy white, division of color being about equal." Mr. S. E. R. Simpson speaks of them as a brown mass—whether it is from the sediment in its general effect on the upper poles I do not know.

Some of the eggs taken July 14, 1923, at Onekio, N. Y. measured from 1.3–1.6 mm. in vitellus, average 1.4, mean 1.4; 2.4–3.0 mm. for the inner envelope, average 2.7 mm.; and 5.6–6.6 mm., average 6.3 mm. for outer envelope. As development proceeds the outer envelope may exceed 7.0 mm. Mr. Bishop made a field measurement and examination. He writes "The individual eggs have 3 envelopes visible with a hand lens: 1st closely surrounds the egg; 2nd about 3 mm. diameter; last 3rd 3/8 inch." The first is the vitelline membrane and the 3/8 inch envelope is between 8 and 9 mm. It is possible some of the older eggs have the envelopes enlarged from 6–7 mm. to even 8 or 9 mm.

HATCHING PERIOD

The two egg masses (quite fresh) taken July 14, 1923 at Onekio hatched July 18 and 19 or about 5 or 6 days after deposition. They were in shallow pans with water between 60° and 70°. Doubtless in nature the hatching would not be more rapid particularly with the deeply laid masses. On July 2, Mr. Bishop and his associates could find no eggs at Clear Lake, Adirondack Lodge. On July 13–15 he found several masses about at the hatching period. Presumably then 11 to 13 days is a maximum for this mid-summer form if the eggs be deep in the water.

MATURE TADPOLE

Color description from life (July 11, 1923.) General coloration is citrine or yellowish olive to dark olive or olive in specimens where hind legs begin to develop well. On the back are small scattered dark spots more or less uniform. When a tadpole has hind legs well developed (forelegs not out) back becomes bluish black and the hind legs stand out by color contrast by being a prominent citrine, buffy citrine, dull citrine or olive citrine. When it reaches the four legged stage the spots of the posterior back are quite well outlined. The mental region is grayish olive and more or less clouded. The pectoral region has a little of greenish color. Where the sides join the belly the body is mottled. Belly straw yellow, colonial buff or deep colonial buff.

Tail. On the lower crest along the edge are many roundish cartridge buff or pinkish buff spots. On the base of the musculature of the tail these collect as pinkish cinnamon spots suggesting somewhat the light areas in a similar place on *Rana grylio* tadpoles. On the rim of the dorsal crest some of the cartridge buff spots are almost whitish. There are very few black specks on the tail in mature tadpoles. A little later the crests have prominent black spots on posterior half of the tail. In two-legged tadpoles a black blotch or blotches appear with pinkish cinnamon spots at the base of the tail and these are very prominent.

Iris black and pinkish cinnamon.

Some tadpoles one month old had on the dorsum three pairs of black or dark spots; one on each nostril; one on or near each eye; and one on each side of the middle of the back. The dark of each eye connected with the back spot by an arc or semicircle of light color. This is the general appearance without a lens.

General appearance. Tadpole large (99 mm.) of the *R. grylio* or *R. clamitans* type, but without black gular area of *R. grylio*. Venter heavily pigmented with white so intestine does not show through in life or preserved specimens. Tail elongate, tip acute. Dorsal crest not as wide as musculature, not extending forward on body much beyond the level of the buds of the hind legs. Spiracle sinistral, directed backward and obliquely upwards, just visible from dorsal aspect. Spiracular opening just touches lateral axis as in *R. grylio*. Eye just above or rarely on lateral axis. Anus dextral on level with lower edge of ventral crest. Muciferous crypts distinct. A short dorsal row of 8 to 10 pores on either side of middle line of back from the dorsal crest forward; from above the middle line of insertion of tail musculature on body to back of eye is a distinct line of pores. Just before it approaches the eye area it sends obliquely upward and backwards toward dorsum a short line in the direction of the end of the first row described. When this main line reaches area just back of the eye, a blind short line starts transversely across occiput but is very short, another continues as supraorbital line to above nostril, another behind eye and under mouth as infraorbital to nostril. The portion behind the eye sends off an upward and backward loop which immediately swings downward parallel with the infraorbital for a short distance, then it descends directed downward to level of upper jaw to be and turns at right angles forward toward the mouth. Another lateral row forms a loop around the tip of the spiracle.

Mouth parts: Teeth 2/3. Edge of upper labium fringed with teeth, the fringe about the length of the horny beak, or somewhat longer. In either corner, beneath this fringe is a short row of teeth one sixth to two fifteenths the length of the upper fringe. The outer end of the lateral row does not reach beyond the edge of the upper fringe. The median space between these two rows is three and one half to four and one half times the length of either row. From above the end of the first upper labial row down to the end of the third row are two or three irregular rows of papillae inside the outer row of papillae. These run to the end of the third row and in one case where the third row is lost it is replaced by papillae inside the usual single row across lower labium. Third lower row therefore about equal to the single row of papillae on lower labium, much less than horny beak, and 1/3 shorter than the first row of lower labial teeth. The first and second rows are about equal to horny beak. The first one often subdivided. In general it is much like *R. grylio* and one adult tadpole has a black line of spots on dorsal crest much like *grylio* tadpoles.

Measurements. Length of body (24–33 mm.) in tail (45–67 mm.) 1.66–2.1, average 1.86. Width (13.5–23.0) of body in its own length 1.3–2.1, average 1.56. Depth (11–19.5 mm.) of body 1.14–1.33 in body width, average 1.23. Depth of body 1.64–2.16 in body length, average 1.85. Depth (12.0–19.0 mm.) of tail in length of tail 3.2–4.7, average 3.87. Depth of tail .85–1.1 in body depth, average 1.97. Muscular part (6.5–13.0 mm.) 1.3–1.9 in depth of tail, average 1.48. Spiracle 1.2–1.3 nearer base of hind legs or vent region (9–18 mm.) than the tip of the snout (16.0–22.5 mm.), average

1.37. Spiracle 1.25–1.6 nearer eye (6.5–12.5 mm.) than base of hind legs or vent, average 1.45. Eye 1.–1.4 nearer tip of snout (8–11 mm.) than spiracle (8.0–12.5 mm.), average 1.14. Nostril 1.0–1.6 nearer eye (4.0–5.5 mm.) than snout (4.0–6.5 mm.), average 1.16. Mouth (4.5–6.5 mm.), usually 1.0–1.3 larger than internasal space (4.0–6.0 mm.), average 1.11. Mouth contained in interorbital distance (6.5–9 mm.) 1.3–1.75 times, average 1.55. Internasal space contained in interorbital space 1.4–1.9, average 1.7.

The dimensions of the largest tadpole are:

	mm.		mm.
Total length	99	Spiracle to vent	18
Body length	32	Spiracle to eye	12
Body depth	19.5	Eye to snout	11
Body width	23.0	Eye to nostril	5.5
Tail length	67.0	Nostril to snout	6.0
Tail depth	18.0	Mouth	6.0
Musculature of tail	13.0	Interorbital distance	9.0
Spiracle to snout	22.5	Internasal distance	5.0

LARVAL PERIOD

Garnier in his point number 4 held that the tadpoles of *R. catesbeiana, R. clamitans* and *R. septentrionalis* require two years to mature. In another place he wrote: "Frog now spawned (July or August) cannot be completed this season, as there are plenty of tadpoles in October and November of *R. catesbeiana, septentrionalis* and *clamitans.* They are seen, all of them, without limbs in spring, and at the present moment they are all three being perfected and assuming the imago, or perfected form. Thus, it requires two years to perfect this little frog."

Inasmuch as *R. clamitans* may transform from 365–400 days from egg deposition doubtless Garnier is in error in believing two years necessary for transformation in *R. septentrionalis* whose tadpoles transform at 29–38 mm. or average 33 mm. *R. clamitans* transforms at a similar size 28–38 mm., average 32 mm., while *R. catesbeiana* transforms 43–59 mm. or 53 mm. average, the latter size, practically a one year old *R. septentrionalis* beyond transformation. If some of the *R. septentrionalis* at 41–44 mm. with stumps are not tardy in losing their tails after transformation possibly *R. septentrionalis* occupies an intermediate position between *R. clamitans* and *R. catesbeiana.* I prefer to believe one year or slightly more the larval period, yet two years in some cases may be required.

TRANSFORMATION

This may come from June to August or September. Garnier (p. 951) "On the 24th ult. (June, 1883) obtained several tadpoles, one a nearly perfect frog with only a small fragment of a tail to be absorbed; several had both legs and arms and others the hind legs with the arms quite ready to make their appearance and the skin confining them at the shoulders, transparent." On July 16th (Copeia, 1915, p. 45) Wright captured at Dorset, Ontario, "one or two frogs with the stump of the tail remaining. These were about 38 mm. (1½ inches from snout to vent, or little below the two largest specimens which were taken (49 mm. or 2 inches). The other specimens which were not lost measured 47, 42, 42, 43, 40, 40 mm. respectively." At the time I did not sense it but these eight were doubtless little past transformation.

On August 8–9, 1917, Pope (Copeia, Dec. 31, 1918, p. 96) found tadpoles transforming and transformed at Tim Pond, Eustis, Franklin Co. Me. "Most of the tadpoles had completed their transformation before this date but I collected a single one with large hind legs, measuring 1 15/16 inches including the tail. Most of the frogs found had evidently completed their change this summer and some retained the stump of a tail. They averaged 1 3/4 inches long, snout to vent. The adults of which I collected four, were nearly twice this size 2 15/16 inches."

In a group of 60 or more specimens taken the middle and last of August, 1919, Mr. S. E. R. Simpson has three just transformed at 32, 35 and 36 mm. This summer (1923) from tadpoles from Onekio, I have two transformed on July 2, two at 30 and 34 mm., and one July 14 at 29 mm. We, therefore, have transformation from June 24 (Garnier) to the last of August (Simpson) at from 29–38 mm. or possibly to 40–49 mm. I believe that sometimes after real transformation they retain the tail for a considerable period. The bulk of transformation doubtless comes in June and July.

Subsequent notes on some of the U. S. National Museum material are as follows:

(a) Mill Creek, Sackett's Harbor, N. Y., Evermann & Clark, July 2, 1894.

No. 39747. Transforming, 4 legs. 34 mm. in body; tail stub 29. Dark band more or less down middle of tail musculature but band broken up.

No. 39748. Transforming, 4 legs. 29 mm. in body, tail stub 27 mm; tail musculature with broken band.

(b) Peterboro, N. Y. Mrs. E. P. Miller—1900.

No. 28455. 37 mm. Not long past transformation.

No. 28456. 36.5 mm.

(c) Peterboro, N. Y. Mr. G. S. Miller, Jr., July 26, 1900.

No. 28338. 36 mm. Just transformed.
" 28339. 38.5 mm. Just past transformation.
" 28340. 38 mm. Just past transformation.
" 28341. 40 mm. Just past transformation.
" 28342. 42.5 mm. Just past transformation.
" 28344. 40 mm. Just transformed.
" 28345. 41 mm. Just past transformation.
" 28346. 39 mm. Just past transformation.

(d) 1st Connecticut Lake, N. H. Bur. Fisheries, July 21, 1904.

No. 36465. 40 mm. Still signs of transformation.
" 36466. 38.5 mm. Apron on back from transformation.

(e) Newport, Clyde R., Vt. Evermann & Bean, July 23, 1894.

No. 39814. 31.5 mm. Just transformed.

(f) Lucknow, Ont.   J. H. Garnier, July 1, 1883.

   No. 13605.   One 30 mm., tail stub small.

               One 31.5 mm., tail stub 46, dark mottling along middle
               of musculature.

               One 30 mm., transformed, slight stub.

All the above U. S. National Museum material apparently came from July 2–July 26 and ranges from 29–40 in transformation size.

GROWTH

If we presume 29–40 inches to be the normal transformation size and the bulk of transformation to be the last of June and through July, possibly some specimens (average 44 mm.) taken the middle and last of August, 1919, at Peat Lake, Dorset, Ontario, may give us some clue to growth. The material sorted into three or four groups: the newly transformed, 3 specimens, 32, 35, 36 mm.; 1 specimen 41–47 mm., average 44 mm.; 27 specimens, 50 mm. ♀–58 mm. ♂, average 53 mm., and 1, 63 mm. ♀. It would seem that they transform in July at 29–38 and by the middle and last of August of the following year they might reach 41–47 mm. in length. One year later they may attain 51–58 or possibly 63, though the latter measurement may be a three year old group. Cope measures 2 specimens 1.92, 49 mm., and 2.25 (58 mm.) inches respectively in body length. Pope (Copeia, Dec. 31, 1918, p. 96) records four 2 15/16 inches (75 mm.).

From Onekio, N. Y., June 10–14, 1923, we took three groups: One of 29, 30, 33 mm. respectively just transformed; the second of 42, 48 ♀ (?) mm. respectively; and the third group of 50 ♀ and 57 ♂ mm. In the same place one month later July 13, 14, 1923, we took three or four groups: 33, 34, 35, 37, 37, 38, 38, 39 mm. near transformation; 41 and 48 mm. sex undeterminable externally: 52 ♀ ?, 52.5 ♂, 53 ♂, 54 ♂, 54 ♂, 56 ♂ mm.; a four group possibly 59 ♂, and 64 ♀ mm. We then have 29–39 mm., 41–48 mm., 50–57 mm., 59–63 ♀ mm., revealed as four groups for Onekio, N. Y.

From Hart Lake or Clear Lake, Adirondack Lodge, Adirondacks, N. Y. June 28, 1923) Drs. S. C. Bishop and C. K. Sibley secured the following six specimens: one 53 mm.; the rest 65, 69, 70, 70, 71 mm. respectively. On July 14, 1923, from same place we have one 51 ♂ mm., and two 60 ♀ and 63 ♀ mm. The 50–53 mm. specimens and 60–71 mm. specimens seem to reveal two groups.

Under (Transformation) it will be revealed that in the U. S. National Museum are 7 or 8 series in which are transformed or past transforming frogs. They range from 29–34 mm. (Sackett's Harbor, N. Y.) to 36–40 or possibly 42.5 mm. (Peterboro, N. Y., G. S. Miller, Jr.). When Mr. Miller took these he also secured a 58 ♀ mm. specimen or when Mrs. E. P. Miller secured 36.5 and 37 mm. specimens she also secured 41, 41, 41, 48 ♀, 47 ♀ mm. specimens. One other lot secured here on July 9, 1900, is 51 ♂ mm., 56 ♂ mm., 57 ♂ mm.; and 61 ♀ mm. and 66 ♀ mm. This Peterboro material shapes as follows: 36–40 mm., possibly 42.5 mm. for transformation; 47 ♀ or 48 ♀–58 ♀ mm.; 61 ♀–66 ♀ mm.

The whole U. S. National Museum series shapes thus 29–40 or possibly 42.5 mm. transformation, average 37 mm.; 41 or 42–47 or 48 mm., average 43.5 mm. first year olds; 48.5–58 or 58.5 mm., average 53.5 mm. two year olds; 60–72 mm., average 64 mm. three year olds. This material and ours combined gives 29–40 mm., average 37 mm., mode 38 mm. at transformation; 40–48 or 50 mm., average 44 for 1st year olds; 47 or 48 or 50 –58or 58.5 mm., average 53.5 mm., mode 51 mm. for two year olds; and 59 or 60 to 72 mm., average 63 mm., for three year olds.

FOOD

Garnier finds that (p. 945) "it preys on water beetles and similar insects, but seems especially partial to the Julus family, having generally found it in the stomachs examined." (P. 947) "the stomachs of many have been examined by me, and they contained mostly Carabus, Julus, and water insects, and on two occasions some little fish, chubs, if I remember correctly, about an inch long. Thus their food is like that of other frogs." In two different instances he found tadpoles eating dead fish, one a brook trout, the other a chub. He saw one (tadpole) rush at, seize a large Ephemera that came near it and swallowed it, yet it had not more than the third of its tail absorbed."

ENEMIES

As already revealed under eggs the newt is a serious foe of the eggs and hatching embryos. Being more common in the southern parts the water-snake is a negligible factor in the life of this species unlike the case of *R. virgatipes*. The great blue heron and other herodiones are amongst the worst foes of the mink frog.

AFFINITIES

Garnier considered "certain peculiarities in the life history and in external forms of these three Ranas (*R. catesbeiana*, *R. clamata* and *R. septentrionalis*) which so thoroughly agree that they may be separated into a group by themselves. These I shall endeavor to point out as concisely as possible:"

"1. They have no 'chant amour' or love notes in spring.

"2. They retire early to hibernate with the first autumnal frosts.

"3. They live in water and lie in wait for their food, but do not hunt for it on land. They poise the body on any floating weeds, lie on the bank or any bit of stick or log that suits their purpose.

"4. The tadpoles of *R. catesbeiana* and *R. fontinalis* require two years to mature, and the mink frog requires the same period.

"5. Adults in all three have no lateral fold, but merely a slight raising of the skin from the angle of the mouth, and which terminates or shades off on the shoulder.

"6. The foot is broader in proportion than in the rest of the family, and the second toe is proportionately shorter, a peculiarity emphatically distinct, and can be seen at an glance by any one who takes the trouble of even a cursory observation, webbed to extremities.

"7. When captured they sometimes utter a cry of distress quite different from their ordinary croaking notes, and I have often seen a bullfrog open his mouth and scream for even a minute, like a child in distress.

"8. When they give their note it is always produced by inflating the throat pouch and suddenly expelling the air, whereas in *R. halecina* there is a pouch near the angle of the jaws, on either side.

"9. They are all tinged, more or less, with yellowish-green on the chin, which soon shades towards the throat and breast, and on the belly is white, more or less, in many subjects most beautifully so.

There is thus an analogy in their life history, and in their external conformation that at once forms them into a group by themselves, and makes a marked section. I am not aware, however, that there is any anatomical difference sufficient to make a genus."

In 1889 Cope (pp. 396, 397) graphically makes this species a central form from which four lines of North American Ranas radiate. "Sometimes the vomerine teeth in *Rana temporaria pretiosa* are not appreciably more posterior in position than in *Rana septentrionalis*, in which case the species approach each other very closely. The *Rana septentrionalis* violates the characters which distinguish the *R. clamata* and *R. catesbeiana* from each other, and would afford a complete connection between them were it not for its inferior size; but even this point does not invariably hold good, as a few specimens of *R. clamata* do not exceed it in dimensions."

"These series (four radiate lines above) are not probably genetic, as some of the species have been most likely derived from the Old World. The *R. septentrionalis*, however, may be very probably ancestral to the forms of the Catesbeiana series, and perhaps of others."

"The variations of the *Rana septentrionalis* are greater than those of any other North American species of the genus. There is, however, no coincidence between them, so that they cannot be regarded as indicating subspecies. The tympanic disc varies greatly in size, the males having it larger than the eye, and the females smaller than the eye. In this respect the species displays its near affinity to the *R. clamata* and *R. catesbeiana*. Some specimens have a dorsolateral dermal glandular ridge, and others have none, such difference being exhibited by specimens from the same locality. The spotting of the dorsal surface varies very much. In some specimens the spots are not closely placed; in others they leave only narrow lines of the lighter ground color between them."

Taking all its characters together, this species occupies a position intermediate "between nearly all the North American species of the genus, and from some such form it might be supposed that all the Ranae of the northern hemisphere have been derived." (Pp. 418, 419).

Boulenger (1920, p. 425) later comments: "I cannot agree with Cope . . .; nor do I think him justified in adding that 'from such a form it might be supposed that all the Rana of the northern hemisphere have been derived,' a statement I would rather apply to *Rana catesbeiana* and *Rana grylio*, regarding *R. septentrionalis* as connecting *R. catesbeiana* with *R. clamitans*."

There is another point of view expressed in H. H. T. Jackson's "The Land Vertebrates of Ridgeway Bog, Wisconsin: Their Ecological Succession and Source of Ingression. (Bull. Wisc. Nat. Hist. Soc. Vol. 12, Nos. 1 and 2, June 1914, pp. 17, 18). "The northern frog, *Rana septentrionalis*, has been considered by some herpetologists to be a subspecies of *Rana clamitans*; specimens of the two forms are often morphologically very similar, but their habits and behavior are so widely at variance that it seems improbable they interbreed. For example, *Rana septentrionalis* is relatively, a sluggish frog; during the summer months it is found along the edge of lakes and streams, usually with the body partly submerged in the water, occasionally on land at the water's edge; when alarmed it utters no sound, makes a feeble leap of two or three feet into the water, settles to the bottom and hides in the mud or under some object where it is easily captured in the hand. Contrast with the behavior of this frog that of *Rana clamitans*; the latter is an active frog; during the summer months it is almost invariably found out of the water on a gently sloping bank; when alarmed it utters a loud startling croak, makes a vigorous leap of five or eight feet into the water, swims some distance under water before hiding, where it remains alert and difficult to capture. There remains, of course, the alternative to explain this as "one species having different mores" (Shelford, 1912a, p. 92), but one can hardly accept this view in the present case."

Such discussions are unsatisfactory. It depends on what characters one knows best, what he is most interested in, or what he accidentally discovers that he uses as his criteria or canes on which he leans. What follows may be of no consequence:

1. Little evidence can link it with *Rana sylvatica* or *R. cantabrigensis*. Sometimes the adults are almost free of spots like *Rana sylvatica*, *R. cantabrigensis*, or some of the Northwestern species. Its eggs are with two jelly envelopes and the above species have the second indefinite. The egg mass is submerged as in *R. sylvatica*, or *R. cantabrigensis* and about of the same size. The woodfrog and northern woodfrog choose woodland pools, etc.; *R. septentrionalis*, peaty lakes, waterlily ponds. The tadpoles are wholly unlike the woodfrog, one transforms the year laid and the other after wintering over at least one season. The two have deep tail crests far forward in body and with labial tooth rows more numerous, while *R. septentrionalis* has the elongate large narrower tail crests of a *Rana clamitans* type and tooth rows 2/3. The two transform at a small size; *R. septentrionalis* transforms at a variable but usually large size. There is little in common with the woodfrogs.

2. *Rana palustris.*

   The pickerel frog (*Rana palustris*) is one of our most poisonous frogs with a decided odor. So also *Rana septentrionalis* is the "mink" frog. Therein they might be associated if secretions be the criterion. Each lays submerged egg masses, each has eggs quite similar in size, envelopes and color. Each adult has about the same degree of vocal sac development in the male.

The adults are unlike in color pattern but *Rana septentrionalis* may have the upper parts with pronounced spots but not regularized. *Rana palustris* tadpole may be held as much *R. clamitans*-like in appearance as *R. pipiens*—(also *sphenocephala, aesopus, areolata*) like but it transforms the same year as eggs laid. The transformation size is smaller and it breeds in late April and May while *R. septentrionalis* belongs to the June–July season of *R. clamitans, R. virgatipes, R. grylio, R. catesbeiana*. But *Rana catesbeiana* breeding in February 1925 in San Antonio, Texas, cured the author of over emphasis on this prop.

3. *Rana clamitans*.

Sometimes it has a suggestion of a dorsolateral glandular fold; its tadpoles winter over at least a season, and the tadpoles have the outline of *R. clamitans* type; sometimes adults have no spots like *Rana clamitans*; sometimes *R. clamitans* in Adirondack and Northern parts are much spotted.

Usually they have no dorsolateral fold, are usually spotted, transform at much larger size than *R. clamitans* though adult is smaller: lays submerged egg mass, not surface films. Its nearest relationship lies doubtless with No. 4.

4. *Rana virgatipes*.

(See *Rana virgatipes* Affinities).

In transformation size *Rana septentrionalis* approaches *Rana catesbeiana* or *Rana grylio* more than *R. clamitans*, while *R. virgatipes* goes into the *R. pipiens* and *R. palustris* class.

5. *Rana pipiens*.

Rana septentrionalis is an associate of this form in the west of its range and may have come from this widespread species. Its egg mass looks more like that of *Rana virgatipes* than *R. pipiens* yet *Rana septentrionalis* has two envelopes on each egg as *R. pipiens* but thisis not to be overemphasized. They are in different tadpole and transformation classes though the adults of the mink frog are smaller than *R. pipiens* However they may approach. Witness A. C. Weed's description of *Rana kandiyohi* from Minnesota where *Rana septentrionalis* and *R. pipiens* are. He writes: "Typical specimens of this species show a color pattern which suggests a blending of *Rana pipiens* and *Rana septentrionalis*. It is as though the black spots of *Rana pipiens* had been superposed on the mottled color of *septentrionalis*. ———." (Weed 1922, p. 109).

BIBLIOGRAPHY

1920 Boulenger, G. A. A Monograph of the American Frogs of the Genus Rana. Proc. Am. Acad. Arts and Sciences, Vol. 55, No. 9, August 1920, pp. 423-425.

1889 Cope, E. D. The Batrachia of North America, U. S. N. M. Bull. No. 34, Wash. 1889, pp. 416-419.

1906   Dickerson, M. C. The Frog Book, 1906, pp. 224-225.

1883   Garnier, J. H. The Mink or Hoosier Frog. The American Naturalist, XVII, Sept. 1883, No. 9, pp. 945-954.

1914   Jackson, H. H. T. The Land Vertebrates of Ridgeway, Wisconsin: Their Ecological Succession and Source of Ingression. Bull. Wisc. Nat. Hist. Soc., Vol. 12, Nos. 1 and 2, June 1914, pp. 17, 18.

1898   Mearns, E. A. Bull. Am. Mus. Nat. Hist., Vol. X, p. 325.

1915   Pope, P. H. The Distribution of the Northern Frog, *Rana septentrionalis* Baird in Maine. Copeia, No. 16, March 15, 1915, pp. 1, 2.

1918   ———. A New Record for *Rana septentrionalis* Baird. Copeia, No. 64, Dec. 31, 1918, pp. 96, 97.

1922   Weed, A. C. New Frogs from Minnesota. Proc. Biol. Soc. Wash., Oct. 17, 1922, Vol. 35, pp. 107-110.

1915   Wright, A. H. The Mink Frog, *Rana septentrionalis* Baird, in Ontario. Copeia No. 23, October 15, 1915, pp. 46-48.

1920   Wright, A. H. The Frog. U. S. Dep't Commerce, Bureau of Fisheries, Doc. 888, 1920, pp. 11, 16, 34, 35.

Rana sphenocephala (Cope)

(Pl. III, Fig. 7; V, Fig. 12; IX, Fig. 3; XI, Figs. 9, 10; XIII, Fig. 2; XVI, Figs, 7, 8; XVII; XL; XLI, Text Figs. 1, 21)

COMMON NAMES

Southern Leopard Frog. Southern Meadow Frog. "Spring Frog." Spotted Frog. Water Frog. Shad Frog.

RANGE

Check list. "Range: Southeastern States." (Stejneger & Barbour 1923, p. 37).

Supplementary records. Deckert (1914, Nos. 3 & 5) gives two meadow frogs at Jacksonville, Florida, each abundant. Whether it be they were puzzling or the two were there or the distinction between the two species be poor we cannot understand. Those just north of Jacksonville, Florida, in Okefinokee Swamp are of the *R. sphenocephala* form. In 1922 the same author (p. 88) finds only *Rana sphenocephala* in Dade Co., Florida. Of these he "saw numbers along the shore of the brackish canal on the right of the Ingraham Highway, between Royal Palm Hammock and Cape Sable. Löding (1922, p. 20) records it in three counties in Alabama. Viosca, Jr., in 1918 (p. 160) records only *R. sphenocephala* but in recent years I believe he has found both *R. pipiens* and *R. sphenocephala* as has Ortenberger (1927, pp. 46, 47) in the panhandle of Oklahoma. Edith R. Force (1925, p. 25) recorded it from Okmulgee Co., Oklahoma. Philip H. Pope (1919, p. 97) carried it westward into Texas as far as Houston, Texas. Ortenberger (1921, p. 75) found each species *R. pipiens* and *R. sphenocephala* in Indiana. The recorded range northward along the Atlantic Coast is to North Carolina where (G. S. Myers, 1914, p. 60) and Brimley & Mabie (1925, p. 15) record it. In 1923 we saw meadow frogs at Lakehurst, N. J. and in southern New Jersey strikingly like *Rana sphenocephala.*

Local Okefinokee records. In 1912 we found it on the outskirts of the swamp as well as in the swamp. We secured mainly tadpoles and young in 1912. In 1921 we recorded it on Billy's Island, Chesser's Island, Suwannee Canal,

Honey Id. Prairie, mainland east of Chesser's Island. In 1922 we took it along St. Mary's River, Chesser Island and mainland between the swamp and St. Mary's River.

GENERAL APPEARANCE

We are provisionally keeping this form as a separate species. If this were a taxonomic paper we would make more measurements and studies to solve it. The southern meadow frog is an alert, active, long-legged and long-snouted spotted frog.

Miss Dickerson chose the long head, circular white tympanic spot and dorsal spots not outlined by white as distinctive of this species in contrast with *Rana pipiens*, the northern meadow frog. Boulenger, G. A. (1920, pp. 438, 439) points out that these characters are not constant and does not recognize *R. sphenocephala* as separate. Of it Miss Dickerson writes (1906, p. 187): "The head is long and pointed, with the eyes set far back. This characteristic and the usual length of the hind legs distinguish this frog at once from *Rana pipiens*, the Common Leopard Frog. It is peculiar also in possessing a circular white spot at the center of the ear. This spot is never lacking, no matter what the coloration of the frog may be at the time. *Rana pipiens* has sometimes a light blotch at or near the centre of the ear, but never this clean-cut circle of white."

COLORATION OF SPIRIT SPECIMENS (1912)

In 1912 we made these distinctions between *R. pipiens* and *R. sphenocephala* on the basis of coloration of spirit specimens. On the back the color may be deep olive to green or purplish brown. On the inner portion of the upper eyelid the blackish brown spot is smaller than in *Rana pipiens* and not so constant. Two or three of the specimens have these two spots absent. In most *R. pipiens* there is a median spot ahead of these two orbital spots and in all these *R. sphenocephala* this is absent. The dark line from snout through the nostril to the front of the eye is possibly more constant and prominent than in *R. pipiens*. Between the lateral folds are two rows of spots more widely separated than in *R. pipiens* and less regularly placed. Below the lateral folds in *R. pipiens* there are two or three irregular rows of smaller spots but in *R. sphenocephala* there is usually one row followed by a more or less vermiculated area, the black sometimes forming more or less horizontal lines. On the fore-arm of *R. pipiens* there are two or three separate spots on the posterior edge of the brachium while in *R. sphenocephala* these are united into one broad brown band; in both there is a brown band on the anterior side of the brachium, in *R. sphenocephala* averaging larger than in *R. pipiens*. In both there is usually a prominent spot on the front of the forearm and usually a band on the posterior edge. These rarely may be absent. The bars of the hind limbs are farther apart and less developed in *R. sphenocephala* than in *R. pipiens* and the small spot below and in front of the anterior femoral bars are more or less separate in *R. pipiens* but generally unite to form a prominent antefemoral dark stripe, particularly in the adults of *R. sphenocephala*. This femoral band often unites with the dark vermiculations or reticulations of the groin. The posterior faces of the thighs in *R. pipiens* have the brown spots more or less separate and the lighter interspaces are equally emphasized to form the reticulum but in *R. sphenocephala* the brown spots become connected and surround the lighter inter-spaces, the dark being the reticulum. The stripe from the snout under the eye to the shoulder is yellowish, much lighter and more prominent than a similar more or less bronzy line in *R. pipiens*. The same difference obtains in the color of the lateral fold. On the upper jaw of *R. pipiens* there is a more or less sharply defined dark line below the above light stripes and below the dark line a clear white or yellowish white edge to the upper lip. In *R. sphenocephala* these two areas are not sharp and the upper and lower lips are more or less dark and light spotted. In *R. pipiens* the lower lip is usually with a few or no dark spots while in *R. sphenocephala* this is the regular coloration. On the throat region and under side of the hind legs dusky fleckings much more frequently enter in the coloration of *R. sphenocephala* than in *R. pipiens*. The under parts are whitish or yellowish white.

In most of the specimens the clear cut distinct white spot in the middle of the tympanum is sufficiently distinctive but in some young and adults the character fails to separate *R. sphenocephala* from *R. pipiens*. Our specimens have not the tibia with complete cross bars but we question its use as a constant distinction because many *R. pipiens* are without complete bars though this latter species inclines more towards the barred state of affairs.

If time were at hand to study as carefully 1921 and 1922 material possibly some of these foregoing distinctions made in 1913 would be changed or recognized as non-distinctive.

STRUCTURAL CHARACTERS (WRITTEN IN 1912)

On the basis of our 1912 specimens these characters are noted. The skin is smooth; on either side of the back is a prominent dorso-lateral fold. Between these two folds on the back there may be no ridges at all or five or six smaller secondary ridges or folds colored like the body and not as the dorso-lateral folds and more or less broken in appearance. These intermediate folds are more prominent in the young specimens. The muzzle is more acuminate than in *R. pipiens*. A prominent fold below the eye to below the tympanum in breeding males or to shoulder in others. Nostril about equidistant from the end of the snout and eye. First finger longer than the second and about equal to the fourth. Third finger larger than the rest. A tarsal fold more or less present; fourth toe of *R. sphenocephala* longer than in *R. pipiens*, sometimes longer by one or two phalanges in specimens of the same size. Three phalanges of the 4th toe free. Inner metatarsal tubercle present. Tongue prominently notched behind; vomerine teeth between inner choanae and in transverse series. These characters not verified with 1921 and 1922 material.

MEASUREMENTS
(Recent Material)

Head to angle of mouth .95 (28 mm.)–.96 (44 mm.)–1.02 (56 mm.)–1.13 (68 mm.)–1.1 (82 mm.) in width of head; head to rear of tympanum .8–.83–

.91–.93–.86 in width of head; head to angle of mouth 2.66–2.83–2.73–2.72–3.5 in length of body; head to rear of tympanum 2.24–2.5–2.43–2.5–2.82 in length of body; snout .66–.88–1.0–.96–.84 in 1st finger; snout .66–.5–.62–.46–.60 in 4th finger; snout .41–.55–.57–.7–.64 in first toe; eye .87–1.0–.85–1.07–1.06 in tympanum; eye 1.5–1.63–1.5–1.85–1.6 in snout; eye 1.0–1.4–1.5 in first finger; tympanum 2.28–2.0–2.33–2.0–2.1 in intertympanic width; tympanum 1.7–1.63–1.75–1.73–1.77 in snout; internasal width .85–.88–1.0–.93–1.05 in upper eyelid width; interorbital width 1.4–1.28–1.37–1.3–1.3 in internasal space; interorbital width 1.2–1.14–1.37–1.2–1.4 in upper eyelid width; interorbital width 3.2–3.14–3.5–3.0–3.6 in intertympanic width.

Forelimb: 1.86–2.0–1.75–2.08–2.1 in length (snout to vent); forelimb 2.73–3.3–3.5–3.7–3.33 in hind limb; first finger 1.375–.93–.85–.80–1.1 in third finger; second finger 1.8–1.33–1.4–1.33–1.29 in third finger; second finger 1.13–1.45–1.7–1.66–1.15 in first finger; third finger 1.0–1.26–1.44–1.4–1.25 in second toe; fourth finger 1.375–1.66–1.35–1.66–1.5 in third finger; fourth finger .63–1.2–.92–1.5–1.07 in first toe; internasal width 1.14–1.7–1.9–1.94–1.68 in first finger; 1.0–1.22–1.08–1.16–1.46 in second finger; 1.55–1.66–1.8–1.55–1.85 in third finger; 1.1–1.0–1.17–.92–1.22 in fourth finger.

Hindlimb: length of body 1.46–1.7–2.0–1.8–1.58 in hind limb; tibia 1.86–1.7–1.55–1.45–1.82 in length; 2.73–2.84–3.1–3.02–2.88 in hind limb; 1.0–.84–.88–.81–.86 in fore limb; 1.33–.88–.91–.93–.91 in hind foot; first toe 2.2–1.9–2.16–1.55–1.78 in second toe; 3.0–2.8–2.75–2.27–2.4 in third toe; 4.4–4.3–4.75–3.77–4.0 in fourth toe; 2.2–3.7–3.16–2.77–2.5 in fifth toe; second toe 1.36–1.47–1.3–1.47–1.4 in third toe; 2.0–2.26–2.2–2.43–2.23 in fourth toe; 1.27–1.9–1.44–1.70–1.40 in fifth toe; third toe 1.44–1.53–1.7–1.7–1.5 in fourth toe; .93–1.32–1.15–1.2–1.0 in fifth toe; fourth toe 1.8–1.06–1.12–1.1–1.3 in hind foot; 1.36–1.2–1.26–1.17–1.3 in tibia; 1.36–1.02–1.1–.95–1.16 in forelimb; fifth toe 1.55–1.16–1.5–1.4–1.6 in fourth toe; internasal width .7–1.1–1.1–1.36–1.3 in first toe; 1.75–2.1–2.35–2.1–2.3 in second toe; 2.03–3.1–3.0–3.01–3.2 in third toe; 3.14–4.8–5.1–5.2–5.1 in fourth toe; 2.0–4.1–3.2–3.7–3.2 in fifth toe.

HABITAT

In 1912 we did not find it commonly in the lakes, runs or prairies. Its habits accorded with those of our northern *R. pipiens* and we did not particularly study the species. More young and tadpoles than adults were taken. They were either in or about the small ponds and pools along the edge of the islands, or in the cypress thickets about the islands. In 1921 and 1922 we made most of our records in cypress ponds or temporary pools, though prairies, runs, Suwannee Canal, river swamps and overflowed roads and ditches and railroad ditches also added to our localities for the species. In the swamp it is ideally of the edge of cypress ponds and bays or small pools and ponds at an island's edge.

Wm. Bartram (1791 pp. 278, 279) describes it thus: "The shad frog, so called in Pennsylvania, from their appearing and croaking in the spring season at the time the people fish for shad: these are a beautiful spotted frog, of a slender form, five or six inches in length from the nose to the extremities;

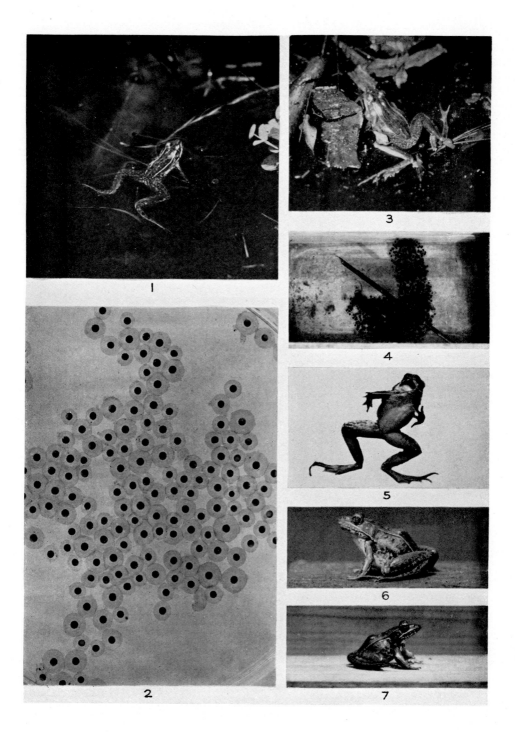

1

2

3

4

5

6

7

of a dark olive green, blotched with clouds and ringlets of a dusky color; these are remarkable jumpers and enterprising hunters, leaving their ponds to a great distance in search of prey. They abound in rivers, swamps and marshes in the southern region; in the evening and sultry summer days, particularly in times of drought, are very noisy, and at some distance one would be almost persuaded that there were assemblies of men in serious debate. These have also a sucking or clucking noise, like that which is made by sucking in the tongue under the roof of the mouth."

FIRST APPEARANCE

In 1910, 1912, 1913, 1914, 1921, 1922 we have records of it from April to October, December and January. In the latter months Francis Harper heard it croaking and in December (1913) J. Chester Bradley found both adult males and females abroad. The months we lack records of it is more because of absence from the swamp than from hibernation by the species. Mr. Percy Viosca, Jr., of New Orleans, La., once told me he believed it might breed every month in the year in Louisiana unless it be one month. Quite the same is possible in the Okefinokee Swamp. Deckert (1914, p. 5) at Jacksonville, Fla., finds it "everywhere from February to November." Later Deckert (1921, p. 21) found it breeding in December at Lemon City, Fla.

GENERAL HABITS

Some of the residents of the swamp maintain its common name of "Spring Frog" is from its ability to leap or *spring*. Others hold it likes *springy* places but usually it is called "spring frog" from its time of breeding and croaking in the *spring* months. It is agile and hard to capture in water or on land. Barbour (1920, p. 56) remarks that "*Rana sphenocephala*, when alarmed while resting on a bank of a stream or pond, usually turns about and escapes inland with leaping bounds, evidently more afraid of enemies in the water than on the land."

On June 1, 1921, we remarked that *Rana sphenocephala* were hopping around the island after breeding, also that they were becoming browner when afield and as the season progressed.

VOICE

Of the croaking position we recorded on April 23, 1921 that "Male *Rana sphenocephala* lie on the surface when croaking or are amongst pickerel weed stems." The rear of the body usually sprawled out (see illustrations) may be at the surface or submerged. The head and upper back are usually emergent. At times they may croak from the edge of a pond like *R. pipiens* or croak beneath the surface or lie amongst drift wood. On May 16 we "heard several males but they were hard to find and ceased croaking after we found them. At 11:20 p. m. we heard *Rana sphenocephala*. Strange we did not hear them when we were near the pond but distance had to sift out the calls. Over in the north part and northeast edge of a pond were males calling amongst the weeds. When a person approaches normally they duck or hop or swim away.

We are having less success in photographing them than croaking males of any
other species encountered." In 1922 we were of the same opinion according to
our note of July 13. At 12.30–1:00 a. m. "We awoke and heard a great
chorus over in the area northwest of our spring. Here in grassy borders of
open spots were plenty of meadow frogs. These would stop croaking when we
approached near them. They are surely shy and begin croaking late at night."

One month later, August 9th, heard two immense choruses, one at 3:00
a. m. and another at 4–5:00 a. m. Went to the latter congress. "Perched on
logs, sticks, and around bases of bushes were plenty of croaking males."

This species begins croaking and breeding early in the season long before
we arrived in the swamp in April. The earlier choruses come by day as well
as at night. On April 23, 1921, it began at night at 8 or 9:00 p. m. A month
later, May 18–May 20 heard it at 8:00 p. m. On May 19 we heard them at
1:00 a. m., on June 7, at 2:30–2:00 a. m., July 1 late in morning before dawn,
July 3 at 2:00 a. m. July 5 at 12:30–1:00 a. m., July 25 before dawn. As
the season advances the later breeders may be heard only in late morning
before dawn except for rare periods in day time before a storm passes or after
its passage.

A resume of the croaking for 1921 and 1922 follows:

1921

April	23.	Began croaking in chorus in cypress pond. Air 58°, water 60°. Began about 8:00 p. m.
"	24.	Heard several meadow frogs.
May	16.	Began to croak after storm had passed.
"	18.	Calling at 8:00 p. m. At times an immense chorus.
"	19.	Several calling 1:00 a. m.
"	21.	In Bufo pond the loudest chorus yet, 8:00 p. m. Air 70°. In several ponds they are calling.
"	27.	One heard.
June	1.	Hear some.
"	6.	Going strong late in the night.
"	7.	Croaking strongly about 2:30–3:00 a. m.
"	23.	Did not hear any tonight.
"	29.	Several heard in midafternoon before thunder storm. Several calling at night.
"	30.	Tonight frogs going strong.
July	1.	Calling in late morning before day. Few calling during day.
"	3.	Calling loudly at 2:00 a. m., Honey Island. A few calling tonight on Billy's Island.
"	5.	Chorus in Long Pond 12:30 a. m.
"	6.	A few croaking after midnight.
"	13.	Heard one in cypress bay.
"	17.	Plenty calling.
"	25.	Late at night before dawn many heard.
"	29.	Plenty of meadow frogs calling on Black Jack Island.
"	30.	Species calling.

1922

July	13.	12:30–1:00 a. m. Great chorus northwest of camp Chesser Island. Also a chorus in Coat Bet Pond.
"	21.	Several calling in the evening.

Aug. 9. 3:00 a. m. Heard a large chorus early this morning. 4–5:00 a. m. another chorus in Coat Bet Pond.

" 11. Plenty in chorus in Coat Bet Pond 1:30 a. m. Air about 72°.

" 20. Chorus before daybreak in Coat Bet Pond.

" 22. Same.

" 29. At dusk and later a few croaking on prairie.

In the 1921 croaking record the temperatures for the day of croaking were from 80–97° for maxima and 52–74° for minima. Most of our camp records for the day time range from 66–79°. Most of the large choruses came during, preceding or subsequent to large downpours of rain. On April 23, they were croaking in chorus when the air was 58° F. and water 60°. Inasmuch as most choruses came at night maxima probably play the most important role of temperatures. The average for all minima for croaking days is 65°. No doubt that or lower temperatures prevailed when southern leopard frogs croak. Humidity is a more important factor than temperature.

The croak itself comes from the swift inflation and deflation of the vocal sacs (each between forelegs and angle of mouth). On April 23 we noted that "the croak of a male sometimes is two croaks, often one or two lower croaks or two or three. Males frequently give two or three clucking-like notes often followed by two or three croaks. Whole performance no more than 4 or 5 seconds. On May 16 we wrote "The croak is 3, 4 or 5 croaks with two or three clucks afterwards. The process may occupy 5 or 6 seconds." Mr. Harper characterizes the croak as follows: "The frog may commence with a series of guttural grunting croaks: *wank-wank-wank*, . . . As a whole chorus tunes up and the clamour increases, the notes become louder and take on a more rattling quality: *wonk-wonk-wonk*. They are easily heard a quarter of a mile, . . ."

MATING

Male (From life, July 3, 1921.) Olive green or jade green or grass green on back, pale chalcedony yellow on upper lip, pale dull green yellow costal fold; center of tympanum chalcedony yellow. Some amber yellow or primuline yellow on under side of fore arm or little on the side of the groin, little on outer side of hind legs and back of crus. Under parts white. Thumb with black swelling. Iris: back part chartreuse yellow; upper part vinaceous buff; inner ring amber yellow or wax yellow; rest black.

Female (From life, June 21, 1921). Top of head to back of eye cinnamon brown to Prout's brown or snuff brown to bister or sudan brown to brussels brown. This color somewhat along inner and outer side of the costal fold, on upper jaw from snout to front of eye somewhat on upper fore limb and somewhat amongst ground color of back. At times it makes most of the ground color of the back. Back ground color of dorsum dark greenish olive to ivy green. Spots of back and sides, fore arms, shoulder bar, and hind legs, black. Those of the back with a thin light green yellow border. Under parts white. Throat and pectoral region dulled with blackish. Lower jaw rim marguerite yellow or sea foam yellow with black. Same color for upper jaw below the stripe from lower eye to arm insertion. Between the sudan brown of the side of the snout and top of the head, and in front of eye through nostril is blackish or greenish. Two or three marguerite or sea foam yellow spots behind the eye. Tympanum argus brown with marguerite yellow or sea foam yellow center. Stripe from under eye over angle of the mouth and just beneath tympanum to over arm insertion marguerite yellow or sea foam yellow.

Iris in front, below and behind pupil black with some pale vinaceous lilac or light pinkish lilac. Rim pinard yellow. Iris above pupil maize yellow. Very top of eye a small black area.

Structural differences. The males begin to show thumbs much enlarged and lateral sacs well developed when 52–58 mm. in length or when presumptive 2-year olds. Our largest females are from 76–81 or 82 mm.; our largest males from 75–78 mm.

Duration. Most mated pairs brought in laid the night of their capture and were broken the next morning after ovulation. In a few cases where impulsive males were brought in with unmated females they persisted in embrace for two or three days. Observations made for *R. pipiens* in Ithaca doubtless obtain for this species. The females probably do not come to the croaking congress until ready to lay, and this may require no more than 15–30 minutes.

Night or day. From April to September it came mainly at night, in latter part of the night, or early in the evening from April to June. Rarely by day when a thunder storm was imminent or after it had passed.

Amplexation.—On May 16 we collected some of our first mated pairs. These were all pectoral in embrace and we have recorded no other form of amplexation in the species. No opportunity was given for cross embrace with other species.

OVULATION

Habitat. In 1921 we made these notes on places of ovulation. On April 24, we found them in a cypress pond. "Center of pond is clear (alligator hole). Then came a circle of *Pontederia* in which are toad and *Rana spheno-cephala* eggs. A circle of sedges; next came bushes; a thin line of gums; and finally the pines." On April 28, of another pond we have these journal notes "Frogs eggs . . . about 8 feet from edge of the pond in water 4–6 inches deep. Two more isolated masses found each at or just below the surface and en-circling the lizard's tail (*Saururus*) which is now in bloom." May 13 one of the boys found eggs in a cypress pond. On May 22 the boys found two masses in ditches beside the railroad; also we found them in edge of cypress bay. In some of the ponds just within a hammock's edge found two masses. Later we found this form breeding in a sphagneous bog on one of the prairies.

Occasionally after severe rains they lay in very temporary places. On June 6, 1921, we found them in a temporary pool in the street. On July 7 we discovered four masses in an open used field just north of camp and near a wood pile.

In 1922 we found masses in water filled pits on high oak-shaded bluffs, beside the open road, in an open pond with saw palmetto border, but no trees, in river swamps, ponds, in cypress ponds and bays and in grassy borders where cypress bay met the open fields of Chesser Island.

Period. In 1912 we found them breeding in May to July. In 1914 (Deckert, 1914, p. 5) at Jacksonville, Florida, "found their spawn, in shallow bayous, in February, March, April, May, August and October." In 1921, basing our statements on 1912 experience we wrote: "The southern leopard frog, as well as the northern leopard frog, breeds normally in the spring, and hence is called the 'spring frog,' but occasionally its breeding period may extend until July 4 or later, after the first eggs of the species are hatched and the tadpoles transformed." In 1923 we (Wright, 1923, p. 34) held that "From April 15 or earlier to September 1st, six forms breed. . . . *Rana sphenocephala*. . . ." In 1924 we (1924, p. 377) held "Species such as *Rana sphenocephala* . . . which begin early in the season, breed during 25 to 30 weeks of the year, if not longer or from February to September or October." In 1918 Pope (1919, p. 97) at Houston, Texas, on October 15, "Found three clusters of hatching eggs, probably of this species, in a rain pool in woods road." In 1920 Deckert (1921, pp. 20, 21) in Dade County, Florida, writes that "The writer has been expecting to hear the calls of the Southern Leopard Frog, but none were heard during or after any of the heavy rains of May and June. During the night of December 5, at Lemon City, after a violent thunder storm the temperature dropped suddenly from 84°F. to 62°F., and when the writer at 1:30 a. m. took a ramble around his yard with a lantern, he heard the croak of what, according to his experience, must have been this frog. The next morning was bright and quite cool, and the writer found, about half a mile from his house, in a rain-ditch in a nearby rock-pit, three batches of frog-spawn."

In 1921 we found the southern meadow frog eggs from April 23 to July 23. In 1922 we found them from June 22–August 9. These accumulated records of others and ours give February to December for breeding. Doubtless January also has its breeding frogs.

Temperature and humidity. Some of our records for ovulation are:

April 23, 1921	May 21, 1921	July 23, 1921
April 24, 1921	June 25, 1921	June 22, 1922
May 13, 1921	June 30, 1921	July 13, 1922
May 16, 1921	July 7, 1921	August 9, 1922

Most of these were laid at night when temperatures range from 50–70°. Our day records for these ovulation records of May–July, 1921, and June–August, 1922, are from 70–78° mainly for midforenoon or earlier. In late April we recorded some air temperatures of 58–65° or lower. The discussion for voice is pertinent to this topic. Humidity and excessive rains are very important in determining onset of breeding.

Egg-laying process. In the field regularly and in camp usually they laid plinth-like masses. We did not see the actual laying. Similarity of egg mass form must make the process akin to that in *R. pipiens*. They do not move from the stick until whole complement is laid.

EGGS

Attachment. In 1921 on April 24, at 9:30 a. m. we found "on the east end of cypress pool in amongst pickerel weed attached to the stems is an area of *Rana sphenocephala* eggs. Twelve masses, one fresh not yet expanded. The eggs are from ⅛–2 inches below the surface of the water. Or, on June 6, in another pond egg masses were "in the middle of a pond and around pickerel weeds. Greatest number of egg masses yet. They are all submerged 2–6 inches below the surface. They are also around the edges of the pond as well as being attached to other plant stems." On May 24 "Around Long Pond in amongst lizard's tail (*Saururus*) are several *Rana sphenocephala* masses hatching." In some of the smaller ponds they are attached to a variety of plants and occasionally are on the bottom unattached.

In 1922 on June 22 at Camp Pinckney in water-filled pit Nos. 2 and 3 found fresh eggs attached to wild rice in the middle of the pits. In the road just before Camp Pinckney found two or three masses, one unattached." Or on July 13 we found them attached entirely to grass blades in a temporary pool.

Egg mass. In 1912 in Okefinokee Swamp we found the egg masses of this species in June and July. In 1918 Pope (1919, p. 97) at Houston, Texas, on October 15 "Found three clusters of eggs, probably of this species, in a rain pool in woods road. The clusters had evidently been round and about four inches in diameter, though considerably softened and expanded by the hatching of the tadpoles."

In 1920, Deckert (1921, p. 21) on December 6, 1920, at Lemon City, Fla., found "three batches of frog-spawn. The masses were partly afloat and attached to weed stems in about 12 to 15 inches of water, milky with disintegrated limestone. Securing one of the masses and placing it in a wooden tub in our arbor, the eggs hatched on the 7th, and the tadpoles, though very small as yet, can be positively said to belong to this frog."

In 1921 on April 24, 1921, we found as in 1912 the "masses are plinthlike, not globular. One mass photographed is 1 inch thick, 2 inches deep and 5 or 6 inches wide. Egg masses look much like those of *Rana pipiens*." In 1922, on July 13 we noted "plenty of masses of eggs submerged. They are plinth masses. The egg envelopes vary in size."

Egg description. On April 24, 1921, we made these field measurements of some eggs as follows: vitellus 1.5–1.8 mm., average 1.6 mm.; inner envelope 3.2 mm., outer envelope 5.4 mm. Later, Mrs. Wright in laboratory measured these same eggs for illustrations and secured the following results: Of 27 eggs the vitelli of two were 1.4 mm., thirteen 1.6 mm., and twelve 1.8 mm., the range 1.4–1.8 mm., mode 1.6 mm., average 1.7 mm.; of the inner envelopes there were ten 2.4 mm., nine 2.6 mm., six 2.8 mm., one 3.0 mm., the range 24–30 mm., mode 2.4 mm., average 2.6 mm.; of the outer envelopes two were 3.4 mm., two 3.6 mm., ten 3.8 mm., thirteen 40 mm., range 3.4–4.0 mm., mode 40 mm., average 3.8 mm. A few inner envelopes were irregular or distorted in shape and look as if due to shrinkage. In 1922 we made the field notes of vitellus 1.5–1.8 mm., inner envelope 3.2 mm. In 1923 we gave the egg complement of this species as 1054 from a field note entry of 1922. On July 16, 1922, we made a count of two egg complements. "The total count of the two complements combined is 2117. These two were relatively small complements. The complement of a large female might reach 1200–1500 eggs or even more."

Dangers. Rapid drying of the ponds is a serious menace. On May 24, 1921, we went to one pond which was drying up fast. The same night we make this note: "Newt Pond much lower and two *Rana sphenocephala* masses left high and dry. These laid a night or so ago. Even though the period of hatching be short eggs attached to plant stems 2–6 inches beneath the surface may be at the surface by hatching time from drying up of ponds. The name Newt Pond above also suggests the one animal, the newt which relishes frogs' eggs.

An amusing mistake is apropos. On May 27, 1921, on Billy's Island in a run we found "some yellowish eggs fastened to a stick. They bother me. What are they?" Because we wanted to see and thought we saw strings (like those in *Amphiuma*) between the eggs we called it Siren Run. Later on May 27, we queried "What are the yellowish white eggs? They are beneath the surface. Flat plinthlike somewhat like *R. sphenocephala* eggs in egg mass form. They are near the edge of the run. Another bunch near the north edge and an area of 6 or 7 bunches on the south side. Shallow water. One mass amongst moss near clean water's edge." Later the same day we found "There were some 6 or 8 more masses of *Siren* other than those I first recorded. In amongst iris several were .5–.33 of an inch below the surface. They are very loose masses. They are yellowish white with no particular animal or vegetable pole so far as color is concerned. They are in areas: one of 5 masses; one of 4; one of 2; and thus it goes. Does each mass represent a female? Did she wind a mass around the stem?" Still later, the same day we noted "5 masses of *Siren*. Two or three inches below the surface. These are near an extending bar of land with a pine tree as its center. About it are *Leucothoë* bushes, etc. All of five are on the south side. Some masses attached to *Leucothoë* branches lying in the water. Another area of four, two at bases of growing iris and two fastened to old iris blades in water. Masses 1–3 inches below the water. Water coffee-colored, sphagnum comes into the water. On the surface above these *Siren* (?) eggs are eggs of *Hyla femoralis*. This *Siren* (?) Run has small pines, *Leucothoë*, *Iris*, *Sphagnum*, *Ilex glabra* outside and *Ilex cassine* saplings, sedges, *Itea*, *Smilax* in run. The water where *Siren* (?) eggs are is at least 85°–90°." Before June 3, we found several more. Now we are satisfied they were not *Siren* eggs but spoiled *R. sphenocephala* eggs. There were as many as 40 or 50 masses in all, similar in color. None of these in the field hatched to our knowledge. We concluded that we were straining our eyes to find a string of jelly between the respective eggs and then knew they were not *Siren* eggs. On June 3 the "run was getting very dry. Some of the eggs are high and dry." Quite likely this happened when the eggs were first laid and they were spoiled by drying. Subsequently it rained to reswell the jelly. Still we are puzzled by one entry in our journal that some of the eggs on May 28 hatched at noon in camp. If this be true they are albinistic but why should 50 pairs of frogs lay albinistic eggs? Herein doubtless lies another mistake on our part, a problem we did not entirely solve.

HATCHING PERIOD

Eggs taken April 24, 1921, 4:00 p.m. from a mass very fresh apparently laid the evening of April 23–24 hatched "a day before April 28." On April 28, we make the entry: "Today some of the eggs of *R. sphenocephala* are hatched. Taken April 24. Four or five days for hatching." The air temperatures at night went down to 60° and by day up to 90° in this period. Of the same eggs in the field we note on April 28 that "over in *Rana spheno-cephala* pond the eggs laid night of April 23–24 have been hatched a day. Temperature of water at 4:00 p.m., 82°." In another pond one of the boys found masses hatching April 28. They were close to the surface where the water at 3:00 p.m. was 90°. On May 13 we found several masses and on May 16 they were hatched and gone. Masses found May 21 were hatched May 24. Other masses found on July 1 and June 30 were hatched and hatching and not yet hatched on July 5.

In 1922 in the morning of July 13 at 12:30–1:00 a.m. we heard a great chorus. Visited the spot and found fresh masses. These eggs were ready to hatch and hatching July 16. The air temperatures ranged from 68° at night to 88° at night in this interval.

We thus have 3–5 days for hatching in these April–July months. Possibly in the late fall and winter months it may require almost as long a period as for our northern *R. pipiens*.

MATURE TADPOLE

Color description from life (June 23, 1921). On sides of the body and over the back yellowish olive or oil green, warbler green or olive green. The back and sides are with conspicuous black spots. On the sides and over the bronchial and pectoral regions is a mottling of light brownish vinaceous or pale vinaceous drab, giving a bronzy appearance. The middle of the belly is a solid color pale cinnamon pink, light vinaceous cinnamon or vinaceous cinnamon.

Tail. The muscular part of the tail, upper and lower crests are with larger black conspicuous spots than the body. The tail has some pale pur-plish gray, purple gray, pale violet-gray or violet-gray.

Iris black heavily punctate with greenish yellow dots; inner rim orange.

General appearance. Tadpole large (74.5 mm.) full and deep bodied. Venter (like that of *R. pipiens*) not strongly pigmented so that viscera clearly show through in life or in preserved specimens. Tail medium in length, tip acute. Dorsal crest in width not equal to depth of musculature and extending on to body somewhat ahead of the vertical of the hind legs. Spiracle sinistral, decidedly upward and backward in direction, just below axis of the body. Eye on lateral axis and nearer lateral outline in dorsal aspect than mid dorsal line. Anus dextral, opening round or elliptical; mucif-

1 2 3 4 5 6 7

erous crypts more or less distinct in mature tadpoles and sometimes quite distinct in half grown tadpoles. The dorsal row of either side starting near the dorsal crest goes diagonally forward and outward to join the principal lateral row which goes from above the middle of the insertion of the tail musculature to back of the eye where a supraorbital and an infraorbital branch goes forward.

Mouth parts: Teeth 2/3 or 3/3. Upper labium edged by a fringe of teeth, the fringe longer than the beak. Below either end of this fringe is a long row of teeth about 2/3–1/3 the length of the upper fringe. The median space one half to one times the length of the lateral row. Usually it is less than once the lateral row while in *R. pipiens* it is almost invariably more than once the lateral row. In many tadpoles as they approach transformation there appear in either corner a short third row of labial teeth on both sides or sometimes on one side only. Also in mature tadpoles it not infrequently appears. For example, in 1912 we secured 23 tadpoles of this species, of which six had the third row on either side, this row .33–.24 the length of the second row and in three specimens the third row was present in only one side. On the lower labium are three rows of teeth. The third row is shorter than the single row of labial papillae, 1/3 to 2/7 shorter than the second or first row, or about 1/6 to 1/5 shorter than the horny beak. First and second lower labial rows about equal and slightly longer than beak. First one is sometimes subdivided in the middle.

Measurements. Length of body (19.0–25.0) in tail (28.5–37.5 mm.) 1.35–1.66, average 1.53. Width (10.–16.5 mm.) of body in its own length 1.56–2.1, average 1.77. Depth (9.0–15.0 mm.) of body .8–1.36 in body width, average 1.1. Depth of body 1.5–2.3 in body length, average 1.95. Depth (10.5–16.5 mm.) of tail in length of tail 2.0–2.66, average 2.65. Muscular part (6.0–9.5 mm.) 1.35–2.35 in depth of tail, average 1.80. Spiracle 1.2–1.7 nearer base of hind legs or vent region (8.0–14.0 mm.) than the tip of the snout (12.5–16.0 mm.), average 1.46. Spiracle 1.1–1.86 nearer eye (5.0–9.0 mm.) than base of hind legs or vent, average 1.46. Eye 1.15–1.3 nearer to tip of snout (5.0–7.0 mm.) than to spiracle (5.0–9.0 mm.), average 1.2. Nostril to snout equal to nostril to both 3.6–5.0 mm. Mouth (3.0–5.0 mm.) usually 9–1.6 larger than internasal space (2.2–5.0 mm.), average 1.25. Mouth contained 1.4–2.0 (average 1.68) in interorbital distance (5.5–7.5 mm.) Internasal space contained in interorbital space 1.4–2.3, average 1.95.

The measurements of the largest tadpole are:

	mm.		mm.
Total length	62.5	Spiracle to vent	14.0
Body length	25.0	Spiracle to eye	7.5
Body depth	15.0	Eye to snout	6.5
Body width	16.0	Eye to nostril	4.5
Tail length	37.5	Nostril to snout	3.5
Tail depth	13.0	Mouth	4.5
Musculature of tail	9.5	Interorbital distance	7.0
Spiracle to snout	15.0	Internasal distance	5.0

General remarks. On April 28 we found mature tadpoles of *R. spheno-cephala*. They are all in the same stage therefore not *Rana clamitans*. Other reasons are: they have bronzy bellies like *R. pipiens* but the tail has prominent black blotches unlike northern *R. pipiens*.

LARVAL PERIOD

Of this common frog we have little data on the actual larval period. Eggs laid April 24, 1921, and hatched April 28 were tadpoles with two large hind legs June 17 and transformed July 4 or 71 days from egg deposition or 67 days from hatching. Others were transforming in some places July 23 or 90 days from laying. This gives 67–86 days for larval period. Much the same period for the northern meadow frog. Frankly I believe the period shorter in the south. Eighty-six days are probably too long for the period in general and many may not live as much as 67 days as larvae. In 1921 we found this species transforming as early as April 1 to April 30. This means at the "67–86 days" determination eggs laid as early as January 23 or January 4 or February 22 or February 3. In these winter months possibly earlier eggs and longer period. In general I suspect 50–75 days may prove to be nearer the true larval period.

TRANSFORMATION

Period. In 1912 we found shortly after our entrance (May 25) into the swamp, transformed specimens. The records are for May 28, 29, June 1, 3, 6, 12, 24. In 1921 we recorded transformed and transforming specimens April 1, May 4, July 4. In 1910 Professor J. C. Bradley secured them in September and October. In 1922 we secured them transforming July 4 and August 14. We thus have every month from April to October for transformation. No doubt every month in the year some southern meadow frogs transform though they are called "Spring Frogs" as breeders.

Size. Under growth we concluded that 20–23 mm. represented the range of transformation. On June 24, 1912, on Billy's Island we found mature tadpoles and transforming frogs. Twelve of the latter measured 18, 18, 19, 20, 20, 21, 21, 22, 22, 22, 22, 23 mm. respectively, the mode 22 mm., the average 21 mm. On July 23, 1921, on the same island we took 19 transformed and transforming specimens in ditches beside the lumber railroad. They measured 22, 23, 24, 25, 25, 25, 25, 25, 25, 25, 26, 26, 26, 26, 27, 27, 27–29, 30 mm. respectively, the mode 25 mm., the average 24 mm. The total range of the two lots is 18–30 mm., the mode 25 mm., the average 23 mm. The total range of our recorded specimens is 18–33 mm.

General remarks. In this species the black spots on the tadpole tail before transformation are very conspicuous. In this regard they seem different from our northern *Rana pipiens* tadpole (of Ithaca, N. Y.) just before transformation.

This species shows considerable variation in transformation sizes. Why one group should range from 18–23 mm., another from, 22–30 mm. and another (not mentioned before) from 26–33 mm. is hard to explain. Are

local conditions of drying up, absence and plentitude of water or food responsible, or are those eggs laid in January, February, or late fall less likely to
reach as large a transformation size as those laid in spring or vice versa?

In 1920 when we wrote that the southern leopard frog transforms during
June and July at .75 to 1 inch in length, the average being seven-eighths of
an inch we were speaking only of our May 28–July 4 experience in the Okefinokee Swamp in 1912. We then suspected it might be any month of the
year but dared not reach beyond our known facts.

GROWTH

In 1920 we gave as the presumptive evidence for *R. pipiens* growth 18–31
mm. at transformation, 31–44 mm. for the first year, 44–52 mm. for the
second year and 52 mm. for the third year.

In 1921 we secured of *Rana sphenocephala* on April 24, five examples 56,
57, 58, 60 and 73 mm., apparently two different growth years. From May
15–23, we secured examples as follows: 52, 58, 62, 64 mm.; 75, 81 mm.—two
groups. On July 5, we secured 67, 68, 70, 77 mm. specimens. On July 23
we took two examples of another growth group, 40, 44 mm. Of transformed
examples we had one, April 1, 33 mm.; one May 4, 28 mm.; one, July 4, 26
mm. The 1921 evidence reveals 26–33 mm. as transformation or just beyond
transformation; 40–44 mm. for 1st year olds; possibly 52–64 mm. for 2nd
year olds, and 67–77 or 81 mm. for 3 year olds. In 1922 on July 4 and 5 we
took transformed frogs at 20, 20, 22 mm., and a female at 71 mm. In August
9–14, we secured one 22 mm. at transformation and a male at 56 mm. In
June (19th and 28th) we caught respectively a 53 mm. and 75 mm. specimen.
We, therefore, had a 20–22 mm. transformation group, 53–56 mm. group;
and a 71–75 group. In 1912, from May 28th–July 15th, we secured transformed frogs at 22, 30, 32 mm.; on May 28–29, two at 22 and 24 mm.; one
of 32 mm. June 1; two 27 mm. and 30 mm. June 3; one 32 mm. June 6.
On June 12, we secured one of 27 mm., one of 37 mm., and one of 71 mm.
—three groups. On June 13–14 we secured one 50 mm. On June 24 we
secured four at 32, 33, 35, 37 mm., one of 49 mm., one 63 mm.,—apparently
three growth groups. From July 15 to November 15 we received three 42
mm., 65 mm., 71 mm. in length. In 1913 a male captured December 26
measured 78 mm., and a female 76 mm.

On the basis of 1912, 1921 and 1922 collections it would seem that transformation came at 20–23 mm.; that one year olds are from 35–50 mm.; that
two year olds are 52–65 mm.; that three year olds are 67–78 or 81 mm.

FOOD

No thorough studies have been made or published on this form. *R.
pipiens* has been studied by Surface, Drake, Frost, Munz and Klugh. No
doubt the two species are quite similar though the range of the southern
meadow frog might cause its diet to be quite different.

After the above was written we chanced on Force's (1925, p. 26) paragraph which follows:

"Of the 46 specimens of Southern Leopard Frog, 10 had empty stomachs, while the remaining 36 had 38% Elateridae, 16% Myrmicidae, 11% larva, 4.5% each Lachnosterna and Coccinellidae, 1.8% each Saldidae, Belostomidae, Scarabaeidae (Tumble Bugs and June Bugs), and Cucujidae, 2.7% each Formicidae and Dytiscidae and .9% each Lamiinae, Cicindellidae, Membracidae and Crayfish."

ENEMIES

On May 6, 1921, I found a cypress pond dried up except for a small center of water filled with fish and *R. sphenocephala* tadpoles. Here Great Blue Heron and Florida Grackles were having a fine feast. On July 7, 1921, we heard subdued croaks of a frog and soon found that the southern water snake (*N. sipedon fasciata*) had a meadow frog which it swallowed in 7–10 minutes. We photographed a water snake with a meadow frog in its mouth.

In 1912 we found these results. A black snake (*Coluber constrictor constrictor*) had swallowed one adult meadow frog. A pied water snake (*Natrix taxispilota*) had two meadow frogs in its stomach while two southern water snakes (*N. s. fasciata*) had each a meadow frog. One ribbon snake (*Thamnophis sackenii*) had swallowed two meadow frogs, and one snake of this species had one meadow frog in its stomach. The true water moccasin also preys on meadow frogs.

AUTUMNAL DISAPPEARANCE

(See First Appearance). Our records of autumnal disappearance mean little for none of us have been in the swamp at the proper autumnal period to record it. Strictly speaking there probably is activity the year through as recorded under First Appearance.

AFFINITIES

Cope first recognized the southern meadow frog as a subspecies of *R. virescens*. Miss Dickerson 1906 (p. 188) by fine illustrations and descriptions did more to bring out the characters than any other author. Of it she writes: "The species is evidently a very distinct one, not intergrading with *Rana pipiens*, but holding its own with the latter frog in the same localities in the southern part of the United States." It is not questionable whether there is such a mixing of ranges. This form seems a Lower Austral offshoot of *Rana pipiens* extending from New Jersey to Texas and up the Mississippi to Indiana. We have treated this form as if it were very distinct from *Rana pipiens* but the whole *Rana pipiens* group is a complex one.

BIBLIOGRAPHY

1920 Barbour, T. Copeia, July 31, No. 84, p. 56.
1925 Brimley, C. S. and W. B. Mabie. Copeia, February 15, 1925, No. 139, p. 15.
1920 Boulenger, G. A. Proc. Amer. Acad. Arts Sciences, August, 1920, Vol. 55, No. 9, pp. 434, 436, 439.
1914 Deckert, R. Copeia, February 14, 1914, No. 3 and April 15, 1914, No. 5.
1921 ————. Copeia, March 15, 1921, No. 92, pp. 20, 21.
1922 ————. Copeia, November 20, 1922, No. 112, p. 88.
1906 Dickerson, M. C. The Frog Book, pp. 186–188.
1925 Force, Edith R. Copeia, April 30, 1925, p. 141.

1922 Löding, H. P. Geological Survey of Alabama. Mus. Paper No. 5, pp. 20, 21.
1924 Myers, G. S. Copeia, June 30, 1924, No. 131, p. 60.
1921 Ortenberger, A. I. Copeia, October 15, 1921, No. 99, p. 75.
1927 ———. Copeia, April-June, 1927, No. 163, pp. 46, 47.
1919 Pope, Philip H. Copeia, December 31, 1919, No. 76, p. 97.
1918 Viosca, Percy. Jr. 3rd Biennial Rept. Department of Conservation Louisiana April 1, 1916-April 1, 1918, p. 160.
1920 Wright, A. H. U. S. Bur. Fisheries Doc. 888, p. 23.
1923 ———. Copeia, February 1, 1923, No. 115, p. 34.
1924 Wright, A. H. and A. A. Wright. Am. Naturalist July-August, 1924, Vol. LVIII, p. 377.

Rana virgatipes Cope

(Pl. III, Fig. 3; IX, Fig. 2; XI, Fig. 13; XIV, Fig. 4; XVI, Fig. 1; XVII; XLII; XLIII; Text Fig. 1, 14)

COMMON NAMES

Sphagnum Frog. Carpenter Frog. Cope's Frog.

RANGE

Check list. "Range: New Jersey to North Carolina. Type Locality: Near Atlantic City, New Jersey." Stejneger & Barbour (1917, p. 39).

Supplementary records. The North Carolina record no doubt referred to Lake Ellis records by C. S. Brimley (1906) 1907 ((1907, p. 159; 1909, p. 133) and by J. Hurter (1907). Dunn (1918) reported it from Norfolk, Va. Wm. Palmer in 1896 secured it at Lake Drummond, Va. Myers (Copeia, 1924, p. 60) reported two from Wilmington, N. C. In 1922 (1923) we reported the extension of its range from N. C. to Okefinokee Swamp, Georgia. In 1922 our party found it and *Hyla andersonii* at Everetts Pond which is .75 or 1.5 miles from the N. C.–S. C. state line. In June 1920 W. T. Davis and Dr. J. Chapin (1922, p. 74) recorded it at Southern Pines, N. C. about 35–50 miles northeast of Everetts Pond. Noble in 1923 (p. 422) remarks "Why *R. virgatipes* has a more extensive range to the south than *H. andersonii* it is impossible to say at this time." Previous to 1921 one would have held *H. andersonii* farther south at Anderson, S. C., and farther north in N. J. (per Miller) than *R. virgatipes*. We found both near the N. C.–S. C. state line (near Cheraw). I believe them more or less associates and confidently expect *H. andersonii* to be found in Georgia.

Local Okefinokee records. In 1921 we recorded it first near Bear House and Hurst Island (near Chesser Island) on July 12 and 13. In the 1st and 2nd dreens or causeways between Chesser's Island and the mainland we heard it from July 15–19 in the wooded swampy parts. Ten days later in a grassy bay or head near Black Jack Island we heard it again. In 1922 we found it around the borders of Chesser Island from June 21 until August 11.

GENERAL APPEARANCE

A small frog with long narrow head, back brownish with four yellowish or golden-brown, longitudinal stripes on the back. The under parts are yellowish white with brown spots. The femur has alternating dark and light stripes.

MEASUREMENTS
(Recent Material)

Head to angle of mouth 1.0 (28 mm. near transformation)–1.04 (36 mm. ♀)–1.08 (36 mm. ♂)–1.06 (44 mm. ♂)–1.2 (56 mm. ♂)–1.0 (56 mm. ♀) in width of head; head to rear of tympanum .87–.92–.96–.95–.857–.95 in width of head; head to angle of mouth 2.8–3.13–2.9–2.5–3.75–3.0 in length of body; head to rear of tympanum 2.43–2.77–2.57–2.5–2.66–2.8 in length of body; snout .95–1.18–.92–.94–.875–1.23 in fourth finger; .76–1.18–1.15–.94–.875–1.3 in first toe; eye 1.3–1.57–1.3–1.23–1.23–1.21 in snout; .61–.85–.7–.69–1.07–.71 in tympanum; 1.12–1.85–1.2–1.0–1.07–1.5 in first finger; tympanum 3.2–3.5–2.7–2.6–1.8–1.64 in intertympanic width; 2.1–1.83–1.71–1.77–1.14–1.7 in snout; internasal width .66–.85–1.0–.66–1.0–.9 in upper eyelid width; interorbital width 1.0–1.5–1.15–1.0–2.25–1.8 in upper eyelid width; 1.5–1.75–1.15–1.5–2.25–2.0 in internasal space; 4.0–5.25–3.15–4.0–6.25–5.4 in intertympanic width.

Forelimb: 1.75–2.0–1.9–1.9–2.43–1.93 in length of body; 2.75–2.6–2.65–2.67–3.2–2.62 in hind limb; first finger 1.33–1.3–1.33–1.46–1.3–1.23 in third finger; second finger 1.5–1.3–1.33–1.35–1.3–1.44 in third finger; 1.12–1.0–1.0–1.0–.93–1.72 in first finger; third finger 1.08–1.17–1.37–1.26–1.44–1.2 in second toe; fourth finger .80–1.0–1.25–1.0–1.16–1.04 in first toe; 1.2–1.37–1.33–1.26–1.5–1.24 in third finger; internasal space 1.5–1.85–1.7–1.44–1.55–2.1 in first finger; 1.33–1.85–1.71–1.55–1.55–1.8 in second finger; 2.0–1.8–2.28–2.11–2.0–2.6 in third finger; 1.66–1.85–1.7–1.66–1.33–2.1 in fourth finger.

Hindlimb: length 1.57–1.3–1.4–1.32–1.34–1.35 in hind limb; tibia 2.07–2.4–( )–( )–2.43–2.33 in length of body; 3.25–3.13–( )–( )–3.26–3.16 in hind limb; 1.18–1.2–( )–( )–1.0–1.20 in forelimb; 1.11–1.33–( )–( )–1.08–1.15 in hind foot; first toe 1.61–1.53–1.46–1.6–1.85–1.4 in second toe; 2.25–2.0–1.93–2.26–2.55–2.0 in third toe; 3.0–2.6–2.6–2.93–3.43–2.45 in fourth toe; 2.0–1.84–1.73–2.0–2.28–1.82 in fifth toe; second toe 1.38–1.3–1.32–1.41–1.38–1.4 in third toe; 1.84–1.7–1.72–1.83–1.83–1.74 in fourth toe; 1.23–1.2–1.18–1.25–1.23–1.29 in fifth toe; third toe 1.33–1.3–1.31–1.3–1.33–1.25 in fourth toe; .88–.92–.90–.88–.88–.93 in fifth toe; fourth toe 1.08–1.35–1.31–1.54–1.04–1.5 in hind foot; 1.12–.88–( )–( )–.95–.90 in tibia; 1.25–1.06–1.0–1.04–.95–1.07 in forelimb; fifth toe 1.5–1.41–1.46–1.46–1.5–1.35 in fourth toe; internasal space 1.33–1.85–2.08–1.66–1.55–2.1 in first toe; 2.18–2.85–3.14–2.8–2.88–3.1 in second toe; 3.0–3.7–4.14–3.8–4.0–4.3 in third toe; 4.0–4.85–5.4–5.0–5.33–5.4 in fourth toe; 2.66–3.4–3.7–3.3–3.55–4.0 in fifth toe.

HABITAT

Davis found (1905, pp. 795, 796) that "Rana virgatipes Cope is also more abundant at Lakehurst than at first supposed and has been found from May to September. In the early summer as many as twelve have been seen in one day without much search having been made for them. They are apt to be in some ditch and seated on the sphagnum moss, or on a floating lily pad, and they are found also in the ditches that border and intersect the cranberry bogs, as well as in the lake."

The other extended account of their habitat is given by Fowler (1905, p. 662, 1906 (1907) p. 123). "Our specimens were obtained at the mouth of the Mare Run, the type locality, and we noticed no other amphibians in this vicinity. Associated in this locality were many examples of *Chrysemys picta* and *Chelopus guttatus*, which were constantly bobbing around in the sphagnum. *Enneacanthus obesus*, *Mesogonistius chaetodon*, *Erimyzon sucetta oblongus* and *Notropis chalbaeus abbottii* were also abundant. The frogs seem to occur exclusively in the almost submerged masses of sphagnum which line the shores in many places and often extend well out in the stream. Here the water is still and the animals rest more or less below, so that their dull colors harmonize well with the surroundings. They were shy and sank quickly out of sight among the aquatic vegetation on the approach of danger. In attempting to escape they would not jump or leap and when caught in the dip-net moved about in a rather slow stupefied manner. They swam for short distances, but were usually able to find suitable shelter close at hand."

Barbour (1916 p. 5) "in search of the Sphagnum Frog, *Rana virgatipes* Cope" at Lakehurst, N. J., writes:

"The afternoons we have usually spent in wandering about the sphagnum bogs and along the cold spring branches which run into the lake, searching for the sphagnum frogs, which we have found at times in considerable numbers. Our observations have confirmed those of Davis and of other observers who have recorded their shy ways and strictly aquatic habits."

For our habitat notes of 1921 see "Voice." In 1922 we camped the night of June 9 on the north side of Everett's Pond (about 5 or 10 minutes by auto from N. C.–S. C. state line), N. C. "In the wooded sections or streams flowing into the lake in dense thickets of *Smilax* (briar) and other plants were *Rana virgatipes* croaking quite generally. Several in different places." The *Hyla andersonii* were in a wooded stream or branch swamp which flowed into the wooded *R. virgatipes* area near the lake.

In 1922 on June 21 in the prairie where we first found the species in Okefinokee and just north of Lake Sego (Seagrove) "heard 7 or 8 *R. virgatipes*. Found one in a grassy place with waterlilies. On a waterlily pad was the one I captured. They like grassy places about or near the edge of a head (islet). Also seem to like some timbered parts or be in timbered parts entirely."

On May 22–23, 1924, we heard a few males croaking on the south side of the west point into the lake at Lakehurst, N. J. "It was at noon with the sun shining. Here in the sphagnum-heath edge caught 4 adults, two females and two males. As we waded along we would see them sometimes wholly out of water or at the lake's edge. Usually they leaped into the water and hid under the vegetation mat or quickly came up under a water lily pad or swam some distance and then poked out their heads. Most of the males were farther out in deeper water. The heaths and birds such as prairie warbler, pine warbler, white-eyed vireo, towhee, bob white, turkey buzzard, etc., suggest a southern environment." On May 23 from the west point northward "the west edge of the lake where the *Rana virgatipes* are normally common had the sphagnum just starting and below the top of the water. Pipeworts (*Eriocaulon*) were just starting. Water lily leaves were yet below the water. Golden club (*Orontium aquaticum*) was in bloom but we saw no adult frogs in this stretch. Some little frogs just ahead of me were continually disappearing. They were probably transformed *R. virgatipes* but of this I could not be sure."

In 1929 in June we planned a trip to Lakehurst, but a mishap befell us. Of the improvised trip June 8, 1929, we have these journal notes.

"Needed a male and a female *R. virgatipes* for photographs. Boarded a train at Ridgewood for Lakehurst and without collecting kit or clothes. It rained until midafternoon; with every handicap we waded the edge of the lake at Lakehurst with no success. The same result along the west point of land extending into the lake. The vegetation mats have not reached the surface to any appreciable degree. Mr. Shinn and his boys have a cottage at the base of the point. They informed us that locally the frogs have long been called 'carpenter frogs.' Some new visitors beside the lake can hardly sleep at night when the species is in full chorus. Mr. Shinn sent the boys out in a canoe to get some on the mats in midlake and along the east side. We went to Emlie's pond. When we returned the boys had 4 males and 1 female and one recently transformed frog. Several they had thrown back. They approached the lily pads and with a scoop of a long handled dip net caught the frogs. The lily pad and mid-lake habits suggest *Rana septentrionalis* of the Adirondack Mts. and the North."

Outside or inside the swamp. *Rana virgatipes* in 1921 we missed in the center of the swamp though one informant claims he has heard them on the south side of Billy's Island. They are not in the center of the swamp in our experience. We found them on the prairies near Chesser Island and between it and the mainland. Also we recorded them from Blackjack Island. This places them in the very southern and eastern part of the swamp, a queer distribution as puzzling as that of the plant *Bejaria* (*Elliottia*) *racemosa*.

FIRST APPEARANCE

In the Okefinokee swamp some of the residents to whose attention we called this frog, said it started croaking in early spring if rainy weather be at hand. They probably appear by mid-April if not before.

VOICE

According to Davis (1907, p. 50) "*Rana virgatipes* may be called the Carpenter Frog, for its note sounds much like the blow of a hammer on a board. It is a quickly uttered *chuck-up*, *chuck-up*, and the frog usually hammers three or four times. For a time I was not sure of the singer, but some captive individuals under the influence of good living have uttered this call-note in my room while I sat by."

In 1907 Fowler writes (1905, pp. 662, 663; 1906, (1907) pp. 123, 124, 125): "The individuals obtained by Cope and Stone did not make any noises, but when we discovered ours, the males were in full cry, which would seem to indi-

1

2

3

4

5

6

7

8

cate that late April was the height of the nuptial season. The males are provided with distensible vocal vesicles, and when about to utter their call these sacs are inflated like little bladders till nearly spherical, and then by degrees the air is allowed to escape. This gives the sac the appearance of collapsing by a series of jerks. As it is done quickly, each jerk at an interval of a second, the result is a sort of a rapping sound. These raps or jerks are about five or six in number. The sound produced is peculiar in that it is difficult at times to detect its source, and if the frog is close is quite startling. This is due not only to the suddenness, but also to the volume of the sound. On one occasion an example which I captured has his vocal vesicles well inflated, and though they partly collapsed as I held him in my hand he did not utter any sound. The call bears considerable resemblance to the sound produced by wood choppers cutting trees a short distance back in the forest, and is different from the cry of any other batrachian, so that when first heard I suspected it was produced by this species."

"Mr. J. A. G. Rehn informs me he heard this frog at Cedar Grove, on the Oswego River, or the east branch of the Wading River, and also at Speedwell during June of 1905. A description of the cluck of a frog, which may possibly have been this species, was given to me by Mr. G. L. Hartman of Palermo, Cape May County, who says that the frogs are common about the Cedar Swamp Creek region. Although diligently searched for in all suitable localities I failed to discover any. Mr. Chreswell J. Hunt informs me that he noted this frog while camping on the dam of the Rancocas Creek at New Lisbon, in Burlington County, on the night of May 15, 1906. During all the evening its voice was the sound most in evidence. It was also abundant at the dam at Brown Mills on May 16th. About the shores at the head of these ponds were masses of sphagnum and in these spots the frogs seemed to abound. Although unsuccessful in securing specimens, he feels certain of the identity of the species as the croak was so different from that of any other with which he was familiar. He also states that he did not hear it anywhere along the Rancocas below New Lisbon, which is well among the pines. During the past summer he heard it at Whiting. On May 30, 1907, Mr. Percy Lorrilliere reports he heard this frog at Dennisville in Cape May County." Again in 1907 Fowler (1908, p. 194) gives us the following: "*Rana virgatipes* Cope—Sphagnum Frog. The clack, clack, clack, clack, clack of this frog could be heard about the Rancocas Creek above New Lisbon, in Burlington County, on May 12th, 1907. It occurred at intervals, interrupting the stillness of a backward spring. Though loud and not often uttered, in comparison with those found at Mare Run, their croaking could be heard at quite a distance. Sometimes the animals must have been quite close, for we could hear them when but a few feet away without seeing them. It may have been that the weather was too cold, for their croaking was always located as coming from among the submerged and overgrown vegetation along the banks. In such places the temperature was considerably higher by mid-day than elsewhere. When Mr. Hunt visited this place just a year previously, the frogs were very numerous. The weather at that time, however, though about the same time in May, was much warmer.

In the evening, during the night, and in the early morning, they were very noisy, but during the day were more or less quiet, only an occasional croak being heard at intervals, or as noted above."

Our first record for *Rana virgatipes* came July 12, 1921, near Chesser Island. We had had to abandon our boat because of low water and wade to shore. Near a head not far from the boat about 5 p. m. we began "to hear a new *Rana* calling in the maiden cane—*cluck–cluck–cluck–cluck*; a rather loud, incisive, distinctive, clucking croak." (F. Harper). The air temperatures were at least 75°. On the following morning (air temperature about 78°; cloudy day) the author with four of the Chesser boys "went for the rest of the equipment at Bear House (2¾ miles from Chesser Island). Heard no end of *Rana clamitans*, *R. grylio* and one or two of the unknown (*R. virgatipes*?). Also over toward Hurst Island heard several (*R. virgatipes*?)". The previous afternoon we instinctively pronounced it *R. virgatipes* though we had never heard it but had read previous characterizations of it. On the night of July 15 after a thunder shower we heard several in the wooded dreens or causeways between Chesser Island and the mainland. Temperature about 70–73 degrees. On July 19 we heard a few before dawn towards the open prairie and at night we caught another in the wooded causeway. On Black Jack Island July 28, 1921, we had one of the hardest rains I ever experienced. In the morning of July 29, 1921, when the temperature was 73 degrees "I heard a Carpenter Frog chorus. . . . Just outside the south bushy edge of Black Jack Island (near camp) were the carpenter frogs. They were scattered in among the small cypress where there was an undercarpet of *Woodwardia* and a little sphagnum. They seemed to be around the base of the cypress trees and on the cypress knees. I saw none of them. In the daytime they are shy. The croak is 4–7 notes in rapid succession, all alike. Then the species has another call of two notes and lower in pitch." Later "on the sphagnum strand many roads out from Chesser Island we heard some carpenter frogs." The period from July 12–19 was a very rainy week throughout southern Georgia and no minima of nearby stations went below 69°, our lowest temperature being 73°. On July 28 almost 3.80 inches of rain fell at Waycross and about 2.4 inches the next day and the temperature ranges from 70°–84°.

In the Okefinokee swamp we heard them at different times of the day. Summarized our 1921 record reads somewhat as follows:

June 19. Heard at night in wooded sloughs.

" 24. "I awoke at 3 a. m. and heard quite a few calling towards the edge of the prairie."

July 2. Harper heard one on prairie at 8–8:30 a. m.

" 21. Calling generally in wooded sloughs.

" 22. One heard in mid-afternoon (2:30 p. m.) in sloughs. Sunlight.

" 22. At night many croaking in slough at temperature 72° until midnight or later. Other frogs not active.

" 25. At night many croaking in slough. Temperature 72°–74°. Air humid. Croaking beyond midnight. Other frogs not active.

" 28. At 3–4 a. m. heard several. At 6:30 a. m. heard one. Air 72° cloudy.

Aug.   8.   Heard two at 8 a. m. (Temp. 79°).
"   9.   At 3 and 4–5 a. m. heard several on prairie or at landing. Heard at
              night in bay.
"   10.   Heard at 7.
"   11.   Calling at midnight.

In other words, they start about dusk or sometimes before and gather strength of chorus as midnight approaches. At 3 or 4 in the morning they go strong. At daybreak one to several may be heard and these may continue until 8:30–9 a. m.

In 1922 on June 21 (Okefinokee Swamp) we have the record of another call. "Male has two prominent lateral pouches. In this respect differs from *Rana grylio*. When held in hand it will open its mouth and make a peculiar call. Often it will swell up when held just as many a frog will when seized by a snake."

On the night of July 21, 1922, when the frogs were actually breeding we made these observations: "Whenever one approached within 5 feet or more usually the male stopped croaking. Seldom indeed did the male croak after the light was put on it. Anna found an area where she heard a scrambling. One croaked under observation. We set up the camera. It moved on. In this area about midnight we secured three exposures. They are strangely silent and wary when one approaches. The croak may be of two parts, sometimes three, four or five parts. Each part occupies a second or less in duration. This species has a pouch on either side. These are round vesicles perfectly round when the frog is croaking and the throat does not inflate. Therein as before remarked they differ from *Rana grylio*, *Rana clamitans* and *Rana catesbeiana*. In this regard they are more more like *Rana sphenocephala*? Are its eggs to be in a film or a mass like *Rana sphenocephala*? Doubtless the former." We made the wrong guess. The next morning revealed the answer.

Our records for 1921–1922 indicate a range of croaking from June 9–Aug. 11. Mr. Benjamin Chesser of Chesser Island says "they croak in the spring and summer alike during wet weather" and his father, R. A. Chesser, considered it one of the first frogs to begin croaking in the spring.

On May 22, 1924, from Mr. Emlie's pond, Lakehurst, N. J. we "heard an immense chorus at Lakehurst lake. It began just before dark." "*R. virgatipes* is more of a night frog. Once in a while we heard it at day in cloudy weather."

F. Harper makes these notes "call 2–5 times in series. Occasionally a minor single note (between or preparatory to series.) Good loud clear note. Frog sprawled in water like *R. sphenocephala*, or sitting half submerged, like *R. clamitans* or perhaps only ¼ under. Seldom less than about 15–30 seconds between calls, intervals apparently irregular. Generally a silent premonitory gulp. No swelling of throat but of lateral sacs, each to about ½ head. Between each note collapse to about ½ size (small marble). At full inflation about size of small persimmon or larger marble. Between series collapse entirely."

MATING

Male (From life, July 15 1921). Stripe down either side from eye to hind leg hazel or fawn color. Back natal brown or chestnut brown. This color with black spots on the back. Natal brown on dorsum of fore and hind legs.

Same color with black on sides. Smaller stripe from angle of mouth halfway on side light or pale ochraceous salmon. This stripe continued over angle of mouth and on to upper jaw pale greenish yellow. Throat sulphur yellow with indefinite brown spots. Rest of under parts cartridge buff to pale chalcedony yellow with beautifully marked bone brown or almost black spots on venter and sides. Back and fore parts of iris neva green. Iris inner rim green and yellow. Iris proper spotted black and empire yellow.

Female (From life, July 22 1922). Back stripe buffy brown and side stripe also. Back color olive brown. Throat sulphur yellow, also inner edge of surface of fore limb. This yellow also from angle of mouth to over arm insertion. Spotting on under parts not so prominent as in male nor so clear cut yet it is conspicuous. Under parts and sides with hardly any wash of yellowish as the male sometimes has on his sides. Females in general on under part look white while males have washes of yellow on throat, sides and slightly on other parts. Front edge and back edge of eye bright green yellow as in the male (see male of July 15, 1921). This female smaller than the four males captured at the same time.

Female (From life, July 25, 1922). This gravid female has as dark a back ground color as a male and in this respect unlike above specimen of July 22, 1922.

Structural differences. In 1906 (1907, p. 121) Fowler notes the males have "Vocal vesicles large and capable of considerable inflation" and presents a striking plate of the distended sacs of the males and the venters of two males and a female. Boulenger (1920, p. 430) says the male has "a large grayish or blackish external vocal sac on each side between the mouth and shoulder; a feeble pad on the inner side of the first finger."

The males have the tympanum enlarged but not so strikingly as in *Rana grylio, Rana catesbeiana, Rana clamitans* or *Rana onca* nor is the thumb quite as large proportionally. I cannot, however, call it a "feeble" pad.

The young males at 25–39 mm. have thumb little swollen, tympana not very large and vocal sacs not well developed. About 40 mm. the thumb begins to enlarge, vocal sacs begin developing and tympana may or may not be large. Certainly by 45 mm. if not before, thumb, vocal sacs and tympana are well developed in the males. However one male at even 38 mm. begins to have thumb enlarging and vocal sacs developing and one male at 42 mm. is almost a full male in tympana, sacs and thumbs.

Duration. Probably of short duration normally.

Night or day. Mainly by night, though by day in cloudy or rainy weather when the climaxes come in breeding.

Amplexation (normal, abnormal, cross). It must be pectoral in this species. No mated pairs have been secured. This species is shy like *Rana grylio* and *Rana catesbeiana.* Unlike toads and tree toads none of the males would seize the gravid females we placed with them.

OVULATION

Habitat. In 1923 (p. 421) Noble lists the breeding habitat of *Rana virgatipes* as "Larger pools of pine barrens." In 1908 Fowler (1908, p. 194) in writing of this species "above Rancocas Creek above New Lisbon, in Burlington County" says "We found a lot of spawn, though were unable to identify it as belonging to this species. It resembled that found at Mare Run, in similar situations, as it was formed in strings and wound about the numerous aquatic plants in still water. These strings were quite long and very abundant. Attempts at their transportation and hatching failed." These strings do not accord in description with our experiences with *R. virgatipes* eggs. In 1922 on July 21 we heard several *Rana virgatipes* in the wooded swampy areas between Chesser Island and the mainland. "At 9 p. m. we started with auto for the first and second dreens. At the first heard a few *Rana virgatipes* males calling. In the area around the pond south of the first crossing were most of the frogs. Other species not calling in great numbers, so we went to the 2nd crossing. To the direct right in the wooded edge of the island we heard several males. These males would be next to a sphagnaceous base of a pine or cypress or between two bushy clumps or sedgy tussocks. Occasionally they were perched on a log. Sometimes they were amongst *Xyris* or *Eriocaulon* stands. There were fallen logs in this area. The water at the deepest was no more than a foot. The places of gathering were near the edge of the wooded swamp. This species seems to be very appropriately a 'sphagnum frog.' There must have been twenty or twenty-five frogs in one small area. We captured four males and saw 10 or 12 more."

The next morning at 11 a. m. M. D. Pirnie and I went to the 2nd dreen to look for the eggs. We found six masses of eggs. Our rough notes describe the area thus: "The area has pine, cypress (young) and gum. More or less open spaces between trees. Around the bases of the trees are sphagneous mounds. More or less wide clear interspaces of water fill most of the rest of the area except for smaller stands of *Eriocaulon, Xyris, Polygala cymosa,* and *Smilax Walteri.* The *Eriocaulon* stands may have *Burmannia, Drosera* with long scapes and white flowers. Some algae and two bladderworts, one purple, one yellow in water interspaces. Sometimes a stand around a cypress or pine is *Rhexia mariana* or *Woodwardia.* Little of latter. Interspersed with trees are *Hyperica*-like bushes of very fine leaves $\frac{1}{2}$–$\frac{3}{4}$ of an inch in length. *Clethra* here and also evergreen "hurrah bushes (*Leucothoë*)." Later in the day we found more egg masses.

Period. In 1923 Noble (p. 425) considers *Rana virgatipes* a protracted breeder, temperature controlled, a form which has hibernated in the water. In Okefinokee Swamp and throughout most of its range I fancy rains and humidity are more important factors than temperature though the latter is an influence as well. We actually found ovulation from July 21–25 but we have presumptive evidence of breeding from June 21–Aug. 11. Probably the species begins the last of April and extends to August.

Egg-laying process. We have not observed the process. It is doubtless similar to that for forms which lay beneath the surface such as *Rana pipiens,*

R. sphenocephala, R. aesopus, R. septentrionalis, R. sylvatica, and other be-
neath-the-surface layers. The process probably requires a few minutes. The
female may start slowly but once the process begins it doubtless is over in
10–30 minutes.

EGGS

Attachment. The masses found July 28 were attached as follows: The
first mass was "found in a clear area attached to a *Xyris* blade and pine needles
and beneath the water, . . ." Six more were found the morning of July 22,
1922. "They were attached to pine needles, upright sticks, *Xyris* or *Eriocaulon* stems." In the afternoon we "found a mass much farther west than
the original area of 5 masses. It looked blue above and when turned over
showed a creamy white impression. The mass like those of *Rana sphenocephala* and *Rana pipiens*, looked white below. The mass was 2¾ x 1¾ inches.
As in *Rana sphenocephala* and *Rana pipiens* it seems to lay in groups as in
case of 5 masses yet this last fresh mass was considerably apart from others
in water 6–8 inches deep. If most of the eggs are laid beneath the algae on
the surface I am lucky to find these few masses. The species may, however,
choose clear water areas with little algae for ovulation." Other observations on
attachment are "Attached to fresh floating pine needles (*Pinus caribaea*). . . .
Attached to rosettes of *Eriocaulon* ½–¾ inches below the surface."

Egg mass. The masses were more like the eggs of *Rana sphenocephala*
than those of *Rana grylio*. The first mass was "not globular but somewhat
elongate. The top of the mass was at or just beneath the surface of the water.
No rain had intervened since last night. The mass may have been 1.5 x 3 to 4
inches." "About eight or ten feet farther into the area were four more masses
two not far apart and two very close together. Isolated was another mass.
These five with original mass found makes six. These were all beneath the
surface. Very small masses for frogs. The temperature when we found them
was 72°."

Other data is as follows: "Sometimes in looking for Cope's frogs' eggs we
mistake the bladders of *Utricularia purpurea* for a mass." ". . . A mass
2 x 2 x 2 inches." "Another mass in water 4 inches deep, 1 inch below surface,
1 inch thick, plinthlike, 2½ x 2½ inches, a perfect duplication of *R. sphenocephala* masses. This last mass 15 feet from two others which are 4 feet apart."
"Another mass, water 3 inches deep. Beneath surface attached to *Eriocaulon*.
Very much like southern meadow frog's mass." "One mass attached to *Eriocaulon* leaves, 1¾ x 4 x 1 inches, a fine plinth but elongate, strap-shaped."
"Another mass attached to *Rhexia mariana*."

One has to be careful. "Right near one of the *Rana virgatipes* mass was a
very large mass as big as some *Rana sphenocephala* masses. Is it *R. sphenocephala*? We took it in to camp. Later in the day we proved it to be *Rana
sphenocephala*. The eggs were different and had inner envelopes."

Egg description. Our first field description of the egg is "The eggs are
large, far apart like *Rana sylvatica* eggs and seem to have no inner envelope."
At camp we made the following hasty notes: Vitellus 1.5, 1.5, 1.7, 1.6, 1.6, 1.4,

1.5, 1.8, 1.6, 1.7, 1.8, 2.5 (embryo elongated) mm.; envelope 5, 5, 5, 5.3, 4.9 x 5, 5, 6 x 6.9, 5, 5.8, 5 x 5.8, 5 x 5.8, 6 mm. Occasionally jelly envelope flattened spheroid-like. Jelly firm—often a flat surface where stuck to adjoining eggs. Envelope single." "Envelope 5.2, 5.5, 5.2–5.8 mm.; vitellus 1.6, 1.5, 1.4 mm." "Several fresh eggs have the envelope 3.8–4.2 mm."

The egg complement is rather small. One mass has 349 eggs. Another had 474. "Some may reach 500 or 600 eggs but 474 was larger than some complements. One mass looked to have little more than 200."

"The eggs are black above and a creamy white (not white as in *Rana sphenocephala* and *Rana pipiens*) i.e. more creamy in fresh eggs than these two species. Soon the black encroaches on the light vegetative pole. The eggs look far apart as do *Rana sylvatica* eggs and being without an inner envelope the parallel goes farther in that the outer envelope of *Rana sylvatica* gets to be as much as 5.8 mm. as does the envelope in this species. Very fresh eggs sometimes look to have sulphur yellow vegetative poles and black animal poles." Comparisons with Ridgway colors made the colors "primrose yellow, naphthalene yellow or light chalcedony yellow. Not so yellow as in *Rana palustris* eggs."

The eggs and egg mass were identified presumptively. We neither saw the eggs laid in the field nor did we capture mated pairs. They are *Rana virgatipes* for these reasons:

1. The female taken the night of July 21 was near where a male *Rana virgatipes* was croaking. We brought her into camp. On July 22 in the afternoon Mrs. Wright when photographing the female accidentally pressed some eggs out. Later July 23 (morning) the female though unattended by a male had laid eggs in the jar. These checked with the eggs of the masses of the field. This was in the nature of direct identification. No end of male Cope's frog were croaking in the area where the female was taken. This is presumptive evidence.

2. They were not films as in *Rana grylio* and *Rana clamitans*. On July 23, 1922 we held there were only four anurans in Okefinokee swamp whose eggs were not surely known: *Scaphiopus holbrookii*, *Pseudacris nigrita*, *Rana aesopus*, and *Rana virgatipes*. They could not be the first two, no gopher frogs were calling that night nor of the first two species. The presumption was that they were *R. virgatipes*. The eggs were of the type of *Rana sphenocephala* or *Rana palustris* but without the inner envelope. In this respect they were like *R. catesbeiana* eggs (but these are in films). No *R. sphenocephala* were calling when we were at area the night of July 22. A mass of this species, however, was later found.

3. On the morning of July 25, 1922, at the boat landing (strand or sphagnum run) "Ridley and Mattie Chesser found a Cope's frog in the boat. It is a female, gravid. Must have leaped into the boat and couldn't get out. This female is smaller than any of the four males captured. When Anna (Mrs. Wright) was cleaning her off for photography the female voided a few eggs. Later I did the same and secured more eggs. These vitelli were somewhat less

than those in the field, being 1.3–1.4 mm. and the inner envelope absent. The jelly did not swell out quite as well as in the field. Our identification of the egg masses of July 22 is certainly correct."

From subsequent studies of the eggs we found the jelly envelope to be 3.8–6.9 mm., the mode 5 mm. the average, 5.4 mm.; the vitellus to be 1.5–1.8 mm., mode 1.6 mm., average 1.6 mm. Egg complement 200–600.

Dangers. On July 22, 1922, when most of the masses were fresh we found one mass about at the hatching stage. It must have been laid in the generally rainy (July 18–21) period for southern Georgia. Doubtless it was laid near the edge of the high water mark. By July 22 receding began. The mass was in water only 3 inches deep and one half of the eggs were white and spoiled. This is the only mass we found caught in this fashion.

HATCHING PERIOD

On July 22, 1922, the masses were all fresh except one. This was laid in the rainy period from July 18–July 21. In the period from July 18–22 the air minima were from 65–73°, maxima 84–96°. The water doubtless in this shallow area kept about 70° or higher. These eggs were probably about 4–5 days in hatching. The egg masses of July 22 in the laboratory hatched in about three days.

MATURE TADPOLE

Color description from life (May 23, 1924). One tadpole very large, brownish olive mummy brown or brownish olive. In general dorsum very dark. A few large widely scattered black spots on the dorsum. The brownish olive on rear sides surrounds lemon yellow or greenish yellow spots. This yellowish color on either side of belly with a few small dark flecks. Middle of belly pale grayish vinaceous or vinaceous buff. Ventral pectoral and branchial region grayish violaceous blue or body color with vinaceous buff and greenish yellow spots.

Tail. In general a grayish color. Along the middle of the upper crest is row of large spots or these connected. This a much broader and more conspicuous row than *R. grylio*, being about 2 inches long. In middle of musculature is a dark line or area to tip of tail paralleling the upper tail crest line of black. The upper tail crest is irregularly black-margined to tail tip. This black more or less outlines pale chalcedony yellow spots. The musculature has numerous pale grayish vinaceous–vinaceous buff spots. Lower tail crest, narrow with irregular black margin in tip region for 1–1½ inches. This crest with numerous pale chalcedony yellow or vinaceous buff spots. Iris largely black with ochraceous salmon or greenish yellow flecks.

One tadpole near transformation buffy citrine, olive lake, or dull citrine a very few inconspicuous spots on dorsum. Tail crests with no black musculature with the vinaceous buff spots. Legs olive lake in color. Iris pinkish vinaceous and black. Belly pale chalcedony yellow, or sulphur yellow.

Mouth parts. Teeth 2/3 or 1/3.

PLATE XLIII

Carpenter frog (*Rana virgatipes*)

1. Male, Chesser Id., Ga. July 22, 1922. Ventral aspect. × 1.2.
2. Female, Chesser Id., Ga. July 22, 1922. Ventral aspect. × 1.2.
3. Eggs in situ, second "Dreen," near Chesser Id., Ga. July 22, 1922. × 1.0.
4. *Rana grylio* transformed for comparison with No. 5. Billy Id., Ga. April 26, 1921. Ventral aspect. × 0.4.
5. *Rana virgatipes*, Chesser Id., Ga. July 15, 1921. × 0.33.
6. 7. Tadpoles, with two legs, with four legs. Lakehurst, N. J. July 4, July 7, 1923. × 1.0.

1

3

2

4

5

6

7

Measurements. Length of body (25–30 mm.) in tail (48–63 mm.) 1.89–2.1, average 1.99. Width of body (14.5–20 mm.) in its own length 1.45–1.86, average 1.61. Depth of body (13–17 mm.) 1.1–1.2 in body width, average 1.14. Depth of body 1.66–2.07 in body length, average 1.84. Depth of tail (16–21 mm.) in length of tail 2.9–3.6 average 3.12. Muscular part (8–11 mm.) 1.62–2.0 in depth of tail, average 1.84. Spiracle 1.17–1.33 nearer base of hind legs or vent region (14–17 mm.) than the tip of snout (17–20 mm.), average 1.23. Spiracle to eye (8–11 mm.) 1.42–1.82 nearer eye than spiracle to vent (13.5–20 mm.) average 1.62. Eye 1.0–1.22 nearer to tip of snout (7–9 mm.) than eye to spiracle (8–11 mm.), average 1.16. Nostril 1.0–1.42 nearer eye (4–4.5 mm.) than eye to snout (4.5–5.5 mm.), average 1.20. Mouth (5–5.5 mm.) usually 1.0–1.37 larger than internasal space (4–5 mm.), average 1.12. Mouth 1.36–1.8 in interorbital space (7–9 mm.), average 1.57. Internasal space (4.5–5 mm.) contained 1.55–1.87 in interorbital space, average 1.74.

The dimensions of the largest tadpole are:

	mm.		mm.
Total length	92.0	Spiracle to vent	16.0
Body length	30.0	Spiracle to eye	11.0
Body depth	15.0	Eye to snout	9.0
Body width	18.0	Eye to nostril	4.5
Tail length	63.0	Nostril to snout	5.5
Tail depth	21.0	Mouth	5.0
Musculature of tail	11.0	Interorbital distance	9.0
Spiracle to snout	20.0	Internasal distance	5.0

General remarks. The eggs of July 22, 1922, hatched out in camp and we kept the tadpoles for a month. The tadpoles a month old had grown very little beyond the size of one week-olds. Our conditions were poor for them.

The last of June, 1923, Mrs. Wright and I were at Lakehurst, N. J., for a very short period and secured no tadpoles. It was probably too late for tadpoles. On May 22–23, 1924, "in a cut off pool from the main pond of Mr. Emlie's pond where considerable sphagnum is are several tadpoles. We tried to capture them with a dip net but didn't succeed. We resorted to a 10 ft. minnow seine and caught 12 or 15 mature tadpoles. They must be *Rana virgatipes* or immense *R. clamitans* or *Rana grylio*. They cannot be the last, yet in coloration have a black line on the upper and lower crests like the condition of *Rana grylio*. One tadpole had 4 labial rows of teeth. Associates of these tadpoles are mud darters (*Boleichthys fusiformis*), mud sunfishes (*Acantharchus pomotis*), little sunfishes (*Enneacanthus obesus*), mud minnow (*Umbra*), American pickerel, and one adult greenfrog."

"In a left over ditch south of Noble's *H. andersonii* breeding pools found plenty of *Rana virgatipes* tadpoles, one with four legs and one transformed. A little water snake in the ditch, also an eastern painted turtle. Mud minnows, the commonest fish. In the large Emlie's pond heard an adult."

LARVAL PERIOD

In 1921 we spent from April 26–Aug. 1 in the center of the swamp and heard no *R. virgatipes*. In the last of July of that year we heard them on the east edge of the swamp and at Black Jack Island in the south part of the swamp. We therefore missed the tadpoles. In 1922 at Chesser Island we found the species laying at July 22 but located no tadpoles from June 10–Aug. 26. Why the mystery? In the first season we were where they were not. In the second season we concluded they wintered over, transformed in May and early June before we arrived and we were not there long enough after egg laying for mature or half-grown tadpoles. Our trip to Lakehurst in 1923, last of June, confirmed us in the supposition that they wintered over, and transformed in May and June. We found only one debatable tadpole. We therefore visited Lakehurst May 22–23, 1924, and found quite a few mature tadpoles, transforming stages and two transformed individuals. We therefore feel they winter over and this places them in the *R. grylio, R. clamitans, R. catesbeiana, R. heckscheri, R. septentrionalis* group in tadpole characters though like others in egg-mass character.

TRANSFORMATION

Period. When we found transforming individuals on May 23, 1924, they were scarce as were mature tadpoles. Stragglers transform to mid-July but the vast bulk of wintering over tadpoles must transform in early spring by May 15.

Since this whole account was written we recently located two transformed specimens of *Rana virgatipes* in our 1922 collections. We assumed we had wholly missed this stage. These two transforming frogs were taken August 15, 1922.

Another addendum of June 8, 1929 is a record of one transformed frog caught on lily pads in Lakehurst Lake by the Shinn brothers (Everett and Whittemore) and R. D. Anderson. At the same time they caught four adult males (51.5, 52.5, 54, 56 mm.) and a ripe female (56 mm.) in the same places.

Size. On May 23, 1924, we secured from Mr. Emlie's pond 1/2 mile south of Lakehurst two *Rana virgatipes* measuring 27 and 29 mm. respectively. On June 5 some of the tadpoles of May 23 capture were approaching transformation and the body length of these were from 25–30 mm. Another of these tadpoles on July 14 transformed at 29 mm. and two on July 2 transformed at 23 and 24 mm.

In 1923 (June 23) Mrs. Wright and I captured a 25 mm. specimen at Lakehurst, N. J. Transformation may in rare cases extend to 32 or possibly 33 mm.

The two specimens taken in Okefinokee swamp August 15, 1922, are respectively 28 and 31 mm. The first is completely transformed and the second has a tail stub 10 mm. Each have the characteristic light stripe from eye to above hind leg insertion as in adults.

We have, therefore, sizes from 23–31 mm.

General remarks. All the tadpoles taken at Lakehurst, N. J., May 22–23, 1924, were of the *Rana clamitans* type. All of them seem to have the left arm coming out first.

Transforming *R. clamitans* from Ithaca and Adirondack Mts., N. Y., and *R. virgatipes* from Lakehurst, N. J., compared are as follows:

Underparts and rear of hind legs and belly heavily blotched with black in *Rana virgatipes*; finely dotted with black in *Rana clamitans*. Light color of under legs and belly to the level of fore legs, in fact to the chin, is white in *Rana clamitans*, in *Rana virgatipes* underparts to level of fore legs with some vinaceous tint. Chin with few if any spots and greenish yellow or sulphur yellow in *Rana virgatipes;* spotted in *Rana clamitans*. Stripe on upper jaw down to middle of side or farther sayal brown, clay color, or tawny olive or buffy brown in *Rana virgatipes*; stripe in *Rana clamitans* only to the shoulder, lettuce green or calliste green on snout to light yellow green or sulphur yellow near the shoulder.

GROWTH

C. S. Brimley (1909, p. 133) has supplied notes on the smallest specimens, taken at Lake Ellis, Craven Co., N. C. "Six specimens taken in 1906 and 38 in 1907, none being over 45 mm. in length of head and body. These little frogs were found in shady places wherever there was water and in such situations acted much like cricket frogs, almost always coming to the surface immediately after jumping into the water, and seldom diving to the bottom and hiding there."

In the U. S. National Museum, Nos. 36629–31 were taken by Brimley Bros. May 11, 1906, from Lake Ellis and measure 32, 36, 42 mm. respectively. The following May (24 and 25) 1907, J. Hurter secured Nos. 57675–78 from the same place. They measure 43, 42, 38 and 39 mm. respectively. A specimen (U. S. Nat. Mus. No. 55447) secured at Lakehurst, N. J., by W. D. Appel May 28, 1905, measure 35 mm. Two specimens (U. S. Nat. Mus. Nos. 37850–51) from the same place taken June 29, 1907, by W. T. Davis measure 40.5 mm. and 42 mm. The first specimens our collection ever received were two taken by Mr. W. T. Davis at Lakehurst, N. J., May 27, 1906. They are 36 and 47 mm.—apparently two growth sizes.

My material falls into these groups: 23–30 mm. at transformation; 36–38 mm. one year old; 40–48 mm. 2 year old, and 49–55 3 year old. The National Museum material is from 32–39 mm. 1 year old; 40.5–47 mm. 2 year old, and 52–55 mm. 3 year old. Boulenger's (1920, p. 431) material falls into three groups: 32–36 mm. 1 year old; 43 mm. 2 year old; 50–56 mm. 3 year old. In general we believe they transform at 23–29 mm., or even at 31 mm., reach 32–39 mm. for 1 year olds, 40–48 mm. for 2 year olds, 49–56 mm. for 3 year olds. The males begin to have enlarged thumbs and somewhat enlarged vocal sacs at 1 year old. Might possibly breed at $1\frac{1}{2}$ years old. Certainly both males and females breed at 2 years and attain near maximum at 3 years.

Since the above was written I have examined the material in the Acad. of Nat. Sciences, Phila. Cope's material of Oct. 1891 falls into sizes 31, 35, 49,

55, 55 mm. Early in the spring of 1905, April 23, T. D. Keim and H. W. Fowler secured a large series at Great Egg Harbor River above May's Landing, N. J. Twenty of them measure as follows: 39, 40, 42, 44, 44, 45, 45, 45, 45, 46, 48, 48, 49, 49, 49, 51, 51, 52, 52, 52, 53, 54, 55, 58 mm., the last two females. Two specimens taken in summer on May 31, 1905 and June 20, 1901 were 45 and 50 mm. The fall (Oct. 1891) group of Cope may show three sizes: 31–35, 49, and 55; the early spring collection of Keim and Fowler apparently fall into two groups: 39–49, 51–58. Or this material might be interpreted as of two groups—the fall collection 31–35, 49–55; the spring 39–49, 51–58; the summer of two, 45 and 50. This would make half year olds or less 31–35, year olds or less 39–49 and two year olds 49–58. Growth conditions vary in N. J. and Ga. no doubt as does growth in bullfrogs in N. Y. and La. (vide Viosca).

In the Museum of Comparative Zoology are the following:

3483	Lakehurst, N. J., W. T. Davis, 1905.		34 mm
2542	Lake Ellis, N. C., C. S. Brimley, May 24, 1907		37 "
2519	" " " " " " " " " "		36 "
2542	" " " " " " " " " "		34 "
3518	" " " " " " " " " "		42 "
712	Beaufort, N. C., J. G. Shute	1863	60 "
3560–68	Lakehurst, N. J., T. & F. K. Barbour, July 1914		

  35, 36 mm. past transformation
  36.5, 40, 42 mm.
  48 mm., 56, 66 mm.

Possibly these big representatives, 60 mm. and 66 mm. represent 4 year olds.

FOOD

Davis noted (1907, pp. 50, 51) that "These frogs domineer over one another to some extent, and when insects were placed in the cage as food, it was common for the more active individual, failing in the attempt to catch a fly, to turn on his companion and butt him until he retreated into the pool or into a corner. The butted individual would hold his head down in the meekest manner, and he became so cowed that if I touched him at any time with my finger, he assumed the humble position. Miss Dickerson in *The Frog Book* says that *Rana pipiens* and *Rana onca* will snap at the head of a companion frog that has taken a worm that he was trying to capture, but she thinks it is probably not an exhibition of anger, but a desire to secure the disappearing worm. However this may be, it is certain that the butting *Rana virgatipes* in the above-mentioned case secured a great advantage over the other frog, for after 'settling' his companion, he captured all of the insects."

ENEMIES

Every associate in the Okefinokee swamp and also at Lakehurst, N. J., if large enough might feed on them. At Lakehurst, N. J., one of their worst enemies is the water snake (*Natrix sipedon sipedon*). We saw several in the sphagnum mat around the large lake. One specimen from Lakehurst had the left arm from elbow down sharply cut off.

AUTUMNAL DISAPPEARANCE

Published records and my own experiences carry their activities from April 23–Aug. 11. They come out earlier than April 23 and must be active at least two months after August 11.

AFFINITIES

(See *R. grylio* for comparison with that species).

A funny episode or joke on the author shows how closely *Rana grylio* and *Rana virgatipes* parallel each other in coloration. Three days after we first heard *R. virgatipes* in the prairie near Chesser Island we went (July 15, 1921) at night to a wooded causeway to catch some we heard. "Harry Chesser caught one. Another put into the water after he put his light on it. We heard several. Caught two frogs which we mistook for *Rana virgatipes* until on the next morning we examined them closely. They are young *Rana grylio*. Two of the three real *R. virgatipes* we saw, escaped."

Boulenger (1920, p. 431) considers "The species does not exceed a length of 60 millimeters from snout to vent, and may be regarded as a dwarfed form derived from the *R. catesbeiana* type."

Previous to 1921, we knew the distribution of *Rana grylio* to be from Florida and Georgia to Louisiana, that of *Rana virgatipes* from New Jersey to North Carolina and that of *Rana septentrionalis* from Canada and Maine to northern New York and possibly to Catskills. One might have thought the three a series with a gap between each species. Now we know the first two to overlap.

In coloration *R. virgatipes* looks most like *R. grylio*. In adult size it is more like *Rana septentrionalis* but smaller or is possibly like a small *R. catesbeiana*. At Lakehurst lake it reminds one of the water prairie form, *R. grylio*; in the sphagnum strands and thickets of the Okefinokee it reminds me of the peat lake species of Canada or beaver lake thicket form of Adirondacks, namely *Rana septentrionalis*. In egg mass it is most like *Rana septentrionalis*, but in individual eggs unlike *Rana septentrionalis*, *Rana clamitans* and *Rana grylio* it has no inner jelly envelope. The individual eggs are more like the eggs of the film species *Rana catesbeiana* but the jelly is firmer. The tadpole reminds one most of *Rana grylio* in coloration but it is more of the *Rana clamitans* type. Like all of the *Rana clamitans* and *Rana catesbeiana* type it winters over as a tadpole. It transforms at a size near that of *Rana clamitans* and may have a larger tadpole than that species. Therein it approaches *R. catesbeiana*, *R. grylio* and *Rana septentrionalis*.

Cope 1891 (pp. 1018, 1019) writes of the species as follows: "This frog is not nearly related to any species of the genus. It has some points of resemblance to *R. temporaria* as the short posterior legs and moderate web: but the interocular space is much narrower, the vomerine teeth more anteriorly placed, and there are no dermal folds. In coloration there is no resemblance to any other species." Of course *Rana grylio* was not then known. If it is to have an European counterpart might it not be that *Rana virgatipes* is rather a dwarfed *Rana esculenta* or *R. esculenta ridibunda*. There might be those who might derive our Atlantic coastal plain species all from Europe or place each close to a European form e.g. *Bufo fowleri* and *Bufo calamita, Scaphiopus holbrooki* and *Pelobates, Rana virgatipes* and *Rana esculenta, Hyla andersonii* and *Hyla arborea*. There are difficulties in the way of such an interpretation and some strong evidence for such an interpretation.

BIBLIOGRAPHY

1916   Barbour, T.   Copeia, No. 26, January 24, 1916, pp. 5-6.
1919   Boulenger, G. A.   Ann and Mag N. H. (9) III pp. 409, 413.
1919-1920   Boulenger, G. A.   Proc. Am. Acad. Arts and Sciences, 55, pp. 415, 429-431.
1907   Brimley, C. S.   Journal Elisha Mitchell Soc. XXII, No. 2, p. 159.
1908   Brimley, C. S.   Ibid XXIV No. 1.
1909   Brimley, C. S.   Proc. Biol. Soc. Washington, p. 133.
1891   Cope, E. D.   American Naturalist, XXV, pp. 1017-1019.
1904, 1905, 1907   Davis, Wm. T.   Am. Nat. XXXVIII, p. 893, 1905, XXXIX, pp. 795-796; 1907, XLI, pp. 49-51.
1922   Davis, W. T.   Jour. N. Y. Ento. Soc., Mar. 1922, Vol. XXX, No. 1, p. 74.
1906   Dickerson, M. C.   Frog Book, pp. 222-224.
1918   Dunn, E. R.   Copeia, p. 21.
1905   Fowler, H. W.   Proc. Acad. Phila., LVII, 1905, p. 662.
1907   Fowler, H. W.   Rept., N. J. S. Mus. 1906, pp. 120-126.
1908   Fowler, H. W.   Rept. N. J. S. Museum 1907, p. 194.
1924   Myers, Geo. S.   Copeia, p. 60.
1923   Noble, G. K.   Zoologica, 1923, pp. 421, 422, 425.
1923   Pratt, H. S.   Vertebrate Animals of the U. S. p. 183.
1917   Stejneger, L. G., and Barbour, T.   Check List N. Amer. Amp. Rept., p. 39; 1923, p. 37.
1906   Stone, W. S.   Am. Naturalist, XL, p. 164.
1923   Wright, A.H.   Copeia, p. 34.
1923   Wright, A. H.   Bull. Ecol. Soc. Am., Vol. 4, No. 2, p. 9.
1923   Wright, A. H.   Anat. Record 24, No. 6, p. 406.
1924   Wright, A. H.   Proc. Biol. Soc. Wash.; 37, pp. 141-152.
1924   Wright, A. H. and A. A.   Am. Nat., LVII, pp. 375-381.

Gastrophryne carolinensis (Holbrook)

(Pl. I, Fig. 6; IV, Figs. 4, 5; V, Fig. 9; VI, Fig. 3; X, Fig. 14; XIV, Fig. 6; XV, Fig. 10; XVII; XLIV; Text Figs. 1, 24)

COMMON NAMES

Narrow Mouth Frog.   Narrow Mouth Toad.   Narrow-Mouthed Frog. Narrow-Mouthed Toad.   Nebulous Toad.   Toothless Frog.   "Rainy Day Frog."   "Rain Frog."   "Frog-Toad."   Carolina Tree Frog.

RANGE

Check list.   "Virginia to Florida, Gulf States to Texas, Northward through central valley to southern Indiana."—Stejneger & Barbour (1923, p. 38).

Supplementary records.   In Florida, Deckert (1922, p. 88) "Heard (*Gastrophryne carolinensis*) from a ditch beside the road, Royal Palm Hammock," Dade County.   In Wilmington, N. C., G. S. Myers (1924, p. 60) took three. Near Charleston, S. C., K. P. Schmidt (1924, p. 68) notes it at Mt. Pleasant. In Alabama, H. P. Löding (1922, p. 21) records it from "Cherokee, Etowah, Calhoun, St. Clair, Tuscaloosa, Mobile and Baldwin counties."   In Alabama, E. G. Holt (1922, p. 95) notes that "A specimen has been taken at Longview, Shelby County, by L. S. Gibson, and I have collected the species at Barachias, Montgomery County." In Doniphan County, Kansas, Jean M. Linsdale (1927, p. 77) records "A narrow-mouthed toad was found on the area in the summer of 1923." In Virginia (1918, p. 22) E. L. Dunn records it in Carolina County. The same year Philip H. Pope records it in Houston, Texas. The next year (1919, p. 82) Doreen Potter records it in Lafayette County, northern Mississippi.

These records of six years 1918–1924 represent its range rather roughly, i.e., from Virginia, North Carolina, South Carolina, Florida to its tip, Alabama, Houston, Texas, eastern Kansas.

Our own records for it in 1917 begin just south of Richmond, Va., May 31. We did not record it again until June 10 when we reached a low woods beyond Tuskagee, Ala., and 30 miles from Montgomery, Ala. Our course through Durham-Charlotte, N. C., Blacksburg–Anderson, S. C., Atlanta–LaGrange, Ga., West Point–Tuskagee, Ala., was too far inland to record this Lower Austral species. In 1926 (p. 83) we placed this species "*Gastrophryne carolinensis* Va.–Fla.–La.," as one of the nine Okefinokee species of the Lower Austral frogs. Strecker (1909, p. 120) restricts it "principally to the humid division of the Lower Austral Life Zone."

In 1922 on June 6 we heard it four miles north of Petersburg, Va., on June 7 at Cary, N. C., and on June 11 at Screven, Ga. (In connection with Virginia records Dunn (1918, p. 22) reports it from Caroline County north of Richmond a considerable distance).

DeKay (1842, p. 65) writes "Dr. Holbrook thinks it possible that a species may be found in this State, for he has heard its peculiar noise in the neighborhood of New York; and Major LeConte informs me that he has seen a species of *Engystoma*, said to have been found in a sandy district of this State." Subsequent records have not yielded it in either New Jersey or New York and fortunately DeKay placed it in the extra limital species.

No one has attempted a critical study of the *Gastrophryne* (*Engystoma*) except J. K. Strecker in 1909 (pp. 115–120). His three conclusions were:

"First, that the narrow-mouthed toad usually reported from Texas is not *Engystoma carolinense* but *Engystoma texense* which is a very distinct species.

"Second, that the *Engystoma carolinense* Holbrook is exceedingly rare in Texas. The only typical specimen examined was from Paris, Lamar County, in the extreme northeastern section of the State.

"Third, that a small form with unusually pustulate upper surfaces, peculiar coloration and short hind feet, from southeastern Texas, is worthy of recognition as a distinct species (*Engystoma areolata* Strecker)". . . In southwestern Texas the new species occurs in localities inhabited by the widely distributed *Engystoma texense*, but in central Texas where the latter species is the prevailing or, or as I am now fully satisfied, the only form of narrow-mouthed toad, no examples have been found that are even an approach to *E. areolata*.

"*Engystoma carolinense* Holbrook. This is the largest of the three forms here considered and the most widely distributed. Examples have been examined from Raleigh, North Carolina; Columbus, Georgia; Milton and Little Sarasota Bay, Florida; Mobile, Ala.; St. Tammany County, La.; Hot Springs, Arkansas; Cliff Cave and Butler County, Missouri; and Paris, Texas. It has also been reported from Johnston and Wayne Counties, North Carolina, Riceborough, Georgia; Clarcona, Lake Jesup and Micanopy, Florida; Greenway, Arkansas; Calcasieu Parish, Louisiana; New Madrid, Missouri; and various localities in Texas; but most of the Texan localities are open to doubt, this species probably being confused with *E. texense*."

His conclusion (1908, p. 57) previous to his revision was that "The range of this interesting batrachian was extensive, covering two-thirds of the State," but in 1909 he credits most of the *Gastrophryne* to *G. texense*, a view with which we with less experience in the State feel inclined to concur.

Strecker (1915, pp. 46, 47) gives as its range in Texas "Eastern Texas south to Victoria. Many of the published records for this species probably refer to *G. texense* Girard, a smaller slenderer, paler, and more uniformly colored animal with unspotted underparts. I have collected typical *carolinense* at Cleveland, Liberty County, and have examined specimens collected at Paris by Hurter, and Victoria by Mitchell. Miss Dickerson reports it from Hitchcock. Mr. Mitchell obtained only one specimen at Victoria, a locality inhabited by both *G. texense* and *G. areolata*."

In 1912 only five adults of the narrow-mouthed toad were secured, but of larval stages to transformation a large series was taken.

GENERAL APPEARANCE

Holbrook (1842, Vol. V, p. 23) gives this "Description. The general form of this animal approaches the oval; the skin is smooth, the head remarkably small and short, though large for the genus; its extent is marked by a delicate fold of the integuments behind the orbits; its shape is triangular, the snout being very pointed; the upper jaw is dark brown, the lower dark grey; the mouth is inferior and minute." Boulenger separates it from *E. ustum* (two metatarsal tubercles) with a "single metatarsal tubercle." "Snout rather obtuse, not twice as long as the diameter of the eye" separates it from *E. elegans*, *E. ovale* and *E. microps*. H. Garman (1892, p. 333) calls it "a small, clumsy toad, with a very small head and disproportionately stout hind limbs."

C. S. Brimley (1907, pp. 157, 159) give its characters as "Upper jaw without teeth. Skin smooth. Size small. Snout pointed. No parotoids . . . . Hind feet not webbed." "Toothless Frog. Wake and Johnson Counties." In 1926 (p. 81) the same author characterizes it as follows: "A transverse fold of skin across neck just behind eyes, snout sharp, legs very short, unwebbed. Size small, color dark."

COLORATION OF SPIRIT SPECIMENS (1912)

In spirits the specimens are whitish or yellowish white below with a prominent reticulation of brownish or grayish brown lines. Their color scheme extends on the under side of the hind- and fore-limbs to the toes.

Throat of the male slaty or blackish. Upper parts black or brown or gray.
In one specimen the whitish color of the under-parts extends on to the lower
tip and sides of the head as a grayish white on a dark background; the other
four have the head uniform black or brown.

STRUCTURAL CHARACTERS (WRITTEN IN 1912)

Skin variable, smooth or finely tuberculate; head pointed, its tip obtuse;
upper jaw projecting beyond the lower jaw; nostrils much nearer the tip of
snout than the eye; a fold of skin extends from the insertion of one arm to
eye, thence to other arm insertion; tympanum concealed; toes free, subarticular tubercle prominent; inner metatarsal tubercle present; in these five
specimens a depressed line across the breast from either arm insertion looks
like an incipient fold. Tongue quite broad, ovate or elliptical, only the caudal
border free and this portion much thinner than the rest of the tongue; tongue
may be rounded or very slightly emarginate. In none of the five specimens
is it so narrow as Cope figures and in only one so relatively long.

MEASUREMENTS
(1912-1914)

The five adults of 1912 measured 24.5–27 mm., average 25.8 mm.; the
head is 4.5–6 mm. long, average 5.0 mm., slightly less than the width of the
head at the rictus oris; the width of the head, 6–7.5 mm., average 6.6 mm.;
the head is contained in the length of the body, 4.1–5.2 times; snout, 3–4
mm., average 3.4, not twice the diameter of the eye, being usually 1.5–1.25
times the eye (in agreement with Boulenger ('81, p. 162) and Cope ('89, p. 385)
but not with Dickerson ('07 p. 48); interorbital distance equal to the eye or
slightly more being from 2.25–3.5 mm. in width; eyelid 1.5 mm. or 1.6–2.3
in the interorbital distance; femur 9–10 mm., average 9.5 mm., equal to or
slightly less than the tibia which is 9.5–10.5 mm., average 9.9 mm.; tarsus
6–7.5 mm., average, 6.7 mm., about equal to the width of the head and
slightly more than its length; rest of foot 11.5–12.5 mm., average 12 mm.,
equal to fore-limb which is 11.5–12.5 mm., average 12 mm.; forelimb slightly
longer than the distance from its insertion to the tip of the snout; posterior-
limb from groin, 27–32.25 mm., average 30.3 mm.; in none of the specimens
does the hind limb to heel reach beyond front of insertion of the fore-limb.
Miss Dickerson ('07 p. 48) gives "head to shoulder one-third total length"
as distinctive of *Gastrophryne texensis* while for *Gastrophryne carolinensis* the
measurement is "head to shoulder one-fourth total length." In our specimens
this measurement is .4–.33 of the total length.

(Recent Material)

Head to angle of mouth 1.4 (20 mm. ♂)–1.44 (20 mm. ♀)–1.33 (28 mm.
♂)–1.43 (28 mm. ♀)–1.64 (36 mm. ♀) in width of head; head to angle of
mouth 4.0–4.4–4.5–5.0–5.1 in length of body; head to rear of tympanum in
length of body; snout .83–.66–.50–.64–.60 in first finger; snout 1.0–1.0–1.0–1.1–
1.1–.90 in fourth finger; snout 1.0–1.0–.70–.88–.70 in first toe; eye 1.5–1.5–1.8–
1.06–1.6 in snout; eye 1.25–1.0–.90–.70–1.0 in first finger; internasal width

1.0–1.0–.72–.64–.66 in upper eyelid width; interorbital width .66–.75–.72–
.55–.50 in upper eyelid width; interorbital width .66–.75–1.0–.87–.75 in
internasal width.

Forelimb: Forelimb 1.8–2.1–2.375–2.5–2.2 in length of body; forelimb
2.35–2.4–2.33–2.4–2.2 in hind limb; first finger 1.8–2.5–2.5–2.5–2.16 in third
finger; second finger 1.5–1.66–1.9–1.5–1.6 in third finger; second finger .83–
.66–.77–.58–.66 in first finger; third finger .88–.80–.92–.90–1.0 in second toe;
fourth finger 1.5–1.66–1.25–1.46–1.44 in third finger; fourth finger .83–.66–
.50–.57–.66 in first finger; internasal width 1.25–1.33–.90–.80–1.0 in first
finger; internasal width 1.5–2.0–1.1–1.35–1.33 in second finger; internasal
width 2.25–3.3–2.2–2.0–2.15 in third finger; internasal width 1.5–1.5–1.8–
1.35–1.5 in fourth finger.

Hindlimb: Length 1.3–1.17–1.0–.94–1.0 in hind limb; tibia 2.36–2.36–2.7–
2.8–2.5 in length; tibia 3.–2.76–2.7–2.64–2.5 in hind limb; tibia 1.3–1.1–1.15–
1.1–1.18 in forelimb; tibia 1.05–1.05–1.05–1.1–1.1 in hind foot without tarsus;
first toe 1.33–1.33–1.64–1.66–1.8 in second toe; first toe 2.3–2.0–2.85–2.6–2.8
in third toe; first toe 3.0–3.16–3.9–3.66–4.0 in fourth toe; first toe 2.0–1.83–
2.5–2.33–2.2 in fifth toe; second toe 1.75–1.5–1.7–1.56–1.5 in third toe; second
toe 2.25–2.37–2.4–2.2–2.1 in fourth toe; second toe 1.5–1.37–1.52–1.4–1.2 in
fifth toe; third toe 1.28–1.5–1.375–1.41–1.4 in fourth toe; third toe .85–.81–
.87–.90–.80 in fifth toe; fourth toe 1.0–.94–1.0–1.0–1.1 in hind foot without
tarsus; fourth toe .94–.90–.94–.91–1.0 in tibia; fourth toe 1.2–1.0–1.1–1.0–
1.18 in forelimb; fifth toe 1.5–1.7–1.57–1.57–1.75 in fourth toe; internasal
width 1.5–2.0–1.27–1.07–1.06 in first toe; internasal width 2.0–2.66–2.1–1.7–
2.16 in second toe; internasal width 3.5–4.0–3.6–4.0–3.33 in third toe; internasal width 4.5–6.33–5.0–4.0–4.6 in fourth toe; internasal width 3.0–3.66–
3.1–2.5–2.66 in fifth toe.

HABITAT

Holbrook (1842, p. 24) writes "The *Engystoma carolinense* passes most of
its days in concealment, near old fences, or under the bark of fallen and
decaying trees, emerging only towards evening and after heavy rains. They
are frequently seen with myriads of the young of the *Bufo lentiginosus*,
apparently washed from their places of concealment by summer showers,
which has led many to suppose that they descended with the rain."

"It is possible that Bosc referred to this animal when he says he observed
in Carolina, a 'crapaud bossu, ou une grenouille' living under the bark of
dead trees, though he describes its skin as so excessively delicate as to prevent
his preserving it alive even for a short time, in order to make a drawing of it.
Now, though the skin of our animal is smooth and delicate, I have kept
them alive for several months, and even sent them from Charleston to Philadelphia, where they not only arrived in safety, but lived a considerable
time after."

Le Conte (1855, pp. 430, 431) refers to Bosc as well. He writes "Very
common in the low country of Georgia under logs."

"In DeTerville's Natural History, Bosc confounds this animal with
Daudin's *Bufo gibbosus*. He says he found it in South Carolina, but brought

none thence to France, as the skin was so thin and tender, that he was unable to preserve or even describe it; to me the skin appears as strong as that of any other species of Ranina of the same size."

H. Garman (1892, p. 333) writes "It has been reported from the most southern part of the State only, and is probably very rare even there. It is the one species which, like the siren, water-moccasin and red-bellied horn snake, mark southern Illinois as a part of a southern Zoological sub-region. Outside of Illinois the species is almost confined to the Southern States. . . . Le Conte found it abundant under logs in Georgia, and others have collected it among weeds. The peculiar form, small immersed head, small withdrawn eyes, and strong hind legs, suggest subterranean habits."

In 1894 Loennberg "found this peculiar little animal under old logs, dry palm-leaves, and such things, near lakes, and in moist places in Orange County, for instance, in the pineland at Clarcona, and in the hammock bordering Lake Jesup. It is not very common."

In 1893 Julius Hurter (p. 253) near St. Louis found "This little toad is quite rare. I have only found it in spring at Cliff Cave, St. Louis County, Mo., nearly on the top of a bluff on the southwestern exposure. They are not easily seen on account of their color and being partially hid in the ground, under rocks and logs." In 1897, the same author (1897, p. 503) writes of it in Missouri. "Dr. Kennicott sent some that he caught in New Madrid County, Mo., to the National Museum. I have found some specimens in Butler County, and three at Cliff Cave, St. Louis County, which is, to all appearance, the most northern locality of this subtropical species. These toads are found under rocks, sometimes on the top of the bluffs. They are very hard to see, as they are partly hidden in the ground and also protected by their color."

In 1895 Rhoads (p. 396) says "The specimens taken (in Tennessee) were found under logs in woodland near running water. Specimens: Raleigh 1 ad.; near Chattanooga, 1 ad."

Percy Viosca, Jr. (1923, p. 40) in discussing the sea beaches of Louisiana writes "Where the beach connects with some alluvial ridge, oaks, bushes and other ridge land forms make up the vegetation and the fauna partakes of the nature of the alluvial species *Hyla squirella* and *Gastrophryne carolinensis* sometimes reaching to the very edge of the Gulf." In (1926, p. 310) he places it in the "Species common to the Atlantic, East Gulf, Mississippi Alluvial and West Gulf Coastal Plains."

In 1911 and 1912 Deckert (1914, No. 3, p. 3) finds at Jacksonville, Florida, "*Engystoma carolinense*...abundant everywhere after heavy rains." In Dade Co., he in 1920 (1921, p. 21) says "Of this, the 'Narrowmouth Toad' about a dozen specimens were taken in Miami, on the borders of a rain-pool in an empty lot at Miama Ave. and 22nd Street. Both sexes were represented. They were hiding under pieces of limestone in black, mucky soil and were heard calling during the night of May 16 in company with Spadefoots and other toads. Several were found at Lemon City under pieces of limestone in a wagon track leading to a rock-pit, and one under a stump in a rock-pit at Little River, in November."

In 1912 we made a few notes on its habitat. They are: It frequents the small ponds around the wooded edge of the islands where some shade is afforded. One performer we took on some fallen saw-palmetto bushes a few inches above a heavily shaded shallow pool which was 3 feet in diameter. This pool was near our camp well. Another specimen was taken under dead leaves. The species is not common but quite widespread. During our stay we took three specimens: one on Honey Island, June 1; one on Billy's Island, June 6; and another, same island, June 12. After July 15, 1912 we received two specimens one taken between July 15–Nov. 15, 1912, and another between Dec. 23, 1913–Aug. 1, 1914. All in all, this species seems decidedly nocturnal, a lover of rain, cover and moist situations.

(For 1921 and 1922 records see Voice, Ovulation, etc.).

FIRST APPEARANCE

In 1921 immediately after we entered the swamp on April 24 "one lad found one under a decaying log." In Texas we found the related species *G. texense* breeding as early as March 25. One can dig *Gastrophryne texense* out of logs in Texas in February and doubtless the same can be done in the southeast for *G. carolinense*. At Biloxi, Miss., G. S. Miller Jr. (U. S. N. M. No. 51120) secured the species in the middle of February.

GENERAL HABITS

Metachrosis: Le Conte (1855, p. 430) says it is capable of "Varying at will very much in color, from dusky to brown, olive-cinerous or yellow cinerous, more or less varied, spotted or speckled with black, beneath pale brownish white, punctate so as to appear spotted."

Variations in color: Holbrook (1862, pp. 23, 24) gives its general color as chestnut brown above. Hallowell (1856, p. 252) has it olive. Gunther (1858, p. 52) has one "rose-coloured." Dumeril et Bibron (1842, p. 743) gives "brun olivatre ou marron." Boulenger has it (1882, p. 182) "brown." Cope (1889, p. 386) considers it "chestnut."

H. Garman (1892, p. 332) discusses coloration and its variation at length: "Color above olive-brown or gray, marked and spotted with dusky; below pale yellowish, closely marbled with purplish, but more yellowish posteriorly on the abdomen and under side of the femora. Two wide, poorly defined pale bands begin at the fold of the skin behind the eyes and pass backward and slightly downward to the insertion of the femora; they are bordered above by a sinuous band of interrupted elongate dark spots, and below by a wider continuous dark band, which in front passes immediately over the fore legs, through the eye and around the snout, where it unites with its fellow of the opposite side. Two dark bands cross the tibia. The throat of adult males is bluish black. The colors vary with age and, to some extent also, at the will of the animal. Old examples are darker, and the markings are in them more obscure. The characteristic markings are consequently more apparent on medium sized specimens because of the paler color and consequent greater contrast between it and the dark marks. Examined with a lens, the skin of the body is seen to be sprinkled with minute dark specks, the closer aggregations of which form the dark spots, while their absence in numerous small irregular areas on the abdomens of the younger examples produces a fine mottling of the under side. Occasionally the pale bands on the sides of the back are so nearly the shade of the ground color as not to be apparent; and they may be rendered still more obscure by the absence of the dark band which generally bounds them above. A very young specimen before me has a series of small dark spots along the middle of the back. The feet are more or less spotted with dark above. A black spot over the vent seems to be constant."

Strecker (1909, p. 117) notes that upper surfaces may be black, brown or gray and under surfaces gray or light brown, speckled with white or light yellow.

General habits: It is so secretive its habits have been little discussed and most of these pertain to its voice. H. Garman (1892, p. 333) held that "Of the habits but little can be written at present." Deckert (1914, No. 9, p. 1) holds "the 'Narrow-mouth Toad' is a common Batrachian here (Jacksonville) but owing to its nocturnal habits, it is not often seen."

This is subterranean species. Its appearance alone indicates it. Never during the day would one find it if he did not hear it bleat during a rain storm or cloudy weather or if he did not unearth it from beneath cover. Often in tearing decaying logs to pieces one finds them within the logs or merely beneath them. Some boys found some under some hay cocks. Rarely during showers one may chance on them by day. Even by day e.g., July 3, 1921, one marvels at the numbers which may appear by day in a drenching rain. Sometimes the din and population is incredible. The species apparently does not have far to migrate at such times.

At times these creatures almost crawl along. They can hop from 2 to 6 or even 9 or 10 inches. Some think they can swim rapidly, others hold them clumsy. At breeding times they often seek cover near the breeding place. For example, on May 22, 1921, at Newt Pond we found eggs laid the night before. In the daytime we turned over a piece of bark which was sticking into the water. A *Gastrophryne carolinensis* male scurried or scrambled or rapidly crawled into the water, but not too rapid for its capture. We have noted under Voice how the males crawl out of the water up the vertical banks at times. One male which the boys found under cut grass climbed the vertical side of a 2-quart can to the top.

VOICE

Holbrook (1842, Vol. V, p. 24) says "It makes a feeble chirp at night and at times when captured; and being but a clumsy swimmer, if thrown into water it repeats this chirp in its endeavors to escape."

In 1855 Le Conte (1855, p. 431) closes his catalogue with the following note: "There is in the water of ponds and ditches a small frog whose note exactly resembles the bleating of a lamb, so truly as to deceive any one. This animal I have seen, but never succeeded in catching it. It is very common in Georgia and I have heard it as far North as Norfolk in Virginia. It is left to the inhabitants of those parts of our country to determine what it is." It is unmistakably *Gastrophryne carolinensis*.

In 1891 J. A. Ryder (1891, p. 838) writes "This interesting Batrachian occurs in the Piedmont section of North Carolina, near Littleton, and within twelve miles of the southern boundary of Virginia. Its presence after a rain may be discovered by its peculiarly plaintive note."

In 1914 Deckert (No. 9, p. 1) writes "After thundershowers, however, every pool and ditch resounds with its cry, which sounds like a nasal 'baa,' or 'bee' and has also some resemblance to the noise made by an electric buzzer." In 1924 (p. 60) G. S. Myers writes of it at Wilmington, N. C. as follows: "The call, as heard in the terrarium reminds one of a loud electric buzzer."

In 1918 Philip H. Pope (1919, p. 94) found them at Houston, Texas, "June 15, 1918. A heavy thunder shower brought out the narrow-mouthed toads. Found them abundant and noisy in a large rain pool about ten o'clock at night. The call is harsh and grating, almost a bleat. It is repeated frequently but not as rapidly as that of the Hylas. The males sit in the water in the thick grass that fringes the pools, and are almost impossible to find with a light, although they are not at all shy. Collected six specimens by treading down the grass into the water and catching them as they swam. They swim slowly with their short legs and webless feet and do not dive when disturbed as frogs and toads do. From this date until the middle of August I heard them frequently, but seldom in any abundance. After a rain one could be heard now and then in a pool or roadside ditch, before sunset as well as at night.

In 1912 we made the following notes: This species was seldom heard during the party's stay within the swamp. Only on the 6th and 7th of June did we hear it. In the evening of the 6th, this curious frog note arrested our attention. To some it sounded like the bleat of a young lamb; to another it resembled the note of a woodcock. All agreed it was very nasal and wholly unlike that of a toad. As one approached the frogs the shrillness of the note became very marked. On the following afternoon the frogs began again during a rain. The natives associate it with such weather and term it the "Rainy Day Frog."

In 1921 our first records on calling came on May 21. Then and on the day before the *Gastrophryne* began to "bleat like a lamb or calf. They stopped to find *Gastrophryne* in a ditch. Sometimes they are under the bank. One was thus. Another was out on the side of the bank. Its throat like a *Bufo terrestris* throat. Black in color." On that date Mr. Harper and I counted the intervals and periods of calls. His record of these 37 intervals is from 3–58 seconds, at least 20 of which were 30 seconds or more and the average 30 seconds. The actual call in most instances occupied 1.5–2 seconds. The intervals of another calling frog were from 1–60, only one below seconds, average 29 seconds. A third frog noted by Mr. Harper on June 26 has 79 intervals from 3–59 seconds, average 30 seconds.

Normally one would not think of *Gastrophryne*'s call as far reaching. Frequently other frogs such as Hylids (*Hyla femoralis, Hyla squirella, Acris gryllus*), *Scaphiopus* or *Bufos* (*Bufo quercicus* and *Bufo terrestris*) may be in chorus in the same place and may break the record or drown its calls. Some of these species interfere with each other or *Gastrophryne* in other ways. Once in a flooded furrow, July 3, 1921, we saw two mated pairs of *Gastrophryne*. One we captured but before we could try for the other a (*Bufo terrestris*) toad had butted the pair and frightened it. To return to its voice. One has to be within 20–60 yards to hear *Gastrophryne* calls under normal conditions. They usually call from the water with rear parts submerged and only fore feet planted on back or some support. Occasionally they may be amongst the trash on surface. Occasionally they are out of water on the bank or in a grassy tussock. On May 26 we observed numerous males in one ditch. At times they would crawl out of the water and up the vertical banks of the ditch a few inches. The white throat is swelled out like the bubble of a toad or spadefoot and the frog becomes vertical or bent backward with the effort. In the interval the frog returns to a position short of vertical, deflates the throat but may pulsate the throat. At times the male has one or two other notes not of the b a a a ... order. The same is true of *Gastrophryne texense*.

1921

May 20. A number heard. Air 68°.
   " 21. A chorus in the evening. Air 70°.
   " 22. Commonly heard in the evening, also in mid afternoon.
   " 24. A few calling tonight. Air 77°, 10:09 p. m.
   " 25. At 12:30 a. m. a great chorus. More *Gastrophryne* calling than ever before. Air 73°.
June 4. Rain of two inches. More *Gastrophryne* than any other time. No end of *Gastrophryne*.
   " 5. Several in late afternoon. Air 71°.
   " 23. Tonight after 2 inch rain all along ditches and elsewhere heard.
   " 24. Abundantly calling at night.
   " 25. Heard plenty of *Gastrophryne*.
June 26. Common tonight.
   " 28. Calling in evening in chorus.
   " 29. Not so common this evening.
   " 30. One calling near cypress bay.
July 1. Heard 5–6:30 p. m. after rain. Common in evening.
   " 2. Less heard than formerly this night.
   " 3. Flood of rain. Never heard such a din.
   " 4. A few calling. Air 75°.
   " 6. A *Gastrophryne* or so; p. m. rain. Several calling in the evening.
   " 7. Commonly heard.
   " 15. One heard.
   " 16. One heard about 7:15 p. m.
   " 23. *Gastrophryne* calling tonight.

July	26.	Last night many heard.
"	29.	One or two heard.
"	30.	No end of *Gastrophryne* calling in the evening.
Aug.	5.	Heard.
"	7.	Heard.
"	16.	Several heard.

1922

July	2.	Heard a few between 8:30 p. m. and midnight.
"	3.	Common at 7 p. m. in meadow below spring.
"	11.	Downpour. Heard a few in evening.
"	18.	Heard near spring in evening.
"	25.	Heard quite a few narrow-mouths 8–11 p. m. after storm.
Aug.	1.	Common at night along Dixie Highway.
"	2.	Common.
"	5.	Commonly calling at 10 p. m.
"	8.	Heard a few 8–11 p. m.
"	11.	Several heard 10–12 p. m.
"	15.	A few only.
"	16.	Several heard.
"	19.	Several heard at night.

Taking the voice record for 1921 we find for stations around the swamp the following data from May 20–July 29. For the day before the record from May 20–June 5 the maxima have an average of 84.5° and range from 78–94° the minima, an average of 68° and a range of 63–70°. The period from June 23 –July 29 have maxima average 92.5° range 80–97° and minima from 67–78°, average 71°. Or the whole period from May 20–July 29 have air maxima of 78–97°, average 89°, minima of 63–78°, average 78.5°.

For the day of the record air maxima from May 20–June 5 are 78–94°, average 85.5°, minima from 62–70°, average 68°. From June 23–July 29 the maxima are 80–97°, average 91.5°, the minima from 67–74°, average 70°. The whole period May 20–July 29 give air maxima from 78–97°, average 89° and minima from 62–74°, average 69°. These records for the day before and for the day of the record correspond closely. The minimum range of 62–78°, averages 68°, 68°, 68.5°, 70° are more important than maxima but not of the consequence of humidity.

Humidity is the important factor in this species in particular. They are truly a "Rainy Day Frog." At three or four stations around the swamp we have this record:

May	20	.58 inches and	1.22 the day before.
"	21	.15 " "	.35 " " "
"	22	.11 " "	.56 " " "
"	24	.01 " "	——— " " "
"	26	.40 " "	——— " " "
"	4	.67 " "	.76 " " "
"	5	2.56 " "	.39 " " "
June	23	——— " "	1.41 " " "
"	24	.98 " "	" " "
"	25	.70 " "	.98 " " "

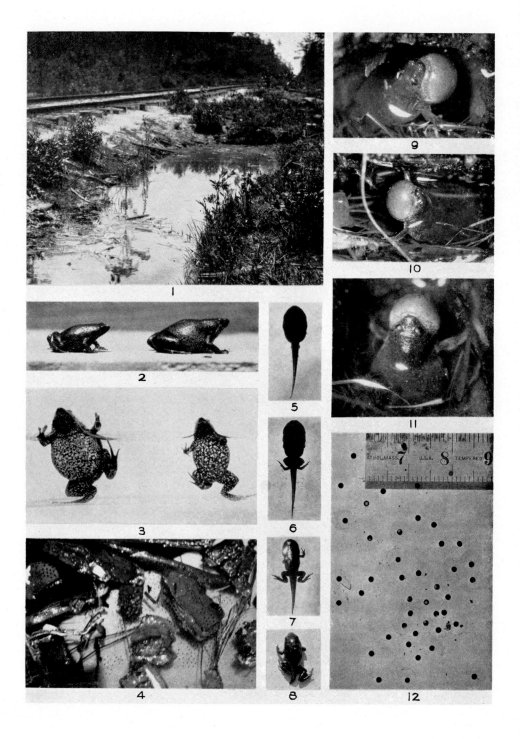

June	26	2.59 inches and		.70	the day before.			
"	28	.57	"	"	————	"	"	"
"	29	3.02	"	"	.57	"	"	"
"	30	2.08	"	"	3.02	"	"	"
July	1	T	"	"	2.08	"	"	"
"	2	.68	"	"	T	"	"	"
"	3	3.47	"	"	.68	"	"	"
"	4	1.00	"	"	3.47	"	"	"
"	6	4.56	"	"	————	"	"	"
"	7	.89	"	"	4.56	"	"	"
"	26	1.32	"	"	1.70	"	"	"
"	29	2.84	"	"	5.13	"	"	"

(For temperature of chorus records see Ovulation).

MATING

Male (From life, April 25, 1921) (Non Ridgway). Top of head and upper eyelids mineral gray, pale smoke gray or with yellowish cast. June 5, 1921. Under parts dusky and bluish-white. White on throat, fine dots not blotches; therefore throat looks blacker in male. All over back dusky with fine bluish-white spots or dots. Pupil circular. Iris black with bluish-white.

Female (From life, June 9, 1921). Lighter, larger. Practically no spots on pectoral region. None on throat. Throat same color as belly. Practically no rusty spots. Ground color of the dorsum more greenish, i.e., olive gray or mineral gray or grayish olive. Sometimes at breeding season males and females may be alike in color, e.g., on April 24, 1921, several were thus, several pairs reddish, one pair gray. Most of pairs however were diverse.

Structural differences. From its first description authors have noted males with a sub-gular vocal vesicle." Or put in the negative H. Garman (1892, p. 330) has males with "no saccular dilations of the skin at the angles of the mouth." His affirmative is "Males with an internal, sub-gular vocal sac."

We found that in the Okefinokee frogs there were some males revealed externally at 21 mm. and females at 22 mm., and our largest male was 29 mm. and largest female 30 mm. In the whole range of the species we found males and females so indicated externally at 20 mm., the largest male 30 mm. and the largest females 31–36 mm. They apparently begin breeding the second spring or summer after transformation.

The male's throat in alcohol may look black, bluish-black, bluish-gray, or in many cases darker than the rest of the underparts. The female has the throat much as the other underparts though the light or bluish-white spots on the throat are smaller than on the venter proper. The male's throat seldom has the lighter spots. Frequently the males in alcohol have the lower throat just ahead of pectoral region thrown into one or two transverse folds or plaits, sometimes it appears as one or more ridges. The lower jaw of the male often has light spots and is brownish-black like venter, but often it is uniform self color like the throat.

The actual measurements of several mated pairs show the males usually smaller. For example one ovulating pair of July 4, 1922, caught at midnight were 24 mm. for the male and 28 mm. for the female. Another ovulating pair of the year before, July 3, 1921, were 23 mm. ♂ and 27 mm. ♀.

Duration, night or day. Amplexation. This subterranean species normally breeds and mates at night. Heavy, warm rains of 1–4 inches may precipitate mating in daylight and rarely one captures a croaking male in mid-day. We took or recorded mated pairs May 21, July 3, July 7, 1921, all taken at night choruses. In every one the amplexation was axillary except in one pair where for a time it was preaxillary.

OVULATION

Habitat. Deckert (1914, No. 9, p. 1) has "caught hundreds of these queer little toads, and on August 28, 1921, came across their spawn in a ditch between two potato hills."

In 1921 we found egg masses or mating or ovulation in the following places: The clearing on Billy's Island was in a hammock with pine barrens on the south and cypress bay on north end. Between the lumber quarters and the bay were the Lee's cleared fields. In the temporary pools in the streets of the lumber quarters after a rain or in any depression they might lay. In the furrows of corn fields or in a walled-in area in a pumpkin patch or in a well beside a shanty they laid. In small ponds at the edge of the clearing or edge of hammock or edge of bay they frequently deposited eggs. The most prevalent places were the ditches in the east and west negro quarters beside the railroad tracks. In any place where a depression will furnish water they ovulate,—places such as a sink hole near a stable, temporary pools in old camp grounds (1912 camp site), pools around a landing, overflows or depressions around a turpentine still or building. At times after a 2–4 inch rain they may appear all over the island in any habitat with water.

In 1922 we found them in deep dug pools on high banks of St. Mary's River at Camp Pinckney, in pools beside wood roads, in ditches along Dixie Highway, in open, artificial and natural ponds in cut over pine barrens, in ponds of *Ilex myrtifolia* or *Hypericum fasciculatum* or shallow cypress ponds or in moist pine barren pools normally dry or in wet meadows.

Apparently whenever a great rain comes they breed wherever much surface water accumulates. Apparently they do not lay so much in the deeper pools and in this respect are much like the fast developing *Scaphiopus holbrookii.*

Period. J. A. Ryder (1891, p. 838) holds that "Oviposition seems to occur in the evening and during cloudy afternoons. It is now late in July, yet two lots of ova have been found by me which have been very recently deposited by the parent female 'frog-toad' as it is known here amongst the natives."

In Raleigh, C. S. Brimley (1896, p. 501) writes that "This species is very abundant in the breeding season, which is in July and August, and possibly the two preceding months. Have never seen any except when breeding; I think they are nocturnal." And Strecker (1909, p. 120) reports that C. S. Brimley says that it "breeds from May to August" at Raleigh, N. C.

In 1921 "we did not find the eggs of this species but the 'pipers' of June 6 and 7 might have been tardy breeders."

In 1921 we have ovulation records May 20, May 21, May 22, May 26, May 28, June 4, June 5, June 23, June 25, July 1, July 2, July 3, July 6, July 7, July 23. In 1922 we have such records on June 22, July 4, August 7, August 9, August 17. We have records of spent females May 23, June 8, July 3, July 4, August 23, and of ripe or gravid females March, May 23, June 11, June 18, July 3, July 22, August, August 23. This gives breeding May 23–August 23 or later.

In 1920 (pp. 29, 30) we wrote "The narrow-mouthed toad is a form whose life-history is not wholly understood .... The author's limited experience with the species suggests that the eggs are usually laid during the spring or early summer." In February, 1923, (p. 34) we state that "From May 15 on to June 1st, five more start (to ovulate)." *Gastrophryne carolinensis* is the third in the list. In 1924 (p. 378) we give the "Season, May 21 to August 17." The records show May, June, July and August the normal months just as Brimley long ago said. Doubtless they begin earlier if our March breeding (1925) date for *G. texense* be indicative.

Temperature and humidity. When eggs were found the minima for the day of the record varied as follows: 63–68°, average 66°, 64–70°, average 69.5°, 70–72°, average 71°, 69–74°, average 72° in 1921 or 64–70°, average 67°, 70–72°, average 71°, and 73–74°, average 73° in 1922. These records 63–74° or averages 66–72° fairly represent the minimum air temperatures of ovulation. The data for mated pairs are much the same. The optimum temperatures are nearer the records for chorus which follow.

The air temperatures which we recorded at camp at the time of 12 choruses of *Gastrophryne* in 1921 range from 70–77°, mode 70°, average 72.5°; the records of 7 fair callings range from 68–75°, average 72.5°. In 1922 for 5 choruses we have 70–78°, average 74°, for four voice records not chorus 70–77°, average 73°. Like *Scaphiopus* it likes drenching rains but will come out on less moisture than the former.

When these choruses, matings and ovulations came a heavy rain preceded or immediately followed the activities. Usually 63–74° are frequent minimal temperatues of ovulation but 70–77° seems the optima of minima.

EGGS

Attachment, egg mass, egg description. J. A. Ryder (1891, p. 838) is the first to describe the eggs of this species. His description follows: "The eggs are heavily pigmented at the upper or animal pole, being darker than the eggs of Rana, and also considerably smaller. They are laid in strings, but so coiled as to form a nearly complete single layer over a considerable surface of water. The gelatinous coating, as in Rana, spreads out under the surface of the water, where by its adhesion to the layer of molecules at the surface a certain amount of support is thus gained for the eggs. It is therefore evident that surface tension is an important agent in keeping the eggs of this genus, and those of Rana, at the surface of the water. Other genera, such as Bufo, do not have the eggs supported on the surface, but are laid in strings formed of one row of eggs, wrapped in a gelatinous cord which lies on the bottom of the pond in which oviposition occurs. Still other forms have the eggs glued together in large masses and supported upon water weeds; this is notably the case with some Urodeles, such as Amblystoma.''

Deckert (1914, No. 9, p. 1) describes them as follows: ''The eggs are laid in oblong jelly-like sheets or flat masses, about 1 1/2 inch long and 1 inch wide. The egg-masses contain about 100 to 150 eggs.''

In 1921 we found them commonly. A few field notes from our journal will reveal some of their characters: ''May 21. Found eggs fastened to vegetation beneath water some 1-2 inches, also saw some floating free and some floating in a mass around a stick on the surface. They were black and white. Thought them at first possibly *Hyla cinerea*. Examination in the camp reveals they have no inner envelope and they look like *Rana clamitans*. Have the habit of free floating eggs. Last night and today it rained an inch or two, so some eggs are immersed.''

''May 22. In ditches by negro quarters were *Gastrophryne* eggs. Each egg stands out distinctly. Ditch 2 feet wide and 1/2-1 1/2 feet deep. Blackish, trashy, oily water. Packets of eggs floating. Some masses 1 x 1 inch in diameter; others 2 x 1 inches; others 2 x 2 inches. Some round masses, others square. Each jelly envelope abuts that of the next in pentagonal or hexagonal fashion. In proper light a mass of eggs makes a mosaic. Some eggs along banks in weeds may be 1 foot 10 inches long and 3 or 4 inches wide. One mass in middle of ditch was amongst chips and was 4 x 7 inches. Few such in mid pond. Believe they lay large masses along edges or amongst brush. Wind scatters them and carries them around on water's surface.''

''In a clean pond (20 x 3 feet) along its edges in amongst grass, one packet of eggs, 100-125 floating. They are brown and yellowish. One mass 6 inches long x 3 wide separated from another mass, round, $2\frac{1}{2}$ x $2\frac{1}{2}$ inches. These three masses are floating films. More eggs in a mass than in a film of *Hyla versicolor*. Insects get into the fresh masses amongst roots.

''We went to Old Hog's Hole. The eggs there we thought *R. climatans* are *Gastrophryne*. Whole pond covered with little masses. These must float away from main mass. Over in Newt Pond amongst weeds are fresh *Gastrophryne* eggs. ... Each egg stands out like glass marbles but attached to each other. Believe eggs are laid in 2-4 large masses or one in amongst brush, grassy edges. Then wind drifts them away in small floats. Finest appearing frog's eggs which float in water. Masses may be at times even triangular, one 7 x 7 x 7 inches.

''May 26. As with other floating egg films, more *Gastrophryne* eggs in Old Hog's Hole Pond are revealed by air bubbles amongst the jelly.

''May 28. New Hog's Hole Pond has many *Gastrophryne* eggs hatching. Newt Pond has numerous masses of fresh and hatching *Gastrophryne* eggs floating. In certain lights each egg looks like a circular oil spot on water. 52, 9, 48 are counts of eggs in three films. Sometimes in a shady place each egg looks to be a milk-white circular ring with a clear hyaline center when hatching. One mass near bank 4 x 8 inches. When I approached in the water the waves separated this mass into 4 masses of 74, 71, 86 and 85 eggs."

In 1923 (p. 34) we write that *"Gastrophryne carolinensis* spawns clear marble-like eggs in films on the surface, these eggs truncated on the top." In 1923 (p. 406) we hold that normally *Gastrophryne carolinensis* "Eggs (are) laid in films." Of this species in 1924 (p. 377) we say that "One form, *Gastrophryne carolinensis*, although it lays at the surface, has the most beautifully distinct, firm eggs of all the species considered." "Egg mass, a surface film. Egg envelope outline always distinct, never lost in the mass; eggs firm and distinct like glass marbles, making a fine mosaic; envelope a truncated sphere, the flat surface above; envelope single 2.8 to 4.0 mm.; vitellus 1.0–1.2 mm.; color black above and white below. Egg complement 869." This egg complement comes from the count of one of the 1921 females. The truncated envelope did not appear until Mrs. Wright tried to manipulate the eggs for drawing. They were hard to turn over.

The detailed study of several eggs by Mrs. Wright gave no inner envelope. The outer envelope ranged from 2.8–4.0 mm. Of 31 eggs, 3 were at 2.8 mm., 11 at 3.0 mm., 1 at 3.2 mm., 4 at 3.4 mm., 3 at 3.6 mm., 4 at 3.8 mm., and 5 at 4.0, average, 3.35 mm., mode 3.0 mm. Of 34 vitelli 17 were at 1.0 mm., 2 at 1.1 mm., and 15 at 1.2 mm., or average of 1.1 mm. We fear that our field record of some eggs brown above and yellow below are of *H. femoralis*. Doubtless it is a mistaken identification when we little knew this form's eggs.

Dangers. No species lays in more transient places than *Gastrophryne* unless it be *Bufo quercicus*. When one finds mated pairs hopping around in sweet potato furrows or finds a congress in a wet meadow which will be dry a few days later, he marvels that any of these forms come through to maturity. Seemingly these subterranean forms breed right where their retreat happens to be. Like *Scaphiopus* they wait for a drenching rain to flood their locality. The toll from these transient breedings must be immense. But even in ponds and bigger ditches great losses happen. For example, on June 25, 1921, we note: "Along the deeper ditches of west negro quarters are plenty of *Gastrophryne* eggs. Many of these are getting stranded even soon after laying. What a frightful waste there is in nature!" Several times we found spoiled white eggs where the eggs were caught and fastened to vegetation. Normally these eggs are free on the surface and drop with the level of the surface.

HATCHING PERIOD

J. A. Ryder's (1891, pp. 838–840) developmental story might be apropos at this point: "The development of the eggs of *Engystoma* is rapid; three days after deposit the larvae escape from the egg-envelopes. Throughout the course of development there is well-marked evidence of geotropism, or of the action of gravity in maintaining the equilibrium of the egg. The animal or black pole remains uppermost, the heavier or light-colored vegetative pole remains lowermost; the whole egg is thus maintained in a position of static equilibrium with the earth's center. There seems to be no tendency to rotate the egg through ciliary action, previous to the closure of the medullary folds. That cilia are entirely absent on the eggs of *Engystoma* is proved by the fact that at the time the medullary groove is still open every egg of the same age is in exactly the same position in respect to the center of the earth, and remains so for a long time, or until the tail fold is well developed and the medullary groove has been closed. Before the closure of the medullary groove, but after the egg has begun to elongate and the paired, secretory, adhesive surfaces of the under side of the head have appeared as rudiments, the position of the animal and vegetative poles is still the same as in the undeveloped ovum. The head end of the egg is slightly elevated above the caudal end. This is due to the forward growth of the head, and the retention of the heavier yolk, farther backward under the posterior half of the medul-lary groove. The medullary groove thus comes to be inclined downward a few degrees from the head toward the tail, but the groove looks exactly toward the zenith, while the yolk looks downward in every egg, even the inclination of the medullary groove with respect to the horizon being the same for every egg of the same age.

"At this stage I neglected to note an extremely important fact,—Viz., whether the cephalic and caudal poles of the same row of eggs were all of them lying in the same direction. The fact that no change of position occurs for a long time in the eggs of *Engystoma* would indicate that possibly we might find that the future cephalic pole of the egg bore a constant relation to the cephalic pole of the parent *Engystoma*, such as is known to be the case in *Batrachus tau*. Such relations between parent and offspring exist to a marked degree, if they are not universal, in plants, and it is desirable to know to what extent the same rule holds with respect to animals. According to what has preceded, the early development of *Engystoma* is peculiarly favorable for the purpose of testing the theory that the cephalic and caudal polarities of the parent are transmitted directly to the offspring, or that the future long axis of the embryo already conforms, even in the egg, to that of the parent.

"The next step in the development of *Engystoma* is somewhat similar to that of *Rana*. As soon as the larvae have the tail-fold well developed they turn over and lie on the side, curved upon themselves, within the egg-evelope. This is the condition of the eggs on the second and early part of the third day. On the third day the larvae leave the egg, and then tend to fall upon the bottom of the pool or receptacle in which hatching occurs. Soon after this they begin to swim about actively, and, singularly enough, instead of swimming like a fish, for some reason, which it is difficult to make out, the larvae revolve on their own axes. This singular mode of locomotion is probably due to the peculiar manner in which the tail is vibrated. This mode of swimming lasts about a day, after which the larvae begin to swim in the usual fish-like way. At this stage, when the larvae come to the surface, the head is in contact with the surface of the water, and when quiescent the axes of the body, when in a condition of equilibrium, assumes an angle of about eighty degrees with the surface. The adhesive organs near the mouth now become functional. Up to this time the light area on the yolk is prominent, and enables one to watch the singular rotation of the larvae. The head now begins to widen rapidly, and the light area on the belly become darker. The tail-fold soon becomes very thin, and bordered all around by a delicate edging of black pigment. The larvae cease to rotate on the fourth day, and no longer take up their angular position at the surface of the water, and now behave very much like the larvae of *Rana*. They are now very heavily pigmented over the whole of the body; the light area over the space where the yolk was formerly placed has disappeared, and the larvae are now black as seen from above."

Deckert's eggs found August 28, 1911, but laid night of August 27, 1911, hatched on August 30. In 1921 on May 24 I have the note. "*Gastrophryne* eggs probably laid night of May 20–21, probably hatched night of May 23–24" or three days later. On the night of May 26–27, 1921, when the air was 72° a great chorus was on, and the following morning many places had fresh eggs. On May 28 in several places some of these were hatching. This makes 1 1/2 days for hatching.

MATURE TADPOLE

Color description from life. General color black overlaid with very fine light purplish gray or quaker drab or hair-brown dots. Transverse stripe of belly divided in middle and is apricot yellow or buff yellow color. Along either side of the belly a light buff stripe. Another such stripe on either side of the gill region. Sometimes whole venter with small light buff or pale orange yellow spot heaviest on belly and sides and lightest on throat. The interspaces are purplish gray, violet gray or plumbeous.

Tail with light buff or white stripe along middle of muscular part of tail. After the first one-half inch the stripe breaks up into spots, which finally disappear caudally. Above and below this continuous stripe is clear black. Above this black is light purplish gray or quaker drab dots. Quaker drab not in lower crest. Lower and upper crests on caudal half with muscular part heavily blotched with black or rather light purplish gray or hair brown giving the tail tip almost a black appearance.

General appearance. Tadpole small, (26.4 mm.) flat, wide, elliptical, snout sometimes somewhat truncate. Tail medium, obtuse or rounded, sometimes with black tip. Dorsal or ventral crest not equal to to depth of the musculature. The dorsal crest scarcely extends on to the body, reaching a vertical somewhat ahead of developing hind legs. Spiracle medium, closely associated with anus, just ahead of it, not very apparent until hind legs begin to appear, when it becomes separated from the anus. Eye is on the lateral axis, distinctly lateral in position. From one eye to snout and around to the other eye the tadpole has a prominent canthus made by the flat ventral and dorsal sides of the head. Anus median at the end of the edge of the ventral crest. Muciferous crypts indistinct.

Mouth parts: Teeth o/o. No horny mandibles; no labial teeth; no papillae; upper labial edge dark and quite emarginate in the middle; just below this emargination is a lower light-colored median beak-like prolongation on the margin of the lower labium.

Measurements. Length of body (9.2–10.8 mm.) in tail (9.8–16.4 mm.) 1.06–1.77, average 1.37. Width (6.5–8.0 mm.) of body in its own length 1.3–1.65, average 1.43. Depth (4.4–5.0 mm.) of body 1.35–1.65 in body width, average 1.5. Depth of body 2.0–2.3 in body length, average 2.15. Depth (3.2–5.0 mm.) of tail in length of tail 2.4–4.25, average 3.15. Muscular part (2.4–3.6 mm.) 1.16–1.66 in depth of tail, average 1.32. Spiracle just in front of vent. Nostril within lateral edge of mouth fold. Mouth (2.0–3.0 mm.) contained 1.5–2.25, (average 1.93) in interorbital distance (4.5–6.5 mm.).

The dimensions of the largest tadpole are:

	mm.		mm.
Total length	26.4	Spiracle to vent	
Body length	10.0	Spiracle to eye	
Body depth	4.8	Eye to snout	4.4
Body width	7.0	Eye to nostril	
Tail length	16.4	Nostril to snout	
Tail depth	5.0	Mouth	2.4
Musculature of tail	3.0	Interorbital distance	4.8
Spiracle to snout		Internasal distance	

General remarks. In 1912 we made the following extended notes on the tadpoles of this species: "In a small pond at the edge of the Lee's clearing and just outside the swampy wooded edge of Billy's Lake we found on June 12, 1912, the tadpoles of the narrow-mouthed toad. In the same pond were *Gambusia affinis, Bufo* tadpoles, *Rana sphenocephala* tadpoles and green frog eggs and adults. The pond was 15 x 10 feet in dimensions and 3 or 4 feet deep. Here we took half grown, mature and transforming tadpoles of this species. On June 24 the same stages could still be found as on the last days of our trip (i.e., in July). Some of the tadpoles would not have transformed before September or October. The description of the tadpoles follows:

"The back is fuscous, olive brown or light brownish olive or raw umber, rarely with a few white spots; the belly may be clear white. On the throat the fine thickly set dusky specks of dorsal color surround small white areas; the rest of the venter is mottled, blotched or reticulated, the white patches being defined by a reticulum of dorsal color. The mottling is most prominent on the sides of the belly. In some the belly is entirely white with no reticulations and with fine speckings. In many on either side where dorsum meets venter there is discontinuous white band from in front of the insertion of the hindlimb well forwards toward the future position of the arm. The belly coloration foreshadows that of the adult only in the latter the white spots are much smaller and not so large or blotch-like. The muscular part of the tail is colored like the back and has usually along the middle a prominent horizontal white band which is from 2–7 mm. long. The caudal crests are more or less translucent with prominent blotches of dorsal color which at the tip wholly covers the crests. The crests are normally low.

"There are *no horny mandibles*. On the lower side of the mouth there is *no labium* and in the position of the lower mandible is a fleshy knob not cornified or differently colored from the surrounding integument. On the upper side of the mouth there is not a normal labium and in preserved specimens it looks like two more or less independent sideflaps which meet on the middle line in an emarginate junction.

"The length of the body is contained 1.43–2.8 in the tail, average 1.8. Width of the body in its own length 1.2–1.6, average 1.4. Eye lateral, visible from venter and dorsum, and exactly on the lateral edge formed by the flattened dorsum and venter of the head and forward part of the body. Spiracle in these spirit specimens undiscoverable and possibly absent in life. Anus median; interorbital space 4.50–7.75 mm., and much greater than the distance of the eye from the snout (3.25–5.0 mm.). Width of mouth slightly less than the distance of the eye from snout and 1.6–2.3 in the interorbital distance. Depth of the tail in its own length 2.2–5.4, the range usually 3.2–4.7, average 4. Depth of the muscular part at the base of the tail in the depth of the tail 1.2–1.8 times. Greatest length 37.25 mm. Greatest length of body 12.75 mm. Greatest length of tail 24.50 mm. Greatest depth of tail 6.0."

In 1920 (p. 32) we wrote "The narrow-mouthed toad, so far as known, transforms the same season during which the eggs are laid. This period was formerly considered to be 90 to 100 days, but Deckert's captives required only 16 days from hatching to transformation, an amazingly short period. The largest of the tadpoles of this species reach a length of 1 2/3 inches and are very easily distinguished from those of other species. The body is very flat, and the depth of it is contained 1 1/2 times in the width, while other tadpoles have round bodies; there is no spiracle (a mistake); there are no horny-edged mandibles, and the lower lip of ordinary tadpoles is not present, while the upper has either a faint row of teeth or none at all. The color of the tadpole is quite conspicuous. On the back and sides it is a uniform brown or olive black. Along the middle of the musculature of the tail there is a bright, clear, white band one-fourth to one-half inch long. Along either side of the belly there is a similar white line and most of the belly is of this clear white. All in all it is our most remarkable tadpole."

In 1923 (p. 34) we have *Gastrophryne carolinensis* as "black flat tadpoles, neither mandibles, not labia, nor labial teeth, the spiracle median and just ahead of anus." By an accident Mrs. Wright discovered the presence of spiracle by observation on the development of the hind legs wherein they separate the two juxtaposed structures, anus and spiracle, the latter going ahead of the hind legs and the anus remaining behind.

LARVAL PERIOD

Deckert (1914, No. 9, pp. 1, 2) gives 16 days for the larval period of some larvae kept in an enamelled pan (see Transformation Size).

The earliest we have taken eggs is May 20, 1921, the earliest transformation we record is June 25, 1922 or June 12, 1912. This gives little evidence but the intervals are 36 days or 23 days. In 1921 in certain ditches the first eggs or egg-laying we discovered came May 20. On June 16 we record mature tadpoles in these ponds 27 days later. On July 23 to 26 we found our first tadpoles transformed in these pools. This gives 64 to 67 days from hatching. In 1921 the earliest transformation of a few tadpoles came July 7 and many transformations July 25 and 26. If these were laid May 20–22 this would give 48 to 50 days from fresh eggs to transformation. In one series of ponds beside the railroad where eggs were first recorded May 22 we first found them transforming July 23 or 62 days later. We thus have possibilities of 23, 27, 36, 48, 50, 62, 64, 67 days for larval periods, but far removed from Deckert's control series. He must have had an optimum of conditions to get 20 days from egg to transformation.

TRANSFORMATION

Period. Deckert's tadpoles transformed September 16 and in 1912 we recorded tadpoles we thought would transform in September or October. If in nature 60 days be allowed for the larval period the eggs we took August 17 would not transform before October 15. In 1912 we have transformation June 12 and June 24, July 4. In 1921 we found transformation from July 7–August 1. In 1922 from June 25 to August 25 we took transformed *Gastrophryne*. For three years it began from June 12–July 7. From mid-June to mid-October seems the approximate period of transformation.

Size. The first note on transformation comes in Deckert's notes (1914, No. 9, pp. 1–2): "Eggs laid, night of August 27, 1911.

Aug. 28. One egg-mass put in flat enamelled pan in about 1 1/2 inches of water. Larvae straightened out, but still in the egg-mass.

Aug. 30. Larvae released from egg-mass, 1/8 inch long, with small tufts.

Sept. 1. Larvae 3/16 inch long, gills disappearing.

Sept. 2. Larvae 1/4 inch long, all have lost gills.

Sept. 8. Hind legs budding, length of larvae 1/2 inch.

Sept. 12. Legs fully developed, arms appearing, tail getting shorter, larvae 5/8 inch.

Sept. 14. Larvae breathing air, tail is but a short stump.

Sept. 16. Tail gone, the young toads measure 3/8 inch from snout to vent."

This is development from egg-laying to transformation in 20 days, almost as rapid as in *Scaphiopus holbrookii*.

In 1912 the sizes of "nineteen young transformed narrow-mouthed toads measure from 11–12 mm., the average is 11.5 mm., the mode 11.5 mm."

In 1920 (pp. 34, 36) we stated that "the narrow-mouthed toad tadpole may transform from the middle of June to September or October. The average size at transformation is 0.5 of an inch (see Fig. 2 and Plate XXII, Fig. 9)".

In 1921 we recorded transformation but strangely enough collected but few. They are: On July 8, 1921, a series of four transformed frogs amongst a large series of two-legged tadpoles, measured 12, 12, 12.5 and 13 mm. respectively. A series of three transformed taken July 23, 1921, (with mature tadpoles, tadpoles 20–21 mm. and small tadpoles 12–14 mm.) measured 11, 11.5 and 11.5 mm. Finally three vials of transformed and tadpole individuals of July 25, 1921 (really one lot) were as follows: Vial where they had dried up 7, 8, 8, 8, 9 mm., another vial with one 9.5 mm. semi-dry, and another vial not much dry 11 mm. In 1922 we took several series of transformation on June 23, June 24, and July 11. In these forms the tadpoles with four legs sometimes retained its tadpole mouth until tail stub reached 7–10 mm. in length, or put in the other way the frog mouth sometimes came in at tail length of 13.5–9 mm., though normally below 10 mm. The measurements of 26 transformed frogs of three series of 1922 are in range from 9–11.5 mm., or two at 9 mm., three at 9.5 mm., eight at 10 mm., six at 10.5 mm., six at 11 mm., one at 11.5 mm. This gives a lower range than in 1912, an average of 10 mm. and mode of 10 mm. The total range then for 1912–1922 is 7 or 8–12 mm., average 10.8 mm., mode 11 mm. Some Raleigh N. C., transformed frogs measure from 11.5–12 mm. for six specimens. One might expect greater variability in size of transformation and doubtless it comes because of the transient character of many of its breeding places. In one or two cases from non-Okefinokee localities we have found transformation as small as 8.5 mm.

General remarks. In 1912 we made these notes on the transformed frogs. They have the dorsal coloration of the adults and on the venter, the under surface of the hind limbs, the throat and upper breast are as in the adults but the belly has more or less of the blotchings and reticulation of the tadpole belly. In none of the various stages from mature tadpole to transformation is there any very apparent evidence of a spiracle and the left arm does not appear before the right. (Later we found the spiracle near the vent).

GROWTH

This species has a size of 8.5–12 mm. at transformation, or an average of 10.8 mm., or mode of 11 mm. We have one record of a specimen taken in the fall 16 mm. long. Another taken in June 9–10, 1917, at LaPlace, Ala., is 15 mm. On April 25 and 26, 1921, we took two specimens 17 mm. and 21 mm. ♂. We apparently have three groups herein indicated on this small evidence, a transformation group 8.5–12 mm., an intermediate group 15–17 mm. sexless externally, and a group sexually visible externally. The group 15–17 come from late fall to late spring or early June. Does this represent 8.5–12 mm. specimens June 15–October 15 transformers or 8.5–12 mm. individuals become 15–17 mm. by November 15–June 15 later or a possible maximum growth of 8.5–5 mm. or minimum of 3 mm. in 5–12 months (winter intervening). None of our 52 adults examined could be sexed externally if below 21 mm. One therefore seems inclined to extend this 15–17 mm. group to 20 mm., and pronounce 21 mm. onward as of the second year group.

On June 11 three females were taken 24, 25 and 28 mm., possibly two modes or groups. On May 23, 1921, we took seven adults one group of four 23 mm. ♂, 23 mm. ♀, 24 mm. ♂, 25 ♂, and a group of three 28 mm. ♂, 29 mm. ♀, 30 mm. ♀. On June 23, we took four specimens 24 mm. ♂, 27 mm. ♂, 28 mm. ♀, 28 mm. ♂. On July 4, 1921, we secured a 24 mm. ♂ and 28 mm. ♀. On July 3, 1922, a 23 mm. ♂, and a 27 mm. ♀. At least 36 of the 52 adults mentioned are 26–21 mm. Our evidence seems to be 8.5–12 mm. at transformation; 15–20 mm. first year olds; 21–26 or 27 mm. second year olds; 26 or 27–30 mm. our largest adults.

Examination of some of the U. S. National Museum material (59 frogs) shows transformed individuals at 11–12 mm. One set of five specimens (U.S.N.M. 9954, 38781–82 F.B. Meek) from Little Sarasota Bay, Florida, are 17.5, 18, 18.5, 18.5 and 18.5 mm. respectively. One group from Calcasieu, La., G. Würdemann (U.S.N.M. 3978) gave 17, 17, 17.5, 19, 21, 22, 23 mm. ♂, specimens—two groups (17–19, 21–23). One other group (U.S.N.M. 25420–21) of two specimens, 18.5 mm. and 22 mm. ♂ represent a sexless stage and a sexual stage externally. Thus far the above material shows transformation at 11–12 mm.; a group 17–19 mm.; and a group of 21 or 22 mm. onward, a sexually mature assemblage.

On April 18, 1897, at Wilmington, N. C., Dr. Paul Bartsch collected 5 specimens, (U.S.N.M. 37060–64) three of which were 20 mm. ♀, 20.5 mm. ♂ and 20 mm. ♂, and two of which were 26 mm. ♂ and 27 mm. ♂. Have we two model groups? Or on May 23, 1910, Julius Hurter, Mobile Co., Ala., takes two (U.S.N.M. 42548–49) 25 mm. ♂ and 28 mm. ♂. Two days and five days later he collects a 28 mm. ♂ (U.S.N.M. 57698) and another 28 mm. ♂ (U.S.N.M. 57697). Or May 15 at New Orleans, La., they (U.S.N.M. 53188–87) have a 20–5 mm. ♂ and 27 mm. ♀.

Or on May 25, 1891, J. Hurter takes in Missouri two females (U.S.N.M. 57700–01) 21.5 mm. and 31 mm. respectively. These selected instances show 11–12 mm. at transformation, 17–19 mm. an intermediate group, a 20–25 mm. group and a 26–31 mm. group. A plotting of the whole 59 frogs reveal 11–12 mm. at transformation, 17–19 mm. apparently first year olds, 20–25 mm. second year olds, 26–31 mm. three year olds. We have no Okefinokee specimeans at 20 mm. The U. S. National Museum material shows sex externally at that size (U.S.N.M. Nos. 37062–64, 53188) and our specimens at 21 mm. Our largest Okefinokee specimen is 30 mm., a female, but the U. S. National Museum collection has several females from 32 (U.S.N.M. 57702, 3707)–36 mm. (U.S.N.M. 57614, 57703–4). We have in our collection four specimens from Raleigh, N. C., August 1893, namely, 26 mm. ♂, 26 mm. ♀, 27 mm. ♂ and 32 mm. ♀. Is the last of a different mode? Are all these 32–32 mm. females more than three year olds? The whole evidence seems to be 8.5–12 mm. at transformation, 15–19–20 mm. for first year olds, 20 or 21 mm.–25 or

27 mm. for two year olds, 25 or 27 mm.–31 mm. for three year olds. Possibly the 32–36 mm. specimens should be three year olds, making that group 27–36 mm.

ENEMIES

On June 5, 1912, we took one garter snake (*Thamnophis sirtalis*) which had eaten this species.

AUTUMNAL DISAPPEARANCE

Our records range from March to September. In the U.S.N.M. collections we find none taken after September. Surely this species must remain out until November at least.

AFFINITIES

Holbrook describes this species in 1836 (p. 83). Later Dumeril and Bibron describes another form *E. rugosum* (1841, p. 744) which today is accredited to *G. carolinense*. Holbrook in his second edition (1842, Vol. V, p. 25) rather testily writes: "Dumeril and Bibron describe an *Engystoma rugosa* as inhabitating the United States, and suppose that I have confounded it with the *Engystoma carolinense*. Now I never saw their *Engystoma rugosa*, and if I had, should never have mistaken it for the *Engystoma carolinense*, which has a smooth skin. The only ecaudate batrachian animal, with which I am acquainted, resembling an *Engystoma* in form and size, is the *Bufo quercicus*; but this is a true toad, with parotid glands, warty skin, etc., whereas all the genus *Engystoma*, as I received it, have smooth skins and no parotid glands. Their *Engystoma rugosa* is probably a Mexican animal, as they say it came from 'des parties meridionales de l'Amerique du Nord.' "

In May, 1854, C. Girard (1856, p. 88) writes: "15 *Engystoma rugosum* Dum. and B. erp. gen. VIII, 1841, 744. Said to occur in the same regions as the preceding species (*carolinensis*). Have never observed it, and therefore cannot endorse it as a North American species."

Hallowell (1856, p. 252) because the Academy specimens and Holbrook's plate of *E. carolinensis* appear brown or chestnut above and his lone specimen from Nebraska and Kansas appears olive, described a new form, *Engystoma olivaceum*. Furthermore he held Holbrook gives the distribution of *E. carolinense* as from Charleston to the lower Mississippi valley.

In 1859 (pp. 169, 170) Chas. Girard described *Engystoma texense*, "This species is allied to *E. carolinense*, and differs from it by a more depressed and flattened head, a more truncated snout, which, as usual, protrudes beyond the lower jaw. The body itself is likewise more depressed, and the limbs assume a slender appearance.

"The head is continuous with the body, and constitutes about the third of their combined length. The cleft of the mouth does not extend as far back as in *E. carolinense*, since it corresponds to a perpendicular line drawn behind the pupil. The longitudinal diameter of the eye is equal to the distance between the orbit and the nostril. The interocular space, measured across the interior rim of the orbits, is greater than the rostral space from the orbits forwards. The symphysis of the lower jaw presents the same structure as in the species just alluded to.

"The skin is perfectly smooth throughout in all the specimens which we have examined; they were collected in April, and are, no doubt, liable to assume a rougher appearance during the hotter and more dry season of the year.

"The ground color of the upper region of the head, body and limbs, is of a light olivaceous brown tint, anteriorly uniform, posteriorly besprinkled with small black spots or dots especially over the coccyx and thighs. A whitish tint prevades uniformly throughout the inferior region.

"Specimens of this species were procured in Texas, by Capt. John Pope."

In 1909 (June 25) John K. Strecker described a new form for the U. S. A., namely, *Engystoma areolata* Strecker. Dr. Stejneger has noted these peculiar specimens. Mr. Strecker uses the pustulate upper surfaces, coloration and short hind feet for some of his characters. Victoria, Refugio County, Texas, the type locality must be an interesting place. The present author was never in it but a few hours. If *G. texense* and *G. areolata* appear together under the same log one wonders if stray *G. carolinense* rarities also in this region would also domicile in the same place. When the first breeding rain came would they recognize their respective kinds? By any chance has *Gastrophryne areolata* any connection with *Engystoma rugosum* (Dumeril and Bibron) which Boulenger reduced to *G. carolinense* synonymy? Or are they the roughened "hotter and more dry season" forms Girard intimates for *G. texense*.

In 1925 we from eggs, call, general appearance and tadpoles concluded that *G. texense* might be different, yet intensive study and careful comparisons need to be made. We have before us detailed measurements of the type 20 mm. of *Gastrophryne areolata* and a 28 mm. ♂, measurements of 20 mm. ♂, 20 mm. ♀ and 28 mm. ♀, *Gastrophryne texense* and 20 mm. ♂, 20 mm. ♀, 28 mm. ♂, 28 mm. ♀ and 36 mm. ♀ of *Gastrophryne carolinensis* from the U. S. National Museum collection, and 28 mm. ♂ and 28 mm. ♀ *Gastrophryne carolinensis* from Okefinokee. These actual measurements do not reveal as many differences in measurements as some of the descriptions might lead one to believe. The *Gastrophryne* have too many "relative" characters not definitely defined, if they can be.

The pustular or rough or tuberculate character is variable. Of one mated pair captured July 3, 1921, in the center of the swamp each is very smooth but a mated pair taken one year later on the esastern edge of the swamp has the female rough to the ridge between the eyes and the male rough for a short distance ahead of the vent. A collection of 7 adults taken May 23, 1921, on Billy's Island separate on larger size and roughness into females (2) and smaller size and smoothness into males (5). The one rough or tubercular character is not a sexual character entirely, nor a wet or dry season character solely. *Gastrophryne* needs careful study.

BIBLIOGRAPHY

1891 Boulenger, G. A. Ann. Nat. Hist. ser. 6, v. 8, p. 453.

1896 Brimley, C. S. Batrachia Found at Raleigh, N. C. Am. Nat. XXX, June 1896, No, 354, p. 501.

1907 ———. A Key to the Species of Frogs and Toads Liable to Occur in North Carolina. Journ. Elisha Mitchell Sci. Soc., Vol. XXIII, No. 4, Dec. 1907, pp. 157, 159.

1926 ———. Revised Key and List of the Amphibians and Reptiles of North Carolina. Journ. Elisha Mitchell Sci. Soc., Vol. 42, Nos. 1 & 2, Oct. 1926, p. 81.

1889 Cope, E. D. The Batrachia of North America, Bull. No. 34, U. S. Nat. Mus. 1889, pp. 385, 386.

1913 Deckert, R. F. List of Salientia from Near Jacksonville, Florida. Copeia, Feb. 14, 1914, No. 3, p. 3.

1915 ———. Further Notes on the Salientia of Jacksonville, Florida. Copeia, Aug. 29, 1914, No. 9, pp. 1-3.

1921 ———. Amphibian Notes from Dade Co., Florida. Copeia, Mar. 15, 1921, No. 92.

1922 ———. Notes on Dade County Salientia. Copeia, Nov. 1922, No. 122, p. 88.

1842 DeKay, J. E. Zoology of New York, Part III, 1842, p. 65.

1841 Dumeril, A. M. C. et G. Bibron. Erpetologie Generale.... Vol. 8, pp. 743, 744.

1918 Dunn, E. R. A Preliminary List of the Reptiles and Amphibians of Virginia. Copeia, No. 53, Jan. 25, 1918, p. 22.

1892 Garman, H. A Synopsis of the Reptiles and Amphibians of Illinois. Bull. Ill. State Lab. Nat. Hist., Vol. III, pp. 331-333.

1856 Girard, Charles. A list of the North American Bufonids, with Diagnosis of New Species. Proc. Acad. Nat. Sci. Phila. Vol. VII 1854, 1855 Phila. 1856, p. 88 May 1854.

1860 Girard, Charles. Herpetological Notices. Proc. Acad. Nat .Sciences, Phila., 1859, pp. 169, 170.

1858 Gunther, A. Catalogue of the Batrachia Salientia.... Brit. Museum, 1858, pp. 51, 52.

1856 Hallowell, E. Reptiles from Kansas and Nebraska.... Proc. Acad. Nat. Sci. Phila., Oct. 1856, p. 252.

1842 Holbrook, J. E. North American Herpetology, Vol. V, 1842, pp. 23, 25.

1924 Holt, E. G. Additional Records for the Alabama Herpetological Catalogue. Copeia, No. 135, Nov. 18, 1924, p. 95.

1893 Hurter, Julius. Catalogue of Reptiles and Batrachians Found in the Vicinity of St. Louis, Mo. Trans. Acad. Sci. St. Louis, Vol. VI, No. II, Dec. 12, 1893, p. 253.

1897 Hurter, Julius. A Contribution to the Herpetology of Missouri. Trans. Acad. Sci. St. Louis, Dec. 31, 1897, p. 503.

1855 Le Conte, John. Decsriptive Catalogue of the Ranina of the United States. Proc. Acad. Nat. Sci. Phila., Dec. 1855, pp. 430, 431.

1927 Lindsdale, J. M. Amphibians and Reptiles of Doniphan County, Kansas. Copeia, No. 164, July-Sept. 1927, p. 77.

1922 Löding, H. P. A Preliminary Catalogue of Alabama Amphibians and Reptiles. Mus. Paper No. 5, Ala. Mus. Nat. Hist. Geol. Survey Ala., Sept. 1922, p. 21.

1894 Loennberg, Einar. Notes on Reptiles and Batrachians Collected in Florida in 1892 and 1893. Proc. U. S. N. M., Vol. XVII, 1894, 1895, p. 338.

1924 Myers, G. S. Amphibians and Reptiles from Wilmington, N. C. Copeia, No. 131, June 30, 1924, p. 60.

1926 Nieden, Fr. Das Tierreich Anura II, pp. 64, 65.

1919 Pope, Philip H. Some Notes on the Amphibians of Houston, Texas. Copeia, Dec. 31, 1919, No. 76, p. 94.

1920 Potter, Doreen. Copeia, Sept. 16, 1920, No. 86, p. 82.

1895 Rhoads, Samuel N. Contributions to the Zoology of Tennessee. No. 1, Reptiles and Amphibians. Proc. Acad. Nat. Sci. Phila. 1895, 1896, Part I, Jan.-March, p. 396.

1924 Schmidt, K. P. A List of Amphibians and Reptiles Collected near Charleston, S. C. Copeia, No. 132, July 15, 1924, p. 68.

1909 Strecker, John K. Notes on the Narrow-mouthed Toads (*Engystoma*) and the Description of a New Species from Southeastern Texas. Proc. Biol. Soc. Wash., June 25, 1909, Vol. XXII, pp. 115-120.

1915 ———. Reptiles and Amphibians of Texas. Baylor Bulletin Vol. XVIII, No. 4, Aug. 1915, pp. 46, 47.

1920 Wright, A. H. Frogs: Their Natural History and Utilization. Rept. U. S. Com. Fisheries, Appendix VI, Doc. 888, pp. 29, 30.

1923 ———. The Tadpoles of the Frogs of Okefinokee Swamp, Georgia. The Anatomical Record, Jan. 20, 1923, p. 406.

1923 ———. The Salientia of the Okefinokee Swamp, Georgia. Copeia, Feb. 1, 1923, No. 115, p. 34.

1926 ———. The Vertebrate Life of Okefinokee Swamp in Relation to the Atlantic Coastal Plain, Ecology, Vol. VII, No. 1, Jan. 1926, p. 83.

1924 Wright, A. H. and A. A. Wright. A Key to the Salientia East of the Mississippi River. The American Naturalist, Vol. LVIII, July-August, 1924, pp. 378, 379.

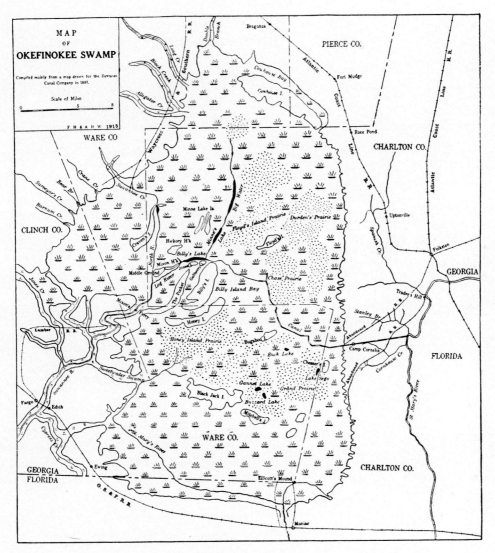

MAP
OF
OKEFINOKEE SWAMP

Compiled mainly from a map drawn for the Suwanee
Canal Company in 1891.

Scale of Miles
0   5   8

F. H. & A. H. W. 1913

PIERCE CO.

WARE CO

CHARLTON CO.

Bragshta

Cowhouse Bay
Cowhouse I.

Fort Mudge

Race Pond

Uptonville

Folkston

GEORGIA

Traders Hill

Camp Cornelia

FLORIDA

CLINCH CO.

Minne Lake Is.
Lake Big Water
Floyd's Island Prairie
Durden's Prairie
Floyd I.

Hickory H'k
Billy's Lake
Chase Prairie
Billy I.
Billy Island Bay
Middle Ground
The Pocket
Honey I.
Honey Island Prairie
Bugaboo I.
Buck Lake
Lake Sego
Grand Prairie
Gannet Lake
Black Jack I.
Buzzard Lake
Mitchell's

Craven I.
Mixon H's

Lumber

Suwanee R.
Sweetwater Swamp I.

Fargo
Edith

GEORGIA
FLORIDA

Ewing

O. B. & F. R. R.

WARE CO.

Ellicott's Mound

Moniac

CHARLTON CO.

St. Mary's River
Cornhouse Cr.
Stanley Br.
Spanish Cr.

PLATE XLV

INDEX

A

Abastor erythrogrammus, 108

Abbott, C. C., 74, 81, 82, 83, 87, 88, 97, 99, 102, 106, 161, 164, 166, 167, 168, 177, 179, 184, 185, 186, 188, 189, 190, 194, 228, 234, 235, 247

Acad, Nat. Sci. Phila., 228, 245, 449, 475

Acadian flycatcher, 314

Acantharchus pomotis, 238, 447

Acer rubrum, 238

Acknowledgments, 1-3

Acris, 13, 26, 29, 30, 50, 65, 68, 117, 191, 192, 193, 194, 202, 203, 211, 213, 220, 225, 272, 282, 289, 304, 305, 330, 369

Acris acheta, 191

Acris crepitans, 68, 156, 157, 164, 166, 168, 191, 192, 193, 194

Acris gryllus, 3, 4, 12, 13, 16, 18, 19, 24, 25, 26, 29, 30, 31, 32, 33, 34, 35, 37, 38, 39, 40, 50, 57, 58, 59, 60, 61, 63, 64, 66, 67, 68, 92, 124, 146, 156-196, 202, 211, 225, 226, 229, 235, 237, 257, 261, 262, 289, 290, 303, 309, 314, 316, 324, 461

Acris gryllus bufonia, 192, 194

Acris gryllus crepitans, 165, 168, 192, 193

Acris gryllus gryllus, 4

Acris nigritus, 194

Acris pickeringii, 192, 194

Adirondack Mts., N. Y., 397, 400, 402, 403, 404, 405, 407, 408, 409, 410, 413, 414, 418, 438, 449, 451

Affinities, 62-67, *S. holbrookii*, 105-106; *B. quercicus*, 131, 132; *B. terrestris*, 153, 154, 155; *A. gryllus*, 190-194; *P. nigrita*, 202, 203; *P. ocularis*, 225, 226; *H. andersonii*, 245-247; *H. cinerea*, 271; *H. femoralis*, 293, 294; *H. gratiosa*, 309, 310; *H. squirella*, 324; *H. versicolor*, 333; *R. aesopus*, 350-352; *R. grylio*, 382, 383; *R. heckscheri*, 396, 397; *R. septentrionalis*, 415-418; *R. sphenocephala*, 434; *R. virgatipes*, 452; *G. carolinensis*, 475, 476

Alabama, 15, 107, 108, 113, 133, 157, 196, 204, 229, 248, 257, 272, 297, 310, 312, 314, 325, 365, 375, 419, 452, 453, 454, 473, 474, 477

Albino frogs, 353, 392

Alders, 407

Alexandria, Va., 255

Algonquin Park, Can., 400

Allapaha, Ga., 4, 204, 272

Allard, H. A., 140, 155

Alleghany Mts., 193

Allen, A. A., 199

Allen, J. A., 76, 106

Allen, M. J., 385

Alligator Swamp, Fla., 384, 386, 393

Alnus incanus, 407

Altamaha River, Ga., 272

Ambystoma, 286, 466

Ambystoma angulatum, 10

Ambystoma conspersum, 6

Amblystoma opacum, 6

Amblystoma punctatum, 6

Amblystoma talpoideum, 6

Am. Mus. Nat. Hist., 3, 228, 318, 323, 348, 349, 384, 398

American spade-foot, 106

Ames, Iowa, 157, 174, 179

Amphiuma means, 4, 429

Anderson, R. D., 448

Anderson, S. C., 228, 240, 435, 453

Anderson tree frog, 28, 31, 235

Anderson tree toad, 227

Anderson's Hyla, 227, 234

Appel, W. D., 449

Arch Creek, Fla., 314

Aristook Co., Me., 409

Arizona, 33

Arkansas, 42, 73, 74, 206, 325, 352, 454

Arlington, Fla., 207, 348, 350

Armstrong, A. J., 1, 9

Aronia, 116

Arrowhead, 386

Arrow arums, 371

Ascaphus truei, 66

Aschemeier, C. R., 209, 213, 217

Athabaska, 201

Atkinson, C., 162, 194

Atlanta, Ga., 453

Atlantic City, N. J., 435

Atlantic Co., N. J., 235

Atlantic coastal plain 107, 108, 133, 196, 419, 452, 457

Atsion Creek, N. J., 235

Auburn, N. Y., 397

Auburndale, Fla., 114, 337, 348

Austroriparian region, 134, 155, 228, 351

Autaugaville, Ala., 114

Autumnal disappearance, 24; *S. holbrookii*, 104-105; *B. quercicus*, 131; *B. terrestris*, 153; *A. gryllus*, 188; *P. nigrita*, 202; *P. ocularis*, 225; *H. andersonii*, 245; *H. cinerea*, 270, 271, 293; *H. femoralis*, 293; *H. gratiosa*, 309; *H. squirella*, 323, 324; *H. versicolor*, 333; *R. aesopus*, 350; *R. clamitans*, 364; *R. grylio*, 382; *R. sphenocephala*, 434; *R. virgatipes*, 451; *G. carolinensis*, 475

Axillary amplexus, 28, 29, 30

Azalea viscosa, 238

B

Babcock, H. L., 157

Bailey, V., 114, 206

Bainbridge, Ga., 9

Baird, S. F. IX, 5, 6, 106, 168, 191, 192, 198, 203, 204, 205, 207, 227, 234, 247, 351, 408

Baker County, Fla., 10, 392

Baldwin Co., Ala., 452

Baltimore, Md., 163, 245

F

Fair Haven, Conn., 78, 79
Fall croaking, 27
Fall fish, 407
Fall mating, 27
Fall ovulation, 27; *Rana sphenocephala*, 27
Farmingdale, N. J., 229, 235
Fayetteville, N. C., 133
Femoral Hyla, 272
Fern bogs, 11
Fern prairies, 11
Fertilization, 26, 27
First Appearance, 24, *S. holbrookii*, 76, 77;
  B. quercicus, 113, 114; *B. terrestris*, 138;
  A. gryllus, 163; *P. nigrita*, 199; *P. ocu-
  laris*, 212-213; *H. andersonii*, 232; *H.
  cinerea*, 252; *H. femoralis*, 276; *H. grati-
  osa*, 297; *H. squirella*, 312; *H. versicolor*,
  326; *R. aesopus*, 337; *R. clamitans*, 355;
  R. grylio, 368; *R. septentrionalis*, 400; *R.
  sphenocephala*, 423; *R. virgatipes*, 438; *G.
  carolinensis*, 458
First Connecticut Lake, N. H., 398, 413
Fisher, G. C., 104, 105, 106
Fitzinger, L. J., 191, 203
Flat Pine Barrens, 10
Flatwood, Ala., 157, 248, 257
Fletcher Lake, Ont., 400
Floating heart, 368
Florida, 10, 15, 16, 41, 42, 44, 46, 47, 49,
  50, 52, 53, 54, 55, 56, 66, 73, 74, 93, 94,
  107, 108, 110, 113, 125, 133, 137, 138,
  139, 155, 156, 157, 158, 162, 165, 169,
  190, 191, 192, 194, 195, 196, 199, 200,
  201, 203, 204, 205, 206, 207, 209, 211,
  212, 213, 217, 223, 226, 229, 248, 252,
  254, 259, 262, 267, 271, 272, 275, 294,
  295, 309, 310, 312, 314, 315, 316, 318,
  322, 325, 334, 337, 340, 342, 343, 347,
  350, 351, 352, 364, 365, 368, 370, 372,
  375, 382, 383, 384, 385, 386, 387, 393,
  419, 423, 427, 428, 451, 452, 453, 454,
  474, 477
Florida blue herons, 379
Florida district, 334, 351
Florida forms, 10, 15, 66, 113, 351
Florida frog, 334
Florida gopher frog, 334, 352
Florida grackles, 190, 379, 396, 435
Florida Hyla, 294
Florida Parishes, La., 108, 275, 294
Florida Keys, 15
Floridan subregion, 134, 334
Florida tree frog, 14, 28, 30, 31, 92, 93,
  124, 294
Florida tree toad, 297
Food, *62*, *S. holbrookii*, 103-104; *B. quer-
  cicus*, 130; *B. terrestris*, 152; *A. gryllus*,
  189; *P. ocularis*, 224; *H. andersonii*, 244;
  H. cinerea, 268-270; *H. femoralis*, 292;
  H. gratiosa, 309; *H. squirella*, 323; *R.
  aesopus*, 349; *R. clamitans*, 364; *R. grylio*,
  382; *R. septentrionalis*, 415; *R. spheno-
  cephala*, 433; *R. virgatipes*, 450
Force, Miss E. R., 325, 333, 419, 433, 434
Fort George Island, Fla., 133
Fort Meade, Fla., 134
Fort Ripley, Minn., 397
Foster, Mr. 154
Fountain, P., 7, 8, 9

Fowler, H. W., 84, 88, 89, 106, 162, 167,
  169, 195, 196, 199, 204, 228, 234, 248,
  327, 333, 352, 437, 438, 442, 450, 452
Fowler's toad, 98, 140, 176
Fox, H., 89
Fox, W. H., 79
Framingham, Mass., 74
Franklin Co., Me., 397, 399, 413
Freneau, N. J., 229
Fried bacon frog, 248, 256
Frog-toad, 452, 464
Frost, S. W., 62, 433
Fruitland Park, Fla., 348
Fry, N. P., 348
Fuertes, L. A., 228, 244
Fulford, Fla., 314
Fulton Lake Chain, N. Y., 397, 400, 409
Fundulus, 153
Funkhouser, W. D., 1, 9

G

Gaige, F. M., 3
Gaige, Mrs. H. T., 162, 195, 336, 352
Gainesville, Fla., 15, 74, 93, 196, 199, 200,
  213, 217, 227, 297, 304, 337, 343, 384, 385.
Gainesville, Ga., 157, 185
Gallberry, 215
Gambusia, 153, 359, 470
Garman, H., 134, 140, 156, 158, 162, 165,
  168, 173, 188, 189, 193, 195, 253, 256,
  271, 454, 456, 458, 459, 463, 477
Garnier, J. H., 399, 400, 401, 402, 405, 407,
  408, 409, 412, 413, 414, 415, 419
Garrison's Creek, N. Y., 397
Garter snake, 131, 152, 292, 475
Gastrophryne, 13, 26, 29, 65, 92, 278, 299,
  360, 453, 460, 461, 472
Gastrophryne areolata, 454, 476
Gastrophryne carolinensis, 12, 13, 15, 16, 18,
  19, 24, 25, 26, 31, 32, 33, 34, 35, 37, 38,
  39, 40, 41, 57, 58, 59, 60, 61, 65, 66, 67,
  71, 92, 265, 278, 312, 452-477
Gastrophryne texense, 92, 454, 455, 458, 461,
  465, 476
Gaylussacia, 116
Gaylussacia dumosa, 199
Gaylussacia frondosa, 277
Geckos, 66
General appearance, *S. holbrookii*, 75; *B.
  quercicus*, 108, 109; *B. terrestris*, 134,
  135; *A. gryllus*, 158; *P. nigrita*, 196-197;
  P. ocularis, 207-208; *H. andersonii*, 229-;
  H. cinerea, 249; *H. femoralis*, 273; *H.
  gratiosa*, 295; *H. squirella*, 311; *R.
  aesopus*, 334; *R. clamitans*, 352; *R. grylio*,
  365; *R. hecksheri*, 385; *R. septentrionalis*,
  398; *R. sphenocephala*, 420; *R. virgatipes*,
  435; *G. carolinense*, 454
General discussion, 15-71
General habits, *S. holbrookii*, 77-86; *B.
  quercicus*, 114-115; *B. terrestris*, 139; *A.
  gryllus*, 164-168; *P. nigrita*, 199, 200; *P.
  ocularis*, 213; *H. andersonii*, 233; *H.
  cinerea*, 252-256; *H. femoralis*, 276-277;
  H. gratiosa, 297, 298; *H. squirella*, 312-
  314; *H. versicolor*, 327; *R. aesopus*, 337-
  339; *R. clamitans*, 355; *R. grylio*, 368-370;
  R. hecksheri, 387; *R. sphenocephala*, 423;
  G. carolinensis, 458, 459